		INITS	DATE
CSO			
GSO2			

ADMIRALTY B.R. 600(5) WAR OFFICE 10224(5) AIR MINISTRY A.P. 3214(5)

The Services' Textbook of Radio

Volume 5

TRANSMISSION AND PROPAGATION

BY

E. V. D. GLAZIER, Ph.D.(Eng.), B.Sc., A.M.I.E.E.

AND

H. R. L. LAMONT, Ph.D., M.A., A.M.I.E.E.

Edited by the Technical Staff of

'WIRELESS WORLD'

LONDON

HER MAJESTY'S STATIONERY OFFICE

1958

Published by
HER MAJESTY'S STATIONERY OFFICE

To be purchased from
York House, Kingsway, London W.C.2
423 Oxford Street, London W.1
13A Castle Street, Edinburgh 2
109 St. Mary Street, Cardiff
39 King Street, Manchester 2
Tower Lane, Bristol 1
2 Edmund Street, Birmingham 3
80 Chichester Street, Belfast
or through any bookseller

Price £1 5*s.* 0*d.* net

The Services' Textbook of Radio

VOLUME 1: ELECTRICAL FUNDAMENTALS

Electricity, magnetism and a.c. theory with a simple introduction to rotating electrical machinery and illumination.

VOLUME 2: TELECOMMUNICATION TECHNIQUES

The basis of communication theory, the principles of telegraphy, nature of speech, the principles of recording and reproducing, the basic principles of telephony, introduction to radio-frequency communications.

VOLUME 3: ELECTRONICS

Valves of all types, semi-conductors, photo-electric devices and cathode-ray tubes.

VOLUME 4: CIRCUITRY

The basic circuits used in radio communication and radar including amplifiers, oscillators, frequency-changers, filters, modulators and pulse generation; measuring and test instruments and power supply circuits.

VOLUME 5: TRANSMISSION AND PROPAGATION

Properties of electrical lines, audio-frequency and radio-frequency considerations, waveguides, radiation and propagation, aerial systems.

VOLUME 6: WIRELESS COMMUNICATION

Characteristics of wireless systems, transmitters and receivers including v.h.f. and u.h.f. types, choice of systems for particular uses including installation considerations, the principles of facsimile and television.

VOLUME 7: RADIOLOCATION TECHNIQUES
(Including Direction Finding)

The principles of direction finding and the various systems in use, characteristics of radar equipment and the factors affecting performance, radar displays and typical radar systems, interference.

Promulgated by Command of their Lordships

J. G. Lang

Promulgated by Command of the Army Council

E. W. Playfair

Promulgated by Order of the Air Council

M. J. Dean

Contents

Foreword

THE SERVICES' TEXTBOOK OF RADIO is a series of seven volumes which has been written primarily to meet the needs of the three Fighting Services for a comprehensive and authoritative work on the theory and technique of radio, including in this term radar and direction-finding as well as telecommunications. Its usefulness, however, is by no means confined to the Fighting Services, for theory and technique are of universal application; it is, therefore, also well adapted for civilian needs and its availability has accordingly not been restricted to the Services.

The authors are all recognized authorities in their own particular spheres. The volumes have been written under the guidance of an Inter-Services Panel and have been edited by the Technical Staff of *Wireless World*.

The seven volumes of the series are listed, with brief synopses, on p. iii. Together they cover the whole range of radio theory from the elementary principles of electricity and magnetism to the advanced techniques of radar and multichannel communication systems. Volume 1, which covers electricity and magnetism, is also Volume 1 of a companion series entitled The Services' Textbook of Electrical Engineering. Volume 2 includes descriptions of a number of telecommunications techniques on which information is not usually readily available, while Volumes 3, 4 and 5 cover the basic theory used in radio. Volume 6 contains information valuable to those responsible for the planning and operation of wireless communication systems. In Volume 7 will be found the principles of radar and direction-finding systems.

In conformity with modern practice, the rationalized m.k.s. system of units is employed throughout. In order to help readers who are more familiar with the c.g.s. system, however, the interrelation between the two and the method of converting from one to the other are fully explained in Volume 1.

The book is intended to meet the needs of three distinct classes of reader. It is for the beginner, who has no prior knowledge of the subject; it is also for the technician and, finally, for the more advanced reader. The attempt to meet these three requirements in one book is an ambitious one and it has resulted in an unusual form of presentation which deserves some explanation.

The text, taken as a continuous whole, provides the full textbook for the technician. Parts of it, however, are too complex to be fully understood by the beginner and these parts are indicated by black triangles, one being placed at the beginning and one at the end of each such part. If the text is read without these marked sections it forms a continuous whole at a level suited to the beginner. In this way, two complete books are obtained at two different levels for two distinct classes of reader. Appendixes to individual chapters include those proofs and analyses which are highly mathematical, and are intended to supplement the main body of the text and assist those with mathematical ability. An extremely detailed index makes the work suitable for use as a reference book and, in this connection also, the appendixes will be found very useful.

Authors' Preface

THIS VOLUME of the Services' Textbook of Radio is concerned with the means by which electromagnetic energy is conveyed from place to place. The first eight chapters deal with transmission lines, which serve to guide the power along paths defined by the conductors. The frequency used determines which one of the various forms of transmission line is most suitable, and this has made it convenient to start with transmission lines appropriate to low frequencies and proceed progressively to the highest frequencies.

Chapters 9 to 14 deal with the radiation of electromagnetic energy from aerials and its propagation in and above the earth's atmosphere, unconfined by conductors. Here again the factors determining both the type of aerial to be used and the mechanism of propagation depend on frequency, and the treatment again progresses through increasing frequency.

In the region of frequencies above 1,000 Mc/s especially, the variety of transmission line components and aerials is so great that it has been possible to select only some typical examples. It is hoped, however, that these illustrate most of the principles involved.

For permission to use as the basis of Figs. 6.5 and 6.24 the drawings by Mr. E. M. Wells we are indebted to Marconi's Wireless Telegraph Company.

The constant advice and guidance of Mr. Cocking of *Wireless World* has been of the greatest assistance to us and is gratefully acknowledged.

E. V. D. GLAZIER

H. R. L. LAMONT

List of Symbols

WHERE A SYMBOL is used with different meanings in different chapters, the relevant chapter numbers are included in brackets in the following list. The symbols are arranged in alphabetical order, capital letters preceding small letters and Roman letters preceding Greek. Minor variations of meaning brought about by the addition of subscripts are not necessarily included.

A	Area
	Constant (5, 6, 8)
	Attenuation factor (14)
B	Magnetic flux density (5, 14)
	Frequency range, bandwidth (10, 13)
	Susceptance (= 1/reactance) (1, 3, 4, 7)
$\mathbf{B}$	Magnetic flux density (vector)
C	Capacitance
D	Distance, linear dimensions, diameter
	Divergence factor (14)
	Electric displacement (1)
E	Electric field strength (scalar)
	Electromotive force (11, 12)
$\mathbf{E}$	Electric field strength (vector)
F	Force (14)
	Array diagram factor (10)
	Field-strength gain factor (11)
G	Conductance
	Gain (9, 13)
H	Magnetic field strength (scalar)
$\mathbf{H}$	Magnetic field strength (vector)
I	Current
J	Bessel function (6)
J	Current density
$\mathbf{J}$	Current density (vector)
K	Constant
	Attenuation factor (1)
K_R	Voltage reflection factor
L	Inductance
	Length (8, 13)
M	Mutual inductance
	Excess modified index (14)
N	Number of turns (11)
	Electrons per cubic metre (14)
	Modified refractive index (14)
P	Power (scalar)
	Atmospheric pressure (14)
$\mathbf{P}$	Power (vector)
P_a	Power per unit area
$P(\theta)$	Polar coefficient of field pattern (10)
Q	$2\pi \times$ Ratio of (energy stored)/(energy dissipated per cycle)
	Charge density (5)
R	Resistance
	Radius (13)
S	Standing-wave ratio
	Signal waveform (2)
T	Period
	Temperature (10)
V	Potential difference
W	Energy
X	Reactance
Y	Admittance (= 1/impedance)
Z	Impedance
Z_0	Characteristic impedance
a	Radius, linear dimension
	Ratio (2, 12)
	Area (5, 8)
b	Radius, linear dimension
	Ratio (2)
	Angle (14)
c	Velocity of light
	Capacitance (1)
d	Linear dimension
e	Electron charge $= 1{\cdot}6 \times 10^{-19}$ coulomb
f	Frequency
g	Conductance

h Height
i Current
Angle of incidence (14)
j Vector operator $= \sqrt{-1}$
j Current density (5)
k Boltzmann's constant $= 1{\cdot}38 \times 10^{-23}$ joule/degree Kelvin
l Length
m Mass
Number (4, 6, 8, 10)
n Number
Index of refraction (13, 14)
p Number
Numerical distance (14)
q Charge per unit length (1)
Numerical height (14)
r Radius
Angle of refraction (14)
Resistance (1, 8)
s Distance (5)
Bessel function constant (6)
t Time
Lens thickness (13)
v Velocity
Voltage (1, 3)
Volume (8)
w Partial pressure of water vapour
Linear Dimension (13)
x Distance
Cartesian co-ordinate
Normalized reactance (3)
Normalized angular frequency (2)
y Cartesian co-ordinate
z Cartesian co-ordinate
α Attenuation coefficient
Angle (6, 10)
β Phase-shift coefficient
Angle (2)
Ratio (8)
γ Propagation coefficient
δ Small increment
Skin depth (1, 5, 6, 8)
Loss angle (1)
ε Base of natural logarithms $= 2{\cdot}71828$
η Efficiency (11)
θ Angle
κ Permittivity
κ_0 Permittivity of free space $= 8{\cdot}854 \times 10^{-12}$ F/m
κ_r Relative permittivity
λ Wavelength
μ Permeability
μ_0 Permeability of free space $= 4\pi \times 10^{-7}$ H/m
μ_r Relative permeability
π Ratio circumference/diameter of a circle $= 3{\cdot}14159$
ρ Resistivity (1, 4, 5)
Reflection factor (7, 14)
σ Conductivity (5)
Echoing area (9)
ν Collision frequency (14)
ϕ Angle
ψ Angle
ω Angular frequency $= 2\pi f$
Δ A small change of
$\varDelta$ Logarithmic decrement (4, 8)
$\varPhi$ Magnetic flux
$\varSigma$ Area (8)

Abbreviations of Units

A Ampere
Å Angstrom unit $= 10^{-10}$ m
F Farad
H Henry
M Mega $= 10^{6}$ (prefix)
V Volt
W Watt
Ω Ohm
c Cycle
c/s Cycles per second
db Decibel
eV Electron-volt
g Gramme
k Kilo $= 10^{3}$ (prefix)
m Metre
Milli $= 10^{-3}$ (prefix)
p 10^{-12} (prefix)
s or sec Second
° Degree
of angular measure
of temperature
°C = degree Centigrade
°F = degree Fahrenheit
°K = degree Kelvin

CHAPTER 1

Properties of Electrical Lines

Introduction

It was explained in Volume 2 that the transmission of electrical power for the purpose of communications is carried out by means of electromagnetic waves, although it was not possible, there, to dwell in detail on the properties of such waves. Owing to the rapid expansion of techniques employing electromagnetic or radio waves it is important to have a clear understanding of these properties. This subject may be approached from two standpoints, one being the propagation of radio waves in free space, the other being the propagation of waves by means of guiding conductors. The latter course will be followed here as it enables the theory to be developed from the circuit theory of Volume 1. To be more specific the study will commence with a consideration of transmission lines formed by two parallel conductors insulated from one another, using the ordinary circuit theory with which the reader should now be well acquainted.

With such transmission lines a generator or transmitter is connected to the two terminals at one end of the line, and the power is received in a two-terminal load impedance connected to the other end. Transmission may be by means of direct-current or alternating-current power, but since the former cannot convey intelligence, interest will centre around the transmission of alternating-current power. All communications signals can be analysed into alternating components of various frequencies, and a knowledge of the performance of a line over these frequencies enables the received signal to be determined. The properties of transmission lines over a wide range of frequencies must be studied, from audio frequencies for telegraphy and telephony up to ultra-high radio frequencies for radio aerial feeders, interconnecting cables for radio apparatus, and transmission-line circuit components.

All transmission lines consist of a conducting medium (the two conductors) and a dielectric medium (the space between the conductors), and there will be electric and magnetic fields in both media. At zero frequency (d.c.) the currents in the two conductors will be equal and opposite since there can be no accumulation of charge in a conducting system. A similar condition exists with a.c. transmission, the currents in the two conductors being equal and opposite in direction at every instant at any cross-section. If the fields in a plane transverse to the direction of the line are examined, the electric and magnetic fields in the dielectric will be found to lie almost entirely in that plane. In fact, as we shall find in Chapter 5, the energy is transmitted along the line mainly by the fields in the dielectric, the conductors merely acting as guides.

The conformation of the two conductors may take on several forms, which may be broadly divided into balanced and unbalanced lines. Two identical wires symmetrically placed with respect to earth or the inside of a tubular conducting screen are representative of balanced lines, while one wire with earth return or at the centre of a conducting tube (concentric or coaxial cable) are representative of unbalanced lines. Cross-sections of these configurations are shown in Fig. 1.1 where the full lines represent the electric field, and the dotted lines the magnetic field. The electric-field lines intersect perfect conducting surfaces at right angles and the electric- and magnetic-field lines intersect one another at right angles.

The type of line shown in Fig. 1.1 (a) is sometimes called an open wire (O.W.) line while (b) is known as a screened pair. The type of line shown at (c) is the single-wire line with earth return, but it is now rarely employed. The cross-section (d) shows a coaxial or concentric line, although the term concentric

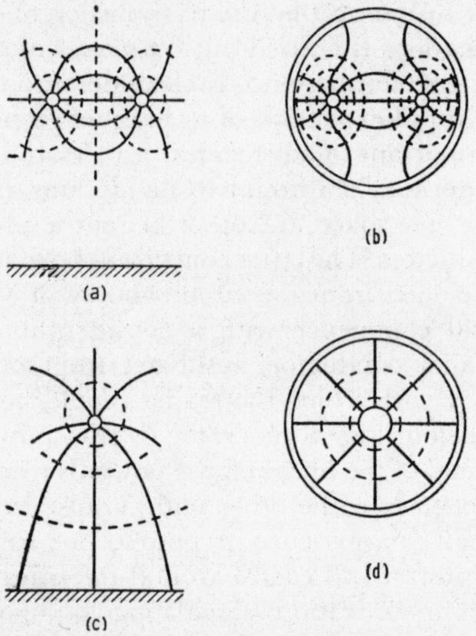

Fig. 1.1. Types of transmission line: balanced, (a) and (b), and unbalanced, (c) and (d). The solid lines represent the electric field and the dotted, the magnetic.

cable is usually reserved for power cable of this type. The fields of (a) and (c) are not confined and they spread out into space. If the screens of lines (b) and (d) are perfect there are no external fields.

Circuits with Distributed Constants

A transmission line has resistance, inductance, leakage conductance, and capacitance, evenly distributed along its length. The leakage conductance is the reciprocal of the insulation resistance between conductors per unit length and is sometimes called leakance. The primary characteristics of a line are defined as follows:

$R =$ The alternating-current resistance per unit length (ohms)
$L =$ The inductance per unit length (henrys)
$G =$ The leakance per unit length (mhos)
$C =$ The capacitance per unit length (farads)

The unit of length employed here is the metre since the m.k.s. system of units is employed in this book. However, the unit employed in telephony is usually the mile and a unit of 100 feet is often employed for radio feeders and cable. Resistance and inductance usually occur in both conductors, and R and L represent the total effect of the two conductors in a manner which will be explained presently.

In Volume 1 the properties of 'lumped' components were studied. For example the reactance $X_L = \omega L$ of an inductive coil was deduced, and the reactance $X_c = 1/\omega C$ (or susceptance $B_c = \omega C$) of a parallel-plate capacitor was determined, $\omega = 2\pi f$ being the angular frequency of the applied alternating voltage. The laws of networks built up from such components were considered. The case of an inductive coil with a resistive winding was simply treated by considering it to be a lumped resistance in series with a lumped inductance. If, however, each turn of such a coil had an appreciable capacitance to the core, it would no longer be admissible to extract the resistance from the coil as the question would arise as to where the capacitances should be connected. The inductance at high frequencies could no longer be measured by a bridge method since the capacitance currents would vitiate the measurements.

This is a similar problem to that which exists in a transmission line. The components R, L, G and C are no longer lumped, but each is distributed evenly

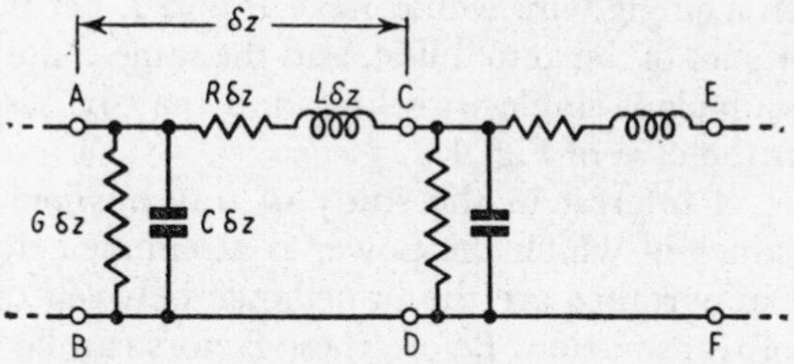

Fig. 1.2. Lumped component representation of a transmission line.

along the length. It is no longer possible to measure one to the exclusion of the others although, of course, there are methods of measurement in which the errors are negligibly small. A length of line may be visualized in terms of lumped components provided it is divided into very short lengths. Thus if a single-wire line is divided into short lengths δz metres long, each may be represented by an inverted L-type network having an impedance $(R + j\omega L)\delta z$ in the series arm and an admittance $(G + j\omega C)\delta z$ in the shunt arm, as shown in Fig. 1.2. The shorter the elements into which the line is divided the more accurate the representation. As will be shown later there is a phase shift between voltage at the input and output of each element, and the representation by lumped networks becomes very inaccurate when, at a particular frequency, the phase shift in one element exceeds about 60°. This representation may give the appearance of being unsymmetrical, and therefore might be thought to give different transmission in the two directions. In fact, if the length δz metres of line represented by one section ABCD of network, is small, this asymmetry is quite insignificant, and only occurs at the terminations of the line.

The primary characteristics R and L are 'series or impedance components' while the characteristics G and C are 'shunt or admittance components'. This follows because the line current flowing in the resistance $R.\delta z$ and the reactance $\omega L.\delta z$ will produce a voltage drop in series with the line, while the voltage between lines will cause a shunt or leakage current to flow into the admittance composed of the conductance $G.\delta z$ and the susceptance $\omega C.\delta z$.

The primary characteristics R and G are power-consuming components, and power lost during transmission appears in them as heat. The primary characteristics L and C are energy-storage components and can consume no power. However, the capacitance C causes the line to take a charging current which flows in the series resistance R and causes greater losses than there would otherwise be.

The series components R and L represent the net resistance and inductance effects of the two conductors of a two-conductor line. Thus R is the sum of the resistances of the two conductors per unit length. If the line is balanced the two resistances will be equal, but if it is unbalanced they will be unequal; but in either case R represents their sum. Similarly we may regard each conductor as having a self-inductance, and L therefore represents the sum of that associated with each of the two conductors. The series components R and L are, therefore, quoted in ohms and henrys per loop metre, per loop mile or per loop 100 feet, it being understood that they represent the total resistance and inductance effect per unit length of line. For theoretical purposes it is often convenient to replace a line by a hypothetical line of a single wire with a zero impedance earth return. Such a single wire would have R and L per unit length equal to the loop characteristics of the actual line, and the same G and C per unit length. It is called the equivalent single-wire line, and may be visualized in lumped components, as in the case of Fig. 1.2.

The main topic of interest in the study of transmission lines is the loss of power, or the manner in which the power is attenuated during transmission. Other features of importance are the impedance between the two conductors, and the velocity of transmission. Before these factors can be studied in detail it is necessary to determine how the primary characteristics depend upon the geometry of a line and the frequency, in a few simple cases.

Resistance per Unit Length

The primary characteristic R of a line is the total resistance per unit length. The zero frequency or d.c. value of resistance is easily calculated from:

$$R = \frac{\rho_1}{A_1} + \frac{\rho_2}{A_2} \text{ ohms per metre} \quad . \quad . \quad . \quad . \quad (1.1)$$

where A_1 and A_2 are the cross-sections of the two conductors in square metres, and ρ_1 and ρ_2 are the resistivities of the material of the conductors in ohms per metre cube.

This simple formula only applies for line-transmission calculations for frequencies up to a few kilocycles per second. At the higher frequencies with which we shall be interested, it is necessary to take account of skin effect. For a qualitative understanding of skin effect we must examine the magnetic field associated with a conductor carrying a current.

Consider a long straight cylindrical wire of radius a metres, carrying a direct current, I amperes, the return conductor being removed to a distance. The magnetic field surrounding a current of I amperes in such a wire may be represented by a series of concentric circles and its intensity at a radius r metres is given by:

$$H = I/2\pi r \text{ amperes per metre} \quad . \quad . \quad . \quad . \quad (1.2)$$

The magnetic intensity in amperes per metre is in a direction tangential to the circles, and should not be confused with quantities distributed along the length of the line. This formula applies down to the surface of the wire. There is also a magnetic field of similar concentric circles within the wire itself. The magnetic field intensity at any radius r (less than a) is caused by the total current confined within that radius, namely $(r/a)^2 . I$ amperes. Thus from equation (1.2) the magnetic intensity at radius r within the conductor is given by:

$$H = Ir/2\pi a^2 \text{ amperes per metre} \quad . \quad . \quad . \quad . \quad (1.3)$$

From equation (1.3) we see that the field is zero at the centre of the wire and increases uniformly up to the surface of the wire. At greater radii the field is given by equation (1.2) and it decreases to zero again at infinity. Fig. 1.3 (a) shows the magnetic field and Fig. 1.3 (b) shows how the field intensity varies with radius in a plane at right angles to the wire.

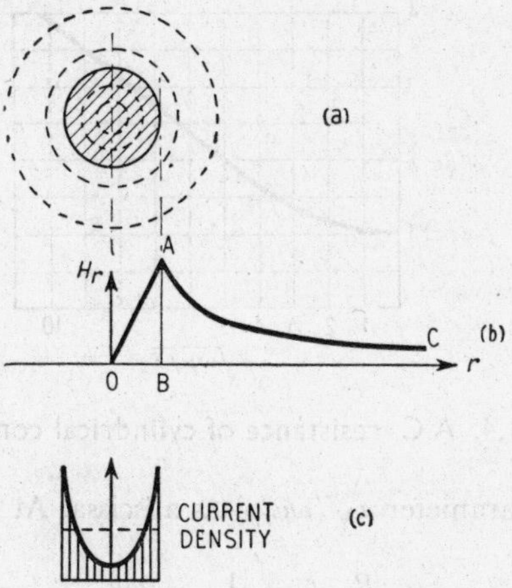

Fig. 1.3. Skin effect in a single conductor with remote return.

The flux density or magnetic induction B in webers per square metre is obtained from H in equations (1.2) and (1.3) by multiplying by:

$$\mu = \mu_r \mu_0$$

where $\mu_0 = 4\pi \times 10^{-7}$ henrys per metre,

and μ_r = relative permeability of the medium.

The ordinates of Fig. 1.3 (b) therefore represent to some scale the flux density.

A filament of conductor at the centre of the wire is linked by the total flux within the conductor plus the total flux outside the conductor; i.e., the whole area under Fig. 1.3 (b). The outer skin of the conductor is only linked by the flux outside the conductor; i.e., the area ABC.

If the current in the conductor is now made to vary sinusoidally, the central filament of conductor will encounter a higher e.m.f. of self-induction than the outer skin, since it is embraced by more magnetic flux. The current density at the centre therefore tends to fall below that at the skin. As the frequency is raised the effect becomes more pronounced and the distribution of current assumes the appearance shown by the curve in Fig. 1.3 (c) the density at the surface rising (for the same total current) and that at the centre falling. The field within the conductor also departs from the form shown in Fig. 1.3 (b). As the frequency is raised still further, the current density within the wire may even reverse (with respect to that at the surface of the wire) at certain radii. In fact, the penetration of the current into the wire at high frequencies behaves after the manner of an attenuated wave travelling from the surface to the centre of the wire. This method of approach will be developed in later chapters.

The actual calculation of the effective resistance per unit length of a conductor is outside the scope of this book. It is usual to express the resistance to alternating current of a wire as a ratio to the d.c. resistance. The value of this ratio $R_{a.c.}/R_{d.c.}$ is a function of the wire radius a, the angular frequency ω, the permeability $\mu = \mu_r\mu_0$ of the conductor, and the resistivity ρ. It is plotted in

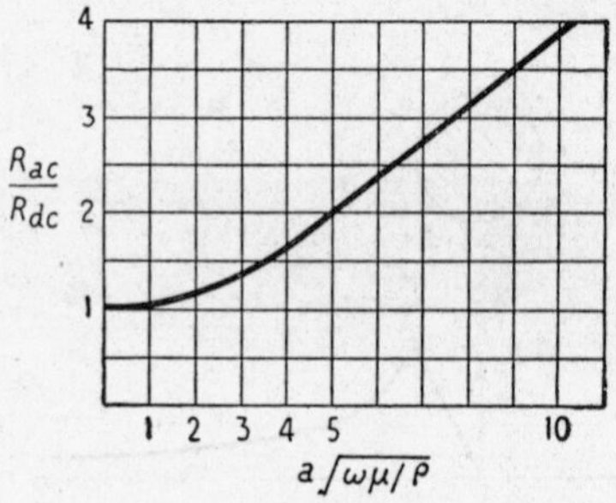

Fig. 1.4. A.C. resistance of cylindrical conductor.

Fig. 1.4 using the parameter $a\sqrt{(\omega\mu/\rho)}$ as abscissa. At high frequencies it can be shown that:

$$\frac{R_{a.c.}}{R_{d.c.}} = \frac{1}{2\sqrt{2}} a \sqrt{\frac{\omega\mu}{\rho}} \quad . \quad . \quad . \quad . \quad . \quad . \quad (1.4)$$

From equation (1.1), $R_{d.c.}$ per metre length is given by $\rho/\pi a^2$, hence $R_{a.c.}$ at high frequencies is given by:

$$R_{a.c.} = \frac{1}{2\pi a}\left(\frac{\omega\mu\rho}{2}\right)^{\frac{1}{2}} \quad . \quad . \quad . \quad . \quad . \quad . \quad (1.5)$$

Thus the resistance at high frequencies is proportional to the square roots of the frequency, permeability and resistivity. Furthermore $R_{a.c.}$ is inversely proportional to the radius a, whereas $R_{d.c.}$ is inversely proportional to a^2. The alternating current may be imagined to flow in a skin, the cross-sectional area of which is $2\pi a$ times the equivalent skin thickness δ so that the resistance of the skin is inversely proportional to a. Then we have:

$$R_{a.c.} = \frac{\rho}{2\pi a\delta} = \frac{1}{2\pi a}\left(\frac{\omega\mu\rho}{2}\right)^{\frac{1}{2}}$$

$$\therefore\ \delta = \sqrt{\frac{2\rho}{\omega\mu}} \text{ metres} \quad . \quad . \quad . \quad . \quad . \quad (1.6)$$

This equivalent thickness is often called the skin depth or thickness.

Thus for low a.c. resistance the radius should be as large as possible and μ and ρ should be as low as possible (e.g., copper). Since the above arguments show that the current at high frequencies is confined mainly to the skin of a wire the effect is termed skin effect. The use of tubular conductors suggests itself for high-frequency work, thereby ensuring a more economical use of conductor material. Although this is rarely possible for long lines it may be desirable for h.f. busbars. Some types of conductor consist of a copper strip bent, rolled and welded around a steel wire. The alternating current is mainly confined to the copper, little penetrating the steel on account of its permeability. This is an economical arrangement and the steel imparts additional strength to the conductor.

So far, attention has been confined to the skin effect of a single wire with a remote return. We must now consider any similar effect in the return conductor,

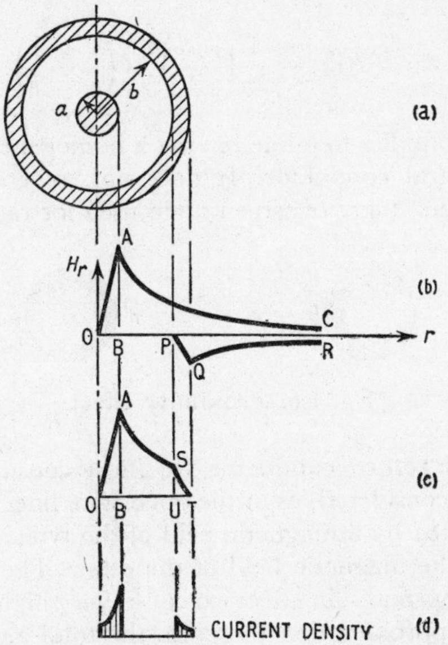

Fig. 1.5. Skin effect in a coaxial line.

and any influence it may have on the original wire. By reason of its symmetry the coaxial line is the simplest case for qualitative study.

The arrangement is shown in Fig. 1.5, the central conductor carrying a steady current I and the tube or screen carrying an equal and oppositely-flowing current. The magnetic field intensity, due to the central wire alone, is represented by OAC in Fig. 1.5 (b) while that due to the screen alone is zero on its inner surface, increasing negatively to the value shown by Q at its outer surface. At this outer surface the fields due to the wire and screen are just equal and opposite and for all greater radii the two fields cancel completely. The net field intensity is then as shown by Fig. 1.5 (c). First, we note that the screen current does not disturb the field distribution in the central wire. From this it can be deduced that as the frequency is increased, the skin effect of the central wire is the same as that for the isolated wire. Now consider a circuit formed from a short length of cable consisting of the central filament of the wire and the outer skin of the screen. The flux linked with this circuit is proportional to the area OAST of Fig. 1.5 (c). For the circuit consisting of the outer skin of the wire and the inner skin of the screen the flux linkages are proportional to BASU of Fig. 1.5 (c). Thus at high frequencies the first circuit encounters a higher e.m.f. of self-induction than the second circuit. The current tends to prefer the second circuit, and the current density rises at the outer surface of the wire and the inner surface of the screen. In other words the current tends to redistribute itself so as to embrace the minimum of magnetic flux. Fig. 1.5 (d) shows a typical current distribution. It can be shown that the equivalent skin thickness for the screen is given by equation (1.6) as for the central conductor. Hence the effective resistance of the screen is less than that of the central conductor owing to its greater radius. If the central conductor radius is *a* and the screen inner radius is *b*, we have from equation (1.5) the following equation for the total a.c. resistance per unit length of coaxial line at high frequencies:

$$R_{\text{a.c.}} = \frac{1}{2\pi}\left(\frac{\omega\mu\rho}{2}\right)^{\frac{1}{2}} \times \left(\frac{1}{a} + \frac{1}{b}\right) \quad . \quad . \quad . \quad . \quad (1.7)$$

This formula only applies to a line having a homogeneous screen of the same material as the central conductor. It does not, of course, apply with any accuracy to the braided types of screen often used for radio-frequency cable.

Fig. 1.6. Proximity effect.

The other type of return conductor we must consider is a parallel wire identical to that first considered, as in the open-wire line. We may imagine that each wire is surrounded by a magnetic field of the type shown in Fig. 1.3, and each wire is cut by the magnetic field of the other. The latter effect does not seriously modify the normal skin effect except at very high frequencies and close spacings. As a first approximation therefore the total a.c. resistance of a two-wire line is simply twice that of a single wire with remote return. At very high frequencies the current density tends to rise on the surfaces of the conductors facing one another. On the surfaces of the conductors remote from one another the current density tends to fall. This phenomenon is known as proximity effect, and it may be understood by a similar argument to that used for skin effect in coaxial cable. Thus referring to Fig. 1.6 the filaments B and B′ enclose less flux than filaments A and A′. As before filaments A and A′ will encounter a higher e.m.f. of self-induction than filaments B and B′, thus the current will tend to congregate on the inner surfaces of the wires, so as to embrace the least flux linkages.

Inductance per Unit Length

It was shown in the previous section that a current flowing in a long straight wire with the return conductor far removed, has a magnetic field which may be represented by concentric circles centred on the axis of the wire. If the current in the wire is changed the flux surrounding it changes, and induces a back e.m.f. of self-induction. That is, the wire has self-inductance, but its value cannot be determined until the return conductor is defined.

Considering first the coaxial line, it has been shown that the magnetic field exists only in the dielectric space between conductors, apart from the small fields in the conductors themselves. The latter will be neglected for the moment, so that the self-inductance per unit length is substantially dependent upon the total flux in the dielectric space. It is shown in Appendix 1.1 that the self-inductance per unit length of coaxial line is given by:

$$L_1 = \frac{\mu}{2\pi} \log_\varepsilon \left(\frac{b}{a}\right)$$

$$= \mu_r \times 2 \times 10^{-7} \times 2{\cdot}303 \log_{10} \frac{b}{a} \text{ henrys per metre} \quad . \quad (1.8)$$

Consider secondly, a return conductor which is similar to the first conductor and parallel to it as in the parallel-wire line. Let us assume that the wire spacing is d metres between the axes of the wires. The first wire may be considered to have the magnetic field of Fig. 1.3 while the second wire has a similar field but oppositely directed. The actual magnetic field in a cross-sectional plane is the vector sum of these two fields and its general configuration is shown by the dotted lines in Fig. 1.1 (a). The total magnetic flux per unit length which cuts the surface between the two wires determines the self-inductance of the line. We neglect again the flux linkages in the conductors themselves. It is shown in Appendix 1.2 that the self-inductance per unit length of parallel-wire line is given by:

$$L_2 = 2\frac{\mu}{2\pi} \log_\varepsilon \left(\frac{d}{a}\right)$$

$$= \mu_r \times 4 \times 10^{-7} \times 2{\cdot}303 \log_{10} \left(\frac{d}{a}\right) \text{ henrys per metre} \quad . \quad (1.9)$$

The inductance of the screened pair type of line cannot be calculated easily, but it will be somewhat less than the corresponding unscreened pair owing to the effect of currents induced in the screen.

In the study of skin effect it was seen that there are internal flux linkages which have been neglected in equations (1.8) and (1.9). These are a maximum at zero frequency but due to the redistribution of current caused by skin effect, the linkages decrease as the frequency is raised. Thus the internal inductance (that due to flux linkages inside the conductor) falls in proportion to $1/\sqrt{\omega}$ as ω is raised. The external inductance (that due to flux linkages outside the conductor) is almost independent of frequency and is usually large in comparison with the internal inductance. For most practical purposes, therefore, the inductance of a parallel-conductor line is independent of frequency.

From a.c. theory the reactance per unit length of a line is $j\omega L$ at an angular frequency of ω, and the impedance per unit length is $(R + j\omega L)$. This impedance is responsible for a drop of voltage in the conductors during transmission.

Leakage Conductance per Unit Length

There is a leakage current between the two conductors of a transmission line due to the imperfection of the dielectric or conductor supporting means. This leakage current consists of two components, one due to the pure leakage resistance, as would be measured by d.c., the other the current which supplies the losses of the dielectric under a.c. excitation. Thus, in a coaxial cable with, say, a polythene dielectric, the leakage current due to the resistance of the dielectric would be very small as polythene has an extremely high specific resistivity, whereas at very high radio frequencies there may be an appreciable loss current to supply the dielectric losses. However, an open-wire line on, say, wet insulators would exhibit an appreciable leakage current due to ohmic resistance between conductors, but the a.c. losses in the air dielectric would be small. The total a.c. leakage resistance is therefore related to the specific resistivity and the power factor of the dielectric.

It is more usual to use the leakage conductance per unit length (called the leakance, G ohms per metre), which is simply the reciprocal of the effective a.c. leakage resistance per unit length, when deducing the transmission performance of a line. The leakance invariably increases as the frequency is raised, but in a manner which is not amenable to calculation.

With solid dielectrics it is possible to predict the value of G from a measurement on a sample of the dielectric. Thus, if a slab of the proposed dielectric is arranged between the plates of a capacitor and its impedance is measured by a suitable a.c. bridge method, the result may be deduced in terms of two parallel connected impedances, a resistance component r', and a reactance component $1/j\omega c'$. The resistance takes a loss current in phase with the voltage while the capacitance takes a reactive current leading the voltage by 90°. The total current leads the voltage by an angle $(90 - \delta)$ where δ is called the loss angle for the dielectric. If v is the voltage applied to the capacitor, we have from the vector diagram of the currents:

$$\tan \delta = \frac{v/r'}{v\omega c'}$$

$$= \frac{1}{\omega c' r'}$$

$$= \frac{g'}{\omega c'}$$

where $g' = 1/r'$ is the conductance.

If from the dielectric and geometry of the line the capacitance per unit length C can be calculated as shown in Appendices 1·3 and 1·4, the leakance per unit length G to be expected is then:

$$G = \omega C \tan \delta$$

The loss angle δ varies with frequency, and the value corresponding to the frequency of interest must of course be used.

Capacitance per Unit Length

If a voltage is maintained between the two conductors of a transmission line an electric field will exist in the dielectric between them. The two conductors resemble the plates of a capacitor and they have a capacitance of C farads per unit length which depends upon the configuration of the line, and the relative permittivity of the dielectric.

When a single wire is remote from other bodies and is maintained at a potential with respect to such bodies, it has an electric field which may be represented by radial lines starting at the surface of the conductor. If now the wire is surrounded by a concentric conducting cylinder, as in coaxial cable, then the radial lines will terminate on the outer conductor as shown in Fig. 1.1 (d). This configuration of field is independent of the way the voltage is varied and thus C is almost independent of frequency. In fact, the permittivity of some dielectrics changes slightly with frequency and temperature but for most practical purposes C may be regarded as a true constant.

The electric field of a two-wire line, remote from other bodies, may be deduced by adding vectorially the two radial fields of the two wires with equal and opposite charges per unit length. This results in a field distribution as shown in Fig. 1.1 (a). However, when the two wires are brought very close together, as in a telephone cable, this method is inaccurate as the charges on the surfaces of the wires are no longer evenly distributed. The charge and electric field tend to concentrate on the surfaces of the two conductors which are closest to one another. The field distribution in such a line is also modified by the proximity of the earth or of a screen in the case of a screened pair. The calculation of capacitance is complex in all but a few simple cases.

It is shown in Appendix 1.3 that the capacitance per unit length of a coaxial line is given by:

$$C_1 = \frac{2\pi\kappa}{\log_\varepsilon (b/a)}$$

$$= \frac{\kappa_r}{18 \times 10^9 \times 2{\cdot}303} \times \frac{1}{\log_{10} (b/a)} \text{ farads per metre} \quad . \quad (1.10)$$

In this equation $\kappa = \kappa_r\kappa_0$, where κ_r is the relative permittivity of the dielectric, and $\kappa_0 = 1/(36\pi \times 10^9)$ farads per metre is the permittivity of free space.

It is shown in Appendix 1.4 that the capacitance per unit length of a two-wire line having a wire spacing between centres of d metres, is given by:

$$C_2 = \frac{2\pi\kappa}{2 \log_\varepsilon (d/a)}$$

$$= \frac{\kappa_r}{36 \times 10^9 \times 2{\cdot}303} \times \frac{1}{\log_{10} (d/a)} \text{ farads per metre} \quad . \quad (1.11)$$

Observe that the capacitances are proportional to κ_r and that squaring the spacing ratio b/a or d/a halves the capacitance.

From a.c. theory the susceptance per unit length of a line is $j\omega C$ mhos at an angular frequency of ω, and therefore the admittance between conductors per unit length is $(G + j\omega C)$. This admittance is responsible for a loss current in the dielectric and a reduction of the current in the conductors during transmission.

Characteristic Impedance

The primary characteristics which have just been discussed are the first stage in the determination of the transmission performance of a line, but before passing on to this, we must consider an important quantity known as the characteristic impedance.

Consider an infinitely long uniform line, and suppose that it is possible to measure the voltage and current at uniformly spaced intervals, as shown in Fig. 1.7, when a.c. power is being conveyed from left to right. Then if we take the ratio of the voltage to the current at each point we shall find that it is constant. This ratio is clearly an impedance, and it is that impedance which would be measured if the line were cut at any point and an impedance measurement made between the two conductors looking to the right. Since by assumption the line is infinitely long and uniform, wherever the line is cut the same

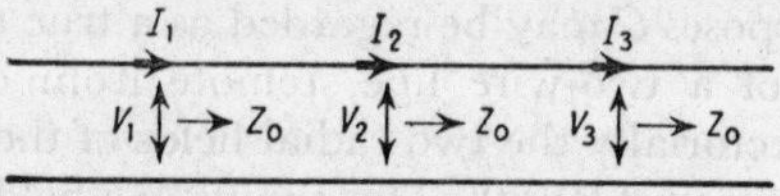

Fig. 1.7. Conception of characteristic impedance.

impedance between conductors will be obtained at a particular frequency. This impedance is called the characteristic impedance of the line and is usually designated by Z_0.

This impedance is in general complex; i.e., it has resistive and reactive components both of which vary with frequency. In all practical lines the reactance is capacitive; that is, the angle of the impedance is negative.

Fig. 1.8 shows a typical impedance–frequency curve for a uniform infinite line. The magnitude of the impedance starts at zero frequency at a high value, which can be shown to be given by $\sqrt{(R/G)}$. As the frequency is raised the impedance falls and it approaches asymptotically the value $\sqrt{(L/C)}$. The angle

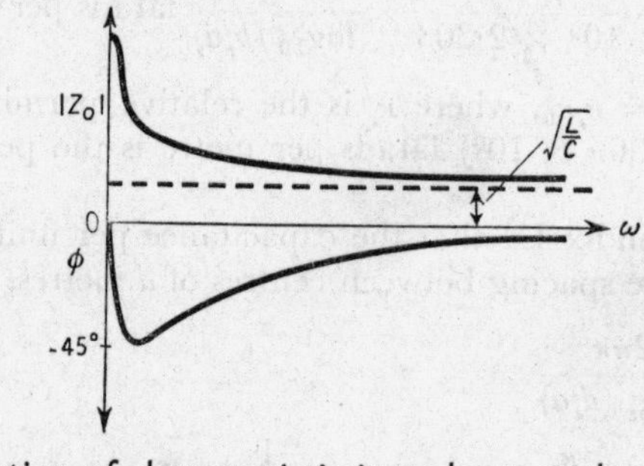

Fig. 1.8. Variation of characteristic impedance with angular frequency.

of the impedance is zero at zero frequency, but for low frequencies it rises to about $-45°$. As the frequency is increased the angle approaches zero again as shown in the lower part of Fig. 1.8.

Thus at very high frequencies the characteristic impedance is a pure resistance, given by:

$$Z_0 = \sqrt{\frac{L}{C}} \quad . \quad . \quad . \quad . \quad . \quad . \quad . \quad (1.12)$$

This is the value of impedance which is used when discussing and classifying lines and cables. It is often called the surge impedance since it is the impedance encountered by the high-frequency components of a surge wavefront.

Practical lines are not infinitely long and they must be terminated at some point in a load impedance. The effects which occur when a line is terminated in any impedance will be considered in Chapter 3, but a special case will be considered here. Suppose it were possible to construct a two-terminal load impedance from lumped components having exactly the characteristic of $Z_0(\omega)$ at all frequencies. Then if a line of finite length having characteristic impedance $Z_0(\omega)$ were terminated with this load impedance, the value of impedance measured at any point of cutting, looking towards the load, would still be $Z_0(\omega)$. That is, it would behave as an infinite line. This procedure is known as terminating the line with a matched impedance and it will be shown in Chapter 3 that this type of termination produces no reflection of energy. For most high-frequency applications it is only necessary to terminate the line with the asymptotic value of Z_0; that is, a pure resistance of value $\sqrt{(L/C)}$.

The characteristic impedance may be deduced from the primary constants in the following manner. Consider an infinitesimally short length δz of line in an infinitely long line, as shown in Fig. 1.9 (a). The resistance and inductance

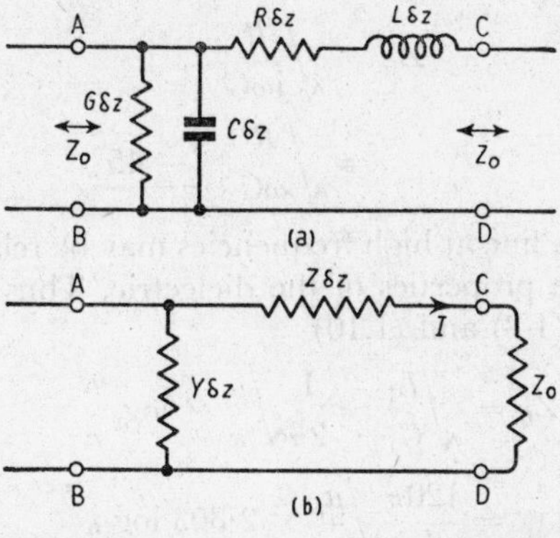

Fig. **1.9. Equivalent network for determining characteristic impedance of a line.**

are assumed to be entirely in the upper conductor, the lower conductor being a zero impedance return.

This short length of line may be represented by an L-network having a series impedance $Z\delta z = (R + \mathrm{j}\omega L)\,\delta z$ and a shunt admittance of $Y\delta z = (G + \mathrm{j}\omega C)\,\delta z$. The impedance in either direction if the line is cut at AB is Z_0. Then from Fig. 1.9 (b) the impedance looking to the right into terminals AB consists of an impedance $Z_0 + (Z\delta z)$ in parallel with an impedance $1/(Y\delta z)$ and it may be equated to Z_0 thus:

$$Z_0 = \frac{\{Z_0 + (Z\delta z)\}\{1/(Y\delta z)\}}{Z_0 + (Z\delta z) + 1/(Y\delta z)}$$

$$= \frac{Z_0 + (Z\delta z)}{1 + Z_0(Y\delta z)}$$

(The product of the two small quantities $Z\delta z$ and $Y\delta z$ is neglected in comparison with either one alone.)

Solving for Z_0 we obtain:

$$Z_0 = \sqrt{\frac{Z}{Y}} = \sqrt{\frac{R + \mathrm{j}\omega L}{G + \mathrm{j}\omega C}}$$

$$= \left(\frac{R^2 + \omega^2 L^2}{G^2 + \omega^2 C^2}\right)^{1/4} \Big/ \underline{\tfrac{1}{2}\left(\tan^{-1}\frac{\omega L}{R} - \tan^{-1}\frac{\omega C}{G}\right)} \quad . \quad . \quad (1.13)$$

A close examination of equation (1.13) enables the results stated above to be deduced. By putting $\omega = 0$ we get the impedance at zero frequency:

$$Z_0 = \sqrt{\frac{R}{G}} \quad . \quad . \quad . \quad . \quad . \quad . \quad (1.14)$$

When ω becomes large enough for R to be neglected in comparison with ωL, and G to be neglected in comparison with ωC, we get:

$$Z_0 = \sqrt{\frac{\mathrm{j}\omega L}{\mathrm{j}\omega C}}$$

$$= \sqrt{\frac{L}{C}} \quad . \quad . \quad . \quad . \quad . \quad . \quad . \quad . \quad (1.15)$$

At a low intermediate frequency where ωL is small compared with R, and G is small compared with ωC, we get:

$$Z_0 = \sqrt{\frac{R}{\mathrm{j}\omega C}}$$

$$= \sqrt{\frac{R}{\omega C}} \; \underline{/-45^\circ} \quad . \quad . \quad . \quad . \quad . \quad (1.16)$$

The impedance of a line at high frequencies may be related to its geometrical configuration and the properties of the dielectric. Thus for a coaxial line we have from equations (1.8) and (1.10)

$$Z_0 = \sqrt{\frac{L_1}{C_1}} = \frac{1}{2\pi}\sqrt{\frac{\mu}{\kappa}} \times \log_\varepsilon \frac{b}{a}$$

$$= \frac{120\pi}{2\pi}\sqrt{\frac{\mu_r}{\kappa_r}} \times 2{\cdot}303 \log_{10} \frac{b}{a}$$

$$= 138\sqrt{\frac{\mu_r}{\kappa_r}} \times \log_{10} \frac{b}{a} \quad . \quad . \quad . \quad . \quad . \quad . \quad . \quad (1.17)$$

since in the m.k.s system of units we have:

$$\sqrt{\frac{\mu}{\kappa}} = \sqrt{\frac{\mu_r\mu_0}{\kappa_r\kappa_0}} = 120\pi\sqrt{\frac{\mu_r}{\kappa_r}}$$

The optimum value of the ratio b/a for minimum attenuation is of the order of 3·6 and substituted in the above equation gives an impedance of about 75 ohms for air-spaced coaxial line. A solid dielectric such as polythene reduces the impedance to about 50 ohms. Values between these two limits are encountered in practice. The relative permeability is normally unity but it should be noted that any method of artificially raising the inductance increases the characteristic impedance.

For a two-wire line, we have from equations (1.9) and (1.11):

$$Z_0 = \sqrt{\frac{L_2}{C_2}} = \frac{1}{\pi}\sqrt{\frac{\mu}{\kappa}} \times \log_\varepsilon \frac{d}{a}$$

$$= \frac{120\pi}{\pi}\sqrt{\frac{\mu_r}{\kappa_r}} \times 2{\cdot}303 \log_{10} \frac{d}{a}$$

$$= 276\sqrt{\frac{\mu_r}{\kappa_r}} \times \log_{10} \frac{d}{a} \quad . \quad . \quad . \quad . \quad . \quad . \quad (1.18)$$

The relationship between high-frequency characteristic impedance and spacing ratio is plotted in Fig. 1.15 (in Appendix 1.4) for air-spaced lines. For paired cable the spacing ratio usually employed gives an impedance of about 150 ohms, while for open-wire lines the figure is about 600 ohms.

Attenuation

In all practical transmission lines there is a loss of power during transmission, and it is necessary to determine the manner in which the input power is decreased or attenuated before arriving in the load impedance.

A transmission line is a linear system; this means that the output power, voltage or current is directly proportional to the input power, voltage or current respectively. This follows because a line is built up from the linear components R, L, G and C (i.e., components which have impedances which obey Ohm's Law at a particular frequency). Thus referring to Fig. 1.7, since the sections are of equal length and the line is infinite, we can state immediately:

$$V_2 = KV_1, \quad V_3 = KV_2, \quad \text{etc.,}$$
$$V_1/I_1 = V_2/I_2 = V_3/I_3 \ldots = Z_0$$
$$\therefore\ I_2 = KI_1, \quad I_3 = KI_2, \quad \text{etc.} \qquad (1.19)$$

where K is a constant less than unity.

We observe that in an infinite line the voltage and current decrease in the same manner. The voltage after two sections of line is:

$$V_3 = KV_2 = K^2V_1$$

and after n sections:

$$V_n = K^nV_1 \qquad (1.20)$$

The curve of voltage against number of sections for a uniform infinite or correctly terminated line is shown in Fig. 1.10. This is the r.m.s. voltage, and phase is not taken into account at the moment.

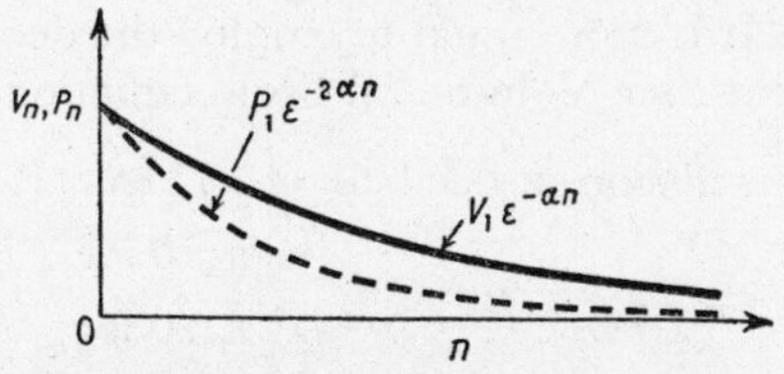

Fig. 1.10. Attenuation of voltage and power in a line.

Quantities which decrease according to the law of equation (1.20) are said to be 'logarithmically attenuated'. The constant K might be called the voltage- or current-attenuation factor, but it is rarely employed since there is a more convenient method of definition. Thus taking logarithms to base ε on both sides of equation (1.20) we obtain:

$$\log_\varepsilon (V_n/V_1) = n \log_\varepsilon K \qquad (1.21)$$

Let

$$K = \varepsilon^{-\alpha} \qquad (1.22)$$

Then

$$\log_\varepsilon (V_n/V_1) = -n\alpha \qquad (1.23)$$

The left-hand side of this equation is defined as the transmission loss or attenuation in 'nepers', a term which is derived from Napier who introduced natural logarithms. The negative sign on the right-hand side merely confirms that we are concerned with a loss. The constant α may be determined from equation (1.22). Thus:

$$\begin{aligned}\alpha &= \log_\varepsilon (1/K) \\ &= \log_\varepsilon (V_1/V_2) \text{ nepers} \quad . \quad . \quad . \quad . \quad . \quad (1.24)\end{aligned}$$

The right-hand side of this equation is the transmission loss of one section in nepers. Normally one section of line in Fig. 1.7 would be unit length, and equation (1.23) shows how to find the attenuation of a length n. The advantage of employing the logarithmic unit is that the attenuation of a number of lengths of line is given by adding the attenuations of the constituent parts as indicated by equation (1.23), whereas if the attenuation factor K were employed it would be necessary to multiply the attenuation factors of the constituent parts as indicated by equation (1.20).

Considering now the attenuation of the power, suppose ϕ is the angle of the characteristic impedance, then power entering the first section:

$$P_1 = V_1 I_1 \cos\phi$$

and that entering the second section:

$$P_2 = V_2 I_2 \cos\phi$$

and so on. Then we have from equation (1.19):

$$\begin{aligned}P_2 &= \frac{V_2 I_2 \cos\phi}{V_1 I_1 \cos\phi} P_1 \\ &= K^2 P_1\end{aligned}$$

or

$$P_n = K^{2n} P_1 \quad . \quad . \quad . \quad . \quad . \quad . \quad (1.25)$$

The attenuation factor for power is the square of that for voltage or current, as shown in Fig. 1.10. It is more usual to employ the decibel as the unit of loss in transmission problems (see Volume 2). From equation (1.25) we then have:

$$\begin{aligned}\text{Transmission in decibels} &= 10 \log_{10} (P_n/P_1) \\ &= n.10 \log_{10} K^2 \\ &= n.20 \log_{10} K \quad . \quad . \quad . \quad . \quad (1.26)\end{aligned}$$

This is again negative, indicating a loss, since K is less than unity. The term $20 \log_{10} K$ is clearly the decibels loss per unit length considered, and to find the loss for a length n it is merely necessary to multiply by n.

Example

A telephone line 12 miles long is correctly match terminated at the receiving end. At a certain frequency the voltage 1 mile from the sending end is 10% below that at the sending end. Find the attenuation per mile in decibels and the received voltage across the load impedance expressed as a percentage of the transmitted voltage.

For an input voltage of 1 volt the voltage after 1 mile would be 0·9 volt. By definition the attenuation per mile is:

$$\begin{aligned}20 \log_{10} (1/0{\cdot}9) &= 0{\cdot}92 \text{ db/mile} \\ \text{Total line attenuation} &= 12 \times 0{\cdot}92 \text{ db} \\ &= 11{\cdot}04 \text{ db}\end{aligned}$$

Let V_2 be received voltage, then:

$$20 \log_{10} (1/V_2) = 11{\cdot}04$$
$$\log_{10} V_2 = -0{\cdot}552$$
$$V_2 = \text{antilog } \bar{1}{\cdot}448$$
$$= 0{\cdot}28$$

or the received voltage is 28% of the transmitted voltage.

The above shows that the voltage, current and power are attenuated logarithmically, but it does not show how the attenuation depends upon the primary characteristics R, L, G and C. This relation may be deduced by reconsidering the element of line shown in Fig. 1.9. Suppose V_z is the input voltage to this section and $V_{z+\delta z}$ the output voltage. If I is the current at the output of the section, then:

$$V_z = I\{Z_0 + (R + \mathrm{j}\omega L)\,\delta z\}$$

Also
$$V_{z+\delta z} = IZ_0$$

Hence
$$\frac{V_z}{V_{z+\delta z}} = 1 + \left(\frac{R + \mathrm{j}\omega L}{Z_0}\right)\delta z$$
$$= 1 + \sqrt{\{(R + \mathrm{j}\omega L)(G + \mathrm{j}\omega C)\}}\,\delta z$$

using the predetermined relation between Z_0 and the primary constants. If we denote $\sqrt{\{(R + \mathrm{j}\omega L)(G + \mathrm{j}\omega C)\}}$ by the Greek letter γ (gamma), and observe that there are $z/\delta z$ elements in a length z, then the input to output voltage ratio for a length z is given by:

$$\frac{V_1}{V_z} = (1 + \gamma\delta z)^{z/\delta z}$$

and expanding by the Binomial Theorem:

$$\frac{V_1}{V_z} = 1 + \gamma z + \frac{z}{\delta z}\left(\frac{z}{\delta z} - 1\right)\frac{\gamma^2 \delta z^2}{2!} + \ldots$$

If δz is made vanishingly small this becomes:

$$\frac{V_1}{V_z} = 1 + \gamma z + \frac{\gamma^2 z^2}{2!} + \ldots$$

or
$$V_z = V_1 . \varepsilon^{-\gamma z} \qquad (1.27)$$

This result is derived by a more rigorous method in Appendix 1.5.

The coefficient γ is called the propagation coefficient and examination of the formula:

$$\gamma = \sqrt{\{(R + \mathrm{j}\omega L)(G + \mathrm{j}\omega C)\}} \qquad (1.28)$$

shows that it is always complex except at zero frequency. Separation of the real and imaginary parts of γ is a little tedious, and will not be attempted here, since approximations are given in Chapter 2. These parts are usually represented by α (alpha) and β (beta), thus:

$$\gamma = \alpha + \mathrm{j}\beta$$

and
$$V_z = V_1 \varepsilon^{-\alpha z} \varepsilon^{-\mathrm{j}\beta z} \qquad (1.29)$$

The coefficient α has already been defined as the attenuation in nepers and it determines the way in which the r.m.s. amplitude of voltage or current is attenuated. The term $\varepsilon^{-j\beta z}$ shows that there is a phase shift or lag between input and output, and β is known as the phase-shift coefficient. The reason for this will be understood from the qualitative argument of the next section.

It can be shown that $\varepsilon^{-j\beta z}$ is related to the circular functions as follows:

$$\varepsilon^{-j\beta z} = \cos \beta z - j \sin \beta z$$

It can be seen from the right-hand side of this function that $\varepsilon^{-j\beta z}$ has a modulus which is always unity and that it represents a unit vector at an angle $-\beta z$ radians to the reference vector. Thus as we proceed down the length of the line this unit vector, and hence the phase of the voltage with respect to the sending end, rotates in a clockwise direction. It may make several revolutions in a long line.

The characteristic impedance Z_0 and the propagation coefficient γ, defined by equations (1.13) and (1.28), are known as the secondary characteristics of a transmission line. The equations show that they are dependent upon frequency and the primary characteristics R, L, G and C. Either set of characteristics completely defines a line, but the secondary characteristics are of more practical value since they determine the impedance of generator and load to be used, and the loss to be expected.

Phase Shift

When a line is transmitting alternating current of angular frequency ω there is a progressive lag of phase of voltage and current during transmission. Returning to Fig. 1.9 we can get a picture of the situation by supposing R and G are

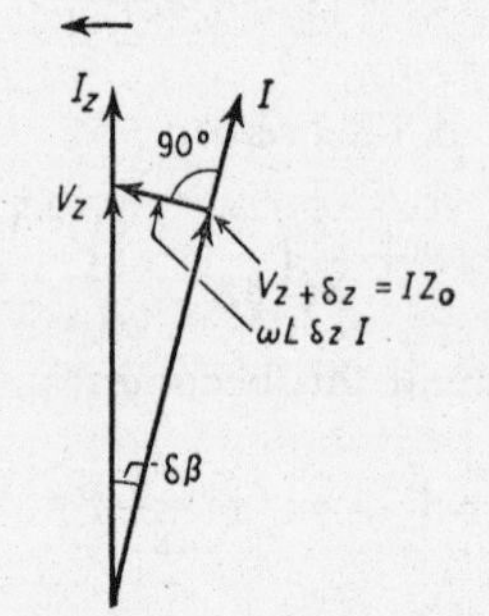

Fig. 1.11. Phase shift in a short section of ideal line.

negligible and therefore $Z_0 = \sqrt{(L/C)}$. If V_z is the voltage across AB and $V_{z+\delta z}$ the voltage across CD, we can construct a vector diagram for the element. If I is the line current at CD, then V_z is equal to the vector sum of IZ_0 and $j\omega LI\delta z$. Provided δz is small the vector diagram will resemble that in Fig. 1.11.

The phase shift or lag for the element is $\delta\beta$ radians, and its value is given by:

$$\delta\beta = \frac{\omega L\delta z I}{IZ_0}$$

$$= \frac{\omega L}{\sqrt{(L/C)}}\delta z$$

$$= \omega\sqrt{LC}\,.\,\delta z$$

The ratio of $\delta\beta$ to δz is the phase shift per unit length usually denoted by β radians per metre. Therefore we have:

$$\beta = \omega\sqrt{LC} \text{ radians per metre} \quad . \quad . \quad . \quad . \quad (1.30)$$

This is in fact the phase shift per unit length for a line carrying a sinusoidal a.c. at a very high frequency. At lower frequencies where R and G are not negligible the phase shift is a complicated function of ω, R, L, G and C. The graph of β against ω is known as the phase characteristic.

This phase shift during transmission can now be identified as a consequence of wave propagation. Suppose we draw vectors showing the phase of the voltage at various points in a line as in the lower part of Fig. 1.12. These vectors all

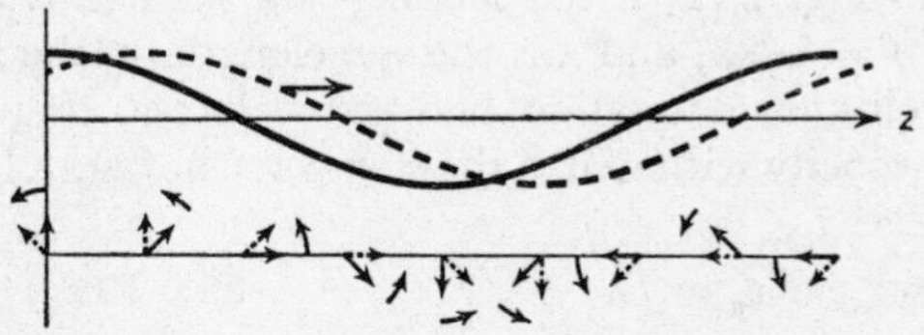

Fig. 1.12. Propagation of voltage or current wave in an ideal line.

rotate anti-clockwise according to convention, but as we pass down the line they lag more and more behind the sending-end vector at the left. If the instantaneous voltage is given by the projection on a vertical axis, the graph of instantaneous voltage between conductors plotted against distance down the line is as shown in the upper part of Fig. 1.12. If we examine conditions a brief instant later the vectors will have rotated to the dotted positions and the voltage wave will have advanced down the line to the dotted position. The voltage at any point can be imagined to be caused by a sine wave of voltage which slides or propagates smoothly down the line. Such a wave is called a progressive or travelling wave.

These results may be expressed in a very convenient mathematical form, which gives the voltage at any point distant z from the sending end. If $V_1 \sin \omega t$ is the voltage applied at the sending end, the voltage at z will lag βz radians behind the sending-end voltage. Hence the voltage at z may be represented by:

$$V_z = V_1 \sin(\omega t - \beta z)$$

$$= V_1 \sin \omega\left(t - \frac{\beta}{\omega}z\right) \quad . \quad . \quad . \quad . \quad . \quad (1.31)$$

This shows that the voltage at z is similar to that at the sending end apart from a delay $(\beta/\omega)z$ seconds. This aspect will be treated more fully in the next section.

The above argument has ignored attenuation, but this can be taken into account by imagining that at the same time the amplitude of the voltage wave is compressed according to the curve of Fig. 1.10. The picture we then get is similar to Fig. 1.13 where the voltage wave propagates to the right, its amplitude always falling within the envelope which may be represented by the curve $\varepsilon^{-\alpha z}$, where z is the distance from the sending end. Equation (1.31) is easily modified to cover this case by multiplying by the attenuation factor, thus:

$$V_z = V_1 . \varepsilon^{-\alpha z} \sin \omega\left(t - \frac{\beta}{\omega}z\right) \quad . \quad . \quad . \quad . \quad . \quad (1.32)$$

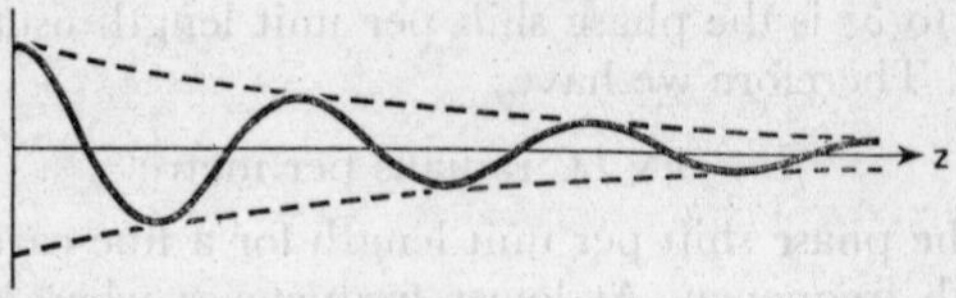

Fig. 1.13. Propagation of voltage or current in an attenuating line.

Velocity of Propagation of Phase

The manner in which the voltage and current, at a point in a line, lag in phase behind the corresponding sending-end quantities suggests a transmission delay. Referring to Fig. 1.12, if the sending-end voltage is a continuous sine wave of frequency $f = \omega/2\pi$, and λ is the wavelength on the line in metres, we may apply the well-known relation between velocity, frequency and wavelength. If v_p is the velocity with which the sine wave of Fig. 1.12 is moving along the line, we have:

$$v_p = f\lambda$$

$$= \frac{\omega}{2\pi}\lambda \text{ metres per second}$$

But λ is the distance for a phase change of 2π radians, and β is the phase change in radians per metre (or $1/\beta$ is the distance for a phase change of 1 radian). Hence we have:

$$\lambda = \frac{2\pi}{\beta} \text{ metres} \quad . \quad . \quad . \quad . \quad . \quad . \quad (1.33)$$

and substituting above we obtain:

$$v_p = \frac{\omega}{\beta} \text{ metres per second} \quad . \quad . \quad . \quad . \quad . \quad (1.34)$$

On the right-hand side of this equation we have radians per second divided by radians per metre which results in a velocity in metres per second. This velocity is known as the phase velocity because it is the velocity with which phase is transmitted down the line. Its reciprocal is the phase delay per unit length.

If the resistance and leakance of a line are negligible then β is a linear function of ω as in equation (1.30). We can then substitute in equation (1.34) and get:

$$v_p = \frac{1}{\sqrt{LC}} \text{ metres per second} \quad . \quad . \quad . \quad . \quad . \quad (1.35)$$

In this instance the phase velocity is independent of frequency. Since a signal can be considered to be made up of a number of frequencies it is clear that in this case the signal is transmitted with no distortion and with the velocity v_p.

On the other hand if β is not directly proportional to ω (i.e., resistance and leakance are no longer negligible) then the phase velocity varies with frequency, a condition which is called dispersion. The existence of this condition implies that there will be phase distortion of a signal consisting of a complex waveform as described in Chapter 2. It is no longer possible to state the velocity of the signal with any precision, since it becomes distorted during transmission. The phase velocity is no longer the velocity of a signal, and it is not the velocity of propagation of energy. It is important to appreciate that when a line is dispersive the phase velocity has only one meaning, namely the velocity with which the phase of a steady sine wave is propagated. Such a steady sine wave cannot convey a signal.

Distance along a line can be measured in metres or, alternatively, in the electrical units of wavelengths or phase shift in radians (for a given frequency). The latter is sometimes convenient particularly when dealing with high-frequency lines. These methods of measurement may be summarized as:

$$z \text{ metres}$$

$$n = \frac{z}{\lambda} \text{ wavelengths}$$

$$\theta = \frac{z}{\lambda}2\pi \text{ radians}$$

$$= \beta z \text{ radians}$$

$$= \frac{\omega}{v_p} z \text{ radians}$$

Returning to equation (1.35) the inductance and capacitance per unit length may be eliminated by using equations such as (1.8) and (1.10) for coaxial line, or (1.9) and (1.11) for parallel wire line. In either case we get the result:

$$v_p = \frac{1}{\sqrt{\mu\kappa}} \text{ metres per second}$$

$$= \frac{1}{\sqrt{\mu_0\kappa_0}} \cdot \frac{1}{\sqrt{\mu_r\kappa_r}}$$

$$= \frac{3 \times 10^8}{\sqrt{\mu_r\kappa_r}} \text{ metres per second}$$

because $\mu_0 = 4\pi \times 10^{-7}$ and $\kappa_0 = \frac{1}{36\pi} \times 10^{-9}$

The constant $\frac{1}{\sqrt{\mu_0\kappa_0}} = 3 \times 10^8$ is the velocity of light or, more generally, of electromagnetic waves in free space, in metres per second. It is usually denoted by c.

Thus we have :

$$v_p = \frac{c}{\sqrt{\mu_r\kappa_r}} \qquad (1.36)$$

This equation shows that the presence of any material medium lowers the phase velocity. The fact that in free space, where $\mu_r = \kappa_r = 1$, the phase velocity turns out to be the velocity of light, suggests that the propagation is similar to the propagation of electromagnetic waves. We shall find in Chapter 5 that the energy transmitted by a line is in fact conveyed by an electromagnetic wave in the dielectric space.

It should be noted that the phase velocity cannot exceed c in the case of line transmission. We shall find in a later chapter another type of transmission using waveguides, in which the phase velocity exceeds c.

▶ Group Velocity

When transmission is dispersive it is necessary to know the velocity with which a signal is transmitted. A continuous sine wave cannot convey any intelligence, so that observations on such a wave will not yield the signal velocity. Our signal must cover a band of frequencies, but this band must be very narrow otherwise the signal would be distorted during transmission so as to be unrecognizable. In the latter event signal velocity has no precise meaning.

We shall take as the signal, therefore, two steady sine waves of equal amplitude, one having an angular frequency ω, the other having a slightly larger angular frequency $(\omega + \delta\omega)$. These two sine waves when plotted and added, produce beats as shown in Fig. 1.14. The envelope will be found to have an angular frequency of $\delta\omega/2$. This can be proved as follows:

$$\text{Input signal} = \cos \omega t + \cos (\omega + \delta\omega)t$$
$$= 2 \cos \frac{\delta\omega}{2}t \left[\cos \left(\omega + \frac{\delta\omega}{2}\right)t\right]$$

The term in square brackets is the mean frequency of the two sine waves and is the frequency of the full line in Fig. 1.14. The term outside the square brackets

Fig. 1.14. Signal for discussion of group velocity.

shows how the amplitude of this curve is varied; that is, it gives the envelope shown dotted. Its angular frequency is $\delta\omega/2$.

Suppose that β is the phase shift for unit length of line at ω, and $(\beta + \delta\beta)$ the phase shift at $(\omega + \delta\omega)$. Then we have for a unit length of line:

$$\text{Output signal} = \cos (\omega t - \beta) + \cos \{(\omega + \delta\omega)t - (\beta + \delta\beta)\}$$
$$= 2 \cos \left(\frac{\delta\omega}{2}t - \frac{\delta\beta}{2}\right)\left[\cos\left\{\left(\omega + \frac{\delta\omega}{2}\right)t - \left(\beta + \frac{\delta\beta}{2}\right)\right\}\right] \quad . \quad (1.37)$$

The term in square brackets is the enclosed frequency, but we are not concerned with this. The term $2 \cos \left(\frac{\delta\omega}{2}t - \frac{\delta\beta}{2}\right)$ is the envelope, and it lags the input envelope by $\delta\beta/2$ radians.

The velocity of the signal is the velocity with which the envelope is propagated. This is known as the envelope or group velocity, and by the argument of the previous section it is given by:

$$v_g = \frac{\delta\omega}{2} \Big/ \frac{\delta\beta}{2}$$
$$= \frac{\delta\omega}{\delta\beta} \text{ metres per second} \quad . \quad . \quad . \quad . \quad . \quad (1.38)$$

The reciprocal is the group or envelope delay in seconds per metre, and it is the differential slope of the β versus ω characteristic.

As a general rule, dispersion is negligible in radio-frequency lines and it only needs to be taken into account when dealing with low-frequency lines which have to transmit signal waveforms very faithfully. However, it reassumes importance in later chapters in connection with waveguide transmission. ◀

APPENDIX 1.1

Calculation of the Inductance for a Coaxial Line

Consider a coaxial line having a central conductor of radius *a* metres and a tube of inner radius *b* metres. The central conductor will have a magnetic field represented by concentric circles and the field intensity at a radius *r* (greater than *a*) due to a current *I* will be given by:

$$H_r = \frac{I}{2\pi r} \text{ amperes per metre} \quad . \quad . \quad . \quad . \quad . \quad (1.39)$$

The outer tube will produce no field within the dielectric space but outside the tube it will produce a field at radius $r > b$ of:

$$H_r = -\frac{I}{2\pi r}$$

This field will however be cancelled exactly by the field due to the central conductor.

The field distribution is therefore of the form given by equation (1.39) in the dielectric space together with a weaker field within the central conductor and within the cross section of the tube. The field in the dielectric space is responsible for the external inductance. The field in the conductors is responsible for the internal inductance. The latter inductance varies with frequency and is related to skin effect, but it is usually small in comparison with the external inductance. Therefore we shall calculate the external inductance only.

The flux linking an area of d*r* radial thickness by 1 metre length along the line is:

$$\frac{I\mu \,\mathrm{d}r}{2\pi r}$$

The total flux linkages are therefore:

$$\int_a^b \frac{I\mu \,\mathrm{d}r}{2\pi r} = \left[\frac{I\mu}{2\pi} \log_\varepsilon r\right]_a^b$$

The inductance per metre is given by the flux linkages per ampere, thus:

$$L_1 = \frac{\mu}{2\pi} \log_\varepsilon \frac{b}{a} \text{ henrys per metre}$$

In this equation $\mu = \mu_r \mu_0$. Normally μ_r is unity, and $\mu_0 = 4\pi \times 10^{-7}$ henrys per metre, the permeability of free space.

APPENDIX 1.2

Calculation of the Inductance for a Paired Line

Consider a paired line consisting of two conductors each of radius a metres and spaced d metres apart between centres. The internal inductance due to flux in the conductors themselves is again neglected.

Then the inductance of the line is caused by the flux due to one conductor from its surface out to the other conductor, plus a similar amount of flux due to the other conductor. If the spacing to radius ratio d/a is large the limits of integration are approximately a to d. Thus flux linkages per metre due to one conductor are:

$$\int_a^d \frac{I\mu \, \mathrm{d}r}{2\pi r} = \frac{I\mu}{2\pi} \log_\varepsilon \frac{d}{a}$$

where I is the current in this line and μ has the same meaning as before.

The flux linkages per metre are double this since there are two conductors. The inductance per metre is given by the total flux linkages per ampere, thus:

$$L_2 = \frac{\mu}{\pi} \log_\varepsilon \frac{d}{a} \text{ henrys per metre} \quad . \quad . \quad . \quad . \quad (1.40)$$

This formula is inaccurate for small values of the ratio d/a. For a spacing to radius ratio of 10 the inaccuracy is about 5%, but for closer spacings the error increases.

APPENDIX 1.3

Calculation of the Capacitance for a Coaxial Line

Consider a coaxial line having a central conductor of radius a metres and a tube of inner radius b metres.

Suppose a voltage V is maintained between conductors and that there is a charge of $+q$ and $-q$ coulombs per unit length on the two conductors. Then in the m.k.s. system of units, the electric displacement D_r at radius r (greater than a and less than b) will be given by:

$$D_r = \frac{q}{2\pi r} \text{ coulombs per square metre} \quad . \quad . \quad . \quad . \quad (1.41)$$

Also $\qquad D_r = \kappa E_r$

where E_r is the electric field intensity at radius r.

Now
$$V = \int_a^b E_r \, \mathrm{d}r$$
$$= \int_a^b \frac{q}{2\pi r \kappa} \, \mathrm{d}r$$
$$= \frac{q}{2\pi\kappa} \log_\varepsilon \frac{b}{a}$$

The capacitance per unit length C_1 is given by q/V:

$$\therefore\ C_1 = \frac{2\pi\kappa}{\log_\varepsilon (b/a)} \text{ farads per metre} \quad . \quad . \quad . \quad . \quad (1.42)$$

In this equation $\kappa = \kappa_r\kappa_0$, where κ_r is the relative permittivity of the dielectric and:

$$\kappa_0 = 1/(36\pi \times 10^9) \text{ farads per metre}$$

the permittivity of free space.

APPENDIX 1.4

Calculation of the Capacitance for a Paired Line

Consider a paired line consisting of two conductors of cross-section radius a metres, spaced d metres between axes. Let $+q$ and $-q$ coulomb charges be placed on each metre length of wire. The electric field distribution in Fig. 1.1 (a) is clearly symmetrical about the central vertical axis. The electric displacement D_r at radius r is the sum of that due to each conductor on a line joining the two conductors, thus:

$$D_r = \left\{\frac{q}{2\pi r} - \frac{-q}{2\pi(d-r)}\right\} \text{ coulombs per square metre} \quad . \quad (1.43)$$

The electric field intensity E_r at radius r is:

$$E_r = \frac{D_r}{\kappa}$$

where κ has the same meaning as in Appendix 1.3.

The voltage between the conductors is twice the voltage between the surface of one conductor and the central vertical axis.

Thus
$$V = 2\int_a^{d/2} E_r \,\mathrm{d}r$$

$$= 2\frac{q}{2\pi\kappa}\left[\log_\varepsilon \frac{r}{d-r}\right]_a^{d/2}$$

$$= \frac{q}{\pi\kappa}\log_\varepsilon\left(\frac{d-a}{a}\right)$$

The capacitance C_2 per unit length is then given by:

$$C_2 = \frac{q}{V}$$

$$= \frac{\pi\kappa}{\log_\varepsilon\left(\dfrac{d-a}{a}\right)} \quad . \quad . \quad . \quad . \quad . \quad . \quad (1.44)$$

This formula is only applicable for large spacing to radius ratio d/a, since at close spacings the charge is not uniformly spread over the surface of the wires. Hence for large spacings:

$$C_2 = \frac{\pi\kappa}{\log_\varepsilon (d/a)} \text{ farads per metre} \quad . \quad . \quad . \quad . \quad (1.45)$$

For a spacing-to-radius ratio of 10, the inaccuracy is about 10% but for closer spacings the error increases.

The results of Appendices 1.1 to 1.4 enable the relationship between characteristic impedance and spacing ratio to be determined. These results

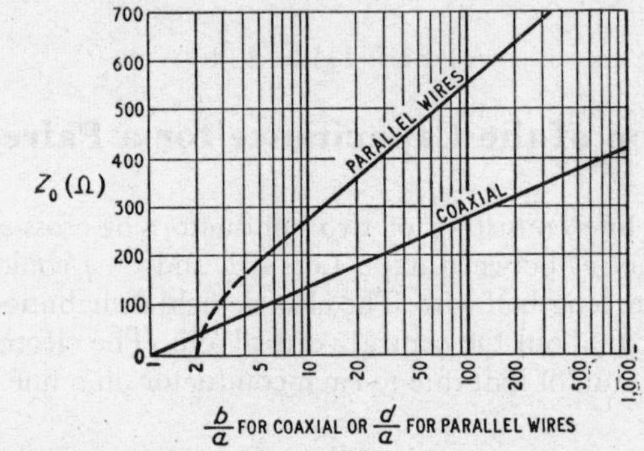

Fig. 1.15. Characteristic impedance of air-spaced coaxial and parallel-wire lines. For coaxial lines, b/a is the ratio of the inside radius of the outer conductor to the outside radius of the inner. For parallel-wire lines d is the spacing between wire centres and a is the radius.

were deduced in equations (1.17) and (1.18). The graphs of characteristic impedance versus spacing ratio are given in Fig. 1.15 for air-spaced coaxial and parallel-wire lines.

APPENDIX 1.5

The Transmission Equations

The differential equation defining the voltage and current distribution in a uniform transmission line, having at some point a voltage of angular frequency ω applied between conductors, can be deduced from Fig. 1.9 (a). Let V be the voltage across the line at a point, distant z from an arbitrary origin.

Considering first of all the drop of voltage in a short length δz we get:

$$\delta V = -(R + j\omega L)I\,\delta z$$

$$\therefore \frac{dV}{dz} = -(R + j\omega L)I \quad . \quad . \quad . \quad . \quad . \quad . \quad (1.46)$$

The negative sign indicates a decrease of the voltage between conductors.

Similarly the loss of current in a short length δz is:

$$\delta I = -(G + j\omega C) V \delta z$$

$$\therefore \frac{dI}{dz} = -(G + j\omega C) V \quad . \quad . \quad . \quad . \quad . \quad . \quad (1.47)$$

Differentiating the first equation and substituting the second we get:

$$\frac{d^2 V}{dz^2} = (R + j\omega L)(G + j\omega C) V$$

$$= \gamma^2 V \quad . \quad . \quad . \quad . \quad . \quad . \quad . \quad . \quad . \quad . \quad . \quad (1.48)$$

where $$\gamma = \sqrt{\{(R + j\omega L)(G + j\omega C)\}} \quad . \quad . \quad . \quad . \quad (1.49)$$

Similarly differentiating the second equation and substituting the first we get:

$$\frac{d^2 I}{dz^2} = \gamma^2 I \quad . \quad . \quad . \quad . \quad . \quad . \quad . \quad . \quad (1.50)$$

Thus voltage and current obey similar equations and it is only necessary to solve one of them. The solution to equation (1.48) is:

$$V = A\varepsilon^{-\gamma z} + B\varepsilon^{\gamma z} \quad . \quad . \quad . \quad . \quad . \quad . \quad . \quad (1.51)$$

where A and B are two constants to be determined since the differential equation is of the second order. The correctness of this solution may easily be checked by differentiation. This result shows that the line will support two waves, one travelling in each direction. The constants A and B are in general complex, and they give the amplitudes and phases of the forward and backward waves respectively at the origin where $z = 0$.

In the case of the semi-infinite line, with a sinusoidal alternating current applied at the sending end ($z = 0$), the voltage across the line when z is infinite is zero, hence the constant $B = 0$. At the sending end $z = 0$, and therefore $A = V_1$ the sending end voltage. The voltage at z is then:

$$V = V_1 \varepsilon^{-\gamma z} \quad . \quad . \quad . \quad . \quad . \quad . \quad . \quad . \quad (1.52)$$

This result was achieved by a less rigorous method in equation (1.27). If this equation is differentiated and substituted in equation (1.46) we get for the current at a point distant z from the sending end:

$$I_z = \frac{V_1 \gamma}{(R + j\omega L)} \varepsilon^{-\gamma z}$$

$$= \frac{V_1}{Z_0} \varepsilon^{-\gamma z}$$

$$= I_1 \varepsilon^{-\gamma z} \quad . \quad . \quad . \quad . \quad . \quad . \quad . \quad . \quad . \quad . \quad (1.53)$$

where $Z_0 = \sqrt{\dfrac{R + j\omega L}{G + j\omega C}}$ is the characteristic impedance of the line.

To obtain the general solution for a finite line, differentiate equation (1.51), substitute in equation (1.46) and we obtain:

$$I = \frac{A}{Z_0} \varepsilon^{-\gamma z} - \frac{B}{Z_0} \varepsilon^{\gamma z} \quad . \quad . \quad . \quad . \quad . \quad . \quad (1.54)$$

If V_S and I_S are the voltage and current at the sending end we have by putting $z = 0$ in equations (1.51) and (1.54):

$$V_S = A + B$$

$$I_S Z_0 = A - B$$

from which

$$A = \tfrac{1}{2}(V_S + I_S Z_0)$$

$$B = \tfrac{1}{2}(V_S - I_S Z_0)$$

Hence equations (1.51) and (1.54) may be written:

$$V = V_S\left(\frac{\varepsilon^{\gamma z} + \varepsilon^{-\gamma z}}{2}\right) - I_S Z_0\left(\frac{\varepsilon^{\gamma z} - \varepsilon^{-\gamma z}}{2}\right)$$

and

$$I = I_S\left(\frac{\varepsilon^{\gamma z} + \varepsilon^{-\gamma z}}{2}\right) - \frac{V_S}{Z_0}\left(\frac{\varepsilon^{\gamma z} - \varepsilon^{-\gamma z}}{2}\right)$$

The terms in brackets may be identified with cosh γz and sinh γz respectively, hence we have finally:

$$V = V_S \cosh \gamma z - I_S Z_0 \sinh \gamma z$$

$$I = I_S \cosh \gamma z - \frac{V_S}{Z_0} \sinh \gamma z \quad . \quad . \quad . \quad . \quad . \quad (1.55)$$

These are known as the transmission equations. It should be noted that the equations must be solved simultaneously and that γz is a complex quantity. Hence it is necessary to have tables of the cosh and sinh of complex quantities. This method of solving transmission-line problems is tending to be replaced by the circle-diagram method described in Chapter 3. The basic theory is, however, the same for either method.

CHAPTER 2

Low-Frequency Transmission Lines

Introduction

The intelligence to be conveyed by a communication system invariably originates as a band of low frequencies. For example, in speech transmission the important range of frequencies to be transmitted is that produced directly by the microphone, namely about 300 c/s to 3,500 c/s. For telegraphy the frequencies are from almost zero (d.c.) to perhaps 100 c/s or more, depending upon the words per minute of the system.

Alternatively the telegraph system may consist of a number of voice frequencies in the speech band which are modulated in accordance with telegraph signals.

In the case of television the band of frequencies may be from zero to 2·5 Mc/s or more. Most systems fall within these limits and the transmission of such signals over two conductor lines, with low attenuation and small distortion, is of considerable importance. Furthermore, the study of such problems is a valuable introduction to high-frequency lines and waveguides. Practical examples of such lines are telephone, telegraph and television lines or cables, and unless they are designed with a full knowledge of the factors involved, serious distortion to signals can be caused. The 'base band' frequencies, which is the term generally employed for the basic frequencies of a system, are usually characterized by a high ratio of upper to lower frequency limits. The transmission of bands with a high ratio of upper to lower frequency limits, with low distortion, is more difficult than the transmission of modulated carrier frequencies.

For example, a system or line transmitting audio frequencies of 300 c/s to 3,500 c/s has a ratio of about 12, whereas if a carrier frequency of, say, 1 Mc/s were modulated with this base band the ratio would be only 1003·5/996·5 = 1·007. A line to transmit the modulated carrier with low distortion would be much easier to design because it would only need to have uniform characteristics over a much smaller frequency interval. However, the attenuation of the modulated carrier signal when transmitted over a line would be vastly greater than that of the base band alone. If we wish to transmit over large distances, the base band must be used and we are, therefore, concerned with the types of distortion that can occur.

The term 'low frequency' in the title of this chapter is intentionally not given a hard and fast definition, although lines for telegraphy and audio and video frequencies are the main consideration. The reason for not closely defining the frequencies we are concerned with is that there is no clear-cut division between the various types of transmission line. Many of the considerations in this chapter apply to lines that would be normally classed as high frequency. For example the sections on attenuation and phase distortion apply directly to television lines where frequencies up to several megacycles per second are often employed.

All the lines considered in this chapter are assumed to be infinitely long or correctly matched with a terminating impedance so that they behave as though they were infinitely long. Thus the deductions of the previous chapter are applicable. Most practical lines for conveying signals of the type just described are employed with correct or approximately correct terminations. The treatment of mis-matched lines is reserved for the next chapter.

Characteristics of Low-Frequency Lines

A wide variety of lines may be used for transmitting low-frequency signals, but they are nearly always of the balanced type shown in Figs. 1.1 (a) or 1.1. (b) of Chapter 1. The reason for the choice of balanced lines is to keep noise interference down to a small value. Most lines are subject to noise interference to a greater or lesser extent. Noise voltages may be induced in lines due to: (a) atmospheric effects (e.g., disturbances due to electromagnetic radiation from near or distant lightning), (b) interference from radio aerials, (c) crosstalk due to electric or magnetic coupling with other lines, (d) man-made interference caused by other electrical apparatus. If a line is balanced with respect to earth (i.e., it is symmetrical with respect to earth such that the impedances to earth of each wire are identical), then interference of types (a) and (b) and sometimes (d) will induce voltages in each wire which are equal in magnitude and phase, or very nearly so.

These voltages are known as 'longitudinal voltages' since they produce currents which flow along the two conductors in parallel, the return path being earth, whereas the wanted signal is a 'transverse voltage' since it produces equal and opposite currents in the two conductors.

If the load at the receiving end of such a line is designed so that it permits the longitudinal currents to flow symmetrically to earth without affecting the transverse signalling circuit, then a substantial improvement in signal-to-noise voltage ratio is possible, as compared with an unbalanced line. This improvement may be as much as 40 decibels; that is, by using a balanced line the residual noise voltage that appears in the transverse circuit (due to minor unbalances such as conductor diameter or resistivity irregularities) is only about 1% of the total longitudinal interference voltage between line and earth.

Interference of the type (c), that is crosstalk from other lines due to electric or magnetic coupling, normally requires other precautions to ensure that it is reduced to a tolerable value. These precautions are twisting of the two conductors of one or both circuits or balancing out the couplings by suitably connected capacitors or mutual inductors.

There are exceptions to the use of balanced lines for low-frequency transmission. One of these is the submarine telephone or telegraph cable which is invariably of coaxial form. The departure is made in this instance because such cables are not normally subject to interference owing to the heavy screening effect provided by the surrounding sea water. Coaxial cable is a more convenient form of construction and has a lower attenuation than balanced cable and is, therefore, preferred. Another instance is the television or multichannel telephony coaxial cable, although this type is hardly in the low-frequency category since frequencies up to 2·5 Mc/s or more are employed. It is, however, an example of an unbalanced cable used for the transmission of base-band frequencies. Even so, the transmission is usually arranged so that the band below 60 kc/s is not employed. Below this frequency interference is likely to arise due to longitudinal interfering currents which flow unequally in the two conductors of a coaxial cable. The coaxial cable will be more fully treated in Chapter 4 under the heading of radio-frequency lines, so that here our thoughts are confined mainly to balanced low-frequency lines.

The next most important consideration is generally the attenuation per unit length of the line, and an inevitable requirement is that it should have as low a value as possible, if a large transmission range is required. The limit to the range of transmission is set by several considerations. First of all there is an economical limit to the power that can be applied at the sending end. This power is usually generated in electronic equipment and it is usually quite uneconomical to raise the sending power above that which can be provided by normal-size valves. The sent power is attenuated during transmission and the limit to which the power may be allowed to fall before being re-amplified is usually set by the residual noise interference in the line. If the required signal is allowed to fall to a level too low in comparison with the noise, then the signal may be impaired beyond the degree desired. Although it may be relatively straightforward to amplify or boost the signals by means of amplifiers distributed along the line, this involves extra equipment and must not be carried beyond economical limits.

We see from these considerations the need for the lowest attenuation that can be economically achieved. It is clear from elementary electrical theory that the lower the line resistance per unit length the lower will be the voltage drop and hence the attenuation. The higher the insulation resistance (i.e., the lower the leakance G) the less will be the leakage current between lines and hence the lower the attenuation. Thus, we must always aim at low R and G to achieve low attenuation.

The requirements on L and C to achieve low attenuation are not so easily formulated by simple deduction. For the moment it will be merely stated that in practical lines to achieve low attenuation the capacitance per unit length C should be kept as low as possible, while an *increase* of inductance per unit length L is usually beneficial to the attenuation.

With these simple rules in mind we may deduce that two copper wires spaced, say, 9 inches apart in air will have a lower attenuation than the same two wires closely spaced in a cable. On the other hand the open-wire line is exposed to the weather and its insulation resistance or leakance will be much more variable than for the cable. The attenuation performance of the open-wire line is thus more liable to fluctuation than that of a cable. So that the reader may become more acquainted with lines of this type, figures and curves showing a comparison of the primary and secondary characteristics of a balanced open-wire line with a balanced-pair screened cable are given in Table 2.1.

The open-wire line consists of two 0·055-inch diameter cadmium-copper wires spaced 9 inches apart on insulators on poles. The cable consists of two annealed copper conductors of the same diameter (0·055 in.) spaced 0·17 inch between centres in a solid dielectric of polyethylene with an external cylindrical screen of 0·35-inch internal diameter. Polyethylene is a low-loss dielectric, with a relative permittivity of 2·3 which is practically the lowest known value for a solid. Similar sized wires have been chosen for the open wire and the cable so that their characteristics may be more easily compared. Actually the open-wire conductor is somewhat light for practical use and is made of cadmium copper to improve its tensile strength. This raises its resistance somewhat, which tends to spoil the comparison of R between open wire and cable. The primary and secondary characteristics are summarized in Table 2.1 and the attenuation, phase and impedance characteristics are shown in Figs. 2.1 and 2.2 over the frequency range of 1 to 100 kc/s.

TABLE 2.1

Comparison between Open Line and Screened Cable with Two 0·055-in. Diameter Conductors

	Open wire (9-in. spacing)			Screened cable (0·17-in. spacing)		
	1 kc/s	10 kc/s	100 kc/s	1 kc/s	10 kc/s	100 kc/s
R (Ω/mile)	42	44	85	36	45·8	97
L (mH/mile)	3·8	3·8	3·6	1·28	1·10	0·92
G (μmhos/mile)	0·5	5·0	50	0	1·5	17·6
C (μF/mile)	0·008	0·008	0·008	0·080	0·080	0·080
α (db/mile)	0·22	0·29	0·7	0·74	1·62	4·0
β (rad/mile)	0·065	0·35	3·5	0·106	0·62	5·4
$\|Z_0\|$ (ohms)	900	750	740	270	127	108
ϕ (degrees)	− 28°	− 6°	0°	− 39°	− 16°	− 5°

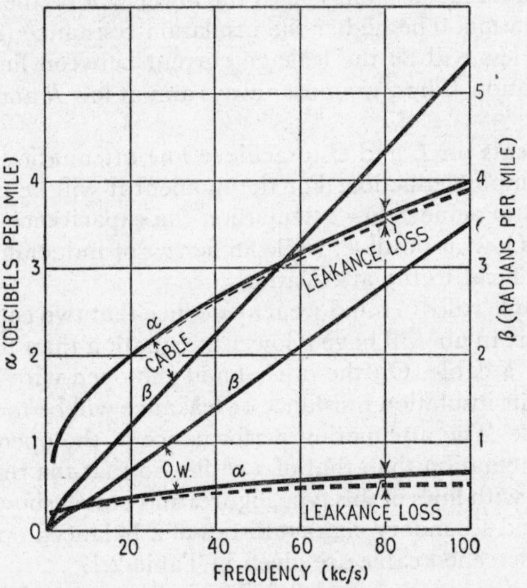

Fig. 2.1. Comparison between open wire and cable; attenuation and phase shift.

Several interesting deductions can be drawn from these figures. Consider first of all the primary constants given in Table 2.1. The figures for R show an increase with frequency as a result of skin effect. In the case of the open-wire line this increase is given by Fig. 1.4 of Chapter 1. In the case of the screened cable the increase of resistance with frequency is more because of the induced currents and consequent losses in the metallic screen.

The figures for L show almost complete independence of frequency for the open-wire case, but a reduction with increase of frequency for the cable owing to the effect of its screen. The important aspect to note is that the open-wire inductance is considerably greater than the cable inductance. This is clearly due to the greater spacing of the wires so that a much higher self-flux is embraced.

The figures for leakance G of an open-wire line must always be regarded as highly variable since leakage over the surface of insulators is dependent upon weather conditions. The figures given are average, and much higher figures are possible in wet weather. In the case of cable the leakance is much more stable. Both show a steady increase of leakance with frequency owing to dielectric losses.

The capacitance C is practically independent of frequency for both open-wire and cable. The higher capacitance of cable as compared with open wire should be noted, this being obviously due to the closer spacing of wires in cables.

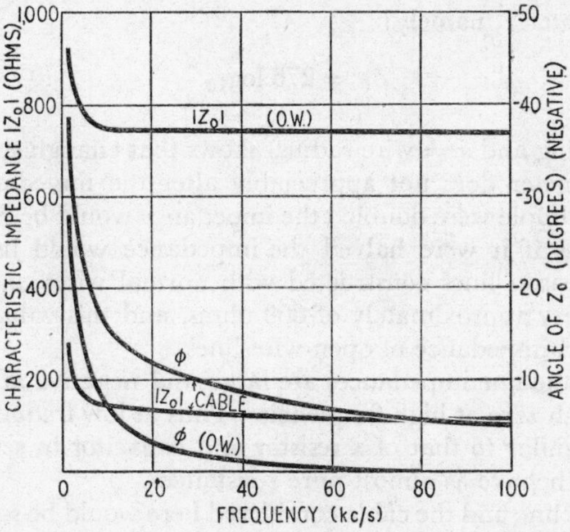

Fig. **2.2. Comparison between open wire and cable; characteristic impedance.**

The secondary characteristics of Fig. 2.1 show that the open-wire attenuation is much less than for cable, although it is much more variable. The cable attenuation is very stable with varying weather owing to the effect of the screen. The rising attenuation with frequency is characteristic of all practical lines. A rough rule for this increase is that the attenuation in decibels is proportional to the square root of frequency. The phase characteristics show curvature at low frequencies with an approach to a linear characteristic at high frequencies; that is, the $\beta-\omega$ curve is asymptotic to a straight line through the origin at high frequencies. The slope of this line for cable is higher than for open wire. Since phase velocity is given by $v_p = \dfrac{\omega}{\beta}$ we see that the cable velocity is less than open-wire velocity. The latter approaches the velocity of light, but the cable velocity is only about $0{\cdot}66c$, where c is the velocity of light. Propagation in a line, which has a dielectric of relative permittivity and permeability each of unity and with no resistance or leakance losses, would be at the same velocity as light. The effect of R and G losses is to lower the velocity slightly and to cause it to vary slightly with frequency. This accounts for the open-wire phase characteristic. It was shown in Chapter 1 that the maximum phase velocity in a line with a dielectric having a relative permittivity κ_r and relative permeability μ_r is given by:

$$v_p = \frac{c}{\sqrt{\mu_r \kappa_r}}$$

This explains why the cable has a velocity of about 0·66 c. The dielectric is polyethylene for which $\kappa_r = 2{\cdot}3$. Thus:

$$v_p = \frac{c}{\sqrt{(1 \times 2{\cdot}3)}} = 0{\cdot}66\, c$$

The impedance–frequency curves of Fig. 2.2 show that the cable, which has a surge impedance of about 105 ohms, provides essentially a low-impedance line, due to its lower inductance and higher capacitance. The open-wire surge impedance is about 740 ohms. The formula for open-wire surge impedance deduced in Chapter 1, namely:

$$Z_0 = 276 \log_{10} \frac{d}{a}$$

(where d = spacing and a = wire radius) shows that changing the wire spacing or the wire diameter does not appreciably alter the impedance. If the wire spacing of the example were doubled the impedance would be increased by only 83 ohms, whereas if it were halved the impedance would be reduced by 83 ohms. For this reason lines constructed with normal wires and spacings have an impedance very approximately of 600 ohms, and this value is taken as the standard nominal impedance of open-wire lines.

The angles of the line impedances are large and negative at low frequencies but they approach zero at high frequencies. Thus at low frequencies, lines have an impedance similar to that of a resistor and capacitor in series, but at high frequencies they behave as almost pure resistances.

The open-wire line and the cable considered here would be suitable for audio-frequency transmission. Since the open-wire attenuation at 1 kc/s is less than half that of the cable, the range of the open-wire would be about double that of the cable, for a given overall transmission loss or attenuation. However, the cable would be less prone to interference owing to its screen, and would have greater uniformity and better impedance balance to earth. The actual choice of the type of line to be used in a particular instance is outside the scope of this book, since many economic factors have to be considered.

▶ The performance of a low-frequency line may be most usefully expressed in terms which show the deviation of the line from the ideal line without losses. The ratios $a = R/\omega L$ and $b = G/\omega C$ are series and shunt dissipation factors which are a measure of the shortcomings of the conductor and dielectric respectively. Where a and b are small compared with unity, several important simplifications to the formulae for the secondary characteristics given in Chapter 1 are possible.

Thus taking the formula for the propagation coefficient:

$$\begin{aligned}\gamma &= \alpha + \mathrm{j}\beta \\ &= \sqrt{\{(R + \mathrm{j}\omega L)(G + \mathrm{j}\omega C)\}} \\ &= \mathrm{j}\omega\sqrt{(LC)}(1 - \mathrm{j}a)^{1/2}(1 - \mathrm{j}b)^{1/2}\end{aligned}$$

Expanding the factors in brackets by the binomial theorem to the third term which is accurate enough for most purposes, we get:

$$\gamma = \mathrm{j}\omega\sqrt{(\mathrm{LC})}\left(1 - \mathrm{j}\frac{a}{2} + \frac{a^2}{8}\right)\left(1 - \mathrm{j}\frac{b}{2} + \frac{b^2}{8}\right)$$

$$= \mathrm{j}\omega\sqrt{(LC)}\left\{1 - \mathrm{j}\frac{(a+b)}{2} + \frac{1}{8}(a-b)^2\right\}$$

Equating real and imaginary parts:

$$\alpha = \frac{a+b}{2}\omega\sqrt{LC}$$

$$= \frac{R}{2}\sqrt{\frac{C}{L}} + \frac{G}{2}\sqrt{\frac{L}{C}} \quad . \quad . \quad . \quad . \quad . \quad . \quad (2.1)$$

$$= \frac{R}{2Z_0} + \frac{G}{2}Z_0 \quad . \quad . \quad . \quad . \quad . \quad . \quad . \quad (2.2)$$

$$\beta = \omega\sqrt{(LC)}[1 + \tfrac{1}{8}(a-b)^2] \quad . \quad . \quad . \quad . \quad . \quad (2.3)$$

where $Z_0 = \sqrt{(L/C)}$ is the surge impedance.

Equations (2.1) and (2.2) are widely used for determining the attenuation of lines. In equation (2.2) the attenuation is given in terms of R, G and the surge impedance. The first term shows the proportion of the attenuation coefficient due to the line resistance, and the second term the proportion due to leakance. For most of the lines considered in this chapter the second term is small but its importance increases with frequency. In Fig. 2.1 the curve shown dotted is that part of the attenuation due to resistance only; i.e., the first term of equation (2.1). It increases approximately in proportion to the square root of frequency owing to skin effect. The remainder of the ordinates between the dotted and the full lines show the attenuation due to leakance. The increase of the latter with frequency should be observed.

Turning now to the simplified equation (2.3) giving the phase characteristic, the expression in square brackets gives the factor by which the practical line deviates from the ideal line. The equation shows that dissipation increases the phase shift or, since $v_p = \omega/\beta$, it decreases the phase velocity (excepting the special case where $a = b$ which will be treated presently). Dissipation causes the phase characteristic to be curved and above the ideal linear characteristic. At high frequencies the characteristic is asymptotic to the linear phase characteristic owing to the diminution of the term $(a - b)$ as the frequency is increased.

The behaviour of Z_0 for lines of this type is best studied by considering the deviation from the asymptotic value $\sqrt{(L/C)}$.

Thus $$Z_0 = \sqrt{\frac{R + \mathrm{j}\omega L}{G + \mathrm{j}\omega C}}$$

$$= \sqrt{\frac{L}{C}} \cdot \sqrt{\frac{1 + R/\mathrm{j}\omega L}{1 + G/\mathrm{j}\omega C}}$$

Using $a = \dfrac{R}{\omega L}$ and $b = \dfrac{G}{\omega C}$ as before, we have:

$$|Z_0| = \sqrt{\frac{L}{C}} \cdot \sqrt[4]{\frac{1 + a^2}{1 + b^2}}$$

and the angle associated with Z_0 is given by:

$$\phi = \tfrac{1}{2}\left(\tan^{-1}\frac{\omega L}{R} - \tan^{-1}\frac{\omega C}{G}\right)$$

$$= \tfrac{1}{2}(\tan^{-1} b - \tan^{-1} a)$$

because $\tan^{-1}(1/a) = \pi/2 - \tan^{-1} a$.

For most lines having good insulation resistance, G is negligible compared with ωC even at low frequencies, thus $b \rightarrow 0$ and we have simplified formulae:

$$|Z_0| = \sqrt{\frac{L}{C}} \cdot \sqrt[4]{1 + a^2} \quad . \quad . \quad . \quad . \quad . \quad (2.4)$$

$$\phi = -\tfrac{1}{2}\tan^{-1} a \quad . \quad . \quad . \quad . \quad . \quad . \quad . \quad (2.5)$$

In general R increases proportionately to $\sqrt{\omega}$ so that $a = R/\omega L$ gradually vanishes as ω is raised. Thus $|Z_0|$ commences at low frequencies at a value considerably larger than $\sqrt{(L/C)}$. As ω is raised, the parameter a falls and $|Z_0|$ approaches $\sqrt{(L/C)}$. The factor $\sqrt[4]{(1 + a^2)}$ gives at every frequency the departure from the asymptotic value.

The simple formula for ϕ shows that at very low frequencies, where a may be large, the angle of the impedance is negative (i.e., the line is capacitive) and in the neighbourhood of 45°. As the frequency is increased and a becomes small, the angle remains negative, but approaches zero. These characteristics are clearly borne out by Fig. 2.2.

Distortion of Signals During Transmission

Any signal may be represented by a graph of an electrical quantity such as voltage or current plotted against time. If it is desired to transmit this signal by means of a line to a distant point, we are interested in the faithfulness with which the voltage-time graph is reproduced at that point, or alternatively the distortion due to transmission.

Before considering the types of distortion which lines can cause, it might be well to mention one type of distortion, common to electronic circuits that does not occur with lines, namely non-linear distortion. If with any 4-terminal network or system to which a sine wave of voltage is applied, the output voltage magnitude is not proportional to the input voltage magnitude, then non-linear distortion is present. Such distortion exists in systems which have an overload limitation; i.e., for some value of input, the output voltage can no longer increase and therefore it ceases to be proportional to the input. Any electrical network or system having input and output terminals wherein the magnitude of the output voltage or current is directly proportional to the input voltage or current respectively, is known as a linear network or system because the graph connecting input and output quantities is a straight line through the origin. Such networks or systems would generally be built from linear components; i.e., impedances which rigidly obey Ohm's Law. Most uniform lines are linear systems and, therefore, do not cause transmitted signals to suffer non-linear distortion.

If the shape of the voltage-time graph is faithfully reproduced at the receiving end of a line, but it has suffered a general diminution in strength due to attenuation, this is not regarded as distortion, since amplifiers of low distortion may usually be employed to restore the signal to its original amplitude. Similarly a constant transmission delay is not regarded as distortion although it might be inconvenient in some applications. The types of distortion with which we are

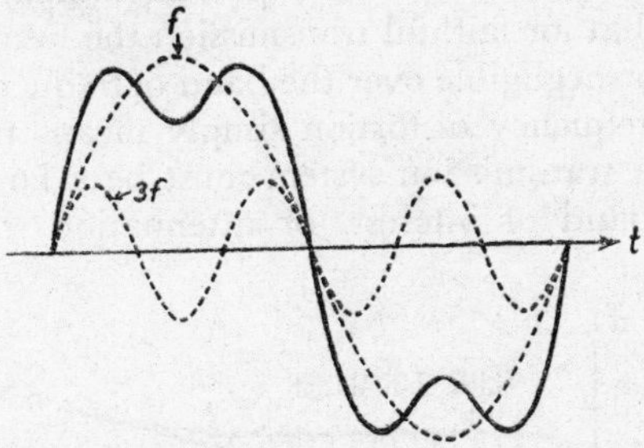

Fig. 2.3. Signal considered for frequency and phase distortion.

concerned here are frequency and phase distortion. Collectively they are sometimes called linear distortion.

Take as a simple example the repeated waveform shown in Fig. 2.3 which is being transmitted down a line in the steady state; i.e., it has been applied to the line indefinitely. This waveform is the sum of a fundamental f and a third harmonic $3f$ which are shown dotted. If during transmission the frequency $3f$ is attenuated more than the frequency f, the received waveform will be as shown in Fig. 2.4 (a) this being a simple example of frequency distortion. It may be

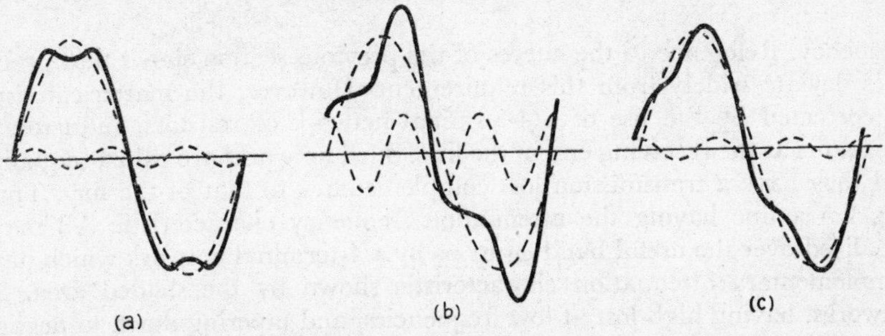

Fig. 2.4. Types of distortion with transmission line; (a) frequency, (b) phase and (c) combined frequency and phase distortion.

defined as follows: Frequency distortion is the distortion of waveforms during transmission due to the variation of attenuation (or gain in amplifiers) with frequency.

Suppose now that the phase shifts of the fundamental and third harmonic during transmission are such that the time relationship at the sending end is destroyed, and the received waveform is as shown in Fig. 2.4 (b). This is then a case of phase distortion.

Fig. 2.4 (c) shows combined amplitude and phase distortion.

The voltage–time graph of all signal waveforms can be analysed (see Volume 1) into a number of steady sinusoidal frequencies, although there may be a large or infinite number of such components. These frequencies are sometimes called the spectrum of a signal or its frequency content. A knowledge of the frequency and phase distortion during transmission enables one to deduce the modified spectrum at the receiving end and hence the received voltage–time graph may be reconstructed. In practice the procedure is long and difficult except for simple signals of the form shown in Fig. 2.3. The method is, however, important and it often assists in drawing qualitative deductions.

It is obvious then that for faithful transmission the frequency and phase distortion must be zero or negligible over the band of frequencies which may exist in the signal. Zero frequency distortion simply means that the attenuation–frequency graph for a transmission system must be a horizontal straight line, over the frequency band of interest, or attenuation should be 'flat' with

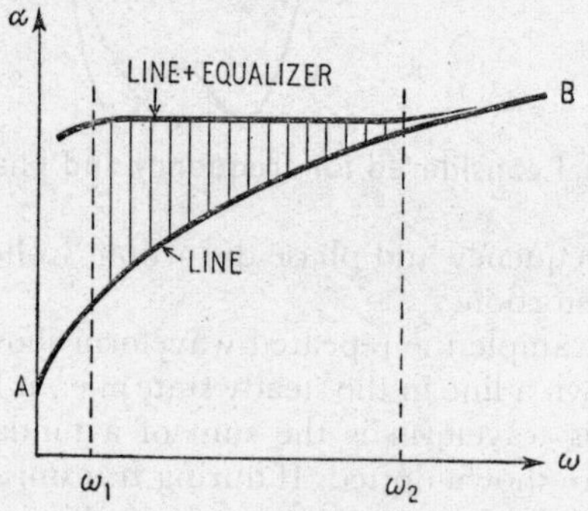

Fig. 2.5. Equalization of frequency distortion.

frequency. Reference to the curves of the previous section shows that practical lines deviate widely from this requirement. However, the matter can usually be corrected by the use of a 4-terminal network of resistors, inductors and capacitors at the receiving end of the line. Such networks are called 'equalizers' and they have a transmission loss complementary to that of the line. Thus in Fig. 2.5 a line having the attenuation–frequency characteristic AB may be equalized over the useful band ω_1 to ω_2 by a 4-terminal network which has the complementary attenuation characteristic shown by the shaded area. Such networks, having high loss at low frequencies, and tapering down to negligible loss at the upper frequency end of the band, must match the line impedance over the desired frequency band. The design of such equalizers is outside the scope of the present book.

Turning now to phase distortion, it was shown in Chapter 1 that if a sinusoidal voltage signal of angular frequency ω is being transmitted in the steady state, the voltage at any point down a line at any instant is given by a sine wave of voltage against distance having a wavelength of $2\pi/\beta$ and sliding down the line at the phase velocity $v_p = \omega/\beta$.

Now suppose that the transmitted signal consists of two angular frequencies ω and 3ω related as in Fig. 2.3, then two voltage waves will progress down the line. If the time relationship of Fig. 2.3 is to be maintained at all points down the line the wavelength of the third harmonic must be exactly one-third of the fundamental wavelength or alternatively the phase velocities of the two voltage waves must be identical.

Since $v_p = \omega/\beta$ then one rule for no phase distortion is that β should be of the form $\beta = \omega \times$ constant. That is, the graph connecting β and ω should be a straight line through the origin, or we say, the phase-frequency characteristic should be linear. From Fig. 2.6 (a), which shows the voltage relationship of the two waves down a section of an infinite line, the phase lag of the fundamental at B behind A is 2π radians, while for the 3rd harmonic the lag is 6π radians, showing that it complies with this rule. In fact, this rule, although true for parallel-conductor lines, is not absolutely inviolable when applied to all transmission networks, and a more general form will be given presently.

Suppose now that the phase velocity for the 3rd harmonic exceeds that for the fundamental, a condition which often exists with dissipative lines, then the voltage picture on the line will be similar to that in Fig. 2.6 (b). At section B

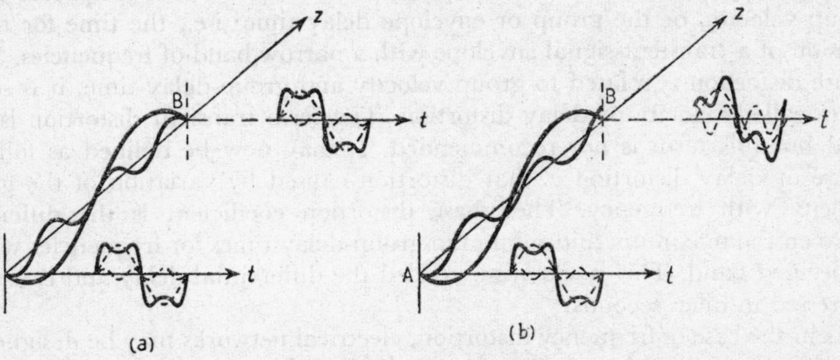

Fig. 2.6. Effect of phase distortion in a transmission line; (a) no distortion, (b) with distortion.

the voltage–time wave will be of the form shown in Fig. 2.4 (b) which shows considerable distortion when compared with Fig. 2.3. The line is then causing phase distortion.

For ordinary speech signals the ear is insensitive to phase distortion provided it does not exceed certain limits. For example, phase distortion of the magnitude shown in Fig. 2.4 (b), if existing in a speech transient, would be quite undetectable to the ear. On a long telephone line with considerable phase distortion, however, the high-frequency components may arrive some milliseconds before the lower-frequency components, so that words are preceded by a distinct whistle. This condition did actually exist on some early long-distance telephone lines.

Phase distortion must be carefully considered for cables or lines carrying telegraph- or television-type signals. The signal in Fig. 2.3 is the first approximation to a square-wave telegraph signal or the square wave of a picture signal produced by scanning across a series of black and white lines. The addition of an appropriately-phased fifth harmonic to Fig. 2.3 would give an even closer approximation to a square wave. A limited amount of frequency distortion such as in Fig. 2.4 (a) does not seriously affect the signal, but the phase distortion of Fig. 2.4 (b) might have objectionable consequences. In the case of telegraphy the points where the wave crosses the zero axis are displaced and if this is excessive it may cause errors, while with picture-type signals the intensity at the crest of the wave is highly distorted.

In the case of lines carrying a carrier wave with a modulation, attenuation and phase distortion are usually of no consequence. This is because the band of frequencies transmitted is usually small compared with the mean frequency of the band and over this band the attenuation characteristic is sensibly horizontal and the phase characteristic sensibly linear.

It can be shown that provided the phase characteristic is linear over the band considered, it need not necessarily pass through the origin. If, when extended backwards, it intersects the vertical axis at $\pm n\pi$ radians where n is an integer, then there is still no phase distortion. If it intersects at points other than these then a type of phase distortion known as intercept distortion occurs, even though the phase characteristic is linear. These rules provide a more rigid definition of the conditions for no phase distortion than the rule derived by the simple example of Fig. 2.6. If the phase characteristic is linear, then it has a constant slope. The value of this slope is, from Chapter 1, the reciprocal of the group velocity, or the group or envelope delay time; i.e., the time for transmission of a transient-signal envelope with a narrow band of frequencies. Since phase distortion is related to group velocity and group-delay time, it is sometimes called velocity or delay distortion. The term transient distortion is also used but this term is not recommended. It may now be defined as follows: Phase or delay distortion is that distortion caused by variation of the group velocity with frequency. The phase distortion coefficient is the difference between the maximum and minimum group-delay times for frequencies within a specified band. This is sometimes called the differential delay and is usually expressed in microseconds.

As in the case of frequency distortion, electrical networks may be designed to correct phase distortion down to small limits. These networks are known as delay equalizers and they are usually built up from inductors and capacitors so that they have negligible loss and effect upon the attenuation characteristic. Such networks are rather complex to design and a discussion of them is outside the scope of this book.

▶ Consider a signal which is composed of a large number of sinusoidal signals in the band ω_1 to ω_2 and represented by:

$$S_1(t) = \sum_{\omega=\omega_1}^{\omega_2} E_\omega \sin(\omega t + \theta_\omega) \quad . \quad . \quad . \quad . \quad . \qquad (2.6)$$

where E_ω and θ_ω are functions of ω.

Suppose this signal is passed through a transmission system (or other 4-terminal network) of attenuation α_ω nepers and β_ω radians phase shift, both of these parameters being functions of ω. Then the received signal will be given by

$$S_2(t) = \sum_{\omega=\omega_1}^{\omega_2} E_\omega \epsilon^{-\alpha_\omega} \sin(\omega t + \theta_\omega - \beta_\omega) \quad . \quad . \quad . \qquad (2.7)$$

For S_2 to have the same wave shape as S_1, then α_ω must be a constant and β_ω must be of the form $\omega t_g \pm n\pi$ over the band ω_1 to ω_2 where t_g is a positive constant and n is an integer.

If these conditions are complied with, the received signal will be given by:

$$S_2(t) = \sum_{\omega=\omega_1}^{\omega_2} kE_\omega \sin\{\omega(t - t_g) + \theta_\omega\} \quad . \quad . \quad . \qquad (2.8)$$

where k is a positive or negative constant.

Comparing this signal with S_1 it is seen to be identical except for a scale factor k and a time delay t_g. The scale factor may be positive or negative depending upon whether n (where $n\pi$ is the intercept of the phase characteristic on the β axis) is even or odd. This sign of the scale factor is usually of no consequence since if negative it can be made positive by reversing the load connections.

Thus the condition for no attenuation distortion is:

$$\alpha_\omega = \text{constant from } \omega_1 \text{ to } \omega_2$$

and for no phase distortion:

$$\beta_\omega = \omega t_g \pm n\pi$$

By differentiating the last equation with respect to ω the delay time through the system is obtained thus:

$$t_g = \frac{d\beta_\omega}{d\omega}$$

This is the group or envelope delay, since it is the reciprocal of the group velocity or the time taken for the transmission of the envelope of a narrow band of frequencies. The condition for no phase distortion may, therefore, be stated alternatively as:

Group delay, $\quad t_g = \text{constant}$
Phase shift (at $\omega = 0$), $\quad \beta_0 = \pm n\pi$

The Distortionless Line

In the early days of telegraphy over lines and submarine cables it was realized that the product RC determined the speed at which they could be used for telegraph signalling. The higher the RC product the lower the signalling speed. For all normal lines the product RC is considerably larger than the product LG. It has already been stated that raising L reduces the attenuation. If the line inductance L is raised by some means until:

$$LG = RC$$

then the line attenuation per unit length falls to its minimum or d.c. value at all frequencies; thus:

$$\alpha = \sqrt{RG}$$

This assumes that R and G are reasonably constant. This only applies up to a limited frequency because of skin effect and dielectric losses, but it is sufficiently accurate for audio-frequency lines.

Furthermore the phase shift per unit length becomes independent of R and G and is given by:

$$\beta = \omega\sqrt{LC}$$

or the phase velocity $v_p = \omega/\beta = 1/\sqrt{LC}$ becomes constant at all frequencies. For such a line the group and phase velocities become equal. The linear relation of β and ω signifies no phase distortion so that raising L until $LG = RC$ provides a line with no frequency or phase distortion. Thus any signal transmitted by such a line of length l will be attenuated by αl nepers, and delayed by a time given by:

$$t_g = \frac{l}{v_g} = \frac{l}{v_p} = \sqrt{LC}.l \text{ seconds}$$

The signal wave shape will not be distorted.

The condition $LG = RC$ is known as the distortionless condition and such lines are called distortionless lines. The same distortionless effect would be achieved by raising the leakance G, but this would grossly increase the attenuation $\alpha = \sqrt{RG}$, a most undesirable feature. Thus if L could be raised without altering G, R and C there would be an all round improvement in transmission. Adding artificial inductance to a line is known as 'loading' and there are two methods of achieving this result. In one method the inductance is added uniformly along the length of the line, and in the other inductance coils or 'loading coils' are inserted in series with the line at uniformly spaced points.

A further feature of the distortionless line is that the characteristic impedance becomes constant at all frequencies, and equal to the surge impedance, thus:

$$Z_0 = \sqrt{\frac{L}{C}} = \sqrt{\frac{R}{G}}$$

This shows that loading increases the characteristic impedance, while the formula for phase velocity shows that loading reduces the velocity. The latter is one of the disadvantages of loading, since for most systems of communication a high velocity is desirable.

The distortionless condition may easily be identified with a state of affairs during transmission in which the energy stored per unit length is equally divided between the magnetic and electric fields. Thus in a short length δx the energy stored in the magnetic field is:

$$\tfrac{1}{2}L\delta x I^2$$

where I is the current, assumed uniform over the length δx, and the energy stored in the electric field is:

$$\tfrac{1}{2}C\delta x V^2$$

where V is the voltage between lines, assumed uniform over the length δx. For the distortionless case:

$$\frac{V}{I} = \sqrt{\frac{L}{C}} = \sqrt{\frac{R}{G}}$$

or

$$V^2 = I^2 L/C$$

Substituing for V^2 in the expression for the energy stored in the electric field it will be found to equal the magnetic field energy.

Furthermore the energy which is dissipated per unit length is equally divided between resistance loss and leakance loss. Thus resistance loss in the short length δx is given by:

$$R\delta x I^2$$

and the leakance loss is given by:

$$G\delta x V^2$$

But $V^2 = I^2R/G$ which on being substituted shows the even distribution of losses between R and G.

When the field theory of transmission is studied we shall find that the energy is conveyed entirely by the magnetic and electric fields, the energy for the R and G losses coming entirely from these fields. Thus the distortionless case is a symmetrical state of affairs in which the energy is transmitted equally by the magnetic and electric fields and the transmission losses are uniformly absorbed from them, to be dissipated as heat equally in R and G.

The distortionless line is mainly of theoretical importance owing to the practical difficulty of raising the inductance up to the desired value.

▶ Oliver Heaviside was able to show in 1887, by mathematical reasoning, that if the inductance of a telephone line could be increased, the attenuation would be reduced. If the relations between the characteristic impedance Z_0, the propagation constant γ, and the primary constants are examined, viz.:

$$Z_0 = \sqrt{\frac{R + j\omega L}{G + j\omega C}}$$

and

$$\gamma = \sqrt{\{(R + j\omega L)(G + j\omega C)\}}$$

it will be observed that raising the inductance until the angles of $(R + j\omega L)$ and $(G + j\omega C)$ are equal, i.e.:

$$\frac{\omega L}{R} = \frac{\omega C}{G}$$

or

$$LG = RC \quad . \quad . \quad . \quad . \quad . \quad . \quad . \quad (2.9)$$

enables the square roots to be easily extracted. Thus, Z_0 becomes the square root of a real number and γ is a vector having the same angle as $R + j\omega L$ or $G + j\omega C$ and with a modulus which is the geometric mean of $|R + j\omega L|$ and $|G + j\omega C|$.

First of all, by simply extracting the square root, the characteristic impedance is seen to be:

$$Z_0 = \sqrt{\frac{R}{G}} = \sqrt{\frac{L}{C}} \quad . \quad . \quad . \quad . \quad . \quad . \quad (2.10)$$

That is, it is independent of frequency (provided R, L, G and C are reasonably constant for the frequency range considered; this is approximately true for audio-frequency lines).

Secondly, we have:

$$\gamma = \sqrt{\left\{R\left(1 + j\frac{\omega L}{R}\right)G\left(1 + j\frac{\omega C}{G}\right)\right\}}$$

$$= \sqrt{(RG)}\left(1 + j\frac{\omega L}{R}\right)$$

$$= \sqrt{RG} + j\omega L\sqrt{\frac{G}{R}}$$

or

$$\alpha + j\beta = \sqrt{RG} + j\omega\sqrt{LC} \quad . \quad . \quad . \quad . \quad . \quad (2.11)$$

or

$$\alpha = \sqrt{RG}$$

and

$$\beta = \omega\sqrt{LC}$$

This last result may be obtained by putting $a = b$ in equation (2.3). ◀

Continuous Loading

The addition of distributed inductance to a transmission line up to the limit given by $LG = RC$ is rarely practicable or even desirable. If the leakance G is small, as is essential for low attenuation, then the value of inductance required becomes very large. Even supposing that such an inductance could be added, the resultant lowering of phase velocity would, for many applications, become intolerable. For example if a telephone circuit could be loaded with distributed inductance such that $LG = RC$, then the phase velocity might be reduced to $0{\cdot}01c$ or even less. The transmission delay for a 1,000-mile telephone circuit would be over half a second, which is considered excessive for comfortable telephony. However, beneficial results from loading can be obtained by adding only a small proportion of the theoretical value corresponding to the distortionless condition. The method of adding inductance must be such as not to deteriorate the other primary constants of the cable. For example R, G and C must not be increased in value, or, at least, if they are increased their effect upon the attenuation must be negligible compared with the improvement due to the higher inductance.

In practice it is very difficult to achieve an increase of distributed inductance over a wide frequency band. If a dielectric could be found with a low permittivity (to preserve a low value of C) and yet having a high permeability, and at the same time having low magnetic and dielectric losses, then no doubt beneficial distributed inductance loading could be achieved. However, so far no such material has been discovered and the best that can be achieved is to wind a fine high-permeability ferromagnetic wire or tape (e.g., nickel–iron alloy) round the copper conductors. This is known as 'continuous loading'. The turns of this wire or tape must be closely spaced, otherwise the effective permeability is low due to the air gap appearing in the magnetic circuit which surrounds the conductor. This ferromagnetic layer tends to increase the capacitance C, but its most serious effect is to increase R, especially as the frequency is raised. In general the latter effect is so serious that this method of loading shows no improvement above a few kilocycles per second. Continuous loading is then only applicable to very low-frequency lines such as long-distance submarine d.c. telegraph cables.

Lumped Loading

Owing to the difficulty and expense of achieving satisfactory continuous loading the use of inductance coils in series with the line has become common in telephone practice. These coils can be made to have a low copper and iron loss and, if correctly spaced, they can provide a substantial reduction in the attenuation of a line; they are usually wound on magnetic dust cores of toroidal form. In the case of balanced lines the coils are wound so as to put an equal inductance into each conductor, as in Fig. 2.7 (a). The effective loading inductance is that which would be measured if the two coils on a core were connected in series aiding. Suppose each coil has a total inductance of L_C henrys and the spacing is d metres, as shown diagrammatically in Fig. 2.7 (b). Then the equivalent smoothed inductance is that which would be obtained by imagining L_C to be uniformly distributed over d; i.e., (L_C/d) henrys per metre. If this smoothed inductance is added to the natural inductance of the line it can be shown that calculations using this value of L in the previous formulae for uniform lines will give an attenuation very close to the true value.

However, this simplification only applies when the frequency is such that the wavelength extends over about 4 coils (i.e., a distance of $4d$ metres) or more. The wavelength to be used here is that calculated from the new total inductance, and is much less than the wavelength in the unloaded line.

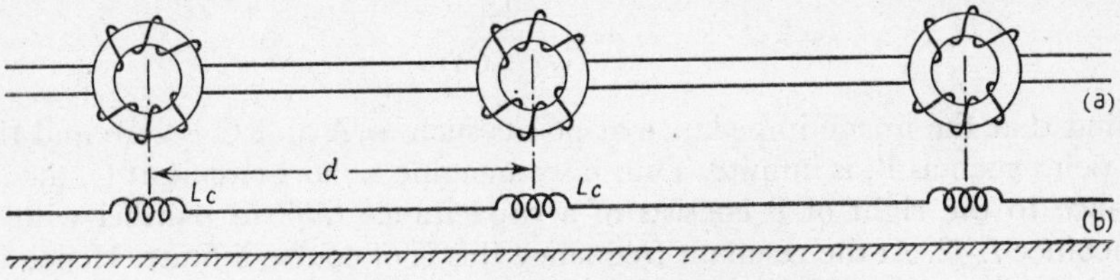

Fig. 2.7. Lumped, or coil loading.

At a frequency corresponding to π coils per wavelength the attenuation rises steeply. This is illustrated in Fig. 2.8 which shows at (a) the attenuation-frequency curve for a line consisting of two 0·05-in. diameter conductors spaced 0·12 in. in air-spaced paper-core cable. When loaded with 88 mH coils spaced

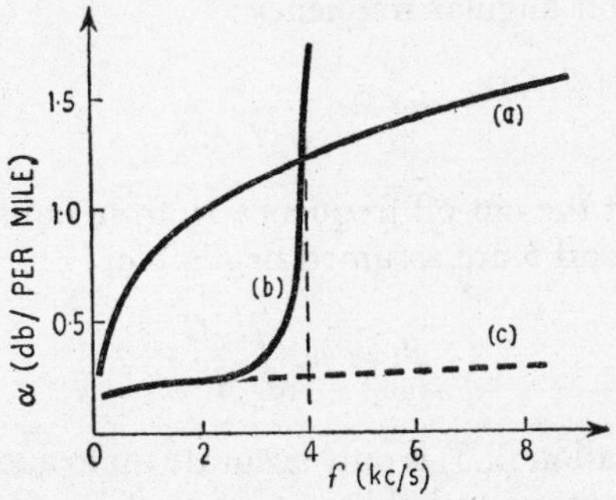

Fig. 2.8. Attenuation versus frequency: (a) without loading, (b) with coil loading, (c) with ideal uniform loading of same mean value.

at 2,000 yards the curve (b) is obtained. Such a cable would be used for audio-frequency telephony and up to a frequency of 3,500 c/s it is seen that a substantial reduction of attenuation is achieved by loading. If the inductance could have been added uniformly (i.e., continuous loading) the dotted curve (c)

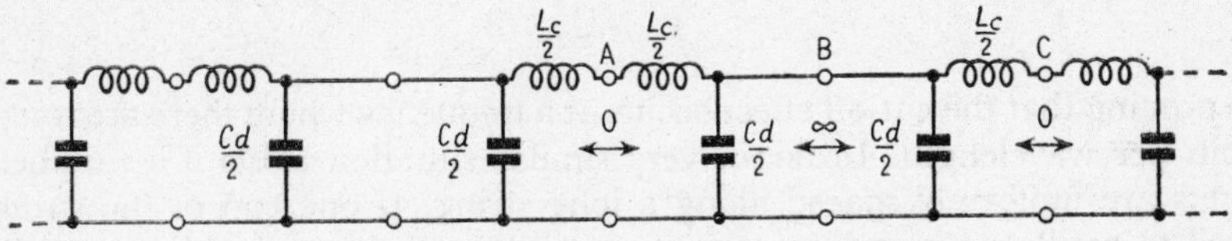

Fig. 2.9. Cut-off effect in coil loaded lines.

would have been obtained. However, owing to the 'lumped' nature of the added inductance there is a cut-off frequency of about 4,000 c/s, in the region of which the attenuation rises steeply as shown by (b).

The existence of a critical or cut-off frequency can be seen by ignoring R and G and drawing the loaded line in lumped form as in Fig. 2.9. The capacitance of a length of cable between coils is Cd and we divide this and the coils into two. The natural inductance of the line is ignored in comparison with the coil inductance. If now we study the behaviour at an angular frequency at which $Cd/2$ and $L_C/2$ resonate,

i.e.,
$$\omega = \frac{2}{\sqrt{(L_C Cd)}}$$

we find that the image impedance at points such as A and C is zero and that at a point such as B, is infinite. Thus if we imagine a short circuit at C, the impedance to the right of B consists of a capacitance $Cd/2$ in parallel with an inductance $L_C/2$. At the resonant frequency this is of course infinite. Hence the impedance in shunt with the capacitance to the left of B is infinite. Thus to the right of A, $L_C/2$ and $Cd/2$ resonate in series producing a zero impedance at A as at C. This condition exists all down the line. At the termination of the line, which should be either the mid-point of a coil or the mid-point of a cable section, it is very difficult to pass power into the line since it presents an impedance approaching either a short circuit or an open circuit respectively. The resonant frequency at which this occurs is, in fact, the cut-off frequency.

Thus we have cut-off angular frequency:

$$\omega_c = \frac{2}{\sqrt{(L_C Cd)}} \qquad (2.12)$$

The phase constant at the cut-off frequency is, from equation (2.3), given very approximately by (a and b are assumed negligible):

$$\beta_c = \omega_c \sqrt{\frac{L_C C}{d}}$$

(Strictly speaking equation (2.3) is only accurate up to about one-half the cut-off frequency but it is assumed to hold up to cut-off because it provides a useful rule.)

Substituting ω_c from equation (2.12) we get:

$$\beta_c = \frac{2}{d}$$

The wavelength at cut-off, λ_c, is related to β_c simply by $\lambda_c = 2\pi/\beta_c$ and substituting for β_c:

$$\lambda_c = \pi d \qquad (2.13)$$

thus proving that the cut-off effect occurs at a frequency where there are roughly π coils per wavelength. In fact a very similar situation exists if a number of weights are uniformly spaced along a long string. If one end of the string is caused to oscillate up and down a wave will travel down the string provided the frequency is such that the wavelength is large compared with πd where d is the distance between consecutive weights. When the frequency is increased so that the wavelength is comparable with πd it becomes very difficult to propagate a wave. The weights near to the applied force move in an unco-ordinated manner and the wave does not progress far down the string.

This cut-off effect was noticed during early investigations into lump loaded telephone lines, and led to the invention of 'wave' or 'frequency' filters. Thus the network in Fig. 2.9 is a low-pass filter because it has the characteristic of passing with small attenuation all angular frequencies from 0 to ω_c and attenuating all frequencies above ω_c. From this the theory of low-pass, high-pass, band-pass and band-stop filters was evolved (see Volume 4).

Artificial Lines

The previous section suggests that a suitable arrangement of lumped components could be made to represent uniform lines subject to certain limitations. Such is, in fact, the case, and these arrangements are called artificial lines. They exhibit, with slight modifications, all the properties of uniform lines. For example a signal at the input is delayed before arrival at the output. Such lines find considerable application in communication and radar systems.

Consider the network in Fig. 2.10 which may be compared with the uniform line of Chapter 1 divided into elementary lengths. A dissipationless line is assumed for the moment. The similarity of the artificial line to the simplified diagram of the loaded line in Fig. 2.9 should also be noted. We may deduce from

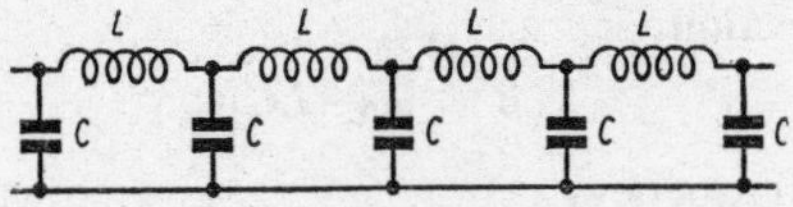

Fig. 2.10. Artificial line.

this similarity that the artificial line will have a cut-off frequency above which transmission will be attenuated.

If this artificial line is extended indefinitely and used for transmitting sinusoidal signals of a frequency low compared with the cut-off frequency (i.e., such that each section is comparable with the elementary length of line in Chapter 1) then several of the deductions of Chapter 1 can be applied. In the case of the artificial line the conception of length or distance does not apply, but the properties may be expressed in terms of a number of sections or simply per section.

For example the inductance per unit length of a line can be compared with the inductance per section of an artificial line and similarly for capacitance. Hence we may deduce immediately that the characteristic impedance of the artificial line in Fig. 2.10 is given by:

$$Z_0 = \sqrt{\frac{L}{C}}$$

However, this only applies for frequencies low compared with the cut-off frequency.

By further analogy with the uniform line we may deduce the phase shift per section. Thus from Chapter 1 the phase shift in radians per unit length of dissipationless line is:

$$\beta = \omega\sqrt{(LC)}$$

where L and C refer to unit length. In the case of the artificial line, L and C refer to one section, hence we have phase shift in radians per section of artificial line:

$$\beta = \omega\sqrt{(LC)}$$

Again the limitation is that ω must be small compared with ω_c the cut-off frequency. Since the components L and C of the artificial line have been assumed dissipationless, there is no attenuation of transmitted signals except above the cut-off frequency.

The cut-off angular frequency ω_c may be deduced by analogy with the loaded line. This frequency corresponds to the resonance of the half-section components $L/2$ and $C/2$, hence:

$$\omega_c = \frac{1}{\sqrt{\left(\frac{L}{2}\cdot\frac{C}{2}\right)}} = \frac{2}{\sqrt{(LC)}}$$

This completes the design formulae for a dissipationless artificial line and the formulae are summarized below:

Nominal characteristic impedance:

$$Z_0 = \sqrt{\frac{L}{C}} \quad . \quad . \quad . \quad . \quad . \quad . \quad . \quad . \quad (2.14)$$

Phase shift per section:

$$\beta = \omega\sqrt{(LC)} \quad . \quad . \quad . \quad . \quad . \quad . \quad . \quad . \quad (2.15)$$

Cut-off angular frequency:

$$\omega_c = \frac{2}{\sqrt{(LC)}} \quad . \quad . \quad . \quad . \quad . \quad . \quad . \quad . \quad (2.16)$$

It will be noted that if the formula for β is assumed to apply approximately up to ω_c, then by substitution for ω_c the phase shift at cut-off is 2 radians per whole section or 1 radian (i.e., about 57°) per half section. The statement in Chapter 1, that lumped-component representation of uniform lines becomes inaccurate when the phase shift per elementary section exceeds about 1 radian, is related to this conclusion. That is, above about one-half of the cut-off frequency the representation begins to break down. For many purposes the delay per section is of more interest than the phase shift. The phase velocity is deduced as in the case of a line as follows:

$$v_p = \frac{\omega}{\beta} = \frac{1}{\sqrt{(LC)}} \text{ sections per second.}$$

The phase delay per whole section is simply the reciprocal of this. Thus delay per section:

$$t' = \sqrt{(LC)} \text{ seconds} \quad . \quad . \quad . \quad . \quad . \quad . \quad (2.17)$$

Within the limits of the assumption that ω is not larger than about $0{\cdot}5\omega_c$ the phase shift per section is almost proportional to ω, so that the phase and group velocities are practically identical. Thus the phase and envelope delays are almost identical. If signals consisting of a sequence of pulses are applied to such an artificial line, and provided that the frequency content of the pulses does not extend much beyond $0{\cdot}5\omega_c$, the pulses will be received at the end of the line in an impedance $Z_0 = \sqrt{(L/C)}$ but after a delay of $t = n\sqrt{(LC)}$ seconds where n is the number of sections. If the line is open- or short-circuited the pulses will be reflected and received back at the sending end after a delay of $2t$ seconds. Delay lines, as they are called, of this type are used in radar systems.

▶ If we wish to study the performance of an artificial line at frequencies approaching cut-off, the full lumped-circuit theory of networks must be used. The artificial line must first be divided into symmetrical 4-terminal networks. From Fig. 2.11 this may be done in two ways.

Division at the points 1, known as the mid-series points, divides the line into a number of symmetrical T networks. Division at the points 2, known as the mid-shunt points, divides the line into a number of symmetrical π networks.

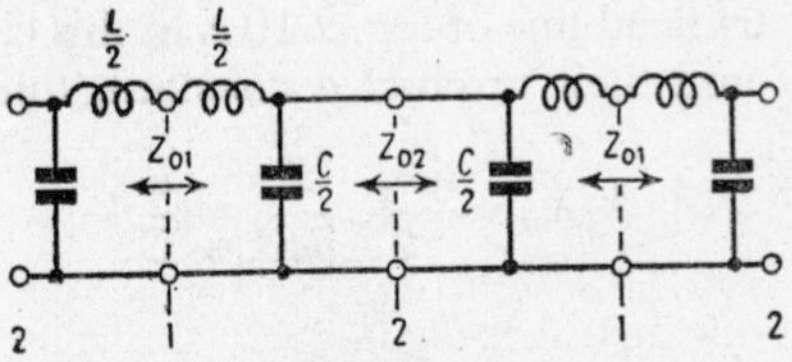

Fig. 2.11. Image impedances in an artificial line.

If the line is infinite the impedance looking in each direction from the mid-series points is the same and is designated Z_{01}. Similarly the impedance in each direction at the mid-shunt points is Z_{02}. These impedances are known as image impedances and they may be determined by analysing a half-section suitably terminated as shown in Fig. 2.12. For convenience the impedance of the series

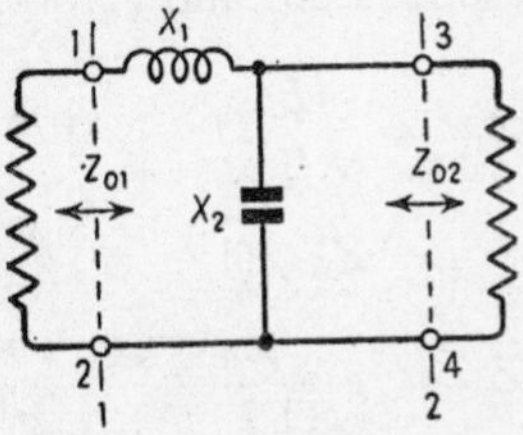

Fig. 2.12. Half section of artificial line.

arm $j\omega L/2$ is taken as X_1 and that of the shunt arm $2/j\omega C$ is taken as X_2. Then Z_{01} may be equated to X_1 in series with a parallel combination of X_2 and Z_{02}. Similarly Z_{02} may be equated to X_2 in parallel with a series combination of Z_{01} and X_1. Thus:

$$Z_{01} = X_1 + \frac{X_2 Z_{02}}{X_2 + Z_{02}}$$

$$Z_{02} = \frac{X_2(X_1 + Z_{01})}{X_1 + X_2 + Z_{01}}$$

These equations yield respectively, the following:

$$Z_{01}Z_{02} + Z_{01}X_2 - X_1X_2 - X_1Z_{02} - X_2Z_{02} = 0$$

$$Z_{01}Z_{02} - Z_{01}X_2 - X_1X_2 + X_1Z_{02} + X_2Z_{02} = 0$$

Addition and subtraction of this pair of equations results in the simple relations:

$$Z_{01}Z_{02} = X_1X_2 \quad . \quad . \quad . \quad . \quad . \quad . \quad . \quad (2.18)$$

$$\frac{Z_{01}}{Z_{02}} = 1 + \frac{X_1}{X_2} \quad . \quad . \quad . \quad . \quad . \quad . \quad . \quad (2.19)$$

Multiplying and dividing these equations gives finally:

$$Z_{01}{}^2 = X_1 X_2 \left(1 + \frac{X_1}{X_2}\right) \quad . \quad . \quad . \quad . \quad . \qquad (2.20)$$

$$Z_{02}{}^2 = \frac{X_1 X_2}{1 + X_1/X_2} \quad . \quad . \quad . \quad . \quad . \qquad (2.21)$$

Networks for which the product $X_1 X_2 = k$ a constant, are known as constant-k networks. The ideal artificial line of Fig. 2.10 is in this class because X_1 and X_2 are inverse reactances and their product is constant, thus:

$$X_1 X_2 = \frac{j\omega L}{2} \cdot \frac{2}{j\omega C} = \frac{L}{C}$$

Also we have:

$$\frac{X_1}{X_2} = -\frac{\omega^2 LC}{4}$$

$$= -\frac{\omega^2}{\omega_c{}^2} \quad \text{from equation (2.16)}$$

$$= -x^2$$

where we set $x = \omega/\omega_c$, the frequency normalized with regard to the cut-off.

Then we have from equations (2.20) and (2.21):

$$Z_{01} = \sqrt{\frac{L}{C}} . (1 - x^2)^{1/2}$$

$$= Z_0 \sqrt{(1 - x^2)} \quad . \quad . \quad . \quad . \quad . \quad . \quad . \qquad (2.22)$$

and

$$Z_{02} = \frac{Z_0}{\sqrt{(1 - x^2)}} \quad . \quad . \quad . \quad . \quad . \quad . \quad . \qquad (2.23)$$

where Z_0 is the nominal characteristic impedance.

From these equations for the range $x = 0$ to 1 it is clear that Z_{01} and Z_{02} are real and positive; i.e., they are pure resistances. The negative roots are inadmissible since they indicate negative resistances which are impossible in a passive network. The manner in which Z_{01} and Z_{02} vary in this band is shown by the full curves of Fig. 2.13. It will be seen that at cut-off $x = 1$, and Z_{01} comes down to a short-circuit, and Z_{02} rises to infinity, confirming the argument used in the section on loaded lines.

Since the network of Fig. 2.12 is composed of non-dissipative reactances it is evident that the total power transmitted into the network must be received in the resistance load terminating the network. Within the band quoted the network permits all frequencies to pass unattenuated, and in fact, it behaves as an impedance-transforming section which matches Z_{01} to Z_{02} without loss. It should be noted that it is not possible to produce Z_{01} and Z_{02} by physical resistors suitable for all frequencies since they vary with frequency. It follows from this that artificial lines cannot be accurately terminated for all frequencies. From Fig. 2.13 it can be seen that up to about half the cut-off frequency, termination with a resistor Z_0 at the mid-series or mid-shunt points provides a reasonably accurate matching impedance.

Returning to equations (2.22) and (2.23), for frequencies greater than cut-off, Z_{01} and Z_{02} become the square roots of negative quantities i.e., reactances. It is not possible to determine by inspection whether these reactances are positive or negative on account of the ambiguity arising from the signs accompanying the square roots. It is obvious from Fig. 2.12, however, that at very high frequencies Z_{01} is a positive reactance approaching the value $j\omega L/2$ and Z_{02} is a

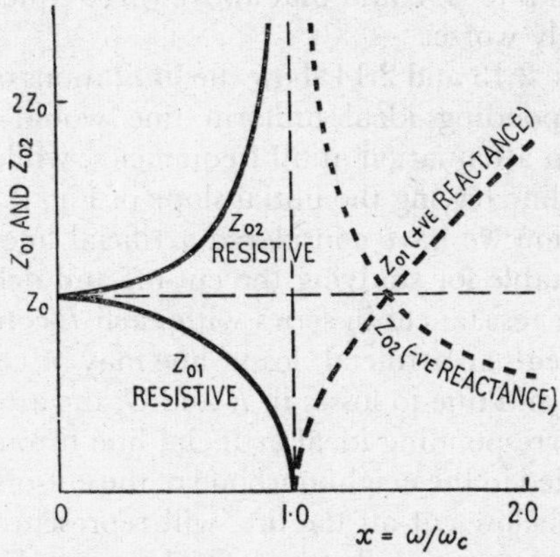

Fig. 2.13. Image impedances versus frequency for artificial line.

negative reactance approaching the value $2/j\omega C$. Hence above cut-off, Z_{01} rises from a zero reactance and approaches $j\omega L/2$ at high frequencies as shown by the dotted curve on Fig. 2.13. Similarly Z_{02} falls from an infinite reactance at cut-off to zero, approaching $2/j\omega C$ at high frequencies as shown in the figure.

It will be noted that Z_{01} and Z_{02} are related to one another inversely through equation (2.18), throughout the entire frequency range.

The determination of the phase shift and attenuation per whole section requires the use of hyperbolic functions and will not be attempted here. The results are, however, summarized in Fig. 2.14. The attenuation curve shows no

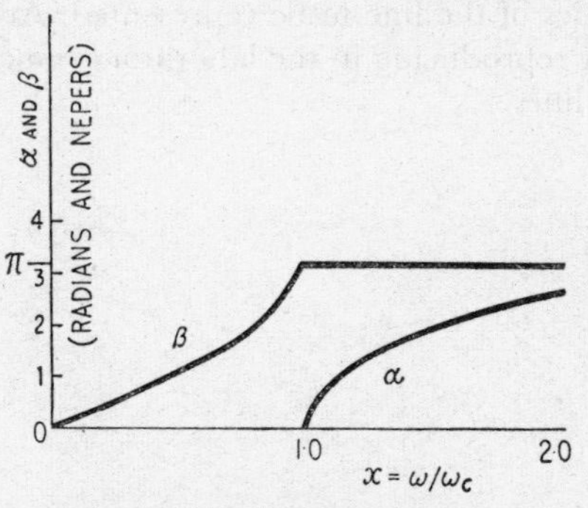

Fig. 2.14. Attenuation and phase shift versus frequency for one whole section of artificial line.

attenuation up to cut-off and a steadily rising attenuation above cut-off. The phase-shift curve for a whole section is approximately linear up to half the cut-off frequency, and thereafter it bends upwards reaching the value π radians per section at cut-off. Thereafter it remains constant. If the initial slope of the phase shift curve is extended up to the cut-off frequency it intersects at 2 radians per section. This assumption was used in the deduction of equation (2.13) and we see that there is an appreciable error. However, the assumption that the phase shift per section is 1 radian at half the cut-off frequency is reasonably accurate. It has already been stated that the artificial line represents the uniform line with good accuracy up to $\omega_c/2$ and that above this frequency the representation becomes progressively worse.

The curves of Figs. 2.13 and 2.14 show the limitations of an artificial line very clearly. The corresponding ideal uniform line would have a constant impedance Z_0 and zero attenuation at all frequencies, while the phase-shift curve would be a straight line having the initial slope of Fig. 2.14.

So far in this section we have considered artificial lines, without losses, since this type is most suitable for studying the cut-off and delay phenomena. However, by introducing resistances in series with each L component, and in shunt with each C component, an artificial 'lossy' line may be constructed. The cut-off effect will still exist, and due to losses in R and G, the attenuation curve will lie above that of the corresponding ideal artificial line throughout. The curve will be much more rounded in the neighbourhood of the cut-off than that of Fig. 2.14. At frequencies well below cut-off the line will represent with good accuracy a practical line with resistance, inductance, leakance and capacitance in similar proportions to the artificial line. The actual length of practical line to be represented by one section of artificial line is determined from considerations of accuracy of representation and cut-off frequency. It has been shown that if linear phase is assumed up to cut-off, the phase shift per section of artificial line at cut-off is 2 radians. If we assume that the accuracy of representation is to be such that the maximum frequency of the line corresponds to half the cut-off frequency of its artificial equivalent then we have the phase shift per section at half cut-off frequency equal to one radian. Hence one section of artificial line must represent a length of practical line having one radian phase shift (i.e., about one-sixth of a wavelength) at the maximum frequency to be transmitted. From this consideration the artificial line component values can be calculated from the known primary characteristics of the line to be represented. Artificial 'lossy' lines are mainly of interest for reproducing in the laboratory something approaching the performance of real lines.

CHAPTER 3

Reflections in Transmission Lines

Introduction

So far only infinitely long lines or perfectly matched lines have been considered. In many applications, for example, an aerial terminating a feeder line, it is difficult to ensure perfect matching. In other instances, it may be desirable to operate lines in the unmatched condition. It is therefore necessary to determine the performance of lines when terminated with any impedance ranging from a short-circuit to an open-circuit.

This problem may be approached in several ways, but perhaps the most informative is to consider an ideal line to which a short pulse of voltage is

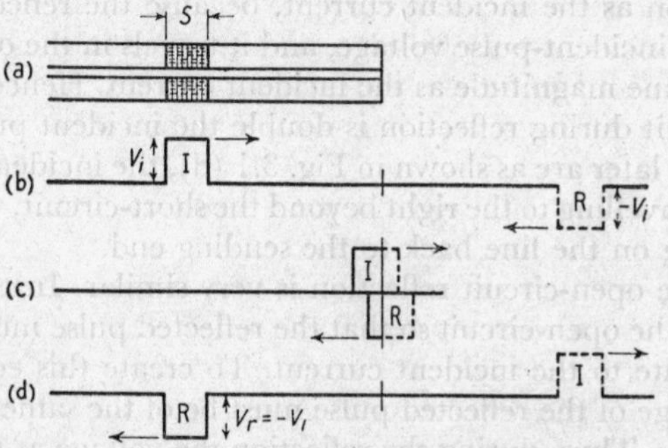

Fig. 3.1. Reflection of a pulse at a short-circuit.

applied. Suppose that this ideal line has primary characteristics L and C. The characteristic impedance is then $Z_0 = \sqrt{(L/C)}$ at all frequencies.

Referring to Fig. 3.1 (a) which shows an axial section through a coaxial line short-circuited at the distant end, the rectangular voltage pulse of length T seconds travels down the line as if it were travelling down an infinite line, since it cannot anticipate the impedance condition at the end of the line. Associated with the voltage pulse is a current or moving charge. The current is obtained from the voltage simply by dividing by Z_0. Since the line is ideal, the pulse is propagated without distortion of its amplitude–time graph at a velocity given by $v_p = 1/\sqrt{(LC)}$ metres/second. The pulse covers a space on the line given by $s = v_pT = T/\sqrt{(LC)}$ metres, where T is the pulse length in seconds. As we have seen for the distortionless line, the energy of the pulse is half in the magnetic field and half in the electric field in the space between the conductors over the length covered by the pulse. Since the line can dissipate no energy, and the short-circuit cannot either, the energy of the pulse cannot be absorbed. Furthermore, since no voltage can be produced across a short-circuit, the electric field must vanish when the leading edge of the pulse reaches the short-circuit. The pulse must be reflected in a rather similar way to the reflection of a wave on a taught string at the point where it is anchored to a wall.

The reflected pulse must have a voltage which will cause the electric field to vanish at the short circuit. Thus the reflected pulse must have an equal and opposite voltage to the incident pulse. This reflected pulse may be imagined to travel from the right in the opposite direction as shown in Fig. 3.1 (b). Thus the imaginary pulse R in Fig. 3.1 (b) is the same distance from the short circuit as the incident pulse I. The two pulses are approaching the short-circuit with the same velocity and Fig. 3.1 (c) shows conditions just after the leading edge of the incident pulse reaches the short-circuit. The real reflected pulse on the line has started to form, although the actual voltage across the short-circuit is zero. When the pulse is half way through its reflection, the electric field is everywhere zero, so that for the first half of the reflection the electric field collapses uniformly and its energy augments the magnetic field. For the second half of the reflection time, the excess magnetic field creates the reversed electric field of the reflected pulse. From energy considerations it can be shown that the current in the short-circuit during reflection is exactly double the current associated with the incident pulse. The same conclusion may be drawn by considering the current in the short-circuit produced by the reflected voltage pulse. This current is in the same direction as the incident current, because the reflected-pulse voltage is opposite to the incident-pulse voltage, and it travels in the opposite direction; it is also of the same magnitude as the incident current. Hence the total current in the short-circuit during reflection is double the incident pulse current. Conditions an instant later are as shown in Fig. 3.1 (d), the incident pulse being now imaginary and travelling to the right beyond the short-circuit, while the reflected pulse is travelling on the line back to the sending end.

The case of the open-circuit reflection is very similar. In this case there can be no current in the open-circuit so that the reflected pulse must cause a current equal and opposite to the incident current. To create this equal and opposite current the voltage of the reflected pulse must be of the same value and sign as the incident pulse. Thus, during the reflection the voltage at the end of the line rises momentarily to double the incident-pulse voltage.

When the line is correctly terminated by a resistance Z_0, the incident pulse is smoothly absorbed, and its energy dissipated as heat in Z_0. For all other values of terminating resistance between zero and Z_0 and between Z_0 and infinity, the pulse is partly reflected and partly absorbed.

Reflection of Continuous Waves

An understanding of the method by which a pulse is reflected from a discontinuity in a line may be easily extended to the reflection of a continuous wave. For, if we consider a sinusoidal wave being propagated down a line in the steady state, it may be imagined to be composed of a large number of contiguous pulses with amplitudes varying in a sinusoidal manner.

Considering again the short-circuited line and referring to Fig. 3.2 the incident sine-wave of voltage is moving from left to right and is considered as a number of pulses so narrow that the flat tops merge to make the smooth wave. Each pulse is reflected and appears as an equal and opposite pulse, so that there is no voltage across the short-circuit. As before, we can imagine the reflected wave as originating from the right and travelling backwards (to the left) with such a phase that the voltage at the short-circuit is always zero. The reflected wave is shown dotted.

The conception of two independent waves existing on the line at the same time is quite correct, but it is not sufficient for all problems. For example, a

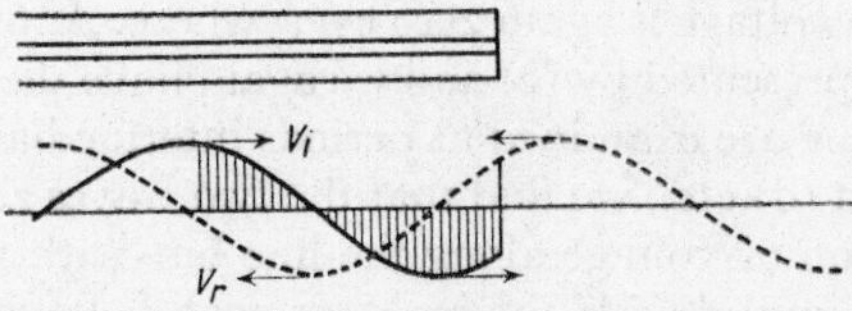

Fig. 3.2. Reflection of a continuous wave at a short-circuit.

simple voltmeter connected across the line could not separate the two waves and it is necessary to know what would be the reading on such a meter. The voltage at any point on a short-circuited line carrying forward- and backward-travelling waves can be determined graphically from Figs. 3.3 (a) to (e). In these figures

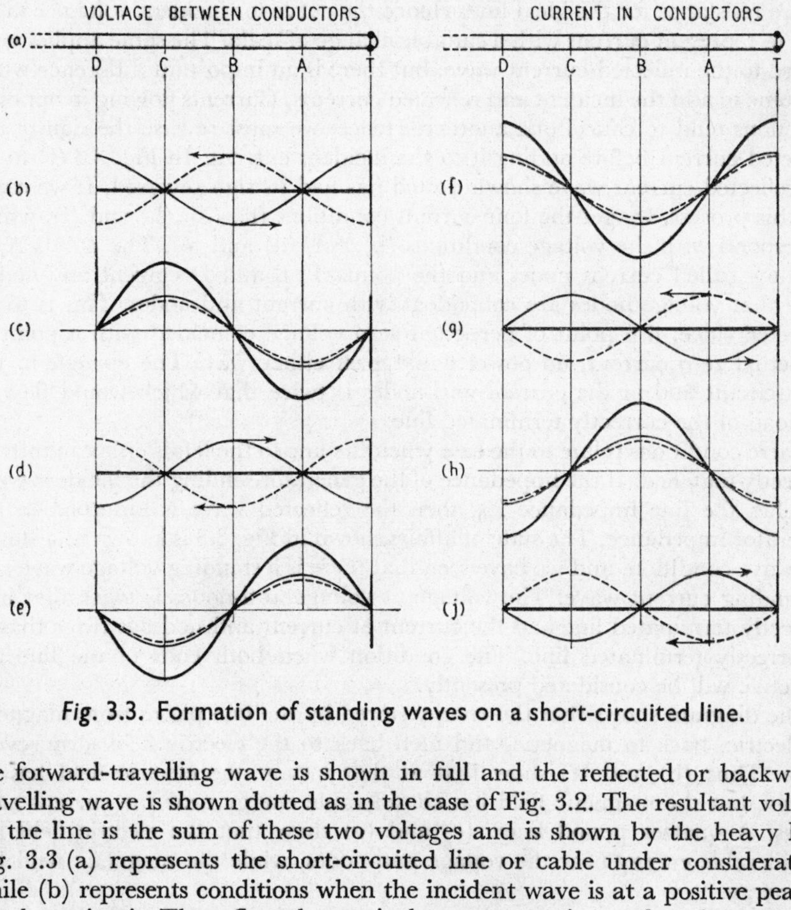

Fig. 3.3. Formation of standing waves on a short-circuited line.

the forward-travelling wave is shown in full and the reflected or backward-travelling wave is shown dotted as in the case of Fig. 3.2. The resultant voltage on the line is the sum of these two voltages and is shown by the heavy line. Fig. 3.3 (a) represents the short-circuited line or cable under consideration, while (b) represents conditions when the incident wave is at a positive peak at the short-circuit. The reflected wave is then at a negative peak and we see that the two waves cancel completely all down the line. Thus at this instant the voltage is zero everywhere. A quarter of a period later we have the conditions represented by (c). The two waves now add to give a sine-wave distribution of voltage along the line, the peak value being twice that of the incident wave. Another quarter of a period later we have the conditions represented by (d) and it can be seen that the voltage is again zero everywhere. Another quarter period later conditions are represented by (e) and we again have the two waves adding. If conditions on the line are examined at periods intermediate between (b) and (c) or between (c) and (d) etc., we find that the two waves add so as to produce a sine-wave distribution of voltage along the line but with a peak value intermediate between zero and double the incident peak voltage. A voltmeter connected across the line at points T, B and D would read zero since the waves cancel here at all times. Such points are called voltage nodes. A voltmeter connected across the line at points A and C would read double the voltage of the incident wave, since the voltage at these points varies sinusoidally with time between the limits of double the incident-wave amplitude. These points of high voltage are called anti-nodes.

The current associated with the incident wave is in phase with it, since Z_0 is a pure resistance for the ideal line. Hence the curve for incident voltage can be used to represent current with a suitable change of scale. The same applies with regard to the reflected-current wave, but there is an important difference when we come to add the incident and reflected currents. Currents flowing in opposite directions tend to cancel one another. Hence, we must reverse the sign of the reflected current before adding it to the incident current. In Fig. 3.3 (f) to (j) the reflected-current wave shown dotted has had its sign reversed. If we carry out this process, we get the four current conditions (f), (g), (h) and (j), which correspond with the voltage conditions (b), (c), (d) and (e). The points A, C are now called current nodes and the points T, B and D current anti-nodes. Note that voltage nodes are coincident with current anti-nodes. This is to be expected since, if a point of perpetual zero voltage coincided with a point of perpetual zero current, no power could pass either way. The current in the short-circuit and at the current anti-nodes is twice that which would flow in the load of the correctly terminated line.

These conditions relate to the case when the line to the left is either infinite or correctly matched. If the impedance of the generator sending the incident wave matches the line impedance Z_0, then the reflected wave is absorbed in the generator impedance. The state of affairs shown in Fig. 3.3 is known as a standing-wave condition, and we have seen that there is a standing voltage wave and a standing current wave. The voltage at voltage anti-nodes is twice that in a correctly terminated line and the current at current anti-nodes is twice that in a correctly terminated line. The condition when both ends of the line are reflective will be considered presently.

The diagram shows that the energy stored by the line passes from magnetic to electric, back to magnetic, and then back to the electric field form, every cycle. Thus (b) and (f) show that at that instant the electric field has no energy, but the magnetic field has considerable energy near the current anti-nodes. A quarter period later, (c) and (g) show that the electric field has considerable energy near the voltage anti-nodes, while the magnetic field has no energy.

The reflection of a continuous wave from an open-circuit can be deduced in exactly the same way. The condition to be observed in this case is that the reflected current wave must be such as to produce no resultant current at the open circuit; i.e., a current node. The reflected voltage will be such as to produce double the incident voltage at the open circuit; i.e., a voltage anti-node. These conditions are shown in Fig. 3.4 and if we compare them with Fig. 3.3 we see that they are very similar except that they are displaced a quarter wavelength with respect to one another. Thus, if we examine Fig. 3.3 at a point a quarter wavelength from the end of the line (i.e., from the short-circuit) the conditions at this point are identical with those at the open-circuit. We could cut a length $\lambda/4$ from the line, leaving it open-circuited, without affecting the

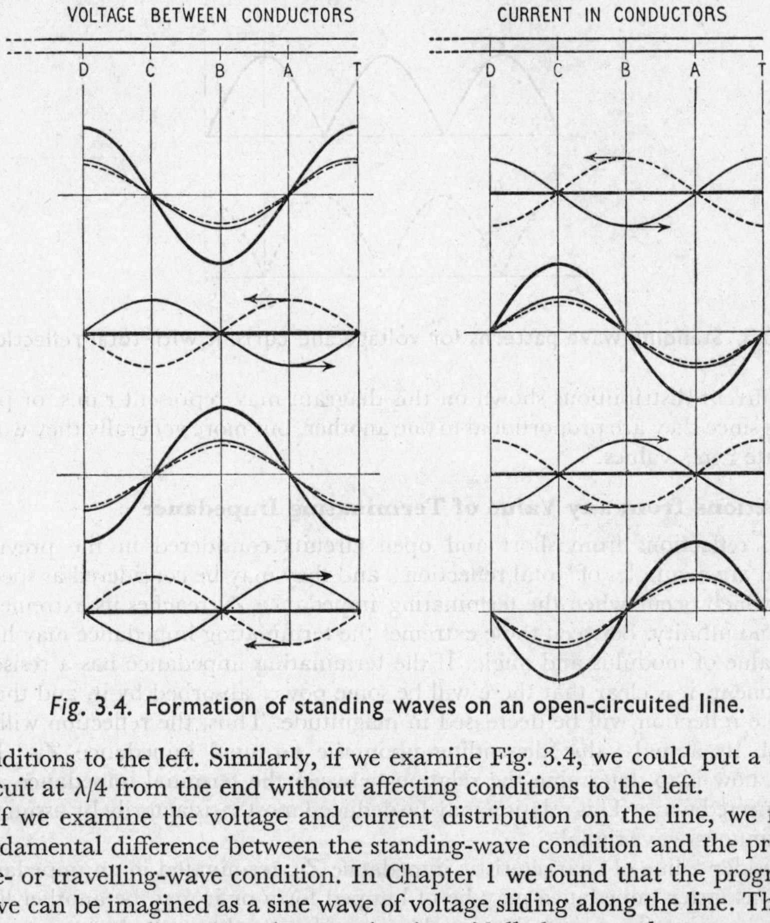

Fig. 3.4. Formation of standing waves on an open-circuited line.

conditions to the left. Similarly, if we examine Fig. 3.4, we could put a short-circuit at $\lambda/4$ from the end without affecting conditions to the left.

If we examine the voltage and current distribution on the line, we find a fundamental difference between the standing-wave condition and the progressive- or travelling-wave condition. In Chapter 1 we found that the progressive wave can be imagined as a sine wave of voltage sliding along the line. Thus, at all points in the line, the voltage varies sinusoidally between the same maxima and minima, the only difference between successive points in the line (ignoring attenuation) being a phase lag of the voltage as we progress down the line. In the standing-wave case, the line is divided into half wavelengths between nodes, and the voltage at each point although sinusoidal in time varies from zero at a node up to a maximum at an anti-node. The voltages at points between two voltage nodes are all in time phase, but there is a phase change of 180° when passing from one side of a node to the other side.

An idea of the type of voltage distribution with standing waves can be obtained from a model in which a wire is bent in the shape of a few cycles of a sine curve. It is then mounted so that it can be rotated horizontally about its zero axis. If viewed from a distance while rotating, the wire will appear to execute the variations of voltage in standing waves.

We are often only concerned with the magnitude of the voltage at points down the line, the relative time phases being unimportant. It is customary therefore to represent the voltage and current distributions, along a line with standing waves, in the manner shown in Fig. 3.5. This diagram has been drawn to cover the case of the open-circuited line or the short-circuited line. For the open-circuited line, the last quarter wavelength is simply omitted. The voltage

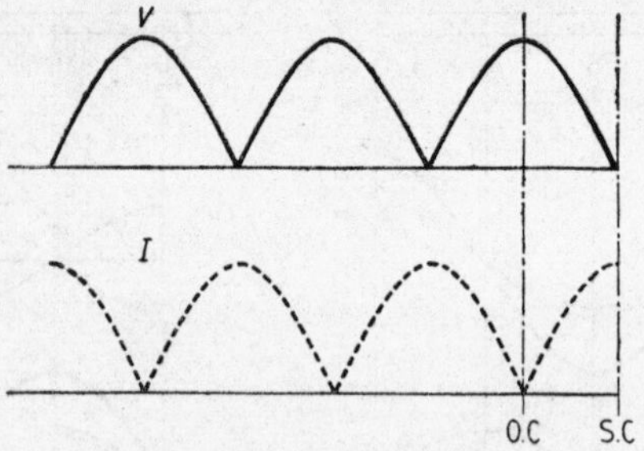

Fig. 3.5. Standing-wave patterns for voltage and current with total reflection.

and current distributions shown on this diagram may represent r.m.s. or peak values since they are proportional to one another, but more generally they would indicate r.m.s values.

Reflections from any Value of Terminating Impedance

The reflections from short and open circuits considered in the previous section are examples of 'total reflection', and they may be considered as special cases which occur when the terminating impedance Z_T reaches its extremes of zero and infinity. Between these extremes the terminating impedance may have any value of modulus and angle. If the terminating impedance has a resistive component, it is clear that there will be some power absorbed by it, and therefore the reflection will be decreased in magnitude. Thus, the reflection will be partial, its actual value depending upon the terminal impedance Z_T. The object now is to determine the relation between the terminal impedance and the reflected wave. This relation may be deduced most satisfactorily by assuming a continuous-wave signal.

Consider a line of characteristic impedance Z_0, terminated in an impedance Z_T. This latter impedance may be of lumped form or it may be another line. At the junction the convention for the signs of the voltages and currents is as shown in Fig. 3.6. A consistent convention such as this is adopted so that the result may give the correct phase relationships between voltage and current for all types of terminating impedance. Considering first of all instantaneous values of voltage and current, let:

v_i, v_r, v_t = incident, reflected and transmitted voltages at the junction, and

i_i, i_r, i_t = incident, reflected and transmitted current.

Then the voltage just to the left of the junction must equal the voltage just to the right, thus:

$$v_i + v_r = v_t \qquad (3.1)$$

Similarly, the current just to the left of the junction must equal the current just to the right, thus:

$$i_i + i_r = i_t \qquad (3.2)$$

It is clear that v_i and v_t are always of the same sign, and so are i_i and i_t. When Z_T is large compared with Z_0, there is a rise of voltage and a decrease of current at the end of the line as in the open-circuit case, hence v must be positive and i

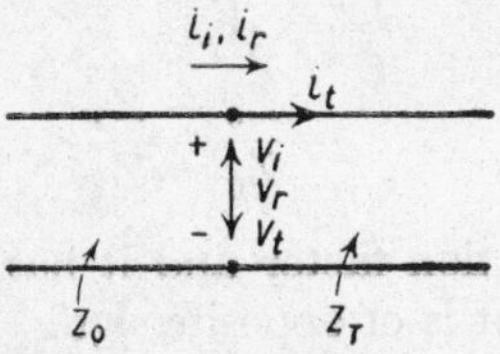

Fig. 3.6. Conventions for voltage and current at an impedance discontinuity.

negative. Similarly, when Z_T is small compared with Z_0 there is a decrease of voltage and an increase of current, so that v_r is negative and i_r positive. Thus, the actual signs of v_r and i_r are always opposite.

If the incident voltage is sinusoidal, then all the voltages and currents are sinusoidal and equations (3.1) and (3.2) are still complied with if vectors are substituted, thus:

$$V_i + V_r = V_t \qquad (3.3)$$

and

$$I_i + I_r = I_t \qquad (3.4)$$

where V_i, V_r, V_t; I_i, I_r and I_t are vector voltages and currents, the subscripts representing the incident, reflected and transmitted waves as before.

Further necessary relations are:

$$\frac{V_i}{I_i} = Z_0 \qquad (3.5)$$

$$\frac{V_r}{-I_r} = Z_0 \qquad (3.6)$$

$$\frac{V_t}{I_t} = Z_T \qquad (3.7)$$

The negative sign in equation (3.6) is necessary because, as we have seen above, v_r and i_r are of opposite sign or, alternatively, because a positive reflected voltage (i.e., in the direction of the convention of Fig. 3.5) causes a current opposite in sign to the convention.

Using equations (3.5) to (3.7) we have from (3.4)

$$\frac{V_i}{Z_0} - \frac{V_r}{Z_0} = \frac{V_t}{Z_T}$$

Eliminating V_t by using equation (3.3) we have

$$\frac{V_i - V_r}{Z_0} = \frac{V_i + V_r}{Z_T}$$

From which:

$$\frac{V_r}{V_i} = \frac{Z_T - Z_0}{Z_T + Z_0} \quad . \quad . \quad . \quad . \quad . \quad . \quad . \quad (3.8)$$

This ratio is called the voltage-reflection factor.

From equations (3.5) and (3.6)

$$\frac{I_r}{I_i} = \frac{-V_r}{V_i}$$

$$= \frac{Z_0 - Z_T}{Z_0 + Z_T} \quad . \quad . \quad . \quad . \quad . \quad . \quad . \quad (3.9)$$

This is the current-reflection factor and it has the same magnitude as the voltage-reflection factor, but is of opposite sign.

Equations (3.8) and (3.9) are in general vector ratios, because Z_T is generally complex; i.e., it has resistance and reactance. The equations are true when Z_0 is also complex although it will usually be a pure resistance equal to the surge impedance. The modulus of the voltage-reflection factor indicated as below:

$$\left|\frac{V_r}{V_i}\right| = \left|\frac{Z_T - Z_0}{Z_T + Z_0}\right|$$

gives the magnitude of the reflected wave relative to the incident wave. The angle of the impedance ratio of equation (3.8) gives the phase at the junction of the reflected wave relative to the incident wave.

These factors are sometimes expressed logarithmically in decibels or nepers. In decibels the reflection factor is often known as the 'return loss', since it gives the level of the reflected or returned wave relative to the incident wave, thus:

$$\text{Return loss} = 20 \log_{10} \left|\frac{Z_T - Z_0}{Z_T + Z_0}\right| \quad . \quad . \quad . \quad (3.10)$$

▶ When expressed in nepers it is sometimes known as the 'echo attenuation'. With this method of expression the attenuation and phase shift of the reflected wave relative to the incident wave appear as the real and imaginary parts of the echo attenuation as below.

$$\text{Echo attenuation} = \alpha + j\beta \text{ say,}$$

$$= \log_\varepsilon \left\{\frac{Z_T - Z_0}{Z_T + Z_0}\right\}$$

$$\therefore \varepsilon^\alpha \varepsilon^{j\beta} = \frac{Z_T - Z_0}{Z_T + Z_0}$$

$$\therefore \varepsilon^\alpha = \left|\frac{Z_T - Z_0}{Z_T + Z_0}\right|$$

$$\beta = \text{angle of } \frac{Z_T - Z_0}{Z_T + Z_0}$$

Hence we have

$$\text{Echo attenuation} = \log_\varepsilon \left| \frac{Z_T - Z_0}{Z_T + Z_0} \right| + j\beta \quad . \quad . \quad (3.11)$$

This form is convenient for adding to the attenuation and phase shift of the line if we wish to determine the reflected-wave amplitude and phase at a point in an attenuating line distant from the termination Z_T.

When $Z_T = 0$ (i.e., the short-circuited line), the magnitude of the reflection factor is unity. When Z_T becomes large compared with Z_0, the magnitude of the reflection factor approaches unity, and in the limit when $Z_T = \infty$ it becomes unity. When Z_T is a pure reactance and Z_0 is a pure resistance, it is easily seen by drawing the vectors $(Z_T - Z_0)$ and $(Z_T + Z_0)$ that the magnitude of the reflection factor is again unity. This is also obvious from the fact that a purely reactive load can absorb no net power. In this case, there is a phase shift between reflected and incident voltages which is dependent upon the sign and magnitude of the terminating reactance. In all other cases, where there is a resistive component in Z_T, the magnitude of the reflection factor is less than unity.

Similar factors can easily be deduced for the transmitted waves. Thus from equation (3.3)

$$\frac{V_t}{V_i} = 1 + \frac{V_r}{V_i}$$

$$= 1 + \frac{Z_T - Z_0}{Z_T + Z_0}$$

$$= \frac{2Z_T}{Z_T + Z_0} \quad . \quad . \quad . \quad . \quad . \quad . \quad . \quad . \quad (3.12)$$

and from equation (3.4)

$$\frac{I_t}{I_i} = 1 + \frac{I_r}{I_i}$$

$$= 1 + \frac{Z_0 - Z_T}{Z_0 + Z_T}$$

$$= \frac{2Z_0}{Z_0 + Z_T} \quad . \quad . \quad . \quad . \quad . \quad . \quad . \quad (3.13)$$

These are known as voltage- and current-transmission factors respectively.

This terminology is satisfactory for low frequencies where impedances can be reliably measured, but for high frequencies it is more convenient to make voltage measurements on the line when actually conveying a signal. From such measurements the standing-wave ratio (s.w.r.) is obtained and can be easily related to the above coefficients.

Standing-Wave Ratio

When the reflection is only partial it causes a backward-travelling wave which is of smaller amplitude than the incident wave. At the load impedance mismatch the amplitude and phase of the reflected wave with respect to the incident wave can be determined by the reflection coefficients of the previous section.

Since the backward-travelling wave is smaller than the incident wave it cannot effect a complete cancellation, neither can it add so as to produce double the incident voltage. Nevertheless, the two voltage waves combine so that points of maxima and minima appear. The maxima are separated by a half wavelength and so are the minima, as in the case of total reflection.

Consider an ideal line with a forward-travelling wave of peak amplitude a, and a backward-travelling wave of peak amplitude b. The forward wave may be imagined to be composed of two co-phased parts (b) and $(a - b)$ as shown in Fig. 3.7 (a) because we have:

$$a = (b) + (a - b)$$

The forward-travelling portion (b) combines with the reflected wave to produce a standing wave of peak value $2b$ similar to the standing waves of total reflection, as shown by curve A of Fig. 3.7 (b). This leaves the forward-travelling progressive wave $(a - b)$ which actually conveys the power to the load. This wave is shown superimposed on Fig. 3.7 (b) as the chain-dotted curve B and it must

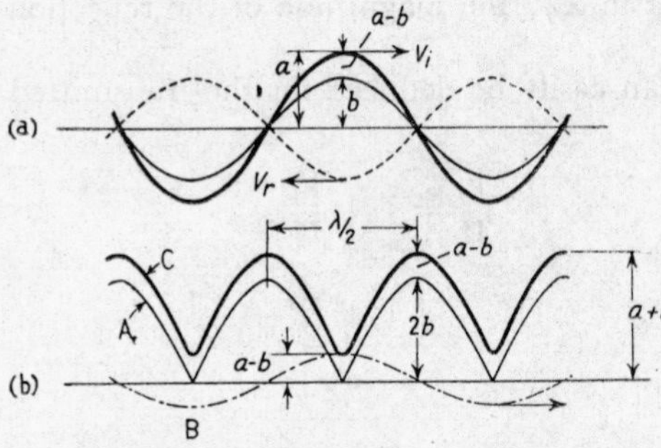

Fig. 3.7. Standing-wave ratio.

be noted that it moves to the right whereas curve A represents a standing-wave pattern. By adding this wave to the standing wave, making due allowance for the time phases, the curve of peak voltages on the line is found and is shown by curve C of Fig. 3.7 (b). The shape of this curve is not a pure sine wave, since the minima are more sharply defined than the maxima. Its actual shape needs a consideration of the time phases, but the maxima and minima, with which we are mainly concerned, are easily found.

Thus, at a minimum, the only voltage is that of the forward progressive wave $(a - b)$. A maximum occurs when a forward-travelling positive peak combines with a backward-travelling positive peak, giving a maximum voltage on the line of $(a + b)$. Thus the peaks of curve C have an amplitude of $(a + b)$ while the troughs have an amplitude of $(a - b)$.

The ratio of the peaks to the troughs is given by:

$$S = \frac{a + b}{a - b}$$

and is called the standing-wave ratio (s.w.r.).* We have been dealing in Fig. 3.7 (a) with sine waves of peak value a and b, but it is more usual to denote

* The inverse of this is sometimes used as the definition of standing-wave ratio, in which case the values of s.w.r. are less than unity.

voltage or current waves by their r.m.s. values. Since the r.m.s. value of a sine wave is simply $1/\sqrt{2}$ of the peak value we can express the standing-wave ratio as:

$$S = \frac{V_{\max}}{V_{\min}} = \frac{V_i + V_r}{V_i - V_r} \quad . \quad . \quad . \quad . \quad . \quad (3.14)$$

where V_i is the r.m.s. value of the incident voltage wave, and V_r is the r.m.s. of the reflected voltage wave. $V_{\max}$ and $V_{\min}$ are the r.m.s. voltages at the peaks and troughs of the standing wave pattern, as would be measured by a voltmeter reading r.m.s. values. Similar remarks apply to the forward- and backward-current waves. The standing-wave ratio can usually be measured quite easily, and it is therefore often used as a measure of the degree of mismatch. In fact, if the position and magnitude of the standing-wave pattern is known, the load impedance may be completely determined.

To find the power passed to the load, it is preferable not to use the wave B of Fig. 3.7 (b) since this requires a knowledge of the load impedance. We can however proceed as follows:

$$\text{Power in incident wave} = \frac{V_i^2}{Z_0}$$

$$\text{Power in reflected wave} = \frac{V_r^2}{Z_0}$$

where Z_0 is the characteristic impedance of the line and is assumed to be resistive.

$$\begin{aligned}
\text{Power passed to load} &= \frac{V_i^2 - V_r^2}{Z_0} \\
&= \frac{(V_i + V_r)(V_i - V_r)}{Z_0} \\
&= \frac{V_{\max} V_{\min}}{Z_0} \\
&= \frac{V^2_{\max}}{SZ_0} \quad . \quad . \quad . \quad . \quad . \quad . \quad (3.15)
\end{aligned}$$

The significance of the standing-wave ratio can be better appreciated by calculating the proportion of the power in the incident wave which is actually delivered to the load, in terms of S. We have by re-arranging equation (3.14):

$$\frac{V_r}{V_i} = \frac{S-1}{S+1}$$

Then the ratio

$$\begin{aligned}
\frac{\text{Power in load}}{\text{Power in incident wave}} &= \frac{(V_i^2 - V_r^2)/Z_0}{V_i^2/Z_0} \\
&= 1 - (V_r/V_i)^2 \\
&= \frac{4S}{(1+S)^2} \quad . \quad . \quad . \quad . \quad (3.16)
\end{aligned}$$

The above proportion subtracted from unity gives the proportion of the incident power which is lost to the load.

In Table 3.1, values of the proportion of power in the load and power lost are given for typical values of standing-wave ratio. In the last column the power in the load relative to the power in the incident wave is expressed as a loss in decibels. The voltage reflection factors $|K_R|$ are also given.

TABLE 3.1

S	$\|K_R\|$	Proportion of power in load	Proportion of power lost	Power loss in decibels
1	0	1·0	0	0
1·25	0·11	0·988	0·012	0·1
1·5	0·2	0·96	0·04	0·2
2	0·33	0·89	0·11	0·5
3	0·5	0·75	0·25	1·3
4	0·6	0·64	0·36	1·9
5	0·66	0·56	0·44	2·6
10	0·82	0·33	0·67	4·8
∞	1·0	0	1·0	∞

It will be observed that the standing-wave ratio is a very sensitive indicator of the loss of power due to mismatch, a ratio of 1·25 indicating only about 1% power loss. However, there is another important reason for keeping the s.w.r. to a low value, preferably 1·1 or less. The insulation of the line is subjected to unnecessary stress at voltage anti-nodes, and if it is working near voltage breakdown the voltage available for the transmission of power to the load is only $1/S$ of the maximum. It is the difference between the forward and reflected waves which determines the power flow while their sum must be used for voltage breakdown considerations. Where large powers are involved, voltage breakdown is often the important criterion and for this reason a low s.w.r. is desirable.

The s.w.r. can be related to the modulus of the reflection factors of the previous section. Thus from equation (3.14)

$$S = \frac{1 + V_r/V_i}{1 - V_r/V_i}$$

$$= \frac{1 + |K_R|}{1 - |K_R|} \quad . \quad . \quad . \quad . \quad . \quad (3.17)$$

where $|K_R|$ is the modulus of the voltage-reflection factor. The corresponding reflection factors are shown in the second column of Table 3.1.

When the line and terminating impedances are purely resistive, the standing-wave ratio may be shown to be simply related to them. Thus, denoting these impedances by R_0 and R_T to show that they are resistive, we have for the case $R_T > R_0$

$$|K_R| = \frac{R_T - R_0}{R_T + R_0}$$

Substituting in equation (3.17) we get:

$$S = R_T/R_0 \quad . \quad . \quad . \quad . \quad . \quad . \quad . \quad . \quad (3.18)$$

For the case $R_0 > R_T$, the voltage-reflection factor is negative, so that its modulus or magnitude is simply obtained by multiplying by -1. Thus

$$|K_R| = \left|\frac{R_T - R_0}{R_T + R_0}\right|$$

$$= \frac{R_0 - R_T}{R_0 + R_T}$$

Substituting in equation (3.17) we get

$$S = R_0/R_T \quad . \quad . \quad . \quad . \quad . \quad . \quad . \quad (3.19)$$

The s.w.r. is by definition always greater than or equal to unity, and we see that in the purely resistive case it is equal to the ratio of the larger to the smaller of the impedances R_0 and R_T. To determine whether the line or terminating impedance is the larger in a particular case, the distribution of nodes and anti-nodes must be examined. From Figs. 3.3 and 3.4, and total reflection phenomena, we can say that a voltage node or minimum at the termination occurs when $R_0 > R_T$, while a voltage anti-node or maximum at the termination occurs when $R_T > R_0$.

The deductions on standing-wave ratio made so far have been based on the voltage waves. Similar results can, however, be determined from the current waves. If the line impedance is assumed resistive, the forward-travelling current wave will be in phase with the forward-travelling voltage wave. Similarly, the backward-travelling current wave will be in phase with the backward-travelling voltage wave. When a peak of the forward-voltage wave is combining with a peak of the backward voltage wave, the peak forward current will be opposed by the peak backward current. Thus, a voltage maximum coincides with a current minimum. Similarly, a voltage minimum coincides with a current maximum. Since the forward current is V_i/Z_0 and the backward current is V_r/Z_0, it can be seen that the ratio of maximum current to minimum current is the same as the standing-wave ratio based on voltage. Thus, when making measurements of standing-wave ratio, either current or voltage-indicating instruments may be used. The standing-wave pattern for current is obtained by dividing the voltage pattern by Z_0 and displacing the curve by a distance corresponding to $\lambda/4$. Thus

$$\frac{V_{max}}{I_{max}} = Z_0 \quad . \quad . \quad . \quad . \quad . \quad . \quad . \quad (3.20)$$

although V_{max} is displaced $\lambda/4$ from I_{max}. Similarly

$$\frac{V_{min}}{I_{min}} = Z_0$$

although V_{min} is displaced $\lambda/4$ from I_{min}.

The measurement of the maximum and minimum voltages or currents on an open-wire line, such as that feeding a transmitting aerial, can be very easily carried out. If a single-loop coil is arranged to couple with the magnetic field at, say, a point a fixed distance below one of the wires, the e.m.f. induced will cause a current to flow in a thermo-couple or rectifier type of meter. A potentiometer or variable resistor is connected in series to protect the meter and to adjust the reading at a maximum to a convenient value. The coil may be moved along the line and the meter reading will be proportional to current. The arrangement shown in Fig. 3.8 is convenient as it may be pulled along the line maintaining a constant coupling with the line. All parts except the wiring are made from insulating materials. The standing-wave maxima and minima can be located and measured, and the ratio gives the s.w.r.

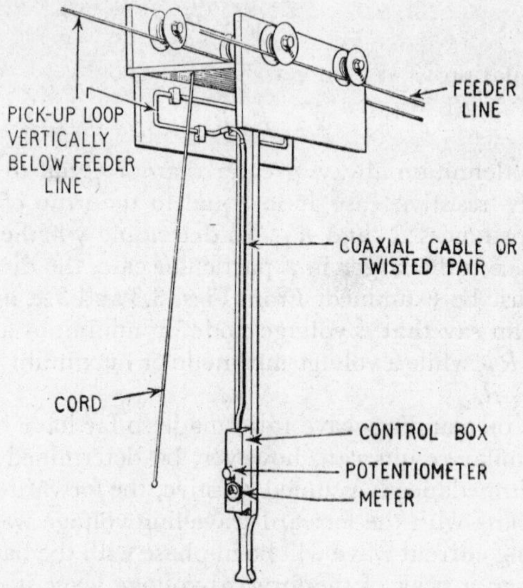

Fig. 3.8. Standing-wave indicator for open-wire line.

The locations of the first maximum and minimum from the termination (e.g., the aerial) also indicate the character of the terminating impedance Z_T. The method of determining Z_T from the s.w.r. and the locations of the first maximum or minimum will be considered presently.

When making these measurements, the current in each wire should be checked by turning the trolley round so that the loop comes under each wire

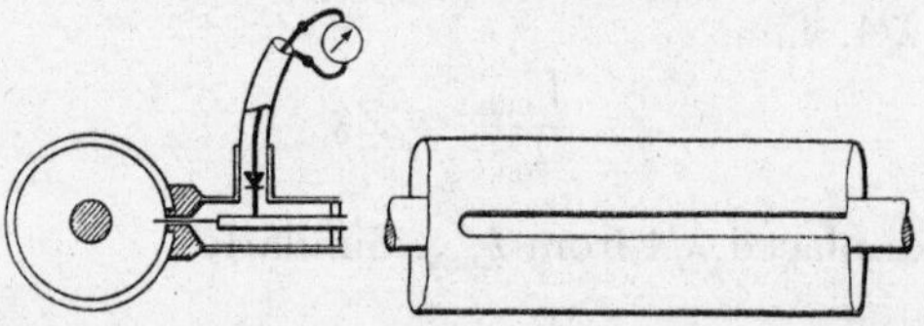

Fig. 3.9. Standing-wave indicator for coaxial line.

in turn. If the currents in the two wires differ by more than a few per cent, a serious unbalance exists and the generator, load, and line should be examined for unbalances. Operation in the unbalanced condition usually means loss of power due to radiation from the transmission line.

At higher frequencies, particularly approaching the microwave region, the measurement of standing-wave ratio is important since it provides a convenient means of measuring impedances. In this method, an air-spaced coaxial line is constructed with a narrow slot in the outer conductor, as in Fig. 3.9, so that standing waves may be detected. The slot should be at least a half wavelength long so that at least one maximum and one minimum can be observed. The slot will have negligible effect if it is narrow, because the current flow is axial, and the voltage distribution between conductors is little disturbed. A wire probe projects into the inner surface of the outer conductor and is used to pick up a voltage proportional to that between the line conductors. The actual power extracted is very small. This voltage is measured by a rectifier, thermal, or other type of meter which has been calibrated from a known condition of total reflection in the line. If an unknown impedance is connected to one end of this line and power is applied at the other end, movement of the probe allows the maxima and minima to be located and their ratio measured. The circle diagram may then be used to determine the unknown terminating impedance, as will be described presently.

These deductions have been based on ideal lines. Where the line has attenuation the standing-wave ratio is greatest near the termination which causes the reflected wave. As we move away from the termination the reflected wave becomes attenuated and the standing-wave ratio is progressively reduced. At a large distance from the termination the standing-wave ratio approaches unity. For many practical r.f. problems, however, the attenuation may be neglected and the s.w.r. can be regarded as constant along the whole line.

The actual curve of maximum voltages in the line can be calculated as follows. Consider a dissipationless line having a forward-travelling wave $V_i\varepsilon^{-j\beta z}$ and a backward-travelling wave $V_r\varepsilon^{j\beta z}$ where V_i and V_r are r.m.s. values as before.

The voltage at any point z is then given by:

$$\begin{aligned} V_z &= (V_i\varepsilon^{-j\beta z} + V_r\varepsilon^{j\beta z}) \\ &= \{(V_i + V_r)\cos\beta z - j(V_i - V_r)\sin\beta z\} \end{aligned}$$

The modulus of V_z is then:

$$\begin{aligned} |V_z| &= \{(V_i + V_r)^2\cos^2\beta z + (V_i - V_r)^2\sin^2\beta z\}^{1/2} \\ &= (V_i^2 + 2V_iV_r\cos 2\beta z + V_r^2)^{1/2} \qquad (3.21) \end{aligned}$$

As $\cos 2\beta z$ varies between the limits ± 1, the value of $|V_z|$ varies between $(V_i + V_r)$ and $(V_i - V_r)$ giving

$$S = \frac{V_i + V_r}{V_i - V_r}$$

The actual plot of the curve of $|V_z|$ against z gives the curve of Fig. 3.7 and shows a minimum which is somewhat more sharply located than the maximum.

Input Impedance of Lines with Total Reflection

If a line is cut at a point and the impedance looking towards the terminating impedance is measured, the value obtained is called the input or sending impedance. It will be denoted by Z_S. It was shown in Chapter 1 that a line of characteristic impedance Z_0, which is terminated in a load impedance Z_0, behaves as an infinite line; i.e., a sinusoidal input signal is propagated smoothly and there are no reflections. Wherever such a line is cut the sending impedance Z_S is equal to Z_0.

If the terminating impedance Z_T differs from Z_0 it is clear that Z_S will in general also differ from Z_0. In this section consideration is given to the value of Z_S at various distances from the end of an ideal line which is either short-circuited or open-circuited.

Suppose a short-circuited ideal coaxial line is cut a quarter of a wavelength away from the short circuit. This point of cutting is from Fig. 3.3 a voltage anti-node and a current node. The ratio of voltage to current at this point is the sending impedance Z_S and it is infinite if the line and short-circuit are ideal. This is an important property which can be put to good use, as will be shown presently.

The voltage and current distribution on the quarter-wave line are as shown in Fig. 3.10 by simply extracting from Fig. 3.3. The voltage at a point P

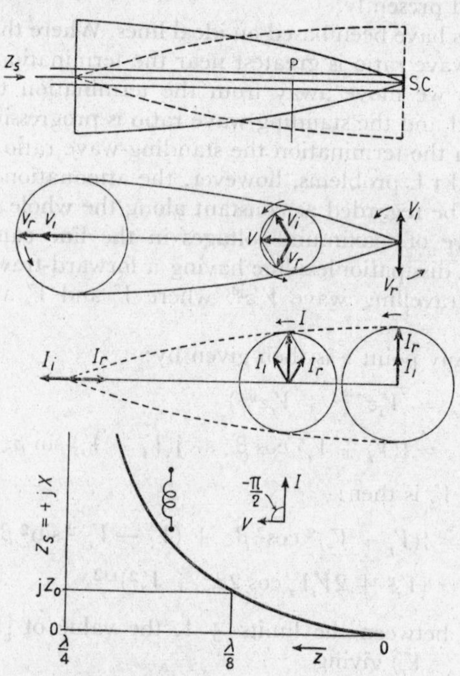

Fig. 3.10. The reactance of a short-circuited line.

oscillates between the limits of the two parts of a sine curve shown in full, while the current at P oscillates to and fro between limits given by the dotted curve. For simplicity, the upper half only of this diagram is usually drawn, it being understood that it represents the positive and negative maxima of the standing wave at all points on the line.

So far, only the space relationship between the voltage and the current has been considered. We must now consider the time relationship and for this purpose it is convenient to use vectors.

In Fig. 3.10 at the end of the line the vector V_i represents the incident wave and the vector V_r, equal and opposite to it, the reflected wave. The sum is at all times zero. If now we move towards the left, the phase of V_i must advance (because V_i lags as we move away from the generator) while the phase of V_r

must be retarded. The advance of V_i must be equal to the retard of V_r, hence the sum is the vector V which gives the net voltage at that point. It will be observed that, as we move from the short-circuit towards the $\lambda/4$ point, the vector V increases according to a sine curve and that the time phase is the same at all points, as we have noted before.

Turning now to the current at the short circuit, I_i is in phase with V_i and I_r is in phase with I_i in order to produce double the current in the short-circuit. Now consider the current to the left of the short-circuit. The phase of I_i must be advanced since it is in phase with V_i and the phase of I_r must be retarded an equal amount. The sum is the vector I which is at right angles to V.

Thus at a typical point such as P, the current lags the voltage by 90°, so that

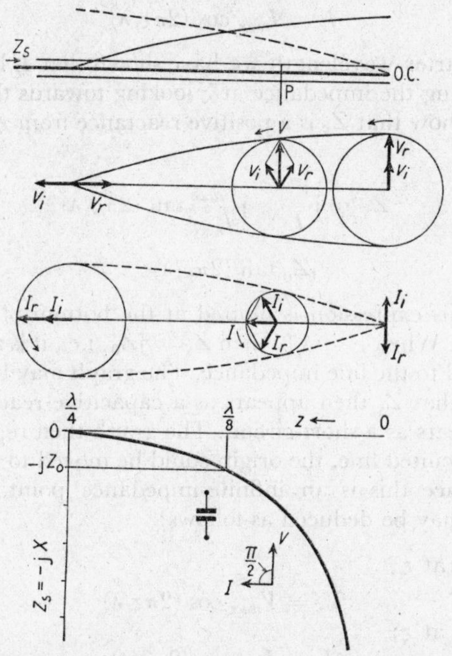

Fig. 3.11. The reactance of an open-circuited line.

if the line were cut at P and the impedance Z_S towards the short-circuit were measured, we should measure a pure inductive reactance. As we proceed towards the $\lambda/4$ point, the voltage rises and the current falls, indicating that this reactance is increasing. At the $\lambda/4$ point, it approaches infinity; i.e., an open-circuit.

Since the line and short-circuit were assumed to be dissipationless, the reactive nature of Z_S is to be expected.

If now we proceed farther to the left, the situation is similar to that just to the left of an open-circuited line. Referring to Fig. 3.11, the current is seen by a similar argument to lead the voltage by 90°. Thus, if an open-circuited line is cut between the open-circuit and the $\lambda/4$ point, its impedance Z_S towards the open-circuit appears as a capacitive reactance. As we proceed back to the $\lambda/4$ point, the voltage falls and the current rises, indicating that this reactance is falling, until at the $\lambda/4$ point it falls to zero; i.e., a short-circuit.

For the $\lambda/4$ line, the following relations between Z_S and Z_T therefore exist:

$$\text{When } Z_T = 0, \quad Z_S = \infty$$
$$\text{When } Z_T = \infty, \quad Z_S = 0$$

In the study of the total reflection of continuous waves, it was deduced that the voltage and current distributions along the line followed a cosine or sine law. Thus, if the origin is taken as the short- or open-circuit and z is measured in metres positively back along the line, we have for the short-circuited line:

Voltage (r.m.s.) at z:

$$V_z = V_{\text{max}} \sin (2\pi z/\lambda)$$

Current (r.m.s.) at z:

$$I_z = I_{\text{max}} \cos (2\pi z/\lambda)$$

For the first quarter wavelength we have shown that I_z lags 90° behind E_z, hence in determining the impedance at z looking towards the short circuit, we must include j to show that Z_S is a positive reactance from $z = 0$ to $\lambda/4$.

Thus:

$$Z_S = \text{j}\frac{V_z}{I_z} = \text{j}\frac{V_{\text{max}}}{I_{\text{max}}} \tan (2\pi z/\lambda)$$
$$= \text{j}Z_0 \tan (2\pi z/\lambda) \quad . \quad . \quad . \quad . \quad . \quad . \quad . \quad . \quad (3.22)$$

The graph of this expression is plotted at the bottom of Fig. 3.10 (z being positive to the left). When $z = \lambda/8$, then $Z_S = \text{j}Z_0$; i.e., it is a positive reactance of magnitude equal to the line impedance. The graph may be extended beyond $\lambda/4$, and it shows that Z_S then appears as a capacitive reactance until the $\lambda/2$ point when it appears as a short-circuit. The graph then repeats itself.

For the open-circuited line, the origin could be moved to the $\lambda/4$ point of the previous graph since this is an infinite-impedance point. Alternatively, the expression for Z_S may be deduced as follows:

Voltage (r.m.s.) at z:

$$V_z = V_{\text{max}} \cos (2\pi z/\lambda)$$

Current (r.m.s.) at z:

$$I_z = I_{\text{max}} \sin (2\pi z/\lambda)$$

For the first quarter wavelength from an open circuit, we have seen that I_z leads V_z by 90°, hence in determining Z_S we must include $-$j to show that Z_S is a negative reactance from $z = 0$ to $\lambda/4$.

Thus:

$$Z_S = -\text{j}\frac{V_z}{I_z} = -\text{j}\frac{V_{\text{max}}}{I_{\text{max}}} \cot (2\pi z/\lambda)$$
$$= -\text{j}Z_0 \cot (2\pi z/\lambda) \quad . \quad . \quad . \quad . \quad . \quad . \quad . \quad (3.23)$$

The graph of this expression is plotted at the bottom of Fig. 3.11. At the $\lambda/8$ point $Z_S = -\text{j}Z_0$; i.e., it is a capacitive reactance of magnitude equal to the line impedance. The graph may be extended beyond $\lambda/4$. The similarity of the graphs for the short-circuit and open-circuit cases is at once apparent, the graph for the open-circuited line being that to the left of the $\lambda/4$ point of a short-circuited line.

One application of these results is the quarter-wave insulator, two examples of which are shown in Fig. 3.12. In Fig. 3.12 (a) a balanced transmission line is supported on a length of line short-circuited at the base. At the point of connection to the line the $\lambda/4$ support will appear as an infinite impedance and will therefore cause a negligible shunt on the line. Similarly in Fig. 3.12 (b) the central conductor of an air-spaced coaxial line is supported on a $\lambda/4$ stub. In

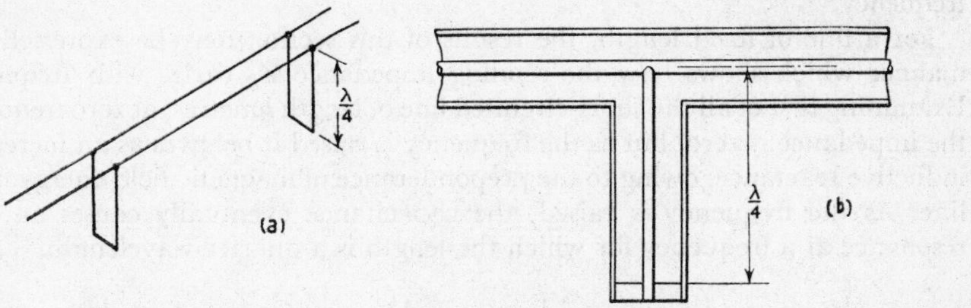

Fig. 3.12. (a) Quarter-wave support for balanced line; (b) quarter-wave stub support.

either case the length of the $\lambda/4$ support line would have to be finely adjusted to give a negligibly small standing-wave ratio on the line. It is important to notice that such devices can only be used at the frequencies for which the support is a quarter wavelength, or for a narrow band on either side of that frequency.

An application of the near-zero input impedance of an open-circuited quarter-wave line is the coaxial rotating joint shown in Fig. 3.13. This may be understood by considering first of all the two-wire line shown in Fig. 3.13 (a). One

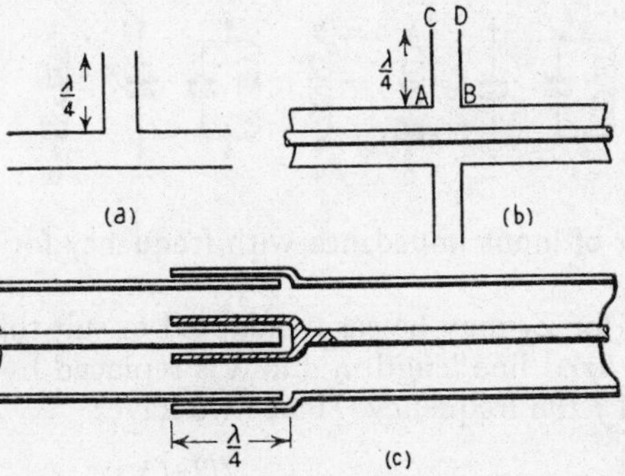

Fig. 3.13. The rotating joint.

conductor of this line is broken and a quarter-wave open-circuited line is inserted in series with it. The input impedance of this quarter-wave branch is zero. Thus the line is electrically continuous, although physically it is broken. The same principle may be applied to the outer conductor of a coaxial line as in Fig. 3.13 (b). The outer conductor is broken, and a flange is connected to each end. The radial length of the transmission line between the two flanges from AB to CD is a quarter wavelength so that the impedance across AB is zero. The next stage is to fold the flange back on to the outer conductor as in Fig. 3.13 (c). The same principles may be applied to the centre conductor as shown in the same figure. We then have electrical continuity for the frequency at which the sleeves are a quarter wavelength and yet the line is physically broken. This enables one section of line to be rotated with respect to the other without friction, a feature which is often employed in radar systems. As in the case of Fig. 3.12, this device is only effective at the one frequency for which the sleeve is a quarter wavelength or for a narrow band on either side of this frequency.

For a line of fixed length, the results of this section may be expressed in a manner which shows how the sending impedance Z_S varies with frequency. Examining first of all the short-circuited line of length l metres, at zero frequency the impedance is zero, but as the frequency is raised it behaves as an increasing inductive reactance, owing to the preponderance of magnetic field energy in the line. As the frequency is raised, the capacitance eventually causes an anti-resonance at a frequency for which the length is a quarter wavelength.

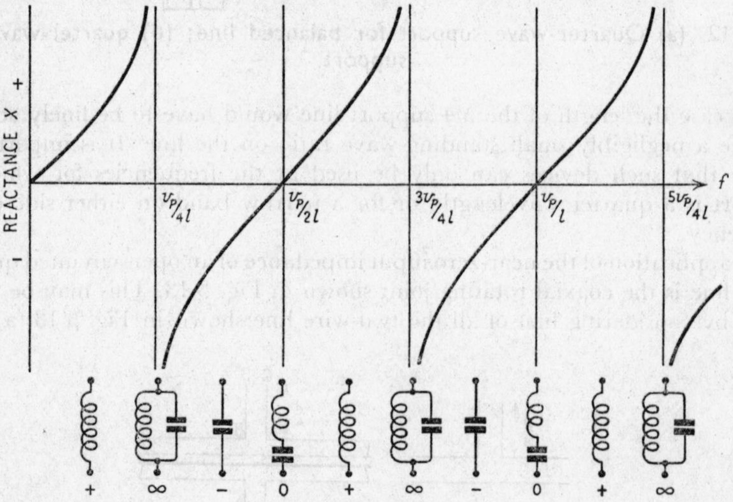

Fig. 3.14. Variation of input impedance with frequency for short-circuited line.

Equation (3.22) for Z_S may be easily adapted to suit this case. The length z is replaced by the fixed line length l, and λ is replaced by v_p/f, where v_p is the phase velocity and f the frequency. Hence we have:

$$Z_S = jZ_0 \tan\left(\frac{l2\pi f}{v_p}\right) \qquad (3.24)$$

If the reactance of Z_S is plotted against f, the shape is that of the tangent curve as shown in Fig. 3.14. The tangent of an angle rises to infinity when the angle is $\pi/2$; i.e.,

$$\frac{l2\pi f}{v_p} = \frac{\pi}{2}$$

or

$$l = \lambda/4$$

As the frequency is raised higher, the tangent function becomes negative, indicating that Z_S is capacitive, its reactance decreasing. In the region where Z_S

passes from plus infinity to minus infinity, the line behaves like a parallel-resonant circuit; i.e., it has an anti-resonance. When the frequency reaches the value where the angle is π radians, corresponding to $l = \lambda/2$, the value of Z_S becomes zero. Just beyond this frequency Z_S becomes a positive reactance again. In the region where Z_S passes through zero, the line behaves like a series resonant circuit.

Thus, as the frequency of the voltage applied to a short-circuited line is increased from zero, the line sending impedance passes from an inductive reactance, through anti-resonance to a capacitive reactance, through resonance to inductive reactance again, and so on.

Taking now a similar open circuited line; at zero frequency the impedance is infinite, but as the frequency is raised the line behaves as a capacitive reactance falling with frequency. Eventually the inductance causes a resonance at a frequency for which the length is a quarter wavelength. The sending impedance is similar in shape to the cotangent curve. Fig. 3.14 can be made to apply to the open-circuited case by moving the frequency scale to the right until its zero coincides with the first anti-resonance.

The nature of the sending impedance at various points on the frequency scale is indicated by the lumped inductances and capacitances shown at the bottom of the figure. By comparison with the straight-line curve representing the reactance of a fixed inductance, the sending impedance of a short-circuited line approximates to it up to a frequency for which the line length is $\lambda/8$. However, beyond this frequency the line reactance rises rapidly and near the infinity of Z_S the best representation is a parallel-resonant circuit. Similarly, the input impedance of an open-circuited line approximates to the reactance of a fixed capacitor up to a frequency for which the line length is $\lambda/8$. Beyond this frequency the line reactance approaches zero rapidly and in the neighbourhood of the zero it behaves as a series-resonant circuit.

The input impedances of a line with closed- and open-circuit terminations have a further significance. If we denote the input impedance of a short-circuited line by Z_C and that of an open-circuited line by Z_F, then by multiplying together equations (3.22) and (3.23) we get:

$$Z_C Z_F = Z_0^2$$

or

$$Z_0 = \sqrt{(Z_C Z_F)} \quad . \quad . \quad . \quad . \quad . \quad . \quad (3.25)$$

This result has been deduced by assuming an ideal line for which Z_0 is a pure resistance. However, it can be shown that the result is quite general and applies when Z_0 is complex.

One method of determining the characteristic impedance of a short line is to measure Z_C and Z_F by a bridge method, and to calculate Z_0 from this equation. With refined impedance-bridge techniques, Z_0 for cables may be determined by measurements on samples a small fraction of a wavelength in length. The attenuation coefficient and the primary characteristics of a line can also be obtained from these measurements as shown in Appendix 3.1. The results of this section are also deduced by more rigid methods in Appendices 3.1 and 3.2.

Input Impedance of Lines with Partial Reflection

Standing waves on a line are caused by the load termination mismatch. It is reasonable to expect, therefore, that the standing-wave pattern, its magnitude and position relative to the termination are a measure of the mismatch. Furthermore, the standing-wave pattern must be related to the input impedance Z_S of a mismatched line. At the standing-wave maxima and minima the input impedance is simply related to the standing-wave ratio in a manner which will now be determined.

For this simplified approach it is necessary to assume a loss-free line, which has therefore a characteristic impedance that is a pure resistance. Consider Fig. 3.15 in which a line of impedance Z_0 is terminated in the general impedance Z_T. The curve of maximum voltage on the line is shown in full, while that for current is shown dotted. The position of the maxima and minima relative to the termination is dependent upon the magnitude and angle of Z_T relative to Z_0.

Consider the section B in Fig. 3.15. The voltage maximum V_{max} occurs when the forward-travelling peak of V_i coincides with the backward-travelling peak of V_r. Since we have assumed an ideal line of surge impedance Z_0, then V_i and I_i are in phase. Furthermore, V_r and I_r are in anti-phase since I_r is flowing to the left. Hence, the resultant voltage $V_{max} = V_i + V_r$ at B is in phase with the

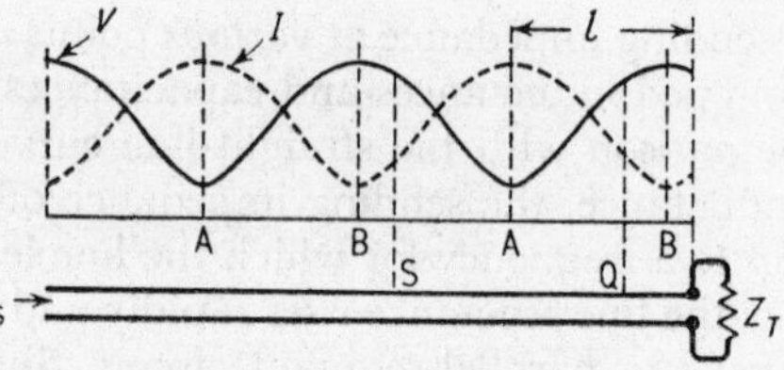

Fig. 3.15. Input impedance of line with partial reflection.

resultant current $I_{min} = I_i - I_r$ at the same point. The ratio of V_{max} to I_{min} thus gives a pure resistance which is the same as the input or sending impedance which would be measured looking towards Z_T if the line were cut at B. Let this input resistance be R_S''.

It has already been shown that:

$$\frac{V_{max}}{I_{max}} = \frac{V_{min}}{I_{min}} = Z_0$$

Hence we have:

$$R_S'' = \frac{V_{max}}{I_{min}} = \frac{V_{max}}{I_{max}} \cdot \frac{I_{max}}{I_{min}}$$

$$= Z_0 S \quad . \quad . \quad . \quad . \quad . \quad . \quad . \quad . \quad (3.26)$$

By a similar argument, the input impedance at points such as A is a pure resistance, given by:

$$R_S' = \frac{V_{min}}{I_{max}} = \frac{V_{min}}{I_{min}} \cdot \frac{I_{min}}{I_{max}}$$

$$= Z_0/S \quad . \quad . \quad . \quad . \quad . \quad . \quad . \quad . \quad (3.27)$$

Between the standing-wave maxima and minima of Fig. 3.15 the input impedance Z_S has resistive and reactive components. If we move away from the load (i.e., towards the generator) from a voltage minimum A to the next voltage maximum B, the resistive component increases. The reactive component rises from zero at A to a maximum and falls to zero again at B. To determine the sign of the reactance we compare the situation with the last quarter-wave section of a short-circuited line. In the latter case the input impedance is a positive reactance, and we deduce therefore that the input impedance towards the load, as we move from A to B towards the generator, has a positive reactance component. Similarly as we continue from B to A towards the generator, the resistive component falls again, while the reactive component is now negative and rises to a maximum value and falls to zero again at the next point A. The determination of the values of the resistive and reactive components is given in the next section and the full theory is given in Appendices 3.1 to 3.3.

When the line has attenuation we have already seen that the standing-wave ratio decreases towards unity, as we move away from the mismatch. It may therefore be deduced that R_S' and R_S'' approach the value Z_0 at large distances from the mismatch with an attenuating line.

Returning to equations (3.26) and (3.27) the standing-wave ratio may be eliminated, thus:

$$S = \frac{R_S''}{Z_0} = \frac{Z_0}{R_S'}$$

whence

$$R_S' = Z_0^2/R_S'' \quad . \quad . \quad . \quad . \quad . \quad . \quad . \quad (3.28)$$

This is a special case of a perfectly general theorem relating the impedances in an ideal line at any two points a quarter of a wavelength apart (or any odd number of quarter wavelengths).

The general form of the theorem states that the input impedance of a quarter wavelength of line of characteristic impedance Z_0 terminated with an impedance Z_T is given by:

$$Z_S = Z_0^2/Z_T \quad . \quad . \quad . \quad . \quad . \quad . \quad . \quad (3.29)$$

It is clear that the same relation exists between the input impedances at any two points in a line a quarter of a wavelength apart, since if Z_S is the input impedance at one point, the input impedance at the second point may be regarded as Z_T.

A quarter-wave line of impedance:

$$Z_0 = \sqrt{(Z_S Z_T)} \quad . \quad . \quad . \quad . \quad . \quad . \quad . \quad (3.30)$$

thus behaves as an impedance-matching transformer, and when connected between Z_S and Z_T it provides the maximum power transfer. If Z_0 is suitably chosen it can function as a step-up or a step-down transformer. When Z_T is a reactive impedance, Z_0 being assumed resistive, the input impedance Z_S is a reactive impedance of opposite sign (i.e., if Z_T is inductive, then Z_S is capacitive and vice versa). Thus if:

$$Z_T = |Z_T| \underline{/\phi}$$

then

$$Z_S = \left|\frac{Z_0^2}{Z_T}\right| \underline{/-\phi} \quad . \quad . \quad . \quad . \quad . \quad . \quad . \quad (3.31)$$

These properties only apply for the frequency at which the line is a quarter-wavelength long, or approximately, for a very narrow band of frequencies on either side of this value. Z_S and Z_T are, of course, image impedances; i.e., if impedances Z_S and Z_T are connected to a quarter-wave line, the line input impedance looking towards Z_T is Z_S and that looking towards Z_S from the other end is Z_T.

This inverse impedance relation should be compared with the similar relation [equations (2.22) and (2.23)] deduced for the image impedances of the constant-k network in Chapter 2. From the artificial-line theory given there, the half-section constant-k network behaves as a quarter-wave device, and is often called a quarter-wave network.

It is clear from Fig. 3.15 and the associated argument for a loss-free line that the impedances at all points such as A are equal, and also the impedances at all points such as B are equal. This result is also a special case of a general theorem, relating the impedance in a line at two points a half wavelength apart (or any number of half wavelengths). Thus, for a half-wavelength line terminated in a load Z_T, the input impedance Z_S is given by:

$$Z_S = Z_T \quad . \quad . \quad . \quad . \quad . \quad . \quad (3.32)$$

A half-wavelength line thus behaves as a unity-ratio transformer. There is one further important aspect which should not be overlooked. By examining Figs. 3.7 and 3.15 at two peaks a half wavelength apart, it can be understood that the impedances at such points are equal, but there is a 180° difference of phase between the voltages and currents. At points one whole wavelength apart, there is no phase difference. These results may be included in the rule that a $\lambda/2$ line behaves as a $1:-1$ transformer, and a λ line behaves as a $1:1$ transformer. Sections of line a half wavelength long are sometimes employed for producing a 180° phase shift in feeders to aerial arrays.

Examples showing the use of quarter-wave lines, and the construction of impedances from transmission lines are given in the next chapter.

The Circle Diagram

Suppose an ideal line of surge impedance Z_0 is terminated in any impedance Z_T such that a standing wave of ratio S exists on the line. If the termination Z_T is a pure resistance, the end of the line will be a voltage maximum or a voltage minimum depending upon whether Z_T is greater or less than Z_0. If the termination Z_T has reactance the maximum or minimum will be displaced from the end of the line.

The input impedance at the voltage maximum has been shown to equal a resistance of Z_0S and that at the voltage minimum a resistance of Z_0/S. The input impedance of the line looking towards the load at points between the maximum and minimum can be obtained from a simple circle diagram.

In order that this circle diagram can be used for a line of any impedance, it is usual to 'normalize' all impedances (i.e., all impedances are divided by Z_0) so that the diagram is drawn for a line with a characteristic impedance of 1 ohm. Thus, when using the diagram it is only necessary to multiply by the value of Z_0 to determine the impedance at any point in a mismatched line of characteristic impedance Z_0.

In Fig. 3.16 resistance is plotted along the OR axis, positive reactance along OX and negative reactance along OX′, using Cartesian co-ordinates. The line characteristic impedance when normalized is the point (1,0) and is designated C.

Taking the standing-wave pattern of Fig. 3.15 as an example (drawn for a s.w.r. of 3) the normalized resistance at a voltage maximum is given by $Z_0S/Z_0 = S$ and this point is marked at B in Fig. 3.16. Similarly the normalized resistance at a minimum is $1/S$ and this is marked at A. It can be shown that the input impedance Z_S at points in the line as we move away from the voltage minimum A towards the generator, is given by vectors such as OP where the point P travels round a circle with centre on the resistance axis which passes through A and B. The circle is described in a clockwise direction, thus as we move towards the generator passing from a voltage minimum A to a maximum B the impedance Z_S looking towards the load has positive or inductive reactance. As we move from a voltage maximum to the next minimum, Z_S has negative or capacitive reactance. If the point under consideration moves towards the load then the circle is described in an anti-clockwise direction. These circles may be called *S* circles since they represent a given s.w.r.

The relation between the position on the actual line and that on the impedance circle is given by the intersections with the curves passing through the

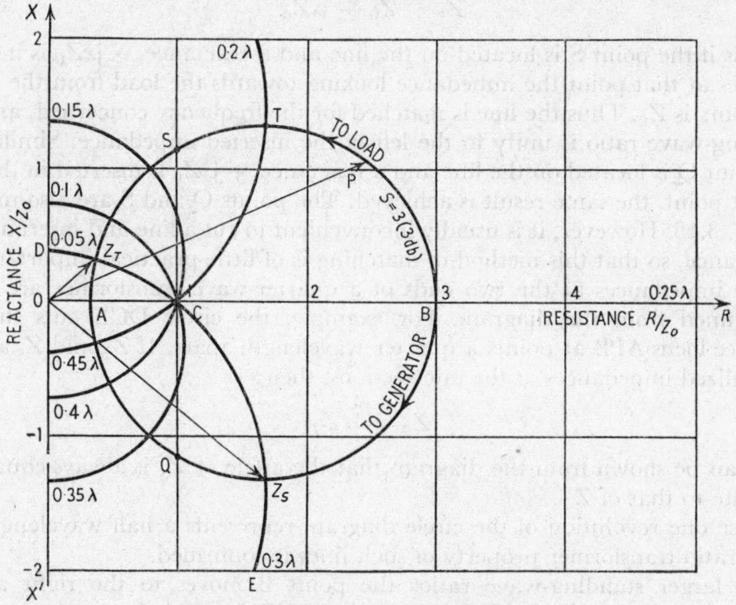

Fig. 3.16. Cartesian circle diagram.

point C and marked in fractions of a wavelength. These curves through C are portions of circles which have their centres on the XOX′ axis. The axis OR is also a portion of one of these circles having an infinite radius. These curves may be imagined to originate and radiate from C. It is usual to mark these curves with distances measured from a voltage minimum. Thus in Fig. 3.16, CO is the curve representing zero distance, and proceeding clockwise and towards the generator the curves are in steps of $0{\cdot}05\lambda$. The curve CR represents the $0{\cdot}25\lambda$ point from a voltage minimum; i.e., a voltage maximum. We then proceed in further steps of $0{\cdot}05\lambda$ until the $0{\cdot}5\lambda$ curve is reached, which coincides with CO, because as we have already seen, the impedances at points a half wavelength apart are identical. These curves are called the $n\lambda$ circles or lines.

The circle diagram gives the impedance at any point in a line, including that at the termination. Given the standing-wave ratio and the location of the first voltage minimum relative to the load it is therefore possible to determine the load impedance. Suppose the standing-wave ratio is 3 as in Fig. 3.15 and the first voltage minimum is say $0{\cdot}3\lambda$ from the load. Starting from A which represents the impedance at the voltage minimum, and moving towards the load (anti-clockwise) round the impedance circle for a distance corresponding to $0{\cdot}3\lambda$, the point T is reached. This point represents the normalized value of the terminating impedance and can be read off as $1{\cdot}7 + \mathrm{j}1{\cdot}3$. The actual value is:

$$Z_T = (1{\cdot}7 + \mathrm{j}1{\cdot}3)Z_0$$

This method is often employed for impedance measurements at the shorter wavelengths, where apparatus such as shown in Fig. 3.9 can be used.

At the points S and Q where QS is the perpendicular through C, the normalized input impedance is of the form $(1 \pm \mathrm{j}x)$, or:

$$Z_S = Z_0 \pm \mathrm{j}xZ_0$$

Thus if the point S is located on the line and a reactance $-\mathrm{j}xZ_0$ is inserted in series at that point the impedance looking towards the load from the left of the point is Z_0. Thus the line is matched for the frequency concerned, and the standing-wave ratio is unity to the left of the inserted impedance. Similarly if the point Q is located on the line and a reactance $+\mathrm{j}xZ_0$ is inserted in the line at that point, the same result is achieved. The points Q and S are also marked on Fig. 3.15. However, it is usually inconvenient to cut a line and insert a series impedance, so that this method of matching is of little practical importance.

The impedances at the two ends of a quarter-wave transformer are easily determined from the diagram. For example, the circle DCE cuts the impedance locus APB at points a quarter wavelength apart. If Z_T and Z_S are the normalized impedances at the intersections, then:

$$Z_S = 1/Z_T$$

It can be shown from the diagram that the angle of Z_S is always equal and opposite to that of Z_T.

Since one revolution of the circle diagram represents a half wavelength the unity ratio transformer property of such lines is confirmed.

For larger standing-wave ratios the point B moves to the right and A approaches the origin O. The impedance circle is much larger and a given electrical distance $n\lambda$ from B in either direction indicates a rapid increase of reactance. This aspect is of importance when considering transmission lines as impedance elements.

The diagram may be used for converting an impedance to an admittance. For suppose it is desired to find the admittance of an impedance Z_T, the point Z_T is located and the S circle is traversed for a quarter wavelength giving the point Z_S. We have then:

$$Z_S = 1/Z_T = Y_T = G_T + \mathrm{j}B_T$$

where $Y_T = G_T + \mathrm{j}B_T$ is the admittance of the impedance Z_T. Thus the impedance Z_T is equal to a conductance G_T in parallel with a susceptance B_T, where G_T and B_T are read off as the components of Z_S.

It follows from this that the input admittance at any point in a line also travels round the S circles. In fact the same diagram may be used as an admittance diagram. In this case the point C represents the normalized line admittance of 1 mho, while A represents the admittance at a current minimum (voltage maximum) and B represents the admittance at a current maximum (voltage

4

ineers

minimum). Points on the circle give the normalized sending admittance at any point in the line as a conductance (along OR) in parallel with a susceptance (along XOX′).

Many other deductions can be made from circle diagrams which are of great importance in r.f. line technique. The form of diagram described here is known as the Cartesian circle diagram and the basic theory is given in Appendix 3.1. A more complete Cartesian diagram showing several S circles is given in Fig. 3.17. It is the preferable form of diagram for discussing the phenomena in transmission lines, but it is not ideal for precise determinations owing to the close spacing of the S and $n\lambda$ circles in the neighbourhood of the origin. For more precise work the polar form of circle diagram described in Appendix 3.3 is to be preferred.

The above arguments have assumed ideal loss-free lines, but the circle diagram is quite general and it can be used to determine the sending impedance of lines having a complex characteristic impedance and attenuation.

The Construction of Terminations

During the explanations of reflection phenomena it has been assumed that it is possible to construct open-circuits, short-circuits, and other terminating impedances (or impedance changes) without any difficulty. Before considering the problem of making terminations it is well to go back and examine the foundations on which the circuit theory of lines is based. In Chapter 1 the theory was developed from calculations for R, L, G and C which assumed infinitely long lines. For example, L and C were calculated on an infinite-length assumption so that the magnetic and electric fields were always (assuming low R) in planes at right angles to the line. If at the end of the line or other discontinuity, the fields depart from this condition, it is to be expected that the circuit theory will not apply with any accuracy.

At low, and most high, frequencies the ordinary conceptions of open-circuits, short-circuits and two-terminal terminating impedances can be used with negligible error, but at extremely high frequencies this is no longer the case. The frequency at which these phenomena begin to assume importance is that for which the wavelength is only a few times larger than the cross-sectional dimensions of the line. For a more complete understanding of these phenomena it is necessary to await the development of field theory given in Chapter 5, but a preliminary insight into the problem can be obtained from a few simple examples.

Consider first of all the construction of a short-circuit for a two-wire line. To preserve the fields in strictly transverse planes a perfectly conducting sheet of infinite extent at right angles to the line must be used, the two wires being solidly connected to this sheet. Of course the sheet need not be absolutely infinite in extent but it should cover the region of appreciable field. For a coaxial line, since there is no external field, it is only necessary to use an accurately fitting plane disc of high conductivity. At the very high frequencies under consideration, a wire short-circuit would be ineffective, no matter how low its resistance, owing to the inductance it would have.

Taking next the case of the open-circuit for a two-wire line. To leave the two wires disconnected does not ensure that the fields are reflected in a plane. There is distortion of the field, and the termination does not behave as an infinite impedance. In fact it behaves as a small capacitance. When the wavelength is comparable with the cross-sectional dimensions of the line it even behaves as a resistance, because energy is radiated from the end of the line. Similar arguments apply for a coaxial line. At extremely high frequencies there is no solution to this problem except perhaps to terminate with a quarter-wave short-circuited line. The latter device only operates at the quarter-wave frequencies however (i.e., $\lambda/4$, $3\lambda/4$, etc.). Alternatively the line may be cut a little short, to reduce the end capacitance but this again is not effective at all frequencies.

The construction of other impedances at very high frequencies is even more difficult. Paired lines are not often used under these conditions except possibly for some types of valve oscillator, so that attention will be confined to the coaxial line. Considering resistive terminations, it is possible to make discs of resistive material in which the radial resistance from the inner periphery to the outer periphery has the desired value. However, it will be found that when used to terminate the line it functions as another impedance owing to capacitance and radiation effects on the far side of the disc. The disc may be made to function at the designed resistance if a short-circuited quarter-wave line is connected to the back of it. This terminates the back of the disc in an infinite impedance, but again it is a frequency–sensitive device. If we have the problem of terminating a coaxial line in its characteristic impedance over a wide band of frequencies, such a device is not permissible. One method of solving this problem is to terminate the line with another line of similar dimensions and the same Z_0, but having a very high attenuation per unit length. If the attenuation of this terminating cable were sufficiently high the final end could be left open-circuited.

APPENDIX 3.1

General Expression for the Sending Impedance Z_S

Almost all the phenomena of unmatched r.f. lines can be deduced from the general formula giving the sending impedance Z_S of a line of characteristic impedance Z_0, propagation coefficient γ, length l with a terminating impedance Z_T.

Taking as origin, the sending end, the voltage V_z at any point z is obtained as in Appendix 1.5, from the sum of a forward-travelling wave and a backward-travelling wave, thus:

$$V_z = A\varepsilon^{-\gamma z} + B\varepsilon^{\gamma z} \quad . \quad . \quad . \quad . \quad . \quad . \quad (3.33)$$

where A and B are constants defining the amplitudes and phases of the two waves at the origin and $\gamma = \alpha + j\beta$.

The corresponding current is given by subtracting the backward-travelling current wave from the forward-travelling current wave, each being obtained by dividing the corresponding voltage wave by Z_0.

Thus:

$$I_z = \frac{A}{Z_0}\varepsilon^{-\gamma z} - \frac{B}{Z_0}\varepsilon^{\gamma z} \quad . \quad . \quad . \quad . \quad . \quad (3.34)$$

At the terminating impedance, $z = l$ and we have:

$$Z = \frac{V_T}{I_T} = \left[\frac{A\varepsilon^{-\gamma l} + B\varepsilon^{\gamma l}}{A\varepsilon^{-\gamma l} - B\varepsilon^{\gamma l}}\right] Z_0$$

or

$$\frac{Z_T}{Z_0} = \frac{A + B\varepsilon^{2\gamma l}}{A - B\varepsilon^{2\gamma l}}$$

also

$$\frac{B}{A} = \varepsilon^{-2\gamma l}\left[\frac{Z_T - Z_0}{Z_T + Z_0}\right] \quad . \quad . \quad . \quad . \quad . \qquad (3.35)$$

B/A is the vector ratio at the sending end of the reflected to the incident wave and it is seen to equal the product of the voltage reflection factor at the termination and the factor $\varepsilon^{-2\gamma l}$ representing the loss in transmission to the termination and back again.

At the sending end, $z = 0$ and we have:

$$Z_S = \frac{V_S}{I_S} = \left[\frac{A + B}{A - B}\right] Z_0$$

$$\frac{Z_S}{Z_0} = \left[\frac{1 + B/A}{1 - B/A}\right] \quad . \quad . \quad . \quad . \quad . \quad . \qquad (3.36)$$

Substituting for B/A we get:

$$\frac{Z_S}{Z_0} = \frac{1 + \varepsilon^{-2\gamma l}\left[\dfrac{Z_T - Z_0}{Z + Z_0}\right]}{1 - \varepsilon^{-2\gamma l}\left[\dfrac{Z_T - Z_0}{Z_T + Z_0}\right]} \quad . \quad . \quad . \quad . \quad . \qquad (3.37)$$

This is the result desired, but it may be manipulated into more convenient forms. By re-arranging the right hand side we obtain:

$$\frac{Z_S}{Z_0} = \frac{(Z_T/Z_0)(\varepsilon^{\gamma l} + \varepsilon^{-\gamma l}) + (\varepsilon^{\gamma l} - \varepsilon^{-\gamma l})}{(Z_T/Z_0)(\varepsilon^{\gamma l} - \varepsilon^{-\gamma l}) + (\varepsilon^{\gamma l} + \varepsilon^{-\gamma l})} \qquad (3.38)$$

This form is suitable for studying ideal quarter- and half-wave lines, but for the general attenuating case it is preferable to employ the hyperbolic tangent form. Thus we have:

$$\tanh \gamma l = \frac{\varepsilon^{\gamma l} - \varepsilon^{-\gamma l}}{\varepsilon^{\gamma l} + \varepsilon^{-\gamma l}}$$

$$\frac{Z_S}{Z_0} = \frac{\tanh \gamma l + (Z_T/Z_0)}{1 + (Z_T/Z_0)\tanh \gamma l} \quad . \quad . \quad . \qquad (3.39)$$

Now:

$$\tanh(\gamma l + \psi) = \frac{\tanh \gamma l + \tanh \psi}{1 + \tanh \gamma l . \tanh \psi}$$

Hence, if we put:

$$Z_T/Z_0 = \tanh \psi \quad . \quad . \quad . \quad . \quad . \quad . \quad . \qquad (3.40)$$

or

$$\psi = \tanh^{-1}(Z_T/Z_0) \quad . \quad . \quad . \quad . \quad . \qquad (3.41)$$

we have

$$Z_S/Z_0 = \tanh(\gamma l + \psi) \quad . \quad . \quad . \quad . \quad . \qquad (3.42)$$

This represents the simplest form for those problems where no approximations are permissible. It lends itself to computations from tables or charts of the complex hyperbolic tangent function. It is also the basis of circle diagrams or charts for determining the impedance Z_S/Z_0. The use of such circle diagrams is tending to replace the tables of the complex hyperbolic tangent function.

The circle diagram of Fig. 3.16 is a form of diagram for transforming from the complex quantity ψ (or $\gamma l + \psi$) to $\tanh \psi$ (or $\tanh (\gamma l + \psi)$) and vice versa. A more complete form of the Cartesian circle diagram is shown in Fig. 3.17. It may be regarded as the superposition of two planes, one having the rectangular co-ordinates R and X, the other having co-ordinates consisting of two systems of orthogonal circles. One system of circles passes through the point $R + jX = 1 + j0$ and each circle is a locus of βl = constant. This is the phase shift in a length of line and can be represented as the 'electrical distance' in radians or wavelengths. These circles are therefore marked in values of $2n\pi$ or $n\lambda$ where n has values 0 to 0·5. The circles repeat themselves for distances greater than a half wavelength. The other system of circles encloses the point $R + jX = 1 + j0$ and each circle is a locus of αl = constant. These circles therefore represent an attenuation and are usually marked in nepers or decibels. Each of these circles also represents a certain standing-wave ratio as will be shown in a moment.

Any point on the diagram therefore has two sets of co-ordinates given by:

$$Z = R + jX$$

and

$$\psi = \alpha l + j\beta l$$

and the diagram is so constructed that:

$$Z = \tanh \psi$$

The procedure in determining Z_S/Z_0 at a point distant l metres from a termination Z_T at the end of a line of characteristic impedance Z_0 is as follows:

(1) Determine Z_T/Z_0 so that the normalized circle diagram may be used and locate this point on the R and X co-ordinates of the circle diagram.

(2) By interpolating if necessary, read off from the orthogonal circles the corresponding complex quantity ψ of equation (3.41) in decibels and radians or fractions of a wavelength.

This operation may be regarded as finding the attenuation and phase shift of a short-circuited line of impedance Z_0 which can replace Z_T. An input signal to such a hypothetical line is transmitted, fully reflected and received back at the input with an attenuation and phase shift equal to that of the reflection factor at the junction of Z_0 and Z_T. To prove this let Z_C be the input impedance of a short-circuited section of the same type of line. By putting $Z_T = 0$ in equation (3.39) we find

$$Z_C/Z_0 = \tanh \gamma l'$$

where l' is the length. Now Z_C has to simulate Z_T, the terminating impedance of the actual line under consideration, or:

$$Z_T/Z_0 = Z_C/Z_0 = \tanh \gamma l' \quad . \quad . \quad . \quad . \quad . \quad (3.43)$$

But from the circle diagram we have:

$$Z_T/Z_0 = \tanh \psi$$

Hence $\psi = \gamma l'$ or the attenuation and phase shift of a short-circuited line of characteristic impedance Z_0 which simulates the impedance Z_T closing the line under consideration.

(3) Add the quantity ψ as read off from the diagram to the corresponding attenuation αl decibels, and the electrical length βl radians of the line corresponding to the distance l to the point where Z_S is desired. This gives $\gamma l + \psi$.

(4) Refer back to the circle diagram, finding the point $\gamma l + \psi$ on the orthogonal circles. Read off the corresponding values of R and X. From equation (3.42) this gives the normalized sending impedance Z_S/Z_0. This may be regarded as finding an impedance which replaces a short-circuited line having an attenuation and phase shift of $\gamma l + \psi$ or alternatively having a length $l + l'$.

The standing-wave ratio S and the positions of the voltage maxima or minima also define the impedance at any point in the line. At the voltage minimum nearest the load the impedance towards the load is resistive for a loss-free line. Suppose its value is R_S', then from equation (3.27):

$$R_S' = Z_0/S$$

From equation (3.41):

$$\begin{aligned}\psi &= \tanh^{-1} (R_S'/Z_0) \\ &= \tanh^{-1} (1/S)\end{aligned}$$

Hence the input impedance looking towards the load at any point on the generator side of the voltage minimum is given from equation (3.42) by:

$$Z_S/Z_0 = \tanh \left(\gamma l_m + \tanh^{-1} \frac{1}{S}\right) \quad . \quad . \quad . \quad . \quad (3.44)$$

where l_m is the distance of the point from the voltage minimum. Knowing the distance of the voltage minimum from the load, the input impedance at any point in the line can be calculated.

Each circle representing a certain attenuation may also be identified with a standing-wave ratio, and the modulus of a reflection factor. The relationship may be determined by the following method.

From equation (3.40) we have:

$$\begin{aligned}Z_T/Z_0 &= \tanh \gamma l \\ &= \frac{\varepsilon^{\gamma l} - \varepsilon^{-\gamma l}}{\varepsilon^{\gamma l} + \varepsilon^{-\gamma l}} \\ &= \frac{\varepsilon^{2\gamma l} - 1}{\varepsilon^{2\gamma l} + 1} \\ \therefore \varepsilon^{2\gamma l} &= -\frac{Z_T + Z_0}{Z_T - Z_0} \\ &= -\frac{1}{K_R}\end{aligned}$$

Taking the modulus of both sides we obtain:

$$\varepsilon^{2\alpha l} = \frac{1}{|K_R|}$$

$$= \frac{S+1}{S-1}$$

from equation (3.17).

Taking natural logarithms:

$$\alpha l = \tfrac{1}{2} \log_\varepsilon \frac{1}{|K_R|}$$

$$= \tfrac{1}{2} \log_\varepsilon \frac{S+1}{S-1}$$

The first form may be compared with equation (3.11). It is seen to be one half of the echo attenuation, if the sign is ignored. It may also be expressed in decibels, in which case it is one-half of the return loss, thus:

$$\alpha l = -\ 10 \log_{10} \left| \frac{Z_T - Z_0}{Z_T + Z_0} \right| \text{ decibels}$$

Thus each attenuation circle of value αl, corresponds also to a certain reflection factor.

The second form may also be expressed in decibels giving:

$$\alpha l = 10 \log_{10} \left(\frac{S+1}{S-1} \right) \text{ decibels} \quad . \quad . \quad . \quad . \quad (3.45)$$

Thus each attenuation circle also represents a certain standing-wave ratio.

Returning to the equation:

$$\varepsilon^{2\gamma l} = -\ 1/K_R$$

if we consider the angle of either side we get:

$$2\beta l = \underline{/K_R}$$

or

$$\beta l = \tfrac{1}{2}\underline{/K_R}$$

Thus the βl circles also represent one-half of the angle of the reflection factor. Any point on the circle diagram represented by the αl and βl co-ordinates therefore represents the modulus and angle of the reflection factor resulting from the impedance represented by that point on the impedance co-ordinates. These circles could therefore be marked with the modulus and angle of the reflection factor.

For a given standing-wave ratio S, if the appropriate attenuation circle is found, and if the line is loss free, that circle will give the value of Z_S/Z_0 at points corresponding to various distances from say, a voltage minimum. If the line has attenuation, but the standing-wave ratio is known in the neighbourhood of a certain voltage minimum, then the standing-wave ratio at other points towards the generator can be found, by adding the appropriate attenuation and referring to the new attenuation or s.w.r. circle. The s.w.r. always falls on moving away from the impedance irregularity towards the generator. The actual curve followed by the sending impedance is therefore a spiral in the attenuating case.

For an infinite s.w.r. (i.e., the case of total reflection) equation (3.45) gives zero decibels, the circle for which is infinite in size, the XOX′ axis being a small portion of it. The reactances on this axis therefore give the reactance of loss-free lines of length corresponding to the intersections with the βl circles. The range of the XOX′ axis on the Cartesian circle diagram is strictly limited, and for this reason other forms of circle diagram have been devised in which the XOX′ axis is bent round into a circle as explained in Appendix 3.3.

For a s.w.r. of 3, equation (3.45) gives the 3-db circle, and for a s.w.r. of unity (i.e., no standing waves) it gives infinite attenuation and the circle collapses to the point C of Fig. 3.16.

Special cases of interest are easily deduced from equation (3.38); thus for a short-circuited line $Z_T = 0$, and the input impedance Z_C is given by:

$$Z_C/Z_0 = \tanh \gamma l \qquad (3.46)$$

And for an open-circuited line $Z_T = \infty$ and the input impedance Z_F is given by:

$$Z_F/Z_0 = 1/\tanh \gamma l \qquad (3.47)$$

Multiplying equations (3.46) and (3.47) together, we get:

$$Z_0 = \sqrt{(Z_C Z_F)}. \qquad (3.48)$$

This is the equation already deduced in (3.25) for a purely resistive Z_0. It is the basis of an important method of measuring the characteristic impedance of a finite line. Thus, if the input impedance is measured by a bridge or other method, first with a short-circuit termination and then with an open-circuit termination, Z_0 can be deduced. From the same measurements, the propagation coefficient can also be deduced, because by dividing equation (3.46) by equation (3.47) we get:

$$\tanh \gamma l = \sqrt{\frac{Z_C}{Z_F}} \qquad (3.49)$$

Reference to tables or the circle diagram enables γ to be deduced. If it is expressed in nepers and radians per unit length, the primary characteristics can be obtained from

$$\gamma Z_0 = R + j\omega L$$

and

$$\gamma / Z_0 = G + j\omega C$$

APPENDIX 3.2

Z_S for Ideal Lines

For ideal lines we assume that the attenuation coefficient α is zero, so that:

$$\gamma = j\beta = j\frac{2\pi}{\lambda}$$

$$\therefore\ \varepsilon^{j\beta l} + \varepsilon^{-j\beta l} = 2 \cos \beta l$$

and

$$\varepsilon^{j\beta l} - \varepsilon^{-j\beta l} = 2j \sin \beta l$$

From equation (3.38)

$$\frac{Z_S}{Z_0} = \frac{(Z_T/Z_0)\cos\beta l + \mathrm{j}\sin\beta l}{(Z_T/Z_0)\mathrm{j}\sin\beta l + \cos\beta l} \quad . \quad . \quad . \quad . \quad (3.50)$$

For the short-circuited line $Z_T = 0$, and the input impedance Z_C is given by:

$$\frac{Z_C}{Z_0} = \mathrm{j}\tan\beta l = \mathrm{j}\tan\frac{2\pi l}{\lambda} \quad . \quad . \quad . \quad (3.51)$$

For the open-circuited line $Z \quad = \infty$, and the input impedance Z_F is given by:

$$\frac{Z_F}{Z_0} = -\,\mathrm{j}\cot\beta l = -\,\mathrm{j}\cot\frac{2\pi l}{\lambda} \quad . \quad . \quad . \quad . \quad (3.52)$$

These results agree with those deduced by reasoning from Figs. 3.10 and 3.11.

If the line is an odd number of quarter wavelengths long, i.e.,

$$l = n\lambda \pm \lambda/4 \quad \text{where } n \text{ is an integer.}$$

then $$\beta l = 2\pi n \pm \pi/2$$

and $$\cos\beta l = 0, \quad \mathrm{j}\sin\beta l = \pm\,\mathrm{j}$$

then from equation (3.50)

$$\frac{Z_S}{Z_0} = \frac{\pm\,\mathrm{j}}{(Z_T/Z_0)(\pm\,\mathrm{j})}$$

or $$Z_S = Z_0{}^2/Z_T$$

or $$Z_0 = \sqrt{(Z_S Z_T)} \quad . \quad . \quad . \quad . \quad . \quad . \quad (3.53)$$

This important relation shows that the quarter-wave line behaves as an inverse impedance transforming device. Ideal lines which are any odd number of quarter wavelengths long behave as a single quarter-wave line; but owing to losses in practical lines, the use of lines as impedance transformers is usually restricted to lines one-quarter of a wavelength long.

If the line is any number of half-wavelengths long, i.e.,

$$l = \frac{n\lambda}{2} \quad \text{where } n \text{ is an integer.}$$

then $$\beta l = n\pi$$

and $$\cos\beta l = \pm\,1, \quad \mathrm{j}\sin\beta l = 0$$

then from equation (3.50)

$$\frac{Z_S}{Z_0} = \frac{\pm\,(Z_T/Z_0)}{\pm\,1}$$

or $$Z_S = Z_T \quad . \quad . \quad . \quad . \quad . \quad . \quad . \quad . \quad . \quad . \quad (3.54)$$

Thus the half-wave line behaves as a 1 : 1 transformer.

The input impedance of ideal lines with reactive terminations can be easily determined from equation (3.50). Suppose the terminating reactance when normalized is given by:

$$\frac{Z_T}{Z_0} = \mathrm{j}\tan\theta$$

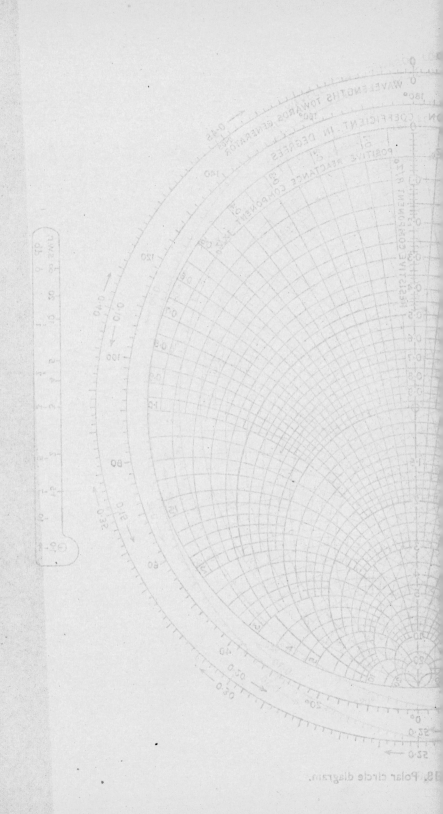

Then from equation (3.50)

$$\frac{Z_S}{Z_0} = \frac{\mathrm{j}\tan\theta + \mathrm{j}\tan\beta l}{1 - \tan\theta . \tan\beta l}$$

$$= \mathrm{j}\tan(\theta + \beta l) \quad . \quad . \quad . \quad . \quad . \quad . \quad (3.55)$$

The input impedance is still a pure reactance. The reactance curve for a short-circuited line plotted against electrical length βl is the tangent curve and the input impedance here is the same curve displaced by θ radians to the left or right depending upon whether θ is positive or negative. In other words the termination is equivalent to a length θ/β of short-circuited line.

APPENDIX 3.3

The Polar Circle Diagram

The Cartesian circle diagram of Fig. 3.17 suffers from the disadvantage that points corresponding to equidistant points in the line are crowded together in some areas of the diagram and widely separated in other areas. Thus, considering the circle of Fig. 3.16 in the region of the voltage minimum A, the electrical distance 0·05λ is quite a small arc of the circle, whereas near the voltage maximum B an electrical distance 0·05λ represents a large arc of the circle. Furthermore the range of resistance and reactance is somewhat limited in the Cartesian form of diagram.

This objection is overcome in the polar form of the diagram shown in Fig. 3.18 where equal lengths of line are represented by equal arcs. This diagram is obtained from the Cartesian diagram by applying a transformation which transforms the circular curves through C of Fig. 3.16 (representing various distances from minima) into equi-spaced radial lines. The circle APB of Fig. 3.16 remains as a circle in the polar diagram although its centre is now at the centre of the whole diagram. This centre is the point $R = 1$, $X = 0$ and corresponds to C in Fig. 3.16.

So far as the R–X system of co-ordinates is concerned, the XOX′ axis of Fig. 3.16 may be imagined to be bent round to form a circle. This circle gives the reactance of a loss-free line, at various points in fractions of a wavelength from the voltage minimum as shown on the peripheral scale. It will be seen that the range of reactance covered by the diagram is $0 \pm \infty$, instead of the rather restricted range of the Cartesian diagram.

To avoid the confusion of too many lines on the polar diagram it is usual to give only the R–X system of co-ordinates. The radial lines representing $n\lambda$ and the circles representing S or αl (db) are omitted, but a scale pivoted at the centre may be used instead. This scale may be rotated to the position $n\lambda$ which may be read off on the periphery. The position is measured from a voltage minimum in terms of $n\lambda$, the direction of travel being clockwise towards the generator, and anti-clockwise towards the load. The standing-wave ratio and attenuation are engraved on the rotating scale.

To illustrate the use of the polar diagram two examples will be given. The first is the previous example used to illustrate the Cartesian diagram.

The standing-wave ratio in a line of negligible loss is 3 and the first voltage minimum is $0{\cdot}3\lambda$ from the load. It is desired to determine the load impedance.

The point corresponding to the voltage minimum is at the radius $S = 3$ from the centre of the diagram on the horizontal axis to the left. To find the load impedance we then have to proceed at radius $S = 3$, towards the load (i.e., anti-clockwise) for an arc of $0{\cdot}3\lambda$. The normalized impedance is then read off as

$$Z_T = 1{\cdot}7 + j1{\cdot}3$$

and the actual load can be obtained by multiplying by the characteristic impedance.

As a second example, the impedance in a dissipative line will be considered.

Find the input impedance of a line of 1-db attenuation, 0·209 wavelengths long, having a characteristic impedance of 50 ohms, which is terminated with an impedance of 150 + j100.

We have
$$\frac{Z_T}{Z_0} = \frac{150 + j100}{50}$$
$$= 3 + j2$$

This point is located on the R–X curves of the polar diagram and the radius is read off as an attenuation, namely 2 db. The position relative to a voltage minimum (on the generator side) is read off as $0{\cdot}223\lambda$. To assist in following the procedure the steps are shown in Fig. 3.19 where this point is marked Z_T.

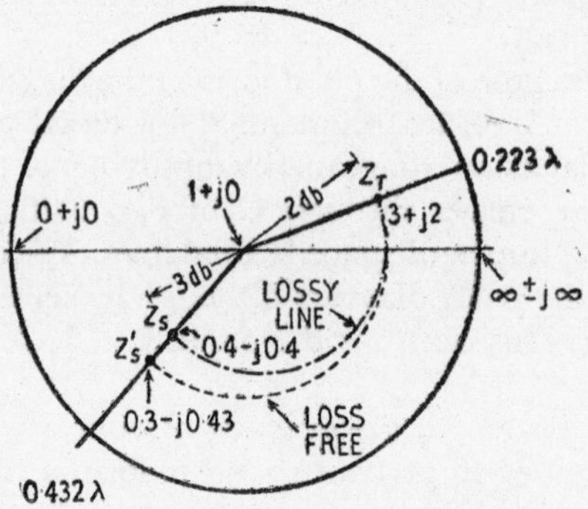

Fig. 3.19. Example showing use of polar circle diagram.

We now proceed towards the generator (i.e., clockwise) a distance of $0{\cdot}209\lambda$ and add 1 db to the attenuation. Hence, the point:

$$3 \text{ db}, \quad 0{\cdot}432\lambda$$

is located at Z_S, and the input impedance read off as:

$$\frac{Z_S}{Z_0} = 0{\cdot}4 - j0{\cdot}4$$

or
$$Z_S = 20 - j20$$

It is interesting to determine the impedance which would exist if the line were loss-free. Thus we locate the point Z_S' on Fig. 3.19 for which the αl and $n\lambda$ co-ordinates are:

$$2\ \text{db},\quad 0{\cdot}432\lambda$$

and read off:

$$\frac{Z_S'}{Z_0} = 0{\cdot}3 - \text{j}0{\cdot}43$$

or

$$Z_S' = 15 - \text{j}21{\cdot}5$$

Thus line attenuation increases the resistive component and reduces the reactive component, as might be expected. The curve Z_T to Z_S in Fig. 3.19 illustrates the manner in which the impedance locus spirals to the centre with a long attenuating line.

CHAPTER 4

Transmission Lines for Radio-Frequency

In this chapter, transmission lines for all frequencies above about 1 Mc/s are considered. A very wide band of frequencies is involved since two conductor lines may be used with advantage up to 3,000 Mc/s and higher. The wavelength of waves on such lines with air dielectric ranges from about 300 m at 1 Mc/s down to about 10 cm at 3,000 Mc/s or considerably shorter than for the low-frequency lines of Chapter 2. A very wide range of applications exists. One important requirement is to convey power from a radio transmitter to a radio aerial with the minimum of losses. Another requirement is to convey the signal from a receiving aerial to radio receiving equipment with the minimum of loss and noise pick up. The distances involved are not often great, so that attenuation is not always the prime consideration. In fact, matching of the load and generator to the line is often more difficult than achieving a low attenuation. For this reason a study of r.f. transmission lines is mainly concerned with generator and load matching by means of a wide variety of devices consisting of short sections of line with intentional mismatch.

Lines with intentional mismatch are often employed as circuit elements, or as resonant circuits for oscillators, and for the construction of filters.

After a brief consideration of the types and characteristics of r.f. lines, their behaviour as circuit elements will be studied. The use of lines for constructing filters and matching devices will be considered, together with the principles of increasing the transmission bandwidth.

Characteristics of R.F. Lines

The types of transmission line used for radio frequencies are, in general, the same as those discussed in Chapter 1. The balanced open-wire line of Fig. 1.1 (a) is the type invariably used for feeding balanced aerials for the h.f. band. The screened-pair line or cable of Fig. 1.1 (b) is not often employed for r.f. purposes, due to its higher attenuation, as compared with a coaxial cable of comparable size. However, there are applications with balanced generator or load wherein this type of cable may be met for h.f. or v.h.f. purposes.

The single-wire line with earth return of Fig. 1.1 (c) cannot be properly classed as a transmission line at radio frequency owing to the appreciable loss of power due to radiation. It is, therefore, preferable to consider this type of line as an aerial, and its treatment is deferred to a later chapter.

The coaxial line of Fig. 1.1 (d) is widely used for radio purposes up to frequencies of about 3,000 Mc/s and sometimes higher. It is immediately applicable to cases where load and generator are unbalanced, and it has the advantage that it is screened; i.e., if the screening efficiency is high, it radiates negligible energy, and negligible energy from the outside penetrates into the cable circuit. It has the lowest attenuation for its cross-sectional dimensions. In many applications conversions from unbalanced to balanced circuits can be carried out easily, thus widening the scope of the coaxial line. Owing to the particular suitability of the coaxial line for r.f. purposes this chapter is mainly concerned with this type. Although the theory of the previous chapters is applicable, several important simplifications in the formulae for the secondary characteristics become possible at radio frequencies, because ωL and ωC become large in comparison with R and G, respectively.

Thus

$$Z_0 = \sqrt{\frac{R + j\omega L}{G + j\omega C}}$$

$$\approx \sqrt{\frac{L}{C}} \quad \ldots \ldots \quad (4.1)$$

At radio frequencies the characteristic impedance Z_0 can be assumed to have reached its asymptotic value, a pure resistance, with negligible error. It must be remembered therefore that in this chapter Z_0 is a pure resistive impedance which is identical with the impedance of a distortionless line, so that the electric and magnetic energies are equal during transmission.

Considering the attenuation coefficient, the approximate formula of equation (2.2) now becomes accurate and is invariably employed at radio frequencies. Thus:

$$\alpha = \frac{R}{2Z_0} + \frac{GZ_0}{2} \text{ nepers per metre} \quad . \quad (4.2)$$

The dissipative primary characteristics R and G both increase with frequency, the first due to skin and proximity effects, and the second due to dielectric losses. The relative importance of the two terms in this equation needs to be examined for every application. Generally speaking R and G are both appreciable for open-wire feeders, but for coaxial cables G is usually negligible except at the highest frequencies of about 1,000 Mc/s and above.

For coaxial cables at frequencies where the attenuation due to G is negligible in comparison with that due to R we may substitute equations (1.7) and (1.17) in equation (4.2) and we get:

$$\alpha = \frac{R}{2Z_0} \quad \ldots \ldots \quad (4.3)$$

$$= \frac{1}{2b} \cdot \left(\frac{\omega\rho\kappa}{2}\right)^{\frac{1}{2}} \cdot \frac{(1 + b/a)}{\log_\varepsilon (b/a)} \quad \ldots \ldots \quad (4.4)$$

If in this equation, the outer conductor inside radius b is held constant and the ratio of conductor radii b/a is varied, the attenuation per unit length will be found to go through a minimum at about $b/a = 3{\cdot}6$. This can be checked by plotting the right-hand factor of equation (4.4) against b/a. It is found that the minimum is not sharply defined so that variation of the ratio from about 2·5 to 5·5 only increases the attenuation about 6% above the minimum. For air-dielectric coaxial line the ratio of 3·6 corresponds to an impedance of about 75 ohms while ratios of 2·5 and 5·5 correspond approximately to 55 ohms and 102 ohms respectively. For a solid dielectric of $\kappa_r = 2{\cdot}3$ the optimum impedance is about 50 ohms while the range for about 6% above minimum attenuation is 37 ohms to 68 ohms.

Rigid coaxial lines for circuit components, filters, etc., are usually specially designed to suit the problem, but flexible coaxial cable is usually made to standardized dimensions and impedances. Since the attenuation is not very sensitive to changes of impedance over the regions quoted above, many flexible cables are designed to an impedance of about 72 or 73 ohms, in order that they may be matched directly to the average impedance of a dipole aerial at resonance. Such cables usually have solid polyethylene dielectric ($\kappa_r = 2{\cdot}3$) so that they may withstand crushing, but where low attenuation is necessary the central conductor is supported by disc spacers separated by uniform intervals along the cable. The characteristics of a few commonly used types of flexible coaxial cable are given in Table 4.1. The attenuation in decibels per 100 ft is given for frequencies of 30 and 300 Mc/s.

TABLE 4.1

O.D. of wire, $2a$ (in.)	I.D. of tube, $2b$ (in.)	Dielectric	Z_0 (ohms)	α (db/100 ft)		Peak voltage (kV)	Mean power (watts)		Relative velocity c_r
				30 Mc/s	300 Mc/s		30 Mc/s	300 Mc/s	
0·056	0·334	Polyethylene	72	1·05	3·8	12	640	130	0·67
0·022	0·133	Polyethylene	72	2·2	7·5	4·5	160	44	0·67
0·155	0·555	Partial air (disc spacers)	75	0·45	1·6	3·5	1,000	300	0·96
0·128	0·755	Partial air (disc spacers)	100	0·30	1·05	6	1,400	380	0·96

The power which such cables can convey is in general determined by one or other of two factors. The first is voltage breakdown of the dielectric, and the second is temperature rise due to losses. Which of these two criteria is the important one depends upon the character of the signal being transmitted by the cable. For signals consisting of short pulses of r.f. power, the power-handling capacity is usually determined by the voltage breakdown. For signals consisting of continuous waves or modulated continuous waves the limitation is usually temperature rise due to transmission losses. However, if a cable or line is carrying c.w. signals and there is a high standing-wave ratio, the power limit may be set by voltage breakdown rather than dissipation of losses. The need for matching, in order to maintain a low s.w.r. and thus raise the power transmitted, was mentioned in the last chapter.

The breakdown voltage is dependent upon the maximum voltage stress in the dielectric, and this maximum stress occurs at the surface of the inner conductor where the electric lines of force are most closely spaced. If the maximum safe stress for the dielectric is known, the maximum safe voltage between the cable conductors can be determined. Knowing the cable impedance, the maximum power which the cable can convey without voltage breakdown can be calculated. The formulae are developed in Appendix 4.1 and the results are quoted here. If E_s volts per metre is the maximum allowable dielectric stress in a coaxial cable then the maximum peak voltage is given by

$$V_p = E_s a \log_\varepsilon (b/a) \text{ volts} \quad . \quad . \quad . \quad . \quad . \quad (4.5)$$

where a and b are the conductor radii. The maximum power P, corresponding to E_s, is given by:

$$P = \frac{E_s{}^2 a^2 Z_0 \kappa_r}{7{,}200} \text{ watts} \quad . \quad . \quad . \quad . \quad . \quad . \quad (4.6)$$

The allowable peak voltages for typical cables are given in Table. 4.1 and they correspond to maximum stresses of about 10^7 volts per metre for polyethylene and $1{\cdot}5 \times 10^6$ volts per metre for air dielectric. It should be noted that the breakdown voltage is independent of frequency, and so also is this power limit.

The power dissipated in a cable by c.w. signals can be easily related to the attenuation. Thus if at a certain point in a cable (with no standing waves) the power flow is P_T and V is the r.m.s. voltage, the power loss per metre is approximately:

$$\begin{aligned} P_L &= \left(\frac{V}{Z_0}\right)^2 R + V^2 G \\ &= \frac{V^2}{Z_0}\left(\frac{R}{Z_0} + G Z_0\right) \\ &= 2 P_T \alpha \quad . \quad . \quad . \quad . \quad . \quad . \quad . \quad . \quad . \quad (4.7) \end{aligned}$$

on comparing with equation (4.2). This power loss will heat up the cable to a temperature at which the heat lost by radiation just balances electrical power loss. For a given safe temperature rise, P_T may be determined, but since

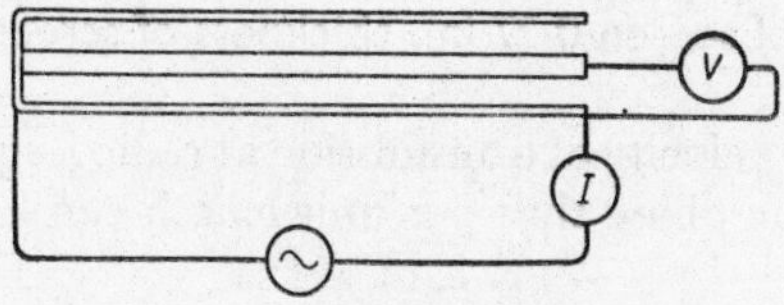

Fig. 4.1. Measurement of coupling impedance for coaxial cable.

attenuation increases with frequency it can be seen from equation (4.7) that the power rating must be reduced for higher frequencies. These factors are taken into account by the manufacturers of cable, who usually provide curves of power rating against frequency. The power ratings of typical cables are given in Table 4.1 at frequencies of 30 Mc/s and 300 Mc/s.

Although a coaxial cable is screened, the screening is not perfect and so it is necessary to know how good it is. Its efficacy can be indicated by the extent to which interfering power from an external circuit is transferred into the cable.

In Fig. 4.1 a current I is shown passing through the outer tube and having an external return. This current penetrates the wall of the tube, and so produces a voltage drop along the inner surface of the tube. This inner surface, however, is common to the proper transmission path of the cable involving both inner and outer conductors. It, therefore, provides a coupling element between the two circuits and so the voltage drop V is recorded on the voltmeter. If this test is carried out for a metre length, the impedance $Z_C = V/I$ is called the coupling impedance per metre, and is an inverse measure of screening efficiency, enabling various cables to be compared. Owing to skin effect, it decreases with frequency; i.e., the screening improves with frequency. At any frequency Z_C decreases with an increase in the thickness and/or the conductivity of the tube wall.

For cables of the rigid type with homogeneous copper tube for the outer conductor, it is not difficult to achieve almost any degree of screening. However, for flexible cables, it is much more difficult to achieve the desired screening. It is often found that the coupling impedance increases with frequency, whereas if the tube were homogeneous it would decrease. The use of spiral tapes or wires for the outer tube to give flexibility introduces inductance in the screen and lowers its effectiveness. Braided screens using wires or tapes in opposite directions are usually the most satisfactory flexible screens. The manner in which Z_C varies with frequency for a coaxial line with a solid tube and for one with a flexible tube of comparable weight is shown in Fig. 4.2.

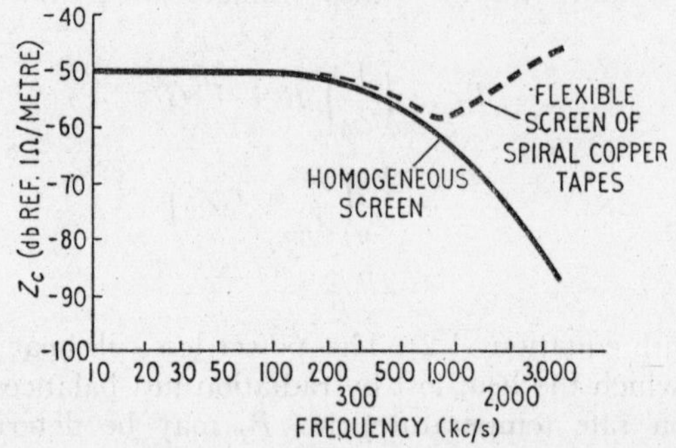

Fig. 4.2. Variation of coupling impedance with frequency for a coaxial cable. Inside diameter of screen 0·27 in., thickness of screen 0·01 in. copper.

Turning now to the velocity of transmission at radio frequencies, the simplified equation (1.30) for the phase shift per unit length can be used with negligible error, thus:

$$\beta = \omega\sqrt{(LC)} \qquad (4.8)$$

The phase and group velocities are therefore equal and constant, thus:

$$v_p = v_g = \omega/\beta = \frac{1}{\sqrt{(LC)}} = \frac{c}{\sqrt{(\mu_r\kappa_r)}} \qquad (4.9)$$

where c is the velocity of electromagnetic waves in free space. Signals at radio frequencies are thus transmitted with negligible phase distortion (i.e., transmission is substantially non-dispersive). The phase velocity in a cable is usually quoted as a fraction of c, thus the relative velocity is:

$$c_r = \frac{1}{\sqrt{(\mu_r\kappa_r)}} \qquad (4.10)$$

Normally μ_r is unity, and κ_r varies from just above unity for a partial air-space cable up to 2·3 for solid polyethylene and higher for other dielectrics. Typical values for c_r are shown in Table 4.1. The wavelength in such cables is easily calculated, thus:

$$\lambda = \frac{v_p}{f}$$

$$= \frac{c}{f\sqrt{(\mu_r \kappa_r)}} \quad . \quad . \quad . \quad . \quad . \quad . \quad . \quad (4.11)$$

The wavelength in a cable is always less than in free space, although in a partial air cable it is only a few per cent less. If a coaxial line has disc spacers, there is a similarity to the loaded line of Chapter 2, viz., there are evenly spaced points of high capacitance or low velocity. By analogy there should therefore be at least π discs per wavelength at the shortest working wavelength in the line otherwise rapid increases of attenuation are possible.

It is interesting to calculate the attenuation per wavelength for r.f. lines. Referring to Fig. 1.13 the ratio of successive peaks is called the decrement, thus

$$\text{Decrement} = \frac{\varepsilon^{-\alpha z}}{\varepsilon^{-\alpha(z+\lambda)}}$$

$$= \varepsilon^{\alpha\lambda}$$

The natural logarithm of this is called the logarithmic decrement, thus:

$$\log \text{dec} = \Delta = \alpha\lambda \quad . \quad . \quad . \quad . \quad . \quad . \quad . \quad (4.12)$$

$$= \text{attenuation per wavelength}$$

Then from equations (4.3) and (4.11) we have:

$$\alpha\lambda = \frac{R}{2Z_0} \times \frac{c}{f\sqrt{(\mu_r \kappa_r)}}$$

$$= \frac{R}{f} \times \text{constant}$$

But from equation (1.7) we see that R is proportional to the square root of frequency so that we have:

$$\alpha\lambda = \frac{\text{constant}}{\sqrt{f}} \quad . \quad . \quad . \quad . \quad . \quad . \quad (4.13)$$

showing that attenuation per wavelength decreases with increasing frequency. This result shows why circuit components made from transmission lines have such small losses, and why attenuation is negligible in lines which are only a few wavelengths long.

The relative merits of coaxial lines and waveguides at frequencies above about 2,000 Mc/s will be considered in Chapter 6, but brief mention will be made here of the upper frequency limit for coaxial lines. When the wavelength in the line is less than about $\pi(a + b)$ (i.e., the mean circumference of the dielectric space), other modes of propagation besides the principal mode discussed so far are possible. Discontinuities and bends are liable to cause loss of power due to these extraneous modes. Unless the line is straight and carefully terminated, as in coaxial resonators for example, it is preferable not to employ coaxial lines at frequencies higher than that corresponding to a wavelength in the line of $\pi(a + b)$. If a coaxial line of the lowest possible attenuation is desired this rule sets the limit to the diameter that may be used. Generally speaking it is possible to keep the cable diameter well below this limit and still have an acceptable attenuation.

Transmission Lines as Impedance Elements

At low frequencies the usual linear circuit components are inductors, capacitors and resistors. Inductors are constructed by winding wire into solenoidal coils with or without ferro-magnetic cores. Capacitors are constructed from two sets of closely-spaced conducting plates separated by air or dielectric material. Resistors are constructed from wire or semi-conducting rods. When these so-called lumped components are used at higher frequencies, difficulties soon arise because they are not pure single reactances or resistances. For example, inductors have capacitance between turns and from turns to core or earth. Capacitors have inductance in the connecting leads and in the plates themselves. Resistors made from wire have inductance and capacitance; when made from high resistance material the inductance and capacitance are still present although to a lesser extent.

The conductors used to interconnect lumped components have distributed inductance and capacitance, and this may affect the performance at higher frequencies.

To allow for these parasitic effects in the design and construction of lumped components becomes more difficult as the frequency is raised. On the other hand, the theory of transmission lines takes full account of distributed inductance and capacitance, and it is applicable up to much higher frequencies. The reactive nature of open- and short-circuited lines has already been deduced and the results are summarized in Fig. 3.14. Thus it is possible to construct reactances from sections of transmission line. When the use of lumped-component circuits becomes difficult or impossible, a transmission-line technique may be used. There is no clearly defined frequency where the change of technique occurs, but in general, the transmission-line methods are preferable above frequencies of a few hundred megacycles per second. It may often be used with advantage at much lower frequencies, for example, in connection with h.f. and v.h.f. aerials and feeders.

When the transmission line from which a reactance is constructed has a low loss, the ratio of reactance to resistance can be remarkably high, and in general is much better than for low-frequency reactances.

Consider the construction of a positive reactance from a low-attenuation line of primary characteristics R, L, G and C, and of length l metres. It can be seen from Fig. 3.14 that a short-circuited line of length between 0 and $\lambda/8$ has approximately the characteristics desired since it has an almost straight reactance–frequency curve. The line should be as long as possible so that end effects due to field distortion at the input end of the line are unimportant, but on the other hand it should not be much longer than $\lambda/8$ because the effect of line capacitance is then causing an appreciable divergence from the straight-line characteristics of an inductance. Generally speaking where no great accuracy is required, a line operating at frequencies up to that corresponding to $\lambda/8$ can be assumed to behave as a positive reactance of ωLl. This follows because at low frequencies the short-circuit would cause a heavy current to flow, determined only by Rl in series with ωLl. The applied voltage would be so small that the current in the admittance of Gl and ωCl would be negligible in comparison with the current in the line. When the line is exactly one-eighth of a wavelength long, equation (3.22) shows that the reactance is:

$$\begin{aligned} X &= Z_0 \\ &= \sqrt{\frac{L}{C}} \\ &= \omega L' \end{aligned}$$

where L' is the apparent inductance corresponding to the actual line reactance.

Now

$$\begin{aligned} \omega &= 2\pi f \\ &= 2\pi \frac{v_p}{\lambda} \\ &= \frac{2\pi}{8l} \cdot \frac{1}{\sqrt{(LC)}} \end{aligned}$$

$$\therefore \quad \frac{\pi}{4l\sqrt{(LC)}} L' = \sqrt{\frac{L}{C}}$$

or

$$L' = \frac{4}{\pi} Ll \qquad (4.14)$$

Thus the apparent inductance is $4/\pi$ times that involved in assuming that an inductance of Ll holds up to frequencies corresponding to $\lambda/8$. This gives a measure of the error involved.

Similarly, with the construction of a negative reactance from an open-circuited line of length l. For frequencies up to that at which the length is one-eighth of a wavelength the line behaves approximately as a capacitance of Cl in parallel with a conductance Gl (due to leakage and dielectric loss).

Suppose now that the frequency is raised until the line is a quarter wavelength long. Fig. 3.14 shows that an open-circuited line behaves as a series-resonant circuit while a short-circuited line behaves as a parallel-resonant circuit. Ignoring for the moment the question of dissipation, let L'', C'' be the components of the equivalent series-resonant circuit, and L', C' the components of the equivalent parallel circuit. For a small frequency on either side of the resonance we can assume that the reactance–frequency curve of the quarter-wave open-circuited line has the same slope as that for the lumped resonant circuit. This enables the lumped components to be determined in terms of the primary characteristics of the line. This is carried out in Appendix 4.2 and we get

$$L'' = \frac{Ll}{2}$$

$$C'' = \frac{8}{\pi^2} Cl \qquad (4.15)$$

In the case of the short-circuited line we must compare the slope of the susceptance–frequency curve with that for the parallel-tuned circuit, because the slope of the reactance–frequency curve is infinite. This is carried out in Appendix 4.2 and we get

$$L' = \frac{8}{\pi^2} Ll$$

$$C' = \frac{Cl}{2} \quad . \quad . \quad . \quad . \quad . \quad . \quad . \quad (4.16)$$

If the line is longer than a quarter wavelength, the equivalent circuits apply at the appropriate multiple quarter-wave points.

So far we have ignored the losses and the effect which they have on the resonances. The effect of R and G can be allowed for if the analogy of transmission lines and lumped circuits is extended further. Consider a series-tuned circuit R'', C'', L'' with a peak current I_p flowing at the resonant frequency. It is known that in such a circuit there is a fixed stored energy which oscillates between the magnetic field of the inductor and the electric field of the capacitor. There is a power loss in the resistance which must be supplied by the energizing source. Then the Q of such a circuit is defined as follows:

$$Q = \omega L''/R''$$

$$= \omega \frac{\frac{1}{2}L'' I_p^2}{\frac{1}{2}R'' I_p^2}$$

$$= \omega \times \frac{\text{stored energy}}{\text{energy loss per sec}} \quad . \quad . \quad . \quad . \quad . \quad (4.17)$$

The latter definition of Q is in fact the more fundamental, although the first definition is the more widely used.

Now we apply this definition to a unit length of cable or line carrying a single travelling wave. The stored energy is equally divided between the electric and magnetic fields. Furthermore the energy passing a point in the line is fluctuating, but we clearly have to take its mean value, which is one half of the peak value.

If V_p and I_p are the peak voltage and current at a point then for a unit length of line we can apply equation (4.17) and get

$$Q = \omega \frac{\frac{1}{2}(\frac{1}{2}LI_p^2 + \frac{1}{2}CV_p^2)}{\frac{1}{2}(RI_p^2 + GV_p^2)}$$

$$= \omega \frac{CV_p^2}{\frac{RV_p^2}{Z_0^2} + GV_p^2}$$

$$= \frac{\omega\sqrt{LC}}{\frac{R}{Z_0} + GZ_0}$$

$$= \frac{\beta}{2\alpha} \quad . \quad . \quad . \quad . \quad . \quad . \quad . \quad . \quad . \quad (4.18)$$

$$= \frac{\pi}{\alpha\lambda} \quad . \quad . \quad . \quad . \quad . \quad . \quad . \quad . \quad . \quad (4.19)$$

This is an important result applicable to a wide range of problems. It should be noted that the length of line does not appear in the result. Equation (4.19) shows that a low attenuation per wavelength is necessary to achieve a high Q, and equation (4.13) shows that the situation becomes more favourable as the frequency is increased. It is not immediately obvious that this result can be applied to a resonant quarter- or half-wave line. A more convincing proof would be to take the standing-wave pattern on the line for voltage and current and to sum the electric and magnetic energies all along the line. The same result would be obtained, however. We can see that equation (4.18) would apply if we regard the standing waves on a resonant line as made up from independent forward- and backward-travelling waves. For each wave we have the same stored energy per unit length and the same energy loss per second per unit length. Hence the average stored energy per unit length is double that for a single travelling wave, and the energy loss per second per unit length is also double. The ratio is thus as given by equation (4.18).

As an example of the order of magnitude of Q we consider the last coaxial cable in Table 4.1 operating at 300 Mc/s. Then we have:

$$\text{Attenuation } \alpha = 1{\cdot}05 \text{ db/100 ft}$$

$$= \frac{1{\cdot}05}{8{\cdot}68} \times \frac{3{\cdot}25}{100} \text{ nepers per metre}$$

$$= 0{\cdot}004 \text{ N/m}$$

$$\text{Wavelength for 300 Mc/s} = \frac{3 \times 10^8}{300 \times 10^6}$$

$$= 1 \text{ metre}$$

$$\therefore\ \beta = 2\pi \text{ radians per metre.}$$

$$\therefore\ Q = \frac{2\pi}{2 \times 0{\cdot}004}$$

$$\approx 800$$

This value is high compared with that normally attainable with lumped components, but it is still much below that attainable with rigid coaxial lines. Thus if instead of considering a flexible cable of small diameter we had taken a rigid line of diameter approaching the maximum allowable we should find that a Q of the order of 10^4 could be achieved.

Considering again the series tuned circuit R'', L'', C'', and its quarter-wave open-circuited line equivalent we have from equation (4.15):

$$Q = \frac{\omega L''}{R''} = \frac{\omega Ll}{2R''} = \frac{\beta}{2\alpha}$$

$$R'' = \frac{\alpha}{\beta}\omega Ll = \alpha l \frac{\omega L}{\omega\sqrt{(LC)}}$$

or

$$\frac{R''}{Z_0} = \alpha l \qquad \qquad (4.20)$$

Similarly for the parallel tuned circuit R', L', C' (where R' is the resistance at resonance) and its quarter-wave short-circuited line equivalent we have

$$\frac{R'}{Z_0} = \frac{1}{\alpha l} \quad \ldots \ldots \quad (4.21)$$

The attenuation per unit length of a line can be deduced from these equations if the resistance at resonance of a quarter wavelength is measured.

If $\pm \Delta f$ is the frequency deviation on either side of the resonant frequency f_r for which the reactance is equal to the resistance (R' or R'') then we have from resonant-circuit theory:

$$Q = \frac{f_r}{2\Delta f} \quad \ldots \ldots \quad (4.22)$$

The modulus of the impedance at these points is $R'/\sqrt{2}$ or $R''\sqrt{2}$ and the angle is 45°. If we assume R' and R'' are approximately constant over this frequency range then the bandwidth $\pm \Delta f$ corresponds to the half-power points; i.e., the power transmitted into the resonant line at these frequency points is 3 db below the maximum power at resonance, for a fixed applied voltage with a series resonance, and a fixed total current for a parallel resonance. For the coaxial cable of the previous example, if we cut a quarter-wave line for 300 Mc/s and measure the bandwidth between the half-power points for either a short-circuit or open-circuit termination we should find from equation (4.22) a bandwidth of:

$$2\Delta f = \frac{f_r}{Q} = \frac{300 \times 10^6}{800} = 375{,}000 \text{ c/s}$$

It is instructive to calculate the effective resistances R' and R'' for this line. From Table 4.1, $Z_0 = 100$ ohms, also we have

$$\alpha = 0{\cdot}004 \text{ N/m}$$

$$l = 0{\cdot}25 \text{ metre}$$

$$\therefore\ R' = \frac{100}{0{\cdot}004 \times 0{\cdot}25}$$

$$= 100{,}000 \text{ ohms}$$

and $$R'' = 100 \times 0{\cdot}004 \times 0{\cdot}25$$

$$= 0{\cdot}1 \text{ ohm}$$

For a rigid coaxial line designed for a Q of the order of 10,000, the bandwidth would only be about one-tenth of that above, and R' would be about one megohm, while R'' would be about 0·01 ohm.

Equations (4.20) and (4.21) apply to lines which are an integral number of quarter-wavelengths long provided l represents the total length. Thus at the resonant points of low resistance the value of the low resistance gradually increases as the length increases. Similarly at the resonant points of high resistance the value of the high resistance falls in proportion to the number of quarter wavelengths. These results can be understood from an example.

Consider a short-circuited line, then at the quarter-wave point the resistance will be high and given by

$$\frac{R_1'}{Z_0} = \frac{1}{\alpha\lambda/4}$$

At the half-wave point we may consider that we have a quarter-wave line terminated in R_1'. The latter may be transformed by equation (3.28) to the half-wave point, but to get the total resistance we must add an allowance for the losses in the second quarter wavelength given by equation (4.20). The resistance at the half-wave point is then

$$R_2'' = Z_0\frac{\alpha\lambda}{4} + \frac{Z_0^2}{R_1'}$$

$$= Z_0\frac{\alpha\lambda}{4} + Z_0\frac{\alpha\lambda}{4}$$

or

$$\frac{R_2''}{Z_0} = \alpha\frac{\lambda}{2}$$

Thus up to a limited number of quarter wavelengths equations (4.20) and (4.21) may be used provided l is taken as the total length. Alternatively for a line of fixed length the same equations may be used provided the value of α appropriate to the frequency is used. The deterioration in the values of the

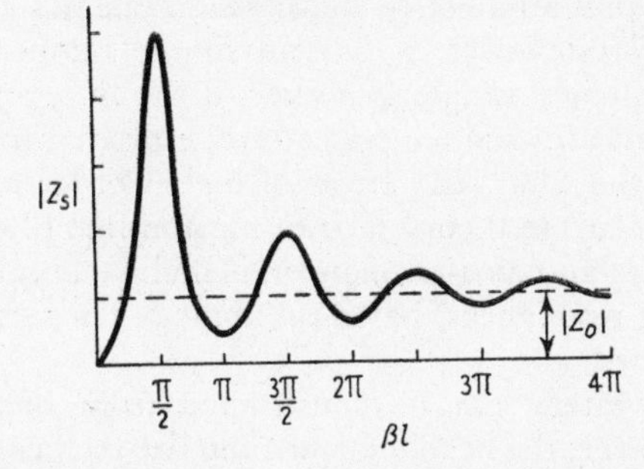

Fig. 4.3. Modulus of Z_S for a lossy line with total reflection.

resistances at the multiple quarter-wave points does not lead to a deterioration in Q, because the reactance change for a given small percentage change of frequency is proportional to the number n of quarter wavelengths. Thus at a low resistance point, the resistance is proportional to n and the reactance for a given small percentage change of frequency is proportional to n. This leads to the result of equation (4.18) that Q is not dependent upon the line length. However the greater the value of n the smaller the fractional bandwidth over which the line behaves as a resonant circuit. It is for this reason that the number of quarter wavelengths in a resonant line should be kept to the minimum.

These results cannot easily be shown on Fig. 3.14 since this is plotted for fully reflective loss-free lines and therefore represents reactance only. However, the magnitude of the sending impedance for an attenuating short-circuited line can be plotted as in Fig. 4.3. As the distance from the short-circuit increases (or as the frequency increases in a fixed line) the impedance oscillates with diminishing amplitude and approaches Z_0 at large distances. This is obvious because in an infinite-lossy line the input impedance is independent of the terminal conditions at infinity.

In comparing transmission lines with lumped circuits, the repetitive nature of the line input impedance may be looked upon as the analogue of the parasitic behaviour of the lumped circuit, the transmission line having the advantage that it can be predicted.

In many problems the reactance to be constructed only has to operate over a very narrow band of frequencies in which case there is no need to restrict the line length to $\lambda/8$. In such cases, the accurate formulae (3.22) and (3.23) must be used.

Filters Constructed from Transmission Lines

The theory of wave filters for low frequencies employing lumped reactances is described in Volume 4. The construction of lumped reactances for frequencies above about 50 to 100 Mc/s presents difficulties as has already been explained. Furthermore, the interconnecting wires have distributed inductance and capacitance which modify the performance. Many frequency-filtering problems occur in radio systems and it is necessary to be able to construct filters over the whole of the band concerned. The manner in which short- and open-circuited lines simulate the behaviour of reactances suggests that filters can be constructed from transmission lines. This technique is quite feasible from 50 Mc/s up to 3,000 Mc/s or more, and a few simple examples will be considered.

Owing to the fact that a reflective transmission line has an infinite number of resonances and anti-resonances, it has no simple lumped circuit equivalent covering a wide frequency range. However, if the lines are used so that their lowest resonances and anti-resonances cause the desired frequency discrimination phenomena of the filter, the effect of higher-order resonances is usually unimportant. The accurate theory of transmission-line filters, allowing for the effect of all resonances and anti-resonances, is highly complex, but a method of design for the lowest resonances, based on analogy with lumped circuit filters, is quite straightforward.

Transmission-line filters can be constructed from balanced lines or unbalanced lines. However, the need for screening between components makes the coaxial line the more suitable. All the filters described here are therefore coaxial filters, although unbalanced two-wire line equivalents may be shown for explanatory purposes.

At the lower end of the frequency range, it is often necessary to construct a high-pass filter to eliminate one sideband of a television transmission in order to economize in frequency spectrum. The lumped equivalent of one section of such a filter is shown in Fig. 4.4 (a) and the two-wire unbalanced form is shown in Fig. 4.4 (b). The capacitance C_1 is simulated by a one-eighth wavelength line of appropriate impedance. The series-resonant circuit L_2C_2 is simulated by a short-circuited line, which is one half-wavelength long at the resonant frequency of L_2 and C_2, connected across the transmission path. The impedance of this line is such that the slope of the reactance curve through the half-wavelength point is equal to the slope of the reactance curve of L_2 in series with C_2. The coaxial form of the filter, which is fully screened, is shown in Fig. 4.4 (c). If we trace the central conductor of the input coaxial line, which corresponds to the upper left-hand terminal of the filter, we see it is connected to the outer tube of a $\lambda/8$ line. The capacitance of this to the vertical conductor is C_1. This vertical conductor is connected to the half-wave line representing L_2, C_2 and the load. A screen is placed over the $\lambda/8$ line, and it must be dimensioned so as to produce a negligible shunt capacitance across the input coaxial line.

At the other end of the frequency range the wavelength is of the order of 10 cm, and quarter-wave lines become very small components. The construc-

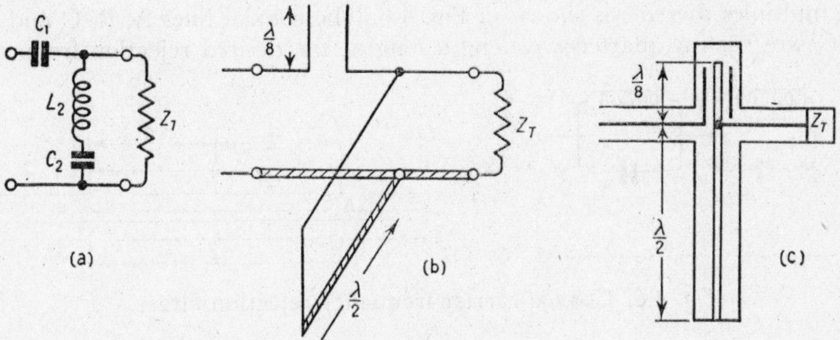

Fig. 4.4. Filter circuit constructed from transmission lines.

tion of filter elements using lathe-turned parts is a widely used technique. The derivation of simple coaxial low-pass and high-pass filters from their lumped equivalents is shown in Fig. 4.5 for cases where it is possible to construct lines within the central conductor of the coaxial line. Considering the low-pass filter of Fig. 4.5 (a), the first series inductance is a short-circuited line of one-eighth

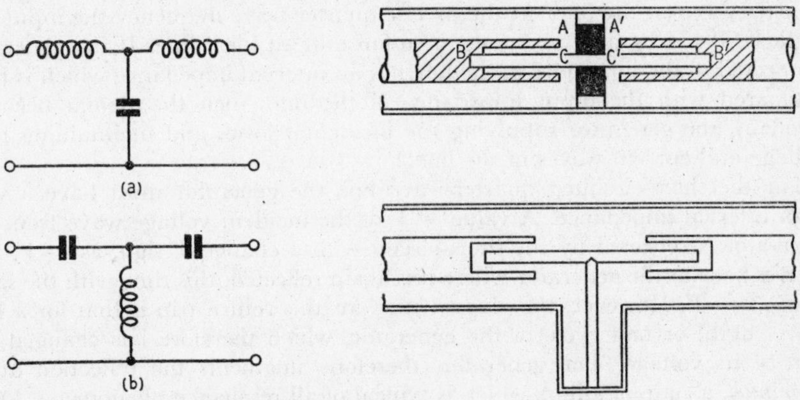

Fig. 4.5. Coaxial transmission-line filters.

wavelength or rather less, at the cut-off frequency of the filter. It is formed by the under-cut line ABC whose input impedance is clearly in series with the central conductor. The shunt capacitance element is short compared with one-eighth of a wavelength so that it behaves as a point capacitance. Its value can be raised by using a disc of low-loss material of high permittivity. The second series inductance is provided by another undercut line A′B′C′ in series with the central conductor. Considering the high-pass filter of Fig. 4.5 (b) similar principles are used. The first series capacitor is provided by an open-circuited undercut line of length rather less than one-eighth wavelength. It is clearly in series with the central conductor. The shunt inductance is provided by a short-circuited stub which supports the central conductor. It can be seen to be connected across the central conductor and the tube. The second series capacitor is another open-circuited short line undercut into the output central conductor.

A carrier-frequency rejection filter of high attenuation at one frequency (and odd multiples thereof) is shown in Fig. 4.6. The coaxial lines A, B, C and A′, B′, C′ are each a quarter-wavelength long at the desired rejection frequency

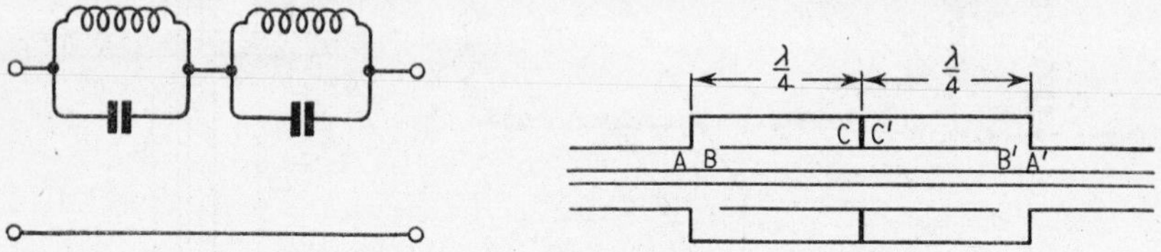

Fig. 4.6. Coaxial carrier-frequency rejection filter.

and they insert a high impedance in series with the outer coaxial conductor of the main line. Thus the impedance across AB and A′B′ becomes high at frequencies near the rejection frequency.

Band-pass filters of wide or narrow fractional bandwidth can also be constructed from transmission lines.

Resonant Lines

It has been shown that the input impedance of a short-circuited line behaves like a parallel-resonant circuit at frequencies near that corresponding to a quarter wave on the line. At the precise quarter-wave frequency the input impedance is a very high resistance or infinite in an ideal line. If the generator connected to the input end of the line has an internal impedance which is high compared with the input impedance of the line, then the system becomes resonant, the generator supplying the incidental losses and maintaining high voltage and current waves in the line.

For the short-circuited quarter-wave line the generator must have a very high internal impedance. A value $+V$ of the incident voltage wave from the generator is reflected by the short-circuit with a change of sign, as $-V$, and arrives back at the generator where it is again reflected, this time with the same sign, as $-V$. However, the elapsed time for this return trip is that for a half wavelength, or half cycle of the generator, which therefore has changed the sign of its voltage. The generator, therefore, augments the reflection at its terminals, a state of affairs which is typical of all resonance phenomena. Once the resonance on the line is established, the generator only needs to supply the losses. If the generator is removed the current and voltage decay with a decrement that can be calculated from the Q of the line.

Similar qualitative arguments may be evolved for the open-circuited quarter-wave line driven by a very low impedance generator; in fact from (a) and (b) of Fig. 4.7 the two cases are identical so far as reflections are concerned, the only difference being the location of the generator necessary to start the resonance and supply the losses.

In (c) of Fig. 4.7 a line is shown which is short-circuited at each end. It has been shown that points of equal impedance in a fully reflecting line are separated by a half wavelength. Thus the minimum frequency for which the line (c) is resonant is that corresponding to a half wavelength. It will also be resonant at an integral number of half wavelengths. The line of (d) in Fig. 4.7 has an open circuit at each end and its minimum resonant frequency is clearly that corresponding to a half wavelength. The full lines show the magnitude of the voltage distribution, and the dotted lines the current distribution.

The generator for supplying the losses of the resonator will normally be a self-oscillating valve, the resonator functioning as its tuned circuit and stabilizing the oscillation frequency. Alternatively the resonator can be used in connection with measurements, on dielectrics for example, in which case it will be excited by a separate oscillator or generator of stable frequency, the frequency of the resonator being adjusted to that of the external oscillator. The manner of

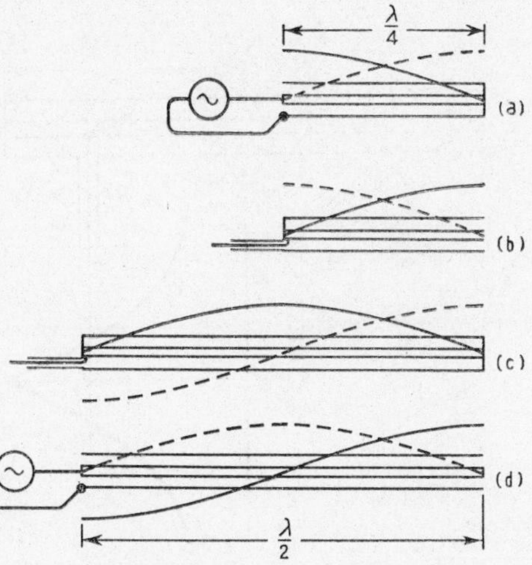

Fig. 4.7. Resonant transmission lines.

coupling the generator to the resonator will normally be determined by which of these two classes it falls into.

In the case of self-oscillators it is usually desired that the tuned circuit should have a high impedance at resonance, and that the impedance should fall rapidly on either side of the resonance. This indicates the use of the high-impedance connection of Fig. 4.7 (a). Ideally the generator should be non-reactive so that there is no phase shift of the reflection at its terminals, and the length of the line then accurately determines the frequency. However this is not attainable in practice, and the generator usually imposes a shunt capacitance across the line. The length of line is then rather less than a quarter wave. We may look upon the line as being inductive and resonating with the self-capacitance of the generator. If C' is the self-capacitance of the generator, the frequency and line length are from equation (3.24) connected by the equation:

$$\frac{1}{\omega C'} = Z_0 \tan\left(\frac{\omega l}{v_p}\right)$$

It is desirable that l should not be much shorter than a quarter wave as the frequency would then be rather dependent upon C' which is not very stable. This indicates that it might be desirable to keep Z_0 somewhat lower than usual. This approach is adopted in the design of coaxial valves. Sometimes it is desirable to maintain d.c. insulation between the line conductors in which case Fig. 4.7 (d) can be employed. The right-hand portion of the line is then exactly a quarter wavelength (ignoring any open-end effect) although the left-hand portion will be shortened on account of the generator capacitance.

In the second type of application where the resonator is driven by a separate generator, the low-impedance or current-loop type of feed is usually to be preferred. This must be introduced at a current antinode and should be arranged to affect the reflection as little as possible, as in Fig. 4.7 (b) and (c). An application of the type of resonant line shown in Fig. 4.7 (c) is the resonant line wavemeter. This may be employed for measuring the wavelength, and hence the frequency, of a microwave power source. The short-circuit at the right-hand

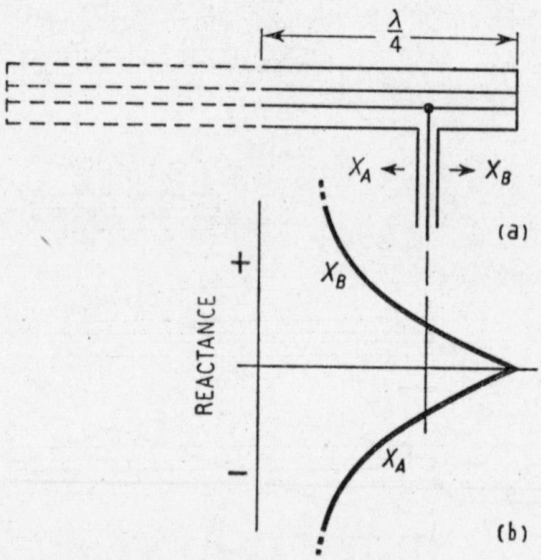

Fig. 4.8. Tapped resonant line.

end is made adjustable in position and the current feed at the left is employed to couple to the circuit under test. A small probe at a point in the outer conductor can be used to detect resonance when the right-hand short-circuit is adjusted. This probe should be near the left-hand end but care should be taken to ensure that direct coupling to the input current feed is small. This probe is connected to a rectifier and meter, or other detector circuit, to indicate maximum voltage corresponding to resonance. Preferably the adjustable short-circuit should range over at least one wavelength so that end effects at the input end are minimized. In use the line is adjusted to half-wave resonance and the length measured on a vernier scale attached to the movable short-circuit. The line is then adjusted to full-wave resonance and the length again measured. The difference gives the half wavelength with a precision that is often better than 1 part in 1,000.

Another method of coupling which is sometimes applicable to oscillators is shown in Fig. 4.8 (a). It is analogous to the tapped parallel-tuned circuit. The impedance at the tapping point is resistive. This can be shown by plotting the input reactance in either direction at a point in the line as in Fig. 4.8 (b). The reactances X_A and X_B are conjugate so that the impedance is resistive and it increases from zero at the closed end to a high value at the open end. A suitable impedance tapping point can therefore be chosen. The length of the tapping connection must be kept as short as possible.

Resonant lines of the type discussed here become practicable above about 300 Mc/s ($\lambda = 1$ metre for an air-spaced line) where the size and cost are reasonable. If constructed of coaxial form, there is no external field to cause losses in external objects, and if plated with silver, very high Q values can be achieved. The use of metals with a low coefficient of thermal expansion enables accurate and stable resonators for oscillators to be constructed. Care must be exercised in the use of open ends to ensure that radiation does not lower the Q. For this reason closed ends are to be preferred, as in the closed resonator shown dotted in Fig. 4.8. Alternatively the open end of Fig. 4.8 could be closed by a well-spaced screen, due allowance being made for the increase of end capacitance.

In some types of oscillator the line consists of two parallel rods with an adjustable shorting bar. Such a line is called a Lecher line and adjustment of the bar changes the oscillator frequency. Oscillators employing resonant lines are described in Volume 3.

Matching in R.F. Lines

Before dealing with the matching problems of r.f. lines, some of the elementary matching theorems of circuit theory will be recapitulated. First of all, consider

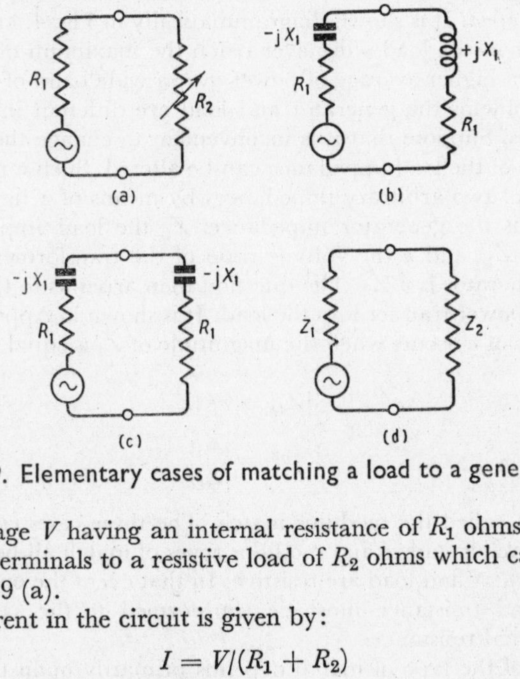

Fig. 4.9. Elementary cases of matching a load to a generator.

a source of voltage V having an internal resistance of R_1 ohms, which is connected via two terminals to a resistive load of R_2 ohms which can be varied as shown in Fig. 4.9 (a).

Then the current in the circuit is given by:

$$I = V/(R_1 + R_2)$$

and the power dissipated in the load by

$$I^2R_2 = \left(\frac{V}{R_1 + R_2}\right)^2 R_2$$

With V constant the right-hand side is zero when $R_2 = 0$ (short-circuited) and zero when $R_2 = \infty$ (open-circuited). Between these two values, the power rises to a maximum when $R_2 = R_1$, as may be shown by a simple application of the calculus or by putting $R_1 = 1$ ohm say, and plotting power in load against R_2. This is the simplest case of matching and is, of course, applicable to the matching of long lines where Z_0 is a pure resistance.

When the generator internal impedance has reactance, then three cases occur. Suppose in (b) of Fig. 4.9 the internal impedance is $R_1 - jX_1$ at a particular frequency. Then a reactance of $+jX_1$ in the load will resonate with $-jX_1$ and produce a circuit which is resistive. If then a resistance R_1 is included in the load, the maximum power will be extracted from the generator and will appear in the load. However, if the frequency is changed, $+jX_1$ and $-jX_1$ will so change as to upset the condition and the power in the load will no longer be the maximum. In this case there is only one frequency at which the power is a maximum, and if the resonance is at all sharp, the power in the load at other frequencies is small. This is known as the conjugate match because the load impedance $R_1 + jX_1$ is the conjugate of the generator impedance $R_1 - jX_1$; i.e., the resistive components are the same, but the reactive components are equal in magnitude and opposite in sign.

If a system has to operate over a wide band of frequencies or at a number of spot frequencies without adjustment, the conjugate match is unsuitable and the true or reflectionless match must be used. In this case the load impedance should equal the generator impedance (in magnitude and phase) at all frequencies of interest. It is shown diagrammatically in Fig. 4.9 (c). It is apparent that the power in the load will never reach the maximum of Fig. 4.9 (b), but it will achieve a higher average of power over a wide band of frequencies.

In some problems the generator and load are different impedances having different angles. Suppose that it is inconvenient to change the angles, but that the magnitude of the load impedance can be altered. Such a problem occurs in the matching of two arbitrary impedances by means of a tight-coupled transformer. If Z_1 is the generator impedance, Z_2 the load impedance (of angle different from Z_1) and n the voltage ratio of the transformer, the impedance seen by the generator is n^2Z_2. The question then arises as to the best value of n for maximum power transfer into the load. It is shown in Appendix 4.3 that the optimum value of n occurs when the magnitude of Z_1 is equal to the magnitude of n^2Z_2 or:

$$|Z_1| = n^2 |Z_2|$$

$$\therefore\ n^2 = \frac{|Z_1|}{|Z_2|} \qquad (4.23)$$

This may be called the modulus match. The three cases considered namely the conjugate, reflectionless and modulus types of match all become equivalent when the generator and load are resistive. In that event the optimum condition is that the load resistance must be transformed to the same value as the generator internal resistance.

The choice of the type of match depends primarily upon the bandwidth to mean-frequency ratio, but other factors have to be taken into account, such as the type of signal to be transmitted and the ease with which the load impedance can be constructed or altered. A fuller consideration of these factors will be given presently when the above fundamental ideas are extended to the case of a transmission line interconnecting a generator and load. Meanwhile it is desirable to be able to calculate what power loss will occur when the match deviates from say the conjugate or reflectionless matches, in order that some appreciation of the power aspects of matching can be given.

Let the actual match which results in a given problem be equivalent to a generator of impedance $Z_1 = R_1 + jX_1$ directly connected to a load of impedance $Z_2 = R_2 + jX_2$ as in Fig. 4.9 (d).

The power in the load is then:

$$P_L = \frac{V^2}{|Z_1 + Z_2|^2} R_2 \quad . \quad . \quad . \quad . \quad . \quad . \quad . \quad (4.24)$$

If Z_2 were made conjugate to Z_1 the power in the load would be:

$$P_L' = \frac{V^2}{4R_1^2} R_1 \quad . \quad . \quad . \quad . \quad . \quad . \quad . \quad (4.25)$$

If Z_2 were made equal to Z_1 for the reflectionless match the power in this load would be:

$$P_L'' = \frac{V^2}{4|Z_1|^2} R_1 \quad . \quad . \quad . \quad . \quad . \quad . \quad . \quad (4.26)$$

The power loss may be expressed in decibels relative to the conjugate match and is usually called the mismatch loss. Thus:

$$\left.\begin{array}{r}\text{Mismatch loss relative}\\ \text{to conjugate match}\end{array}\right\} = 10 \log_{10} \frac{P_L}{P_L'}$$

$$= 10 \log_{10} \frac{4R_1R_2}{|Z_1 + Z_2|^2} \text{ decibels} \quad . \quad (4.27)$$

This will always be negative indicating a loss, excepting the case when Z_2 is conjugate to Z_1, when the loss is zero.

The mismatch loss relative to the reflectionless match is given by:

$$10 \log_{10} \frac{P_L}{P_L''} = 10 \log_{10} \frac{R_2}{R_1} \cdot \frac{4|Z_1|^2}{|Z_1 + Z_2|^2} \text{ decibels} \quad . \quad . \quad (4.28)$$

This expression can be positive, indicating a gain, at frequencies near the conjugate match. This merely means that near the conjugate match more power is delivered to the load than in the case of the reflectionless match.

These ideas may be extended to the case where a transmission line (or any 4-terminal network) connects a generator to a load. Typical problems occur with transmission lines between radio transmitters and aerials and between receiving aerials and radio receivers. The usual requirements are high transmission efficiency and small standing-wave ratio, particularly for high power transmitters, and in some systems, for example, television, freedom from reflection or echo effects. In the general case, the generator impedance Z_G, the line characteristic impedance Z_0, and the load impedance Z_T, are all different, and the choice of matching system depends upon the line attenuation and the particular requirements.

Broadly speaking, there are two systems. The first is an application of the reflectionless match in which the load Z_T is matched by some device to Z_0, and the generator impedance Z_G is matched to the line input impedance, which will be Z_0. This is known as the untuned or flat feeder. The second is an application of the conjugate match in which Z_T is connected directly to the line without matching, and the line input impedance Z_S is conjugate matched to Z_G. This is known as the tuned feeder. These two cases will be examined in more detail.

The untuned or flat feeder is illustrated in Fig. 4.10 (a). Some type of matching device is necessary at each mis-match. This method of operation must be employed when the feeder loss exceeds a few decibels, because any mismatch loss at the termination cannot then be recovered by tuning at the input, as in the case of the tuned feeder. Alternatively, for a given power in the load, more power is required in the incident wave for a large mismatch or s.w.r. at the termination, and since from equation (4.7) the power lost in the feeder increases in proportion to the power in the incident wave, the need for matching can be appreciated. It must also be used where a low standing-wave ratio (1·1 or 1·2) is necessary; for example, with high-power systems where it is necessary to

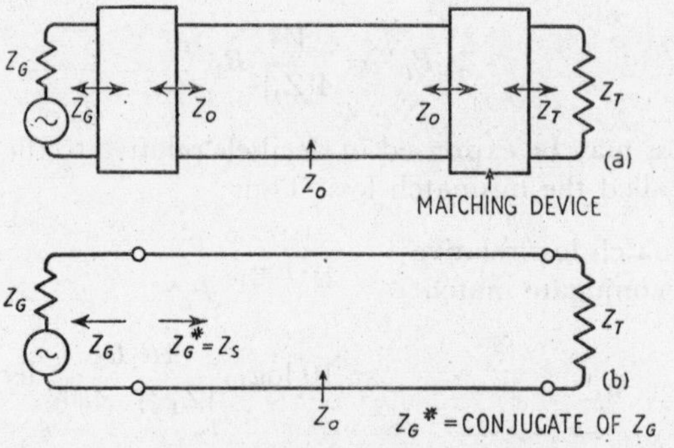

Fig. 4.10. (a) The untuned or flat feeder; (b) the tuned feeder.

minimize the voltage on the feeder in order to avoid voltage breakdown, arcing or corona. The matched feeder must also be employed where the signal to be transmitted is liable to be impaired by reflection or echo effects. For example, a television-system feeder or cable having two or more impedance irregularities greater than a certain minimum distance apart, can cause a delayed signal to be superimposed on the wanted signal.

The matching devices must, of course, be efficient and cause considerably less power loss than the mismatch loss which they are designed to eliminate. If the matching devices are also untuned, for example, broadband transformers, then the system can operate at a number of frequencies within the band without adjustment. This desirable state of affairs is achieved in some applications, for example, with feeders connected to broadband aerials, such as the rhombic aerial. Where the load impedance has reactance, it is usually necessary to tune this out in some way before matching, in which case the system is in fact tuned, although the feeder operates in the untuned manner; i.e., with no standing waves.

Turning now to the case of the tuned feeder, this is illustrated in Fig. 4.10 (b). The transmission line is unmatched at the termination and it may operate with an appreciable standing-wave ratio. In order to achieve a good power delivery into Z_T, the generator impedance Z_G is matched to the line input impedance Z_S using the conjugate match. This method is only applicable to short feeders having an attenuation of less than a few decibels, because otherwise it is not possible to recoup the termination mismatch loss by tuning at the line input. If the line loss is very low, then the efficiency can be as high as the flat feeder, because the loss and complexity of the matching devices are not involved. It is, of course, a single-frequency device and the impedance Z_S may change rapidly with frequency, so that it is unsuitable for generators whose frequency is sensitive to load impedance changes. It can be seen that within reasonable limits, the choice of characteristic impedance Z_0 for the feeder is not important.

There is an interesting deduction that can be made for the tuned feeder when its transmission loss is negligible. Since the generator is conjugate matched to the line, all the transmitted power must appear in the load Z_T and an equal amount will be dissipated in Z_G regardless of the value of Z_0. Hence at all sections of the line and at the load terminals there must always be a conjugate match. This deduction applies to any loss-free reactive four-terminal network which connects a generator and load with a conjugate match.

For problems such as aerial feeders for aircraft or projectiles in which the transmission line is short, say less than about one or two wavelengths, and operation is at a fixed frequency, the tuned feeder is often a satisfactory solution provided the bandwidth for effective matching is adequate for the signal. If Z_T and Z_0 are known, then Z_S can be found by the circle-diagram method. The feeder length may be adjusted to give a value of Z_S which conjugate matches Z_G or suitable reactances can be connected in series or shunt at the generator terminals to achieve the same result.

Considering now the matching devices that must be used with flat feeders, there are several forms available. Coupled coils suitably designed for the frequencies and impedances involved may be employed as impedance transformers, but these are only as a rule satisfactory for the h.f. band. Such transformers usually have the advantage of broadband operation. We are mainly concerned here with matching devices employing transmission-line technique. Such principles may be used from the h.f. band, through the v.h.f. band into the microwave region.

As an example of the use of the circle diagram, it has been shown how to locate points on a misterminated line where

$$Z_S = Z_0 \pm jxZ_0$$

Further it was explained that if the line were cut at such a point and a series reactance equal in magnitude and opposite in sign to that of Z_S were inserted, then the line on the generator side of that point would be matched. The inserted reactance could be conveniently constructed from a length of line with a short-circuit whose position could be adjusted to give the required reactance. However, this procedure of cutting the line is inconvenient and an equivalent result may be achieved by using a shunt reactance whose position on the line can be adjusted. The shunt reactance can be constructed from a section of line with an adjustable short-circuit as before. Such a line is known as a stub line. Where the stub line has to provide capacitive reactance it may be an open-circuited line or the short-circuit may be moved further away so as to make the short-circuited line longer than a quarter wavelength.

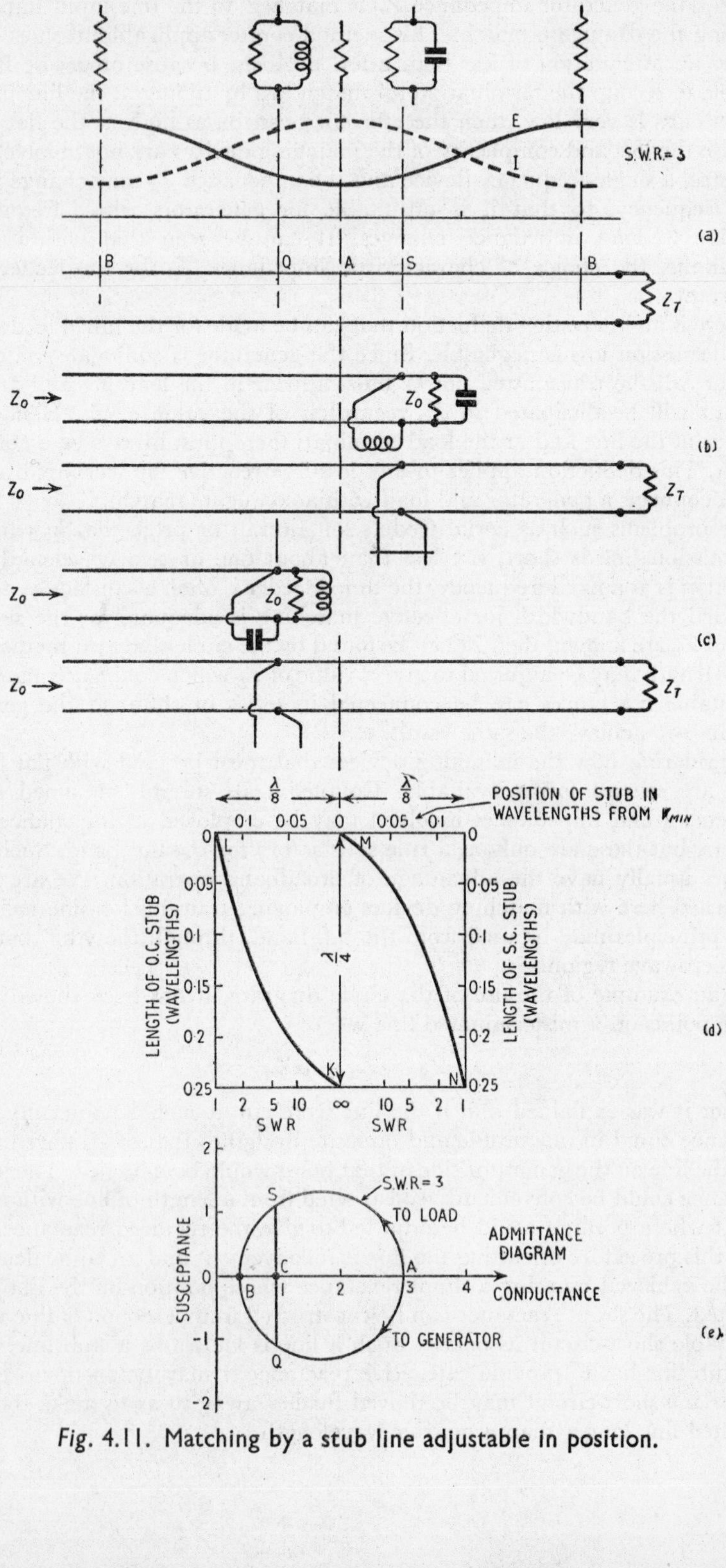

Fig. 4.11. Matching by a stub line adjustable in position.

The principle of the shunt stub is shown in Fig. 4.11 where a line of impedance Z_0 is terminated in Z_T. A point S has to be located where Z_S is a resistance Z_0 in parallel with a reactance. Then a stub line must be connected in shunt at S and adjusted so as to provide an anti-resonance with this reactance. Since we are dealing with parallel-connected components, it is more convenient to work in terms of admittance, conductance and susceptance. It has already been explained that the circle diagram is equally applicable to normalized admittances. An admittance-circle diagram for the standing-wave pattern at the top of Fig. 4.11 for which s.w.r. $= 3$ is shown at the bottom of the figure. The circle gives normalized sending admittances $Y_S = G_S + jB_S$, the actual sending admittance being obtained by multiplying by the actual line characteristic admittance $(1/Z_0)$. The point B on the circle now corresponds to the current minimum of Fig. 4.11, and the point A the current maximum. Then the correct location of S is found at the intersection of the perpendicular through C and the circle, the distance from B or A being read off in fractions of a wavelength. The ordinate SC gives the normalized susceptance of the line at S; in the present example it is positive, indicating shunt capacitance. The susceptance to be shunt connected at S must be such as to annul SC, or it must be negative susceptance; that is, shunt inductance. This can be provided by a short-circuited stub line of

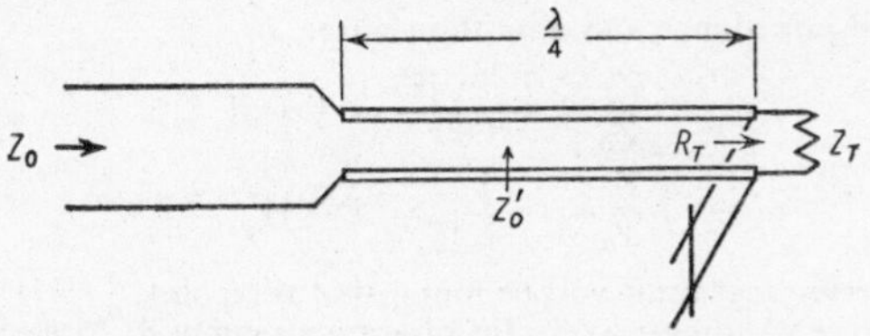

Fig. 4.12. Matching by a fixed stub line and a quarter-wave impedance transformer.

length up to a quarter wavelength. The actual length can be found by determining the desired reactance from the annulling susceptance and using the circle diagram or a curve such as Fig. 3.14. Fig. 4.11 (b) shows diagrammatically the susceptance annulling process. Similarly, another point Q can be found where the shunt resistance component of the input impedance looking towards the load is also equal to Z_0. The opposite type of stub reactance is required here and it can be provided by a suitable length of open-circuited line or a short-circuited stub line of suitable length greater than a quarter wavelength. Fig. 4.11 (c) shows the process in this case. This matching procedure using a circle diagram can be simplified by using the abac of Fig. 4.11 (d); knowing the standing-wave ratio, the curves LK and MN give the position and length of a stub of similar characteristics to the line itself. To the left of the voltage minimum the curve LK gives the position and length of open-circuited stub, and to the right the curve MN gives the position and length of short-circuited stub. The standing-wave ratio determines the position of the stub immediately, as may be checked from the circle diagram for admittance.

An alternative method of matching is shown in Fig. 4.12. In this method the adjustable stub is connected at the load and adjusted to annul the load susceptance. The load now appears as a pure resistance R_T say, which has to be matched to Z_0. This is effected by a quarter-wave matching line of impedance

$$Z_0' = \sqrt{(Z_0 R_T)}$$

In the balanced-line case this matching line is made by adjusting the spacing and diameter of the two wires to give the desired value of Z_0'.

Example

A 600-ohm balanced feeder line has to supply power at 30 Mc/s to a load of 75 ohms resistance in series with 75 ohms positive reactance. Calculate the loss that would occur due to direct connection of the load, and the standing-wave ratio. By annulling the load susceptance, calculate the impedance of a quarter-wave matching line.

It is assumed that the generator is matched to the characteristic impedance of the line so that the source impedance feeding the load when directly connected is 600 ohms. From Fig. 4.9 (d) and the method of equation (4.27) we have:

$$Z_1 = 600 + j0$$
$$Z_2 = 75 + j75$$
$$Z_1 + Z_2 = 675 + j75$$

and the ratio of power in the directly connected load, to the optimum (i.e., a load of 600 ohms) is:

$$\frac{V^2 75}{|675 + j75|^2} \cdot \frac{(1{,}200)^2}{V^2 600} = \frac{4 \times 600 \times 75}{|675 + j75|^2}$$
$$= \frac{4 \times 75/600}{|1\frac{1}{8} + j\frac{1}{8}|^2} = \frac{\frac{1}{2}}{82/64} = 0{\cdot}39$$

Thus more than half the power is lost by direct connection. The mismatch loss is:

$$-10 \log_{10} 0{\cdot}39 = 4{\cdot}1 \text{ db}$$

The normalized load impedance and admittance are:

$$\frac{Z_T}{Z_0} = \frac{75 + j75}{600} = \tfrac{1}{8} + j\tfrac{1}{8}$$
$$\frac{Y_T}{Y_0} = \frac{1}{\frac{1}{8} + j\frac{1}{8}} = 4 - j4$$

From a complete circle diagram it will be found that the points $\frac{1}{8} + j\frac{1}{8}$ and $4 - j4$ fall on a circle corresponding to a standing-wave ratio of approximately 8. Alternatively the reflection factor can be calculated, thus:

$$\text{Voltage reflection factor} = \frac{Z_T/Z_0 - 1}{Z_T/Z_0 + 1}$$
$$= \frac{-\frac{7}{8} + j\frac{1}{8}}{\frac{9}{8} + j\frac{1}{8}}$$

Taking the magnitude:

$$\frac{V_r}{V_i} = \sqrt{\frac{(\frac{7}{8})^2 + (\frac{1}{8})^2}{(\frac{9}{8})^2 + (\frac{1}{8})^2}}$$
$$= \sqrt{\frac{50}{82}} \approx 7/9$$
$$\text{S.W.R.} = \frac{V_i + V_r}{V_i - V_r} \approx \frac{1 + 7/9}{1 - 7/9} \approx 8$$

This means that for a given allowable maximum voltage on the line, the power that can be transmitted is only one-eighth of that which the line could carry. [See equation (3.15).] This is perhaps one of the most important reasons for matching the line, especially if any appreciable amount of power is to be delivered to the load.

We have found the normalized load admittance, namely:

$$4 - j4$$

from which the actual load admittance is:

$$\frac{4}{600} - j\frac{4}{600}$$

This can be visualized as a resistance of 150 ohms in parallel with a positive reactance of 150 ohms. This positive reactance is to be resonated with an equal negative reactance (capacitance) connected across the load. When this is carried out the load will appear as a 150-ohm resistive impedance. Thus the quarter-wave matching line impedance will be:

$$\sqrt{(600 \times 150)} = 300 \text{ ohms}$$

The shunt capacitance required across the load is given by:

$$\frac{1}{\omega C} = 150$$

or

$$C = \frac{10^{-6}}{150 \times 2\pi \times 30} \text{ farads}$$

$$= 35{\cdot}5 \text{ pF}$$

This may be provided by a suitable open-circuited line not exceeding one quarter of a wave-length; i.e., less than 2·5 metres, since the wavelength is 10 metres.

If the feeder line spacing-to-radius ratio is d/a that of the quarter-wave line should be $\sqrt{(d/a)}$ since the characteristic impedance of a two-wire line is given by $276 \log_{10} (d/a)$ ohms. This formula gives a ratio of $d/a = 150$ for a 600-ohm line and $\sqrt{150} = 12{\cdot}2$ for a 300-ohm line. Thus a line of 0·16 inch diameter wire, spaced 12 inches would have an impedance of 600 ohms and the spacing would have to be about 1 inch to bring the impedance down to 300 ohms. This is unduly close, and the quarter-wave section of 2·5 metres length, should be constructed of copper tubing of say 1-inch diameter spaced about 6 inches to give 300 ohms impedance.

Two slightly different methods of matching are shown in Fig. 4.13. The first shown at (a) consists of a phasing section of line AB and an adjustable quarter-wave matching section BC. Without the matching section present, the point B

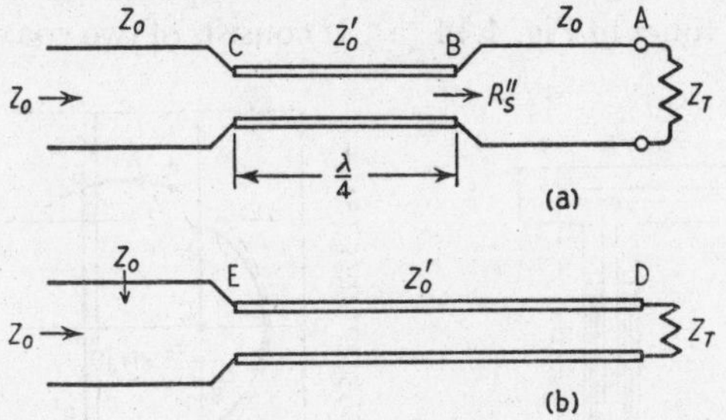

Fig. 4.13. (a) Matching by a phasing section and a quarter-wave transformer; (b) matching by a combined phasing section and quarter-wave transformer.

would be a voltage minimum so that Z_S at B would be a pure resistance R_S'', which is less than Z_0 the characteristic impedance of the line. Hence the characteristic impedance Z_0' of the matching section should be

$$Z_0' = \sqrt{(Z_0 R_S'')}$$

This is constructed as in the previous case by two tubes a quarter-wave long where spacing can be adjusted to give the desired value of Z_0'. The second method shown in Fig. 4.13 (b) is similar except that the phasing and trans-forming sections are combined into the one section DE. The length of this section is chosen such that E is a voltage maximum of the standing-wave pattern on DE. Then if Z_0' is the characteristic impedance of section DE the input impedance at E is given by SZ_0' and for matching to Z_0 the value of Z_0' must be chosen such that

$$Z_0 = SZ_0'$$

Note, however, that S, Z_0' and Z_T are dependent upon one another according to the circle diagram.

Matching in Microwave Lines

The considerations of the previous section are applicable to transmission lines for frequencies corresponding to centimetre wavelengths. However, such lines are normally of the coaxial type, and the mechanical problems often dictate the type of matching device to be employed. For example, the single adjustable shunt stub of adjustable position is not very practical for a coaxial line, owing to the mechanical difficulties involved with wide screened slots and sliding contacts on the inner conductor.

The methods of Fig. 4.12 and 4.13 can be adapted to coaxial microwave lines when Z_T is known beforehand but they do not lend themselves to adjustable matching devices. The sections of low impedance such as Z_0' would be constructed from a metal sleeve over the central conductor thus reducing the b/a ratio and lowering the impedance, but there is no convenient means of adjusting this impedance.

Before considering the more usual types of adjustable matching device it is necessary to note that they must always comprise at least two variables. This has already been noted in connection with Fig. 4.11 but it really follows from the fact that the standing-wave pattern has two degrees of freedom viz., the s.w.r. and the position of the nodes.

The most widely used matching device for air-spaced coaxial microwave lines is the double-stub tuner of Fig. 4.14 (a). It consists of two coaxial-line stubs fixed

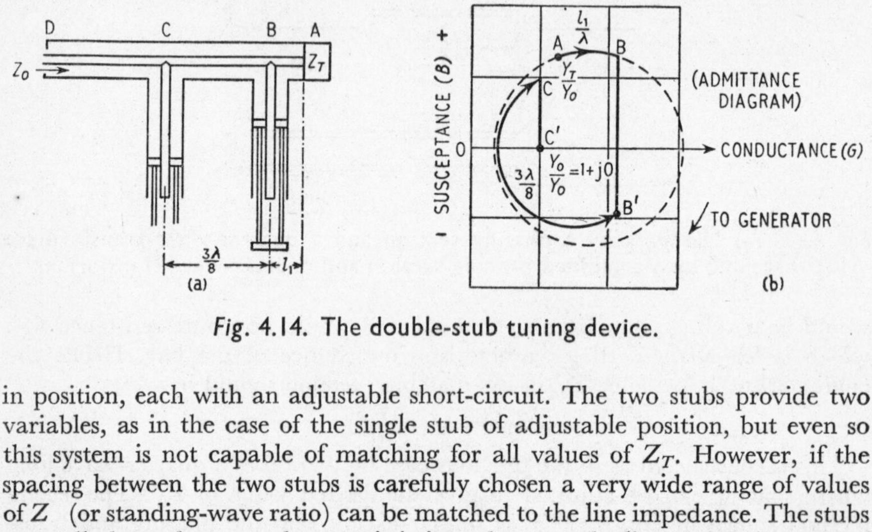

Fig. 4.14. The double-stub tuning device.

in position, each with an adjustable short-circuit. The two stubs provide two variables, as in the case of the single stub of adjustable position, but even so this system is not capable of matching for all values of Z_T. However, if the spacing between the two stubs is carefully chosen a very wide range of values of Z (or standing-wave ratio) can be matched to the line impedance. The stubs normally have the same characteristic impedance as the line and their range of adjustment should be rather greater than a half wavelength. The two stubs should be placed near the load, and the best compromise spacing between the stubs is usually considered to be about $3\lambda/8$. The stubs can of course, be located farther away from the load, and if suitably adjusted the standing-wave ratio on the generator side of the line can be reduced to a low value.

The method of adjustment may be one of trial and error, or one of preliminary computation and final trial and error. In the former case the stub nearest the load is set at a number of points over its range. At each point the other stub is ranged backwards and forwards between its limits, the standing-wave ratio being continuously monitored on a device of the type shown in Fig. 3.9 connected in the generator side of the line. In the latter method an approximate knowledge of the load impedance relative to the line impedance is necessary.

The approximate susceptances to be added or subtracted by each stub can then be determined from a circle diagram. The admittance diagram is used because the stubs are in shunt. The method may be understood from Fig. 4.14 (b) where Y_T/Y_0 is the normalized load admittance and B represents the point where the first stub is connected. The distance round the S circle from A to B corresponds to the distance l_1 of the first stub from the load. Two verticals are then drawn, one through B and the other through $(1 + j0)$, the point corresponding to the normalized line characteristic admittance Y_0/Y_0. An S circle must then be found having a sector B′C which in the direction towards the generator is $3\lambda/8$, the electrical distance BC between the stubs. The distances BB′ and CC′ then give the required susceptances at B and C. In the example shown in Fig. 4.14 (b) both susceptances are subtracted from the line susceptance and the stubs must therefore be negative susceptances or positive reactances; i.e., they would be short-circuited stubs less than $\lambda/4$ long. Knowing the actual susceptance or reactance required the actual length of stub can be determined from the XOX′ axis of a circle diagram. Final adjustment is then made by trial and error.

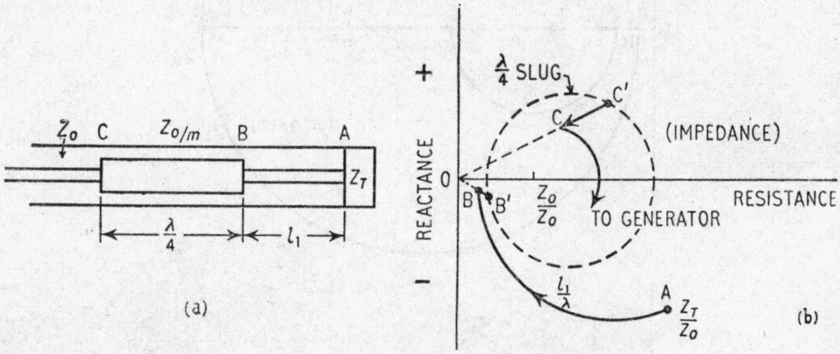

Fig. 4.15. Circle diagram for an adjustable slug.

It has already been noted that such a double-stub tuner does not match for all values of s.w.r. The most general form which is capable of coping with any value of Z_T or s.w.r. consist of three adjustable shunt stubs, usually spaced $\lambda/8$ apart.

The second type of matching device is based on the use of an adjustable slug such as that shown in Fig. 4.15 (a). This slug could be a metal sleeve $\lambda/4$ long sliding in contact with the central conductor, or a dielectric cylinder nearly filling the dielectric space and $\lambda/4$ long at the velocity for the dielectric (i.e., of length $\lambda/(4\sqrt{\kappa_r})$ where λ is the wavelength in the air spaced line and κ_r is the relative permittivity of the dielectric slug). In either case the slug can be adjusted in position by dielectric supports passing through a narrow slot in the line and fixed to a suitable moving carriage. The effect which such a slug has on the impedance of a mismatched line can be deduced from the impedance circle diagram of Fig. 4.15 (b). The line impedance is Z_0 and that of the slug section is Z_0/m where m is greater than unity. The circle diagram has to serve for lines of two characteristic impedances. Circles corresponding to the Z_0 sections are shown in full, and circles corresponding to the slug or Z_0/m sections are shown dotted. Z_T/Z_0, the load impedance normalized with respect to Z_0, is located on the circle diagram and the distance l_1/λ is traversed around the corresponding circle until the point B is reached. To the left of B in Fig. 4.15 (a) the impedances must be normalized with respect to Z_0/m; i.e., the impedance at B must be multiplied by the factor m. This is effected by drawing a line through O and B making OB′/OB equal to m. We can then proceed from B′ around the dotted circle remembering that impedances on this circle are normalized with respect to Z_0/m corresponding to points in the slug section. The dotted circle is followed for a distance $\lambda/4$ and then the impedance changes again. To bring the

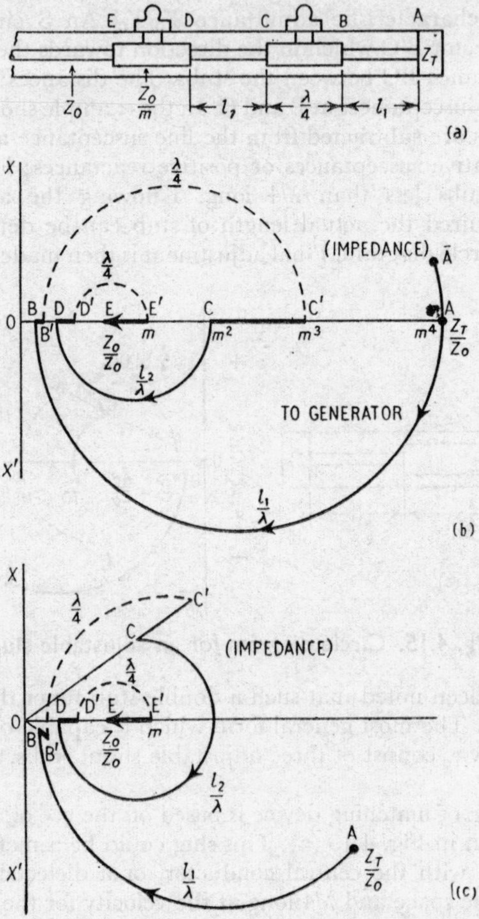

Fig. 4.16. The double-slug tuning device.

impedances back to normalization with respect to Z_0 we must now divide by m. We thus arrive at the point C where OC/OC′ $= 1/m$. If we proceed further towards the generator we follow the full circle shown.

In order to provide two variables such an adjustable slug can be used in conjunction with a single-stub tuner, but it is more usual to provide two slugs. The latter case is shown in Fig. 4.16 (a) and will be considered in more detail. The distances l_1 and l_2 have to be determined so that s.w.r. on the left of the device is reduced to a low value. This may be effected by trial and error as in the case of a stub tuner, but adjustment of the double-slug device is somewhat easier. This is because it is roughly true that l_1 is determined by the phase of the standing-wave pattern and l_2 is determined by the s.w.r. In some forms of this device l_2 is adjusted by a right- and left-threaded screw coupling the two slug carriages, while l_1 is adjusted by a separate screw which moves the two carriages together. Thus there are two controls one for s.w.r. and one for the phase of the pattern. When the two slugs are touching together they act as a half-wave transformer and produce no effect in the line.

It is somewhat complex to trace the action of the double-slug tuner on the circle diagram, but it is instructive to do this in the special case where $Z_T = m^4 Z_0$. Referring to Fig. 4.16 (b) which is an impedance diagram normalized with respect to Z_0, point A is located corresponding to the normalized value of Z_T. The circle is followed towards the generator for a distance $\lambda/4$ until B is reached. This is the point $(1/m^4, 0)$ from circle-diagram theory. As before the impedance must be multiplied by m so that the dotted circle represents points in the slug normalized with respect to Z_0/m. The dotted circle is followed for a distance $\lambda/4$ until the point C′ or $(m^3, 0)$ is reached. We must now divide by m to bring the diagram back to impedances normalized with respect to Z_0; i.e., the point C or $(m^2, 0)$ is reached. We now proceed a distance l_2 corresponding to CD which in the simple case assumed is in fact $\lambda/4$. This brings the impedance to $1/m^2$ corresponding to a point just to the right of D. By a similar process the second slug is traversed. The point D′ is $(1/m, 0)$ and the dotted circle gives impedances along the second slug section if the diagram is considered to be normalized with respect to Z_0/m again. The slug is $\lambda/4$ in length and the point $(m, 0)$ is reached corresponding to a point just to the right of E in Fig. 4.16 (a). The final step is to divide by m to give the impedance normalized with respect to Z_0 in the line to the left of E. In the simple case chosen this can be seen to be the point $(1, 0)$ or the centre of the circle diagram corresponding to the line characteristic impedance Z_0. Thus the s.w.r. has been reduced to unity or the load is matched. The manner in which the impedance spirals towards the centre should be noted.

If Z_T had been any other impedance falling on the large circle, matching could still be effected provided l_1 were adjusted accordingly. Thus, if the point $\bar{A}$ on Fig. 4.16 (b) had been the point corresponding to Z_T, the distance l_1 would be rather more than $\lambda/4$ corresponding to the sector $\bar{A}$B. If Z_T falls outside the large circle complete matching cannot be achieved. This device is therefore effective for all cases where the s.w.r. corresponding to Z_T is less than m^4. If Z_T falls within the large circle matching can still be achieved, but l_1 and l_2 both differ from $\lambda/4$. A typical diagram for such a case is shown in Fig. 4.16 (c). The distance l_1 and l_2 must be such as to bring the impedance just to the right of D, to the point $(1/m^2, 0)$. Thereafter Fig. 4.16 (c) is the same as Fig. 4.16 (b). An accurate method of construction for determining l_1 and l_2 can be evolved, but it is somewhat complicated.

The slug impedance can be made one-half of the line impedance (i.e., $m = 2$), without difficulty so that a maximum s.w.r. of 16 can be dealt with. This can be achieved with a metal slug if the radius ratio is made the square root of the radius ratio in the line. Thus if b/a for the line is 3·6, then b/a for the slug of $\sqrt{3{\cdot}6} = 1{\cdot}9$ makes the slug impedance one-half the line impedance. With the dielectric slug a relative permittivity of 4 produces the same effect, although a higher value is necessary if the slug does not fill the whole dielectric space of the line.

Broadbanding

It will be observed that the transmission-line matching devices described so far are true for one frequency only (apart from the multiple resonances). The actual range on either side of this frequency for which the match is satisfactory must be examined in every case. Where the signal transmitted has a bandwidth which is an appreciable fraction of the carrier frequency, or where the latter can take on several values, it may be necessary to modify the system to give matching over the broader band. This is known as 'broadbanding'.

There is another important aspect to this question. If the bandwidth of the matching system is very narrow, it can be shown without difficulty that there must be high standing-wave ratios existing in the matching device. The high voltages in this device might limit the power that could be transmitted into the load. For example consider a quarter-wave matching transformer joining a line to a resistive load. At the design frequency we may imagine that it works by the cancellation of two reflections. Thus, looking towards the load from the

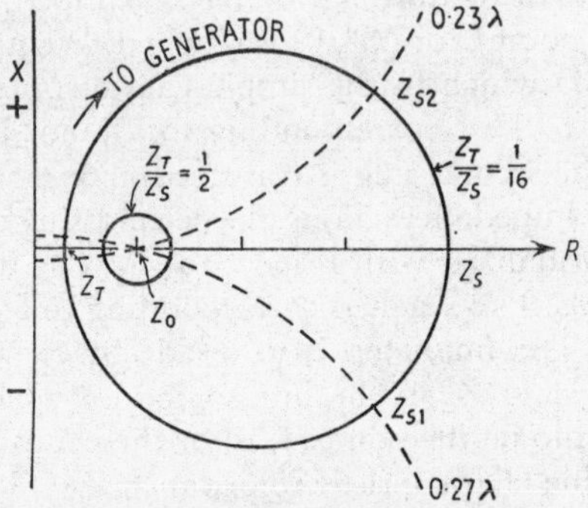

Fig. 4.17. Circle diagram for quarter-wave transformer, showing narrow bandwidth for high transformation ratios.

generator, the first reflection comes from the first junction and the second is due to the load. These two cancel out in the line, although the standing-wave ratio in the transformer may be high. Now suppose the frequency is changed, the phase of the second reflection will change so that cancellation is no longer complete. The second reflection lags the first reflection by an angle corresponding to twice the length of the transformer. A 1% increase of frequency means about a 1% decrease in wavelength (or the transformer is 1% too long) so that the second reflection is retarded by about 1% of π radians. The resultant of the two reflections is thus roughly $0{\cdot}01\pi$ times the magnitude of one reflection. A high standing-wave ratio in the transformer therefore means that the net reflection back to the generator increases rapidly for a small change of frequency. Or alternatively a narrow bandwidth is associated with a high standing-wave ratio in the matching device.

We may follow this argument from the Cartesian circle diagram of Fig. 4.17, where Z_0 represents the impedance of the transformer line, Z_T the load impedance, and Z_S the input impedance seen by the line at the matching frequency. An increase of frequency means that the length of the transformer line is now rather more than a quarter of a wavelength long, so that the corresponding point on the circle is Z_{S1}. Similarly for a decrease of frequency the input impedance is given by a point such as Z_{S2}.

Now we consider various matching ratios Z_T/Z_S or various sizes of circle in Fig. 4.17. The curves through Z_0 are for a given small fractional change in frequency or wavelength so that is is clear that the larger the circle the greater the change of reactance and sending impedance for changes in frequency. Thus the higher the impedance ratio, the higher is the s.w.r. on the transformer, and

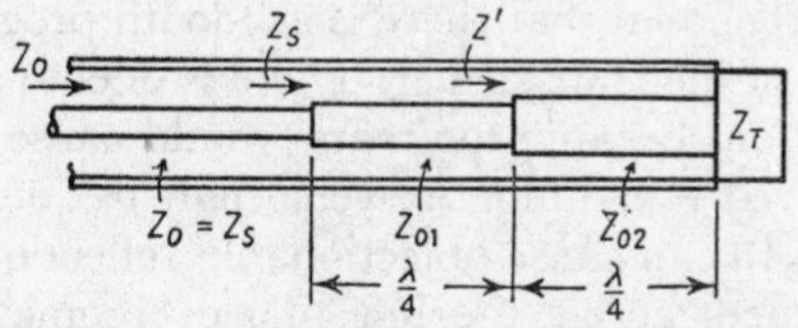

Fig. **4.18.** Double quarter-wave transformer.

the narrower the bandwidth. For small impedance ratios the small circle shows that Z_S does not vary greatly for large changes of frequency.

If the load impedance does not change over the frequency of interest, the bandwidth over which matching is effective may be broadened by using two or more quarter-wave transformers in tandem as shown in Fig. 4.18. Consider two quarter-wave transformers in tandem between Z_T and Z_S. Then we have to choose two characteristic impedances Z_{01} and Z_{02} for the transformer lines to give the best match. If the impedance at the junction of the two transformer lines is Z' then it can be shown that the best choice of impedances is that in which Z_S, Z_{01}, Z', Z_{02} and Z_T are in geometrical progression, or:

$$\frac{Z_T}{Z_{02}} = \frac{Z_{02}}{Z'} = \frac{Z'}{Z_{01}} = \frac{Z_{01}}{Z_S} \quad . \quad . \quad . \quad . \quad . \quad (4.29)$$

This clearly conforms to the quarter-wave transformer impedance rules:

$$Z_{02} = \sqrt{(Z_T Z')}$$
$$Z_{01} = \sqrt{(Z_S Z')}$$

Furthermore $$Z' = \sqrt{(Z_S Z_T)}$$

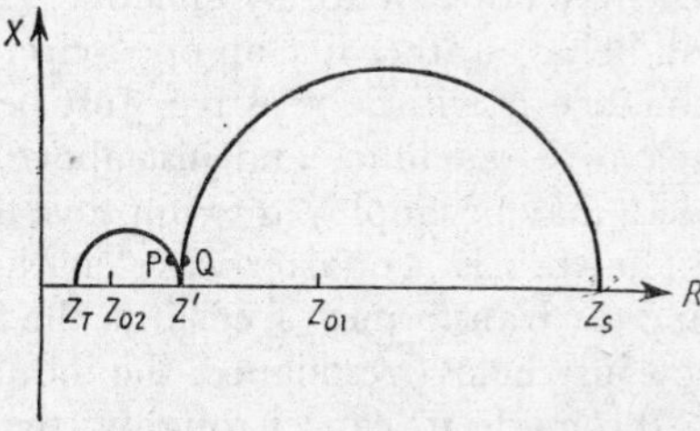

Fig. **4.19.** Circle diagram for double quarter-wave transformer.

We can see how this two-stage transformer works, from the special circle diagram of Fig. 4.19 in which the five impedances are marked along the resistance axis. Then for the design frequency, the impedance at various points in the transformers looking towards the load is on the two semi-circles shown. This may be seen by drawing normalized diagrams for the two transformers and then scaling up the higher impedance transformer and superimposing it on the other diagram. Then a small decrease in frequency brings the impedance at the middle junction, looking towards the load, to the point P in Fig. 4.19. At this reduced frequency Q is the impedance terminating Z_{01} which would make the input impedance equal to Z_S. The points P and Q are practically coincident so that matching is maintained over a broader band. It is not difficult to appreciate that the matching is broader in bandwidth if there are several quarter wavelength transformers so chosen that there is a smooth progression of impedances looking in either end of the transformer. There is of course an economical limit to the number of sections because too many would cause extra loss, out of proportion to the improved matching. At very high frequencies the steps in the coaxial lines of Fig. 4.18 can cause objectionable reflections, because they place small shunt capacitances across the line. To overcome this, it is possible to design tapered matching sections in which long cones are used instead of the stepped cylinders.

The effectiveness of broadband matching is usually determined by measuring the standing-wave ratio on the input line, for various frequencies on either side

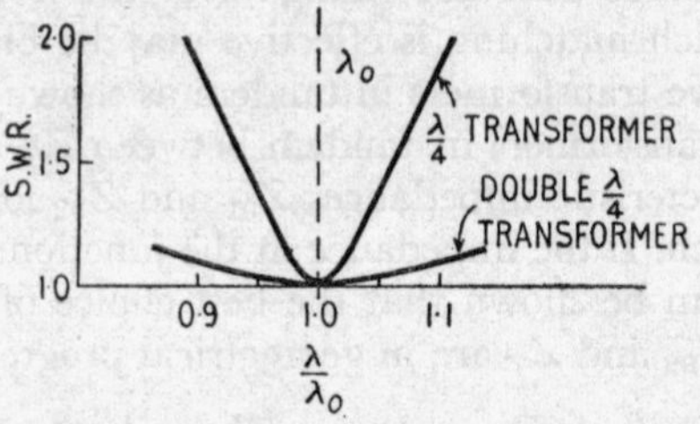

Fig. 4.20. Wavelength sensitivity of curves for single and double quarter-wave transformer.

of the perfectly-matched frequency. Curves such as in Fig. 4.20 are obtained and are sometimes called wavelength or frequency sensitivity curves. The curves shown compare single and double quarter-wave transformers for a total impedance-transformation ratio of 16.

If the load impedance changes appreciably over the band of interest, the procedure just described may not be entirely effective. Generally speaking the load (e.g., an aerial) will behave rather like an open-circuited resistive quarter-wave line. Thus at resonance it will be resistive. Just below the resonant frequency it will have capacitive reactance and just above, inductive reactance. The shunt stub of Fig. 4.12 may be employed to improve the matching on either side of the resonance. The stub is a quarter-wavelength long at the resonant frequency so that the line (or transformer) feeds into the resistive impedance of the load. At a frequency just below resonance, the inductive reactance of the short-circuited stub can be made to cancel roughly, the capacitive reactance of the load. Just above resonance the stub becomes capacitive whilst the load becomes inductive and a similar cancellation takes place. Such a stub is not always convenient in practice, and there is then no alternative but to use other methods of broadening the load or aerial bandwidth as explained in Chapter 12.

A combination of these principles is employed to broadband the stub support of Fig. 3.12 (b). The method is shown in Fig. 4.21 (a). Here the main line has a sleeve a half-wavelength long at the centre frequency, while the stub is a quarter-wavelength long at this frequency. Thus for signals at the centre frequency the stub presents a negligible shunt whilst the sleeve acts as a 1 : 1 transformer, so that if the load on the right is matched to the line impedance, the impedance seen from the left is matched. Now consider impedances at the junction of the T at a frequency somewhat below the mid-frequency. The impedance looking towards the load just to the right of the stub will now have

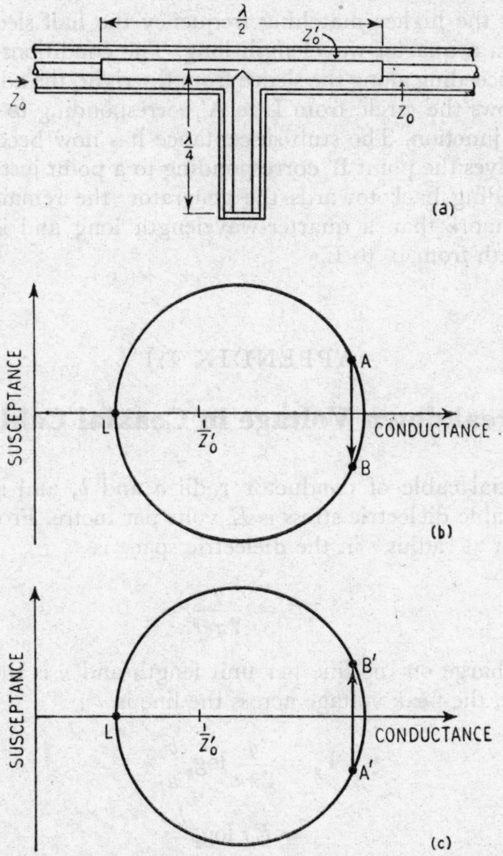

Fig. 4.21. Broad-band stub support for coaxial line.

some capacitance. The stub will be inductive and its characteristic impedance should be chosen so that it more than cancels this capacitive reactance looking towards the load. Thus the impedance looking towards the load at a point just to the left of the stub can be made to have an inductive component. Proceeding now towards the generator, the remaining portion of the sleeve transforms this inductive load back to the load impedance. Similar arguments apply just above the centre frequency. By a suitable choice of sleeve and stub characteristic impedances, it is possible to achieve correct matching at three frequencies, and very reasonable matching over the band between them. The action of this stub at the lower matching frequency can be traced on the admittance circle diagram of Fig. 4.21 (b). The admittance diagram is used because the stub impedance is in shunt with the line. The point L represents the load admittance. Proceeding along the sleeve from the right, the admittance to the right follows the circle from L round to A corresponding to the point just to the right of the junction because the distance is rather less than a quarter wavelength. The shunt susceptance due to the stub is represented by AB and must be added to the admittance at A to give the admittance at B corresponding to the point just to the left of the junction. Proceeding now towards the generator, the remainder of the sleeve transforms the admittance at B back to the load admittance represented by L. At the higher matching frequency the half sleeve and stub are rather more than a quarter-wavelength long. The conditions are as shown in Fig. 4.21 (c). Proceeding along the sleeve from the right, the admittance looking to the right follows the circle from L to A′ corresponding to the point just to the right of the junction. The stub susceptance has now become positive and added to A′ it gives the point B′ corresponding to a point just to the left of the junction. Proceeding back towards the generator, the remaining part of the sleeve is rather more than a quarter-wavelength long and is represented by the clockwise path from B′ to L.

APPENDIX 4.1

Breakdown Voltage in Coaxial Cables

Consider a coaxial cable of conductor radii a and b, and suppose that the maximum allowable dielectric stress is E_s volts per metre. From Appendix 1.3 the field strength at radius r in the dielectric space is

$$E_r = \frac{q}{2\pi\kappa r}$$

where q is the charge on the line per unit length and κ is the permittivity in m.k.s. units. Also the peak voltage across the line is

$$V_p = \frac{q}{2\pi\kappa} \log_\varepsilon \frac{b}{a}$$

$$= E_r r \log_\varepsilon \frac{b}{a}$$

E_r is a maximum at radius a (i.e., at the surface of the inner conductor), hence,

$$V_p = E_s a \log_\varepsilon \frac{b}{a} \quad . \quad . \quad . \quad . \quad . \quad (4.30)$$

This equation connects the peak voltage on the cable and the maximum stress in the dielectric. The maximum power which corresponds to this voltage is:

$$P = \left(\frac{V_p}{\sqrt{2}}\right)^2 \frac{1}{Z_0}$$

$$= \frac{E_s^2 a^2}{2Z_0} (\log_\varepsilon b/a)^2$$

but from equation (1.17) we have

$$\log_\varepsilon \frac{b}{a} = 2\pi \sqrt{\left(\frac{\kappa}{\mu}\right)} Z_0$$

where $\mu = 4\pi \times 10^{-7}$ and $\kappa = \kappa_r \times (1/36\pi) \times 10^{-9}$

Substituting in the above equation

$$P = \frac{E_s{}^2 a^2 Z_0 \kappa_r}{7{,}200} \quad . \quad . \quad . \quad . \quad . \quad . \quad . \quad (4.31)$$

APPENDIX 4.2

The Equivalence of Tuned Circuits and Quarter-wave Lines

An open-circuited quarter-wave line behaves as a series L'', C'' circuit over a very narrow band of frequencies. These lumped components may be determined in terms of the length of the line l and its inductance L and capacitance C per unit length by equating the slope of the reactance–frequency curves.

Thus for a series circuit we have for the reactance

$$X'' = \omega L'' - \frac{1}{\omega C''}$$

$$\frac{\mathrm{d}X''}{\mathrm{d}\omega} = L'' + \frac{1}{\omega^2 C''}$$

$$= \frac{1}{\omega}\left(\omega L'' + \frac{1}{\omega C''}\right)$$

At resonance we have:

$$\frac{\mathrm{d}X''}{\mathrm{d}\omega} = 2L''$$

The input reactance of an open-circuited loss-free line is from Chapter 3:

$$X_S = -Z_0 \cot \frac{l\omega}{v_p}$$

$$\therefore \frac{\mathrm{d}X_S}{\mathrm{d}\omega} = Z_0 \frac{l}{v_p} \operatorname{cosec}^2 \frac{l\omega}{v_p}$$

At quarter-wave resonance:

$$\frac{l\omega}{v_p} = \frac{\lambda}{4} . \frac{\omega}{f\lambda} = \frac{\pi}{2}$$

$$\therefore \frac{\mathrm{d}X_S}{\mathrm{d}\omega} = Z_0 \frac{l}{v_p}$$

Equating slopes for the tuned circuit and the quarter-wave line we get:

$$2L'' = Z_0 \frac{l}{v_p}$$

$$= Ll$$

$$L'' = \frac{Ll}{2} \quad . \quad . \quad . \quad . \quad . \quad . \quad . \quad . \quad . \quad . \quad (4.32)$$

The resonant angular frequency for the tuned circuit is:

$$\omega = \frac{1}{\sqrt{(L''C'')}}$$

and that for the quarter-wave line is obtained from:

$$v_p = f \times 4l$$

or

$$\omega = \frac{2\pi v_p}{4l} = \frac{2\pi}{4l\sqrt{(LC)}}$$

$$= \frac{1}{\sqrt{\left(\frac{4}{\pi^2} LlCl\right)}}$$

Equating and using equation (4.32) we get:

$$C'' = \frac{8}{\pi^2} Cl \quad . \quad . \quad . \quad . \quad . \quad . \quad . \quad . \quad (4.33)$$

A similar method may be used to deduce the equivalence of a parallel-tuned circuit and a quarter-wave short-circuited loss-free line. If $L'C'$ are the components of the parallel circuit we find that the slope of the susceptance–frequency curve at resonance is:

$$\frac{\mathrm{d}B'}{\mathrm{d}\omega} = 2C'$$

and the slope for the line is:

$$\frac{\mathrm{d}B_S}{\mathrm{d}\omega} = \frac{l}{Z_0 v_p}$$

giving:

$$C' = \frac{Cl}{2} \quad . \quad . \quad . \quad . \quad . \quad . \quad . \quad . \quad (4.34)$$

By equating the resonant frequencies we get:

$$L' = \frac{8}{\pi^2} Ll \quad . \quad . \quad . \quad . \quad . \quad . \quad . \quad . \quad (4.35)$$

APPENDIX 4.3

The Optimum Transformer Ratio for Matching

Let the impedances in Fig. 4.9 (d) be:

$$Z_1 = R_1 + \mathrm{j}X_1$$
$$Z_2 = R_2 + \mathrm{j}X_2$$

A transformer is to be connected between Z_1 and Z_2 of voltage ratio $n:1$ from primary to secondary. It is required to find the best value of n for the maximum power dissipation in Z_2.

From transformer theory the impedance looking into the primary terminals is:

$$n^2Z_2 = n^2R_2 + \mathrm{j}n^2X_2$$

If V is the generator voltage the power in the load is

$$P = \frac{V^2}{|R_1 + n^2R_2 + \mathrm{j}X_1 + \mathrm{j}n^2X_2|^2}n^2R_2$$
$$= \frac{V^2}{(R_1 + n^2R_2)^2 + (X_1 + n^2X_2)^2}n^2R_2$$

For a maximum we must differentiate with respect to n but it is easier to differentiate the reciprocal of P and then equate to zero for a minimum

$$\frac{1}{P} = \frac{(R_1/n + nR_2)^2 + (X_1/n + nX_2)^2}{V^2R_2}$$

$$V^2R_2\frac{\mathrm{d}(1/P)}{\mathrm{d}n} = 2(R_1/n + nR_2)(R_2 - R_1/n^2) + 2(X_1/n + nX_2)(X_2 - X_1/n^2)$$
$$= 0$$
$$(n^2R_2{}^2 - R_1{}^2/n^2) + (n^2X_2{}^2 - X_1{}^2/n^2) = 0$$
$$(R_1{}^2 + X_1{}^2) = n^4(R_2{}^2 + X_2{}^2)$$

or

$$|R_1 + \mathrm{j}X_1| = n^2|R_2 + \mathrm{j}X_2|$$

Thus the best value of n is that which makes the modulus of the impedance looking into the transformer towards Z_2 equal to the modulus of Z_1 or

$$|Z_1| = n^2|Z_2|$$

CHAPTER 5

Electromagnetic Waves

Introduction

In the preceding chapters the treatment has mainly concerned voltages and currents, and the properties of circuits have been described in terms of such quantities as resistance, inductance, capacitance, etc. It is known, however, that with a voltage there is always associated an electric field, for example, an electric field exists in the space between the plates of a charged capacitor; and that a current flowing in a conductor always sets up a magnetic field in the space surrounding the conductor. These electric and magnetic fields must not be regarded as merely secondary effects. They have just as much reality as voltages and currents, and are only different aspects of the same phenomenon; sometimes it is more convenient to use currents and voltages, sometimes more convenient to use fields. In dealing with the propagation of radio waves in space, and for certain types of transmission line, it is convenient and often necessary to use the ideas of electric and magnetic fields. Along with them it is necessary to use the properties of the medium in which the waves travel, such as conductivity, permeability and permittivity.

In order to state the value of the electric or magnetic field at any point in a medium we must know two things about it—its magnitude and its direction at that point. Quantities of this kind which possess not only magnitude but also direction are known as vector quantities or *vectors*. They are usually printed in heavy type to distinguish them from quantities such as voltage, which have only a magnitude but no direction, and are called scalar quantities or *scalars*. Thus **E** is the vector symbol usually used for the value of an electric field, and **H** for the value of a magnetic field. These vectors are not to be confused with the rotating vectors used to represent alternating quantities.

There can exist in a space a stationary electric field without the presence of a magnetic field in the same space, and alternatively a stationary magnetic field can exist alone without an electric field. However, if the fields are *changing* it is impossible for either to exist separately; a changing electric field will produce a magnetic field, and a changing magnetic field will produce an electric field.

Just as a disturbance set up at one point in a pond, such as is caused by a stone thrown into it, is not confined to that point but spreads out in ripples over all the pond, so a disturbance in an electric or magnetic field is not confined to the point where it occurs. A changing magnetic field induces a changing electric field not only in the region of the change but also in the surrounding region. The changing fields in this surrounding region in turn induce further fields in a still more distant region, and so the energy is propagated outwards.

The laws which connect these changing fields, when expressed in their general mathematical form, give rise to relations which are similar in form to those existing between mass and elasticity in an ordinary material medium. If the moving charges which give rise to the fields oscillate continuously with the motion of an alternating current, then the solution of the equations will indicate the existence of waves rather similar to waves travelling in an elastic medium, for example, sound waves in air. These *electromagnetic waves*, as they are called, require no material medium to support them and can be propagated just as well in completely empty space as in the atmosphere.

When a quantity of electromagnetic energy is set up in an unbounded space it cannot remain at rest, but must travel as a wave until the energy is dissipated. When energy is radiated from a simple aerial into space, it travels out more or less in all directions. On the other hand electromagnetic energy may be guided in a desired direction by means of a system of conductors. Examples of such guiding systems are the parallel wire and coaxial transmission lines discussed in the preceding chapters. There the treatment has been in terms of circuit theory or current and voltage but, from the alternative viewpoint of fields, we can also picture such lines as guides for the electromagnetic energy carried by the electric and magnetic fields set up in and around the conductors. We shall find that the two methods of approach can be made completely compatible with one another.

The laws defining the relationships between electric and magnetic fields were first stated in their mathematical form by James Clerk Maxwell (1831–1879), and are known as Maxwell's equations. They express very general laws of nature covering much of what is known about electricity and magnetism, laws deduced experimentally over a long period and owing much to the experimental genius of Michael Faraday (1791–1867). Their complete statement is beyond the scope of this book, but a simplified approach is given in Appendix 5.1.

This chapter is mainly concerned with electromagnetic waves in free space but it is also a preliminary to the study of guided waves in hollow tubes. First we must consider the nature of the electric and magnetic field vectors, **E** and **H**.

Electric Field

The electric field at any point in space may be found by introducing a unit positive charge at the point and measuring the magnitude and direction of the force exerted on it by the field. The electric field is then defined as equal in magnitude and direction to the measured force on the electric charge. When the vector is thus determined at every point, the whole field may be represented by a family of curves drawn so that each curve follows the direction of the field at every point. Such lines are called electric lines of force, and are directed from positive to negative charges. To connect electric field with the more familiar idea of potential it may be stated that potential is defined in such a way that the rate of change of potential with distance measured along a line of force, is equal but opposite in sign, to the electric field at the point. The unit of electric field is thus expressed in the m.k.s. system as a rate of change of potential with distance, namely, in volts per metre. It is often called the field strength.

Magnetic Field

Magnetic field at a point is also defined in terms of a force, namely, the force which would act on an isolated north pole placed at the point, the direction of the field being the direction in which the isolated pole would tend to move. Any value of magnetic field at a point, which may be produced by currents or permanent magnets or both, can be simulated by placing a long solenoid with its centre at the point, orientating the solenoid and adjusting the current through it so as to produce the same magnetic effect at the point as the original field. The field thus produced is proportional to the current and to the number of turns per unit length on the solenoid. This explains the unit in which magnetic field is measured, ampere–turns per metre, **H** being thus a measure of magnetic field in terms of a current which can duplicate that field.

The magnetic field can be represented by a family of curves, the direction of the curve at any point being that of the field at that point.

Dynamic Fields and Boundary Conditions

The above definitions of electric and magnetic fields are based on static considerations. However, in this chapter we are mainly concerned with dynamic fields, that is fields at a particular point which change with time, because it is only such fields which are associated with the propagation of electromagnetic energy. The simplest form of dynamic field is a sinusoidal alternating field. The vector symbols **E** and **H** can still be used to represent sinusoidally alternating fields, by simply multiplying them by a sinusoidal quantity such as sin ωt or the real part of $\varepsilon^{j\omega t}$. This means that the family of curves representing the field is unchanged but the intensity varies sinusoidally, from a maximum in the positive direction, through zero to a maximum in the other direction and back to zero and so on. However it is hardly necessary to include the sinusoidal term when it is understood from the outset, and it only needs to be introduced when studying the detailed behaviour of some quantity with respect to time. In the following discussion we shall assume that the fields and associated quantities vary sinusoidally, but the sinusoidal factors will be suppressed for convenience. The symbols may represent peak or r.m.s. values according to convenience, but peak and r.m.s. values must not be mixed in the same equation.

When constructing equations relating vector quantities we should strictly speaking use the methods of vector analysis so that the magnitudes and directions on the two sides of an equation are equal. However, vector analysis will not be introduced here; the directions of the various vectors will be given by description, and the magnitudes will be given by equations containing the magnitudes of vectors only. This will be indicated by vertical bars, thus $|\mathbf{E}|$ and $|\mathbf{H}|$ means that we are taking the magnitudes of **E** and **H** and ignoring the directions. When it is not necessary to emphasize the vector nature of **E** and **H**, the normal type E and H will be used, it being understood that magnitudes only are to be inserted in the equation.

It is now necessary to consider what happens when dynamic electric and magnetic fields meet a perfectly conducting surface. The laws to be obeyed by the field vectors at such a boundary are readily deduced from Maxwell's equations, and are known as *boundary conditions*. A thorough grasp of these simple conditions is essential to the further understanding of wave propagation. The four boundary conditions are stated as follows:

1. Inside a perfect conductor all electric field must vanish, since in a perfect conductor no gradient of potential can be set up to establish an electric field. If there exists at a point in the space just outside a plane conducting sheet an electric field which is perpendicular (more usually called *normal*) to the sheet, there will be no corresponding field in the conductor, but electric charge will

flow to the surface to balance the field. The density of this surface charge Q is given by the equation:

$$Q = \kappa_0 |\mathbf{E}_n| \text{ coulombs per square metre}$$

where $|\mathbf{E}_n|$ represents the magnitude of the normal electric field just outside the conductor surface, and κ_0 is the permittivity of the medium, assumed here to be free space.

2. An electric field which is tangential to a perfectly conducting boundary must vanish at the boundary.

3. For the magnetic field the conditions are reversed. A magnetic field perpendicular to a perfectly conducting boundary must vanish at the boundary.

4. A magnetic field parallel to a perfectly conducting boundary is associated with a surface current I in the conductor, whose magnitude is given by:

$$I = |\mathbf{H}_t| \text{ amperes per metre}$$

where $|\mathbf{H}_t|$ represents the magnitude of the tangential magnetic field just outside the conductor surface. This current is in the nature of an infinitely thin current sheet flowing on the surface of the conductors. Its direction is at right angles to the magnetic field producing it, as is shown in Fig. 5.1

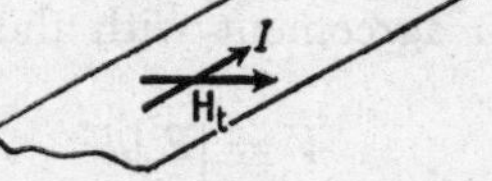

Fig. 5.1. Boundary condition for current and magnetic field at a conducting surface.

Briefly, with subscripts t and n for tangential and normal fields, the boundary conditions are:

$$\left.\begin{aligned} &(1) \quad \kappa_0|\mathbf{E}_n| = Q \\ &(2) \quad \mathbf{E}_t = 0 \\ &(3) \quad \mu_0\mathbf{H}_n = 0 \\ &(4) \quad |\mathbf{H}_t| = I \end{aligned}\right\} \quad . \quad . \quad . \quad . \quad . \quad (5.1)$$

The permeability of free space is included in the third equation merely to preserve the symmetry.

When dealing with waveguides and cavities in later chapters we shall discuss the various field patterns which can exist inside metal conductors of different shapes. The fields will in all cases be subject to these laws, which require that lines of electric force always meet a conductor at right angles, and that lines of magnetic force always flow tangentially past a conductor.

Of course, in practice, conductors are not perfect. The presence of small resistivity in the conductor, however, affects the boundary conditions in only a minor way which need not concern us here.

The Parallel-Strip Transmission Line

These boundary condition concepts may be illustrated by a hypothetical system known as a parallel-strip transmission line. This example also serves to relate very closely the circuit theory method developed in Chapter 1 with the field theory now being considered.

Imagine two perfectly conducting parallel planes of infinite extent. Let the separation be d metres and suppose that the medium between the planes is characterized by permeability μ and permittivity κ. It is also assumed that the medium is loss free.

Consider infinitely long strips one metre wide, in the two planes, one above the other as illustrated in Fig. 5.2.

These two strips may be imagined to form a transmission line. Let V be the voltage between strips in an arbitrary plane at right angles to the plane con-

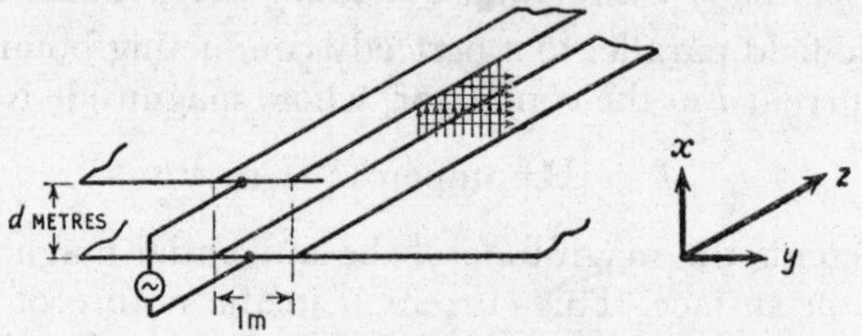

Fig. 5.2. The parallel-strip transmission line.

ductors and the direction of the strips. The electric field $\mathbf{E}_n$ between the strips is normal to the planes in agreement with the boundary conditions of the previous section.

$$\therefore \; V = |\mathbf{E}_n| d \qquad (5.2)$$

Also we have for the charge per square metre on say the positive strip:

$$Q = \kappa |\mathbf{E}_n| \qquad (5.3)$$

Therefore we can deduce a capacitance per unit width and per unit length of the strip transmission line, thus:

$$C = \frac{Q}{V} = \frac{\kappa}{d} \text{ farads per metre} \qquad (5.4)$$

This could have been deduced from the ordinary theory for the capacitance of a parallel-plate capacitor.

Now let I be the current flowing in the parallel-strip line. The magnetic field $\mathbf{H}_t$ between the strips is parallel to the planes and at right angles to the current. By the previous section we have:

$$I = |\mathbf{H}_t| \qquad (5.5)$$

The flux linkages between the strips per metre length are:

$$\Phi = \mu |\mathbf{H}_t| d$$

Hence the inductance of the strips per metre length is given by:

$$L = \frac{\Phi}{I} = \mu d \text{ henrys per metre} \qquad (5.6)$$

From equation (1.13) the characteristic impedance per metre width of the strip line is:

$$Z_0 = \sqrt{\frac{L}{C}} = \sqrt{\frac{\mu}{\kappa}} . d \qquad (5.7)$$

If now V and I are taken to be sinusoidal quantities of angular frequency ω, we have:

$$Z_0 = \frac{V}{I} = \frac{|\mathbf{E}_n|}{|\mathbf{H}_t|} d$$

or

$$\frac{|\mathbf{E}_n|}{|\mathbf{H}_t|} = \sqrt{\frac{\mu}{\kappa}} \quad . \quad . \quad . \quad . \quad . \quad . \quad . \qquad (5.8)$$

These results apply regardless of the frequency of V and hence I. The ratio of $\mathbf{E}_n$ to $\mathbf{H}_t$ is of the nature of an impedance (often called the wave impedance) and is in fact the impedance per metre width of the strip line when the spacing d is one metre. We have for the value of this impedance:

$$\frac{|\mathbf{E}_n|}{|\mathbf{H}_t|} = \sqrt{\frac{\mu_r}{\kappa_r}} \times \sqrt{\frac{4\pi \times 36\pi \times 10^9}{10^7}}$$

$$= \sqrt{\frac{\mu_r}{\kappa_r}} \times 120\pi \quad . \quad . \quad . \quad . \quad . \quad . \quad . \qquad (5.9)$$

For free space where μ_r and κ_r are unity, the wave impedance is 120π or 377 ohms. At any cross-section of the line V and I are in time phase since the characteristic impedance is resistive. Therefore $\mathbf{E}_n$ and $\mathbf{H}_t$ are in time phase although they are in space quadrature. From transmission line theory we know that a wave of V and I travels down the line, and therefore we have a wave of $\mathbf{E}_n$ and $\mathbf{H}_t$ travelling down the dielectric space between the strips.

The wave between the two planes is known as a plane electromagnetic wave because $\mathbf{E}_n$ and $\mathbf{H}_t$ oscillate entirely in plane surfaces normal to the direction of propagation.

Instead of the parallel infinite planes we could have deduced the same results by considering a coaxial cable in which the radii a and b are made very large keeping the dielectric thickness $d = (b - a)$ at a constant value. It can be seen from this that the wave in a coaxial cable is similar in many respects to a plane wave. Thus **E** and **H** are in time phase and space quadrature, and both are perpendicular to the direction of wave propagation. The waves in ideal parallel conductor lines are therefore known as transverse electromagnetic (TEM) waves.

In fact the energy transmitted in transmission lines flows through the dielectric, and not through the conductors which merely act as guides. The losses in the conductors of lossy lines are supplied by a lateral flow of energy from the dielectric into the conductors, so that the waves in lossy lines are not entirely plane.

We have already seen in Chapter 3 the limitations of circuit theory when considering the construction of terminations, and in Chapter 4 the limitations when the wavelength is comparable with the line cross-section. In such cases the complete field theory with appropriate boundary conditions is the correct approach, although it is more complicated than the simplified treatment given here.

The phase shift per metre length of the strip line can be calculated from equation (1.30). Thus:

$$\beta = \omega\sqrt{(LC)} = \omega\sqrt{\frac{\mu d\kappa}{d}} = \omega\sqrt{(\mu\kappa)} \quad . \quad . \quad . \quad . \qquad (5.10)$$

From equation (1.33) the phase velocity is:

$$v_p = \frac{\omega}{\beta} = \frac{1}{\sqrt{(\mu\kappa)}} = \frac{c}{\sqrt{(\mu_r\kappa_r)}} \quad . \quad . \quad . \quad . \quad . \quad (5.11)$$

With a free-space dielectric the wave velocity is the velocity of light. The attenuation of the wave in the dielectric is of course zero, since we have postulated non-dissipative dielectric and guiding conductors.

▶ The parallel-strip transmission line may be used to provide results of more general interest. If the medium between the planes is assumed to have a conductivity $\sigma = 1/\rho$ in addition to permeability μ and permittivity κ, the transmission of plane waves in a wide range of gases, liquids and solids can be studied. The parallel planes must still be assumed to be infinitely conducting otherwise the wave transmitted will no longer be plane. For simplicity the planes are assumed to be one metre apart. There will now be a conduction current between the planes in addition to a capacitance current, and there will clearly be dissipation of power.

Then by analogy with equation (1.13) and (5.7) the complete expression for Z_0 is:

$$Z_0 = \sqrt{\frac{j\omega\mu}{\sigma + j\omega\kappa}} \quad . \quad . \quad . \quad . \quad . \quad (5.12)$$

Similarly the propagation coefficient for the medium is by analogy with equation (1.28) given by:

$$\gamma = \sqrt{\{j\omega\mu(\sigma + j\omega\kappa)\}} \quad . \quad . \quad . \quad . \quad (5.13)$$

This equation is of value for determining the attenuation and phase shift (or wavelength) in poor conductors such as sea water, soil, etc. Equation (5.12) can be used to determine the wave impedance in poor conductors. If we have a

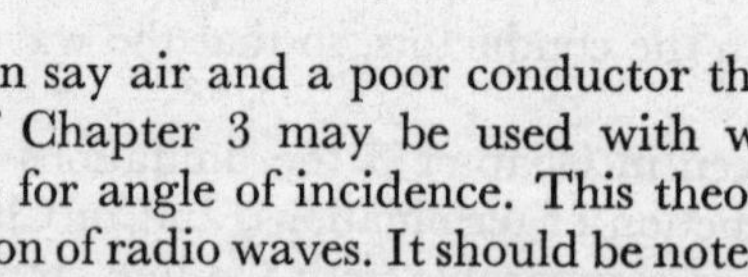

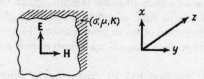

Fig. 5.3. **Propagation of a normal plane wave into a semi-infinite medium.**

plane interface between say air and a poor conductor the reflection and transmission coefficients of Chapter 3 may be used with wave impedances, due allowance being made for angle of incidence. This theory proves useful when considering the reflection of radio waves. It should be noted from equation (5.12) that **E** and **H** are not in time phase in the dissipative case, although they remain in space quadrature.

If **E** and **H** in Fig. 5.3 are the transmitted wave components in a medium at a frequency where $\omega\kappa$ is large compared with σ then equation (5.12) and (5.13) can be simplified somewhat, thus:

$$Z_0 = \sqrt{\frac{\mu}{\kappa}} \quad . \quad . \quad . \quad . \quad . \quad . \quad . \quad (5.14)$$

and
$$\gamma = j\omega\sqrt{(\mu\kappa)}\left(1+\frac{\sigma}{j\omega\kappa}\right)^{1/2}$$
$$\approx \frac{\sigma}{2}\sqrt{\frac{\mu}{\kappa}} + j\omega\sqrt{\mu\kappa}$$

or
$$\alpha \approx \frac{\sigma}{2}\sqrt{\frac{\mu}{\kappa}} \text{ nepers per metre} \quad . \quad . \quad . \quad . \quad . \quad (5.15)$$
$$\beta \approx \omega\sqrt{(\mu\kappa)} \text{ radians per metre}$$

These simplifications usually apply above about 50 Mc/s for the earth's top soil and comparable poor conductors. It should be noted that α is independent of frequency (provided σ is constant) and the depth of penetration for a reduction of the wave amplitude to $1/\varepsilon$ of its surface value is:

$$\frac{1}{\alpha} = \frac{2}{\sigma}\sqrt{\frac{\kappa}{\mu}} \text{ metres} \quad . \quad . \quad . \quad . \quad . \quad . \quad (5.16)$$

Although σ is constant for a wide range of frequencies it is not constant at centimetre and millimetre wavelengths where absorption bands are possible. The depths of penetration for a few typical poor conductors at selected frequencies are given in Table 5.1

TABLE 5.1

Frequency (Mc/s)	Depth of penetration (metres) for 1 neper attenuation		
	Poor soil $\sigma = 0{\cdot}001$ $\kappa_r = 5$	Normal soil $\sigma = 0{\cdot}01$ $\kappa_r = 15$	Sea water $\sigma = 5$ $\kappa_r = 80$
0·1	51	16	0·71
0·3	30	9·3	0·41
1	18	5·4	0·23
3	13	3·5	0·13
10	12	2·3	0·07
30	12	2·1	0·04
100	12	2·1	0·02
300	12	2·1	0·15

The attenuation per wavelength for poor conductors is from equation (5.15):

$$\alpha\lambda = \frac{2\pi\alpha}{\beta} = \frac{\pi\sigma}{\omega\kappa} \quad . \quad . \quad . \quad . \quad . \quad . \quad (5.17)$$

It has already been shown in equation (4.19) that attenuation per wavelength is π/Q. Hence we have for the Q of a poor conductor:

$$Q = \frac{\omega\kappa}{\sigma} \quad . \quad . \quad . \quad . \quad . \quad . \quad . \quad (5.18)$$

a logical definition by analogy with circuit theory.

Although equations (5.12) and (5.13) were derived from a consideration of the dielectric in a strip transmission line, they also may be applied to plane waves in metals of finite conductivity. In this case $\omega\kappa$ is negligible compared with σ hence:

$$Z_0 = \sqrt{\frac{\mathrm{j}\omega\mu}{\sigma}}$$

$$= \sqrt{\frac{\omega\mu}{2\sigma}} + \mathrm{j}\sqrt{\frac{\omega\mu}{2\sigma}} \quad \ldots \ldots \quad (5.19)$$

$$\gamma = \sqrt{\mathrm{j}\omega\mu\sigma}$$

$$= \sqrt{\frac{\omega\mu\sigma}{2}} + \mathrm{j}\sqrt{\frac{\omega\mu\sigma}{2}} \quad \ldots \ldots \quad (5.20)$$

$$\therefore \alpha = \beta = \sqrt{\frac{\omega\mu\sigma}{2}}$$

$$= \sqrt{\frac{\omega\mu}{2\rho}} \quad \ldots \ldots \quad (5.21)$$

The last equation gives the attenuation, in nepers per metre, of a plane wave being propagated into an infinite block of metal. Its reciprocal is the depth of penetration for 1 neper attenuation into an infinite block with a plane surface (i.e., the depth at which voltage and current are $1/\varepsilon$ of that at the surface). For metals this depth is very small, and decreases as the frequency is increased. It has already been quoted in equation (1.6) as the skin thickness in connection with skin effect. The skin thickness at various frequencies is discussed in Chapter 6. The impedance given by equation (5.19) is sometimes called the surface impedance of the metal. The distance of the propagation along the z-axis of Fig. 5.3 is now small compared with the distance between the hypothetical perfectly conducting planes, and Z_0 is the impedance per metre width between the two planes one metre apart; i.e., it is the surface impedance per metre width and per metre length along the surface. An application of this result to the calculation of the power loss in a conducting plane having a plane wave travelling parallel to its surface is given in Appendix 5.3. ◀

Plane Waves in Space

If an electromagnetic wave starts from a point in space and spreads out uniformly in all directions it will form a spherical wave. However, an observer situated at a great distance from the source will be able to observe only the small part of the wave in his immediate neighbourhood, and it will appear to him as a plane wave, just as the ocean appears flat to someone who can only see a few miles around him.

At a great distance from the source the wave has similar properties to the plane waves in the strip line. By analogy with the strip line we can therefore summarize the properties of a plane wave in free space as follows:

1. The electric field **E** and the magnetic field **H** are at right angles to each other and to the direction of propagation. A cross-section of the wave is illustrated in Fig. 5.4, $0x$, $0y$, $0z$ being a set of three mutually perpendicular axes.

The wave is moving in the direction $0z$, **E** is parallel to $0x$, and **H** is parallel to $0y$. Both **E** and **H** are constant in direction and magnitude throughout their plane.

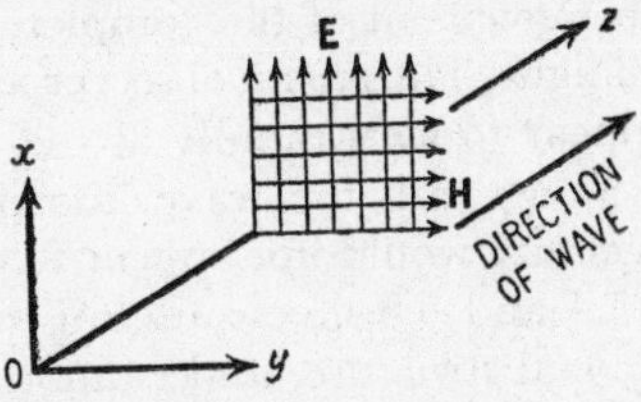

Fig. 5.4. Relationship of **E** and **H** in a plane wave.

2. The velocity of propagation of the wave in free space is given by:

$$v = \frac{1}{\sqrt{(\kappa_0 \mu_0)}} \text{ metres per second,}$$

where κ_0 is the permittivity of free space, and μ_0 the permeability of free space. The values of these constants are:

$$\kappa_0 = \frac{1}{36\pi} \times 10^{-9} \text{ farad per metre}$$

$$\mu_0 = 4\pi \times 10^{-7} \text{ henry per metre}$$

Thus we find:

$$v = \frac{1}{\sqrt{\{(1/36\pi) \times 10^{-9} \times 4\pi \times 10^{-7}\}}}$$

$$= 3 \times 10^8 \text{ metres per second}$$

This is the value used in most calculations, but the value given by the most recent exact measurements is $2{\cdot}99790 \times 10^8$ metres per second.

3. **E** and **H** always oscillate in phase, and the ratio of their amplitudes is always constant and equal to $\sqrt{(\mu_0/\kappa_0)} = 377$.

All electromagnetic waves in free space travel at the velocity stated above, whatever their frequency. Light is also composed of electromagnetic waves, although the frequencies are much higher than those of radio waves, and it also

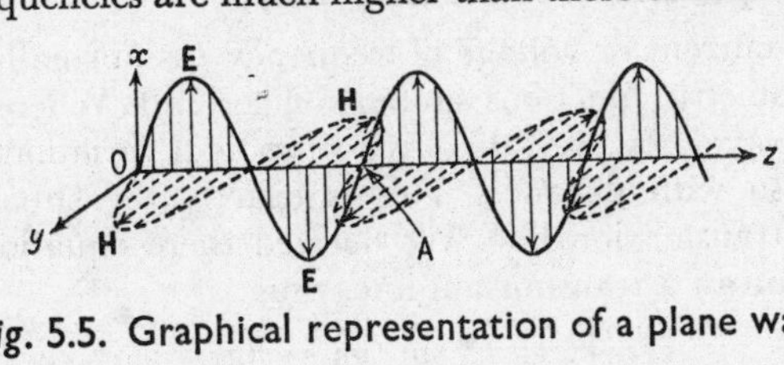

Fig. 5.5. Graphical representation of a plane wave.

travels at this same velocity. In fact, the value 3×10^8 metres per second is usually called the 'velocity of light' even when it refers to radio waves, and is always represented by the symbol c.

If we consider a plane wave of frequency f c/s, its progress may be graphically represented as in Fig. 5.5, where the **E** vectors always lie in the plane $x0z$, and the **H** vectors (shown dashed) are always in the plane $y0z$. The length of each vector represents its value at that distance along $0z$. They vary with distance in a wave-like manner, the distance for a complete cycle, for example the distance 0A, being the *wavelength* λ. The connection between wavelength and frequency is, of course, the well-known relation $f \times \lambda = c$. The motion of the wave can be pictured as a movement of the complete field pattern of Fig. 5.5 along $0z$ at the velocity of light. Thus to an observer at a fixed point on $0z$ the values of **E** and **H** will appear to vary rapidly as the field rushes past him. If, however, he could move along with the wave, moving with its velocity, the values of **E** and **H** in his vicinity would not appear to change.

The diagrams of Figs. 5.4 and 5.5 give quite an incomplete picture of the wave. It is a three-dimensional structure, and cannot well be represented in a simple diagram. Moreover these pictures show only the wave at one instant of time. They should, however, help the reader to visualize the motion of electromagnetic waves.

A plane wave is *transverse*, since its field vectors lie in a plane which is transverse to the direction of travel. At any instant **E** and **H** are constant in magnitude and direction over the whole surface of any plane set up perpendicular to the direction of propagation. Such a plane is known as a wave front. More generally a wave front is a surface over which the phase of **E** or **H** is constant. For example, a surface in which **E** and **H** have their maximum values, is a wave front.

Polarization

A wave in which the directions of the **E** and **H** vectors reside in fixed planes as the wave progresses, is said to be *polarized*. The plane in which the electric vector moves is called the *plane of polarization*. Thus in Fig. 5.5 the plane $x0z$ is the plane of polarization and, if this is vertical, the wave is vertically polarized. A wave whose electric vector oscillates in a horizontal plane is horizontally polarized. In the case of an unpolarized wave, the electric and magnetic vectors change direction as the wave proceeds, but they always remain at right angles to one another.

Usually we shall be dealing with polarized waves and a wave may be defined very simply by specifying the plane of polarization and the field strength **E** in volts per metre. It is usual to employ the r.m.s. value of the vector **E** in this definition.

Mathematical Expression for a Plane Wave

Any oscillatory current or voltage of frequency f is normally represented by one of the trigonometric functions $\sin 2\pi ft$ or $\cos 2\pi ft$. Where we are dealing with a travelling wave, however, there is a sinusoidal variation of field not only with time but also with distance. This is exactly the situation we had in Chapter 1 for a transmission line. We derived there equation (1.31) for the voltage at any point in a transmission line, thus:

$$V_z = V_1 \sin (\omega t - \beta z)$$

The same principles apply for a plane wave travelling in the direction of the z axis. Referring to Fig. 5.5 the phase at the origin changes by ωt in time t. Whilst moving to the right a distance z, the phase changes by $2\pi z/\lambda$. Since the wave is moving to the right the phase at z lags that at the origin, hence at time t the phase at z is given by:

$$\omega t - \frac{2\pi}{\lambda} z = \omega t - \beta z$$

The phase coefficient $\beta = 2\pi/\lambda$ has the same meaning as in Chapter 1 at equation 1.33. However when dealing with free space, a non-dispersive medium at ordinary frequencies, β is proportional to frequency and equation (1.34) becomes:

$$c = \frac{\omega}{\beta} = f\lambda$$

The trigonometric term to describe the variation of quantities in a plane wave then becomes:

$$\sin(\omega t - \beta z) = \sin(\omega t - 2\pi z/\lambda) = \sin \omega(t - z/c) \quad . \quad . \quad . \quad . \quad (5.22)$$

In the last form the term z/c may be identified as the time delay for the wave to travel from the origin to the point z. A wave travelling in the backwards direction, i.e. to the left, would be described by a term of the form:

$$\sin(\omega t + \beta z) = \sin \omega(t + z/c)$$

The field components of the wave shown in Fig. 5.5 can therefore be written as:

$$\left.\begin{aligned} E_x &= A \sin(\omega t - \beta z) \\ H_y &= A(\kappa_0/\mu_0)^{1/2} \sin(\omega t - \beta z) \end{aligned}\right\} \quad . \quad . \quad . \quad (5.23)$$

in which the constant A defines the amplitude of the electric vector. Note how this satisfies the requirements for a plane wave; viz. the field components E_x and H_y are in time phase, and in directions perpendicular to each other and to the direction of motion of the wave; the ratio of the amplitudes of E_x and H_y is $\sqrt{(\mu_0/\kappa_0)}$.

In the above example the wave is referred to a co-ordinate system of three perpendicular axes—known as a Cartesian system—which is normally chosen so that one of the axes coincides with the direction of propagation and the other

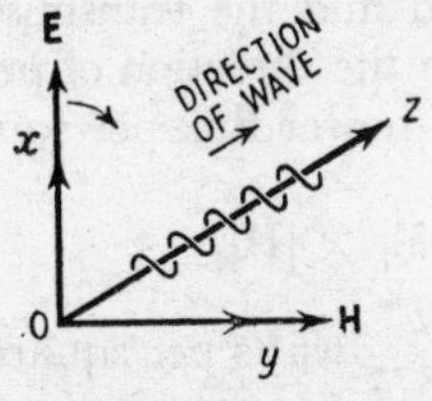

Fig. 5.6. Sign conventions for a plane wave.

two with the electric and magnetic field vectors. The relative directions of the three axes in a Cartesian system are chosen in such a way that, if a right-handed corkscrew were placed along 0z, screwing it in the direction from 0x towards 0y would move it in the direction from 0 towards z, as shown in Fig. 5.6. The relative directions of **E** and **H** in an electromagnetic wave are also given by this rule. Turning the corkscrew from **E** towards **H** should move it in the direction of motion of the wave.

It is to be noted that any vector can be split up into components lying along the three Cartesian axes. Thus in general **E** could be split up into three components E_x, E_y, E_z. In this particular example the axes are chosen so that **E** lies along $0x$ and thus has only the one component E_x, the other two, E_y and E_z, being zero. Similarly **H** has only one component, H_y.

A more rigorous deduction of these results is given in Appendix 5.2.

The Power Flux of a Plane Wave

An electromagnetic wave conveys electrical power. The direction of power flow or flux is at right angles to the plane containing **E** and **H**, i.e. normal to the wave front, and in the direction of propagation. For a plane wave in free space, the amount of power flowing through a square metre normal to the direction of propagation may be calculated without difficulty.

Consider a parallel strip transmission line consisting of two perfectly conducting planes one metre apart, the width of the line also being one metre. The voltage applied to the line V is then equal to the field strength $|\mathbf{E}_n|$ in the dielectric space of the line. From equation (5.7) the characteristic impedance of the line is

$$Z_0 = \sqrt{\frac{\mu}{\kappa}}$$
$$= 377 \text{ ohms}$$

for free space. This is a pure resistance so that we can determine the power input to the line by taking the product of the applied voltage V and input current I. Thus input power to line:

$$P = VI$$
$$= |\mathbf{E}_n| \times |\mathbf{H}_t| \quad . \quad . \quad . \quad . \quad . \quad (5.24)$$

remembering that $|\mathbf{H}_t| = I$. Strictly speaking this should be written as an equation in vector analysis, but here we indicate by the vertical bars that we take the product of the magnitudes, and remember that the direction of power flow is at right angles to **E** and **H** according to the rule of Fig. 5.6.

Since the line is uniform and infinite, there are no reflections and this amount of power must pass through every cross-section of the line. If we now imagine the conductors to be removed and the transmission line to be a tube of one square metre cross-section in the direction of propagation of an infinite plane wave, we may state that the power flux per square metre of a plane wave in free space is

$$P_T = |\mathbf{E}| \times |\mathbf{H}|$$
$$= \frac{E^2}{377} \text{ watts per square metre} \quad . \quad . \quad . \quad . \quad (5.25)$$

In this formula E is of course, the r.m.s. field strength in volts per metre.

APPENDIX 5.1

Maxwell's Equations

It can be proved from first principles that electromagnetic waves can be propagated in an unbounded space or other isotropic medium. The equations from which the laws of propagation may be deduced are known as Maxwell's equations, and they are based on two fundamental laws of magnetism and electricity introduced in Volume 1. These two laws, Ampère's Law and Faraday's Law, are illustrated by Fig. 5.7.

We may formulate these fundamental laws in mathematical form. Thus from Fig. 5.7 (a), the line integral of magnetic field round a closed curve is equal to the total current:

$$\oint_C H_s \, ds = \int_S J_n \, da \quad . \quad . \quad . \quad . \quad . \quad (5.26)$$

On the left-hand side, H_s is the component of magnetic field along the closed curve C of which ds is a short element. On the right-hand side J_n is the normal

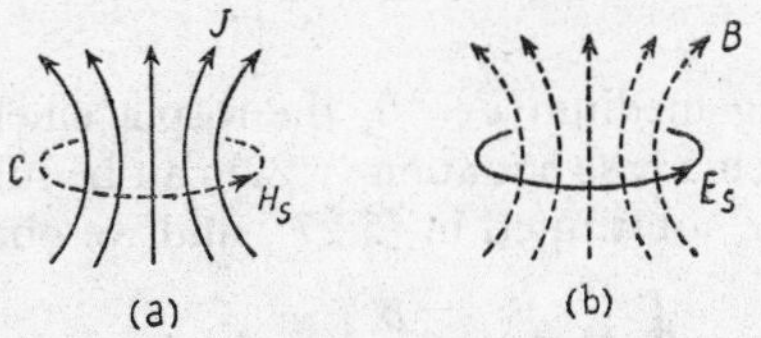

Fig. 5.7. (a) Illustrating Ampère's Law; (b) illustrating Faraday's Law.

component of current density flowing through an elemental area da of a surface S which is bounded by the curve. The circle on the integral sign indicates that the integral is taken round a closed curve.

From Fig. 5.7 (b) the line integral of electric field round a closed curve is equal to minus the time rate of change of total magnetic flux linking the curve, or:

$$\oint_C E_s \, ds = -\frac{\partial}{\partial t}\int_S B_n \, da \quad . \quad . \quad . \quad . \quad . \quad (5.27)$$

On the right-hand side B_n is the normal component of magnetic flux density crossing an elemental area da of a surface which is bounded by the curve round which the electric field is integrated.

These two equations may be reduced to relations between two vectors only, namely **E** and **H**, by substitution from two further equations. The first connects flux density and magnetic field:

$$\mathbf{B} = \mu \mathbf{H} \quad . \quad . \quad . \quad . \quad . \quad . \quad (5.28)$$

where **B** and **H** are vectors in the same direction. The second equation connects electric field and current density. If the medium is conducting with conductivity σ there is one component of current density given by:

$$\mathbf{J}' = \sigma \mathbf{E}$$

where **J**′ and **E** are vectors in the same direction. There is however another component of current density, which as Maxwell pointed out assumes great significance when the quantities are varying at a high frequency. This component is the displacement-current density, which is analogous to the capacitive current which flows between the plates of a capacitor. When an electric stress or field strength **E** is set up in a dielectric, there is momentary displacement current in the direction of **E**. The displacement current is therefore proportional to the rate of change of **E**. In the m.k.s. system of units the displacement current density is:

$$\mathbf{J}'' = \frac{\partial \mathbf{D}}{\partial t} = \kappa \frac{\partial \mathbf{E}}{\partial t}$$

where **D** is the electric displacement and κ the permittivity of the medium. **J**″, **D** and **E** are vectors in the same direction or components of such vectors. Experiment confirms the existence of such a displacement current, in space or near conducting systems. This current produces a magnetic field in the same way as any other current. The total current density is then:

$$\mathbf{J} = \sigma \mathbf{E} + \kappa \frac{\partial \mathbf{E}}{\partial t} \quad . \quad . \quad . \quad . \quad . \quad . \quad . \quad . \quad (5.29)$$

In a non-conducting medium $\sigma = 0$, the displacement current is the only current existing. In such a case equation (5.29) can be substituted in (5.26) and equation (5.28) can be substituted in (5.27), and we obtain:

$$\oint_C H_s \, \mathrm{d}s = \kappa \frac{\partial}{\partial t} \int_S E_n \, \mathrm{d}a \quad . \quad . \quad . \quad . \quad . \quad . \quad . \quad (5.30)$$

$$\oint_C E_s \, \mathrm{d}s = -\mu \frac{\partial}{\partial t} \int_S H_n \, \mathrm{d}a \quad . \quad . \quad . \quad . \quad . \quad . \quad . \quad (5.31)$$

These equations are the integral form of Maxwell's equations for space or non-conducting dielectric. The two equations are interconnected in a way which cannot easily be seen until they are applied to an element of space or dielectric in a co-ordinate system. The symmetrical form which the fundamental laws have taken on should be noted.

There are two further equations which are usually included in Maxwell's equations although they are not independent of equations (5.30) and (5.31). These equations express the fact that there are no free magnetic poles or free electric charges in the space or medium under consideration.

Thus if the outward normal component H_n of the magnetic field is integrated over a closed surface, the result is zero, or

$$\oint_S H_n \, \mathrm{d}a = 0 \quad . \quad . \quad . \quad . \quad . \quad . \quad . \quad . \quad (5.32)$$

The circle on the integral sign indicates that the integral is over a closed surface. This result is implicit in equation (5.31) because the surface is not defined and therefore the integral is equal for each surface chosen. Thus the integral over two surfaces bounded by C of the outward normal component of H_n is zero.

Similarly for the outward normal component E_n we have

$$\oint_S E_n \, \mathrm{d}a = 0 \quad . \quad . \quad . \quad . \quad . \quad . \quad . \quad (5.33)$$

These equations must now be applied to a small volume of space or medium in a Cartesian co-ordinate system as shown in Fig. 5.8. The z axis is directed to the right since we shall often be interested in waves propagated along that axis. Consider the element of area $\mathrm{d}y \times \mathrm{d}z$ at the point (x, y, z) and apply equation

(5.30). The upward electric field strength out of the face is E_x and the magnetic field round the edge of the face is as shown. We have then

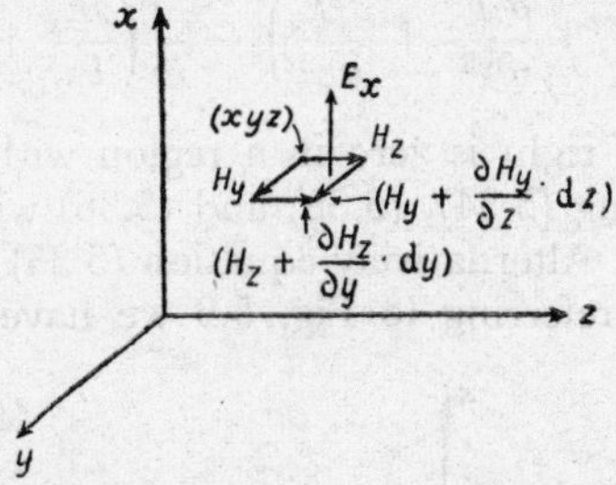

Fig. 5.8. Element of space in Cartesian co-ordinates for Maxwell's equations.

$$\kappa\frac{\partial}{\partial t}.E_x\,dy\,dz = H_y\,dy + \left(H_z + \frac{\partial H_z}{\partial y}dy\right)dz - \left(H_y + \frac{\partial H_y}{\partial z}dz\right)dy - H_z\,dz$$

$$= \left(\frac{\partial H_z}{\partial y} - \frac{\partial H_y}{\partial z}\right)dy\,dz$$

$$\therefore\ \kappa\frac{\partial E_x}{\partial t} = \left(\frac{\partial H_z}{\partial y} - \frac{\partial H_y}{\partial z}\right) \qquad (5.34)$$

By a similar process we have for the E_y and E_z components of the E vector:

$$\kappa\frac{\partial E_y}{\partial t} = \left(\frac{\partial H_x}{\partial z} - \frac{\partial H_z}{\partial x}\right) \qquad (5.35)$$

$$\kappa\frac{\partial E_z}{\partial t} = \left(\frac{\partial H_y}{\partial x} - \frac{\partial H_x}{\partial y}\right) \qquad (5.36)$$

In a similar way equation (5.31) can be applied to the three surface elements, and we get:

$$-\mu\frac{\partial H_x}{\partial t} = \left(\frac{\partial E_z}{\partial y} - \frac{\partial E_y}{\partial z}\right) \qquad (5.37)$$

$$-\mu\frac{\partial H_y}{\partial t} = \left(\frac{\partial E_x}{\partial z} - \frac{\partial E_z}{\partial x}\right) \qquad (5.38)$$

$$-\mu\frac{\partial H_z}{\partial t} = \left(\frac{\partial E_y}{\partial x} - \frac{\partial E_x}{\partial y}\right) \qquad (5.39)$$

Equations (5.34) to (5.36) are now differentiated with respect to time. The first equation is typical and will be considered alone:

$$\kappa\frac{\partial^2 E_x}{\partial t^2} = \left(\frac{\partial^2 H_z}{\partial t\partial y} - \frac{\partial^2 H_y}{\partial t\partial z}\right) \qquad (5.40)$$

We now differentiate equation (5.39) with respect to y and equation (5.38) with respect to z and substitute in (5.40). The result is found to be:

$$\kappa\frac{\partial^2 E_x}{\partial t^2} = -\frac{1}{\mu}\left(\frac{\partial^2 E_y}{\partial x\partial y} - \frac{\partial^2 E_x}{\partial y^2} - \frac{\partial^2 E_x}{\partial z^2} + \frac{\partial^2 E_z}{\partial x\partial z}\right)$$

If we add $\frac{\partial^2 E_x}{\partial x^2} - \frac{\partial^2 E_x}{\partial x^2} = 0$ to the right-hand side we get:

$$\mu\kappa \frac{\partial^2 E_x}{\partial t^2} = \left(\frac{\partial^2 E_x}{\partial x^2} + \frac{\partial^2 E_x}{\partial y^2} + \frac{\partial^2 E_x}{\partial z^2}\right) - \frac{\partial}{\partial x}\left(\frac{\partial E_x}{\partial x} + \frac{\partial E_y}{\partial y} + \frac{\partial E_z}{\partial z}\right) \quad . \quad (5.41)$$

The last term on the right is zero in a region with no charge, as may be checked by differentiating (5.34), (5.35) and (5.36) with respect to x, y and z respectively and adding. Alternatively equation (5.33) could be applied to the volume element. Thus referring to Fig. 5.9 we have for the surface A, the

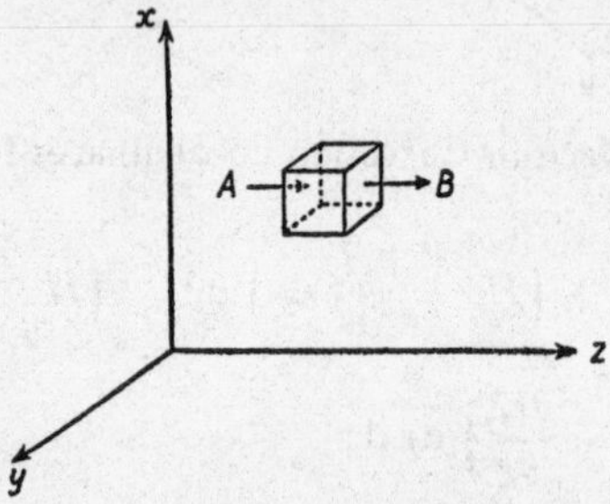

Fig. 5.9. Element of space for equations of continuity.

product of the normal component of **E** and the area:

$$- E_z \, dx \, dy$$

and for surface B:

$$\left(E_z + \frac{\partial E_z}{\partial z} dz\right) dx \, dy$$

The net value of the integral for surfaces A and B is therefore:

$$\frac{\partial E_z}{\partial z} dx \, dy \, dz$$

Similarly for the other directions we get:

$$\frac{\partial E_x}{\partial x} dx \, dy \, dz \text{ and } \frac{\partial E_y}{\partial y} dx \, dy \, dz$$

Hence equation (5.33) shows that:

$$\left(\frac{\partial E_x}{\partial x} + \frac{\partial E_y}{\partial y} + \frac{\partial E_z}{\partial z}\right) dx \, dy \, dz = 0$$

or

$$\frac{\partial E_x}{\partial x} + \frac{\partial E_y}{\partial y} + \frac{\partial E_z}{\partial z} = 0 \quad . \quad . \quad . \quad . \quad . \quad . \quad (5.42)$$

A similar expression can be deduced for the magnetic field in a region with no free magnetic poles thus:

$$\frac{\partial H_x}{\partial x} + \frac{\partial H_y}{\partial y} + \frac{\partial H_z}{\partial z} = 0 \quad . \quad . \quad . \quad . \quad . \quad . \quad (5.43)$$

These equations express the fact that the fields **E** and **H** are continuous and are called the equations of continuity. The equations 5.34–5.36, 5.37–5.39, 5.42 and 5.43 are Maxwell's equations in their differential form.

Returning to equation (5.41) and substituting equation (5.42) we get:

$$\therefore\ \mu\kappa\frac{\partial^2 E_x}{\partial t^2} = \frac{\partial^2 E_x}{\partial x^2} + \frac{\partial^2 E_x}{\partial y^2} + \frac{\partial^2 E_x}{\partial z^2} \quad . \quad . \quad . \quad . \quad (5.44)$$

Similar equations can be evolved for E_y and E_z. These three equations for the components of vector **E** can be written in shorthand form:

$$\mu\kappa\frac{\partial^2 \mathbf{E}}{\partial t^2} = \nabla^2\mathbf{E}$$

or

$$\frac{\partial^2 \mathbf{E}}{\partial t^2} - \frac{c^2}{\mu_r\kappa_r}\nabla^2\mathbf{E} = 0 \quad . \quad . \quad . \quad . \quad . \quad . \quad . \quad (5.45)$$

The symmetry of equations (5.34) to (5.39) shows that if we had differentiated the second three equations with respect to t and carried out substitutions from the first three we should have got the result:

$$\mu\kappa\frac{\partial^2 \mathbf{H}}{\partial t^2} = \nabla^2\mathbf{H}$$

or

$$\frac{\partial^2 \mathbf{H}}{\partial t^2} - \frac{c^2}{\mu_r\kappa_r}\nabla^2\mathbf{H} = 0 \quad . \quad . \quad . \quad . \quad . \quad . \quad . \quad (5.46)$$

Equations (5.45) and (5.46) are wave equations, and represent the solution of Maxwell's equations for free space or non-dissipative dielectric. They indicate a wave of **E** and **H** travelling with a velocity of $c/\sqrt{(\mu_r\kappa_r)}$. The solutions depend upon the boundary conditions. The simplest solutions are those corresponding to plane, cylindrical, or spherical waves. The plane-wave solution is considered in Appendix 5.2.

APPENDIX 5.2

Plane Waves in Space

The plane wave previously discussed under this heading (p. 136) represents the simplest solution of Maxwell's equations for an unbounded space. To deduce the properties of the wave from Maxwell's equations we may start by postulating a field having an electric vector which is constant in direction. This may be represented by a field E_x directed along the x-axis, E_y and E_z being zero. Substituting in equations (5.34) to (5.39) and assuming free space we get:

$$\left.\begin{aligned} \kappa_0\frac{\partial E_x}{\partial t} &= \frac{\partial H_z}{\partial y} - \frac{\partial H_y}{\partial z} \\ -\mu_0\frac{\partial H_x}{\partial t} &= 0 \\ -\mu_0\frac{\partial H_y}{\partial t} &= \frac{\partial E_x}{\partial z} \\ -\mu_0\frac{\partial H_z}{\partial t} &= -\frac{\partial E_x}{\partial y} \end{aligned}\right\} \quad . \quad . \quad . \quad . \quad . \quad (5.47)$$

From the second equation it is seen that H_x must be zero. If we make the further simplifying assumption that there is no magnetic field along the z-axis, the equations become:

$$\left.\begin{aligned} \kappa_0 \frac{\partial E_x}{\partial t} &= -\frac{\partial H_y}{\partial z} \\ \mu_0 \frac{\partial H_y}{\partial t} &= -\frac{\partial E_x}{\partial z} \end{aligned}\right\} \quad . \quad . \quad . \quad . \quad . \quad (5.48)$$

Differentiation of these with respect to t and z respectively gives:

$$\kappa_0 \frac{\partial^2 E_x}{\partial t^2} = -\frac{\partial^2 H_y}{\partial t \partial z}$$

$$\mu_0 \frac{\partial^2 H_y}{\partial z \partial t} = -\frac{\partial^2 E_x}{\partial z^2}$$

The order of differentiation is immaterial, so that:

$$\frac{\partial^2 H_y}{\partial t \partial z} = \frac{\partial^2 H_y}{\partial z \partial t}$$

and hence the two equations reduce to:

$$\frac{\partial^2 E_x}{\partial z^2} - \kappa_0 \mu_0 \frac{\partial^2 E_x}{\partial t^2} = 0 \quad . \quad . \quad . \quad (5.49)$$

This is the differential equation to be satisfied by E_x. Had we eliminated E_x instead of H_y from equation (5.48) we should have obtained an equation exactly the same as (5.49) but containing H_y in place of E_x. Thus E_x and H_y have to satisfy the same equation. Equation (5.49) is a special case of (5.45) and could have been deduced directly from it.

This is a simple form of what is known as the *wave equation*. If the wave is of angular frequency ω then it is easy to show that (5.49) will be satisfied by an expression of the form:

$$E_x = A \sin \omega\{t - (\kappa_0 \mu_0)^{1/2} z\} \quad . \quad . \quad . \quad . \quad . \quad (5.50)$$

in which A is an arbitrary constant. This represents a wave travelling along $0z$, in which E_x will have the same value at time t_2 and position z_2 as it had at time t_1 and position z_1, provided that

$$t_1 - (\kappa_0 \mu_0)^{1/2} z_1 = t_2 - (\kappa_0 \mu_0)^{1/2} z_2$$

Hence the velocity of the wave is given by

$$\begin{aligned} \text{Velocity} &= \frac{\text{distance interval}}{\text{time interval}} \\ &= \frac{z_2 - z_1}{t_2 - t_1} = \frac{1}{(\kappa_0 \mu_0)^{1/2}} \quad . \quad . \quad . \quad . \quad (5.51) \end{aligned}$$

This velocity—the 'velocity of light'—is always represented by c. Equation (5.50) can now be written as

$$\begin{aligned} E_x &= A \sin \omega(t - z/c) \\ &= A \sin (\omega t - \beta z), \quad . \quad . \quad . \quad . \quad . \quad . \quad (5.52) \end{aligned}$$

as in equation (5.23). Then from either of equations (5.48) we find:

$$H_y = A(\kappa_0/\mu_0)^{1/2} \sin(\omega t - \beta z) \quad . \quad . \quad . \quad (5.53)$$

Equations (5.52) and (5.53) give the complete field of a plane wave, and show that the magnetic and electric fields oscillate in phase and are perpendicular to each other and to the direction of propagation z.

A cosine form could equally well be chosen as the solution of (5.49), and any linear combination of sine and cosine will also be a solution. It often simplifies the analysis to choose the solution in the complex form as

$$\left.\begin{aligned} E_x &= A\{\cos(\omega t - \beta z) + \mathrm{j}\sin(\omega t - \beta z)\} \\ &= A\varepsilon^{\mathrm{j}(\omega t - \beta z)} \\ H_y &= A(\kappa_0/\mu_0)^{1/2}\varepsilon^{\mathrm{j}(\omega t - \beta z)} \end{aligned}\right\} \quad . \quad . \quad . \quad (5.54)$$

When this notation is used it should be understood that the physical quantity concerned (here E_x or H_y) is represented by only the real part of the exponential expression. This should be stated by prefixing the equations with a symbol indicating 'Real part of', but in practice it is often left to the reader's understanding.

APPENDIX 5.3

A Plane Wave Travelling Tangentially to a Conducting Plane

In the study of the parallel strip transmission line, the conducting planes were assumed to have infinite conductivity, so that no power could be dissipated in them. The electric field could therefore be assumed to meet the conducting plane normally. We now consider the case where the conducting plane has a

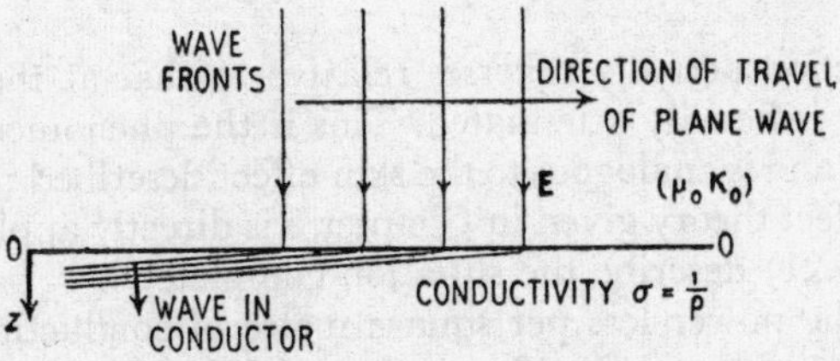

Fig. 5.10. Exaggerated view of wavefronts for a plane wave travelling tangentially to a conducting plane.

finite conductivity which is nevertheless high, such as would exist with a metallic plane. We need only consider one metallic plane, the other being removed to a great distance, so that we have the case of a plane wave travelling tangentially to a conducting plane, the plane of polarization being at right angles to the conducting plane. It is desired to estimate the power loss per square metre in this conducting plane.

In this case the waves will be tilted forward very slightly near the conducting plane so as to have a wave component normal to the plane in order to provide the losses in the plane. For high conductivities the waves in the conductor will be nearly normal to the surface. A very exaggerated view of the wave fronts is given in Fig. 5.10, the actual curving back of the wave front near the conductor being much smaller than shown. The magnetic field vector is parallel to the plane and from boundary condition number (4) currents will be set up therein. The surface current of the perfectly conducting plane is replaced by a current density varying with depth into the conductor in the finitely conducting case. Since the wave in the metal is nearly normal the current may be assumed to flow in thin laminae parallel to the surface. The current in an infinitesimally thin lamina will alternate backwards and forwards along the direction of the primary wave and with the same frequency. The distribution of current density in the thin laminae will vary with depth into the conductor according to an exponential attenuation law the propagation coefficient being given by equation (5.20). Thus the current density j_z at a depth z is given by:

$$\begin{aligned} j_z &= j_1 \varepsilon^{-\gamma z} \\ &= j_1 \varepsilon^{-(\sqrt{0\cdot5\omega\mu\sigma})z} \varepsilon^{-j(\sqrt{0\cdot5\omega\mu\sigma})z} \qquad (5.55) \end{aligned}$$

where j_1 is the surface value of the current density. The first exponential factor gives the attenuation of the current density whilst the second exponential factor gives the phase by which the current density at a lamina of depth z lags that at the surface. At the depth given by:

$$\sqrt{\frac{\omega\mu\sigma}{2}}.z = 1$$

or

$$z = \delta = \sqrt{\frac{2}{\omega\mu\sigma}} \qquad (5.56)$$

the current density is attenuated by one neper. This depth is the skin thickness δ. At a depth given by:

$$\sqrt{\frac{\omega\mu\sigma}{2}}.z = \pi$$

the current direction actually reverses relative to that at the surface. At this depth however it is heavily attenuated. This is the phenomenon of skin effect in a plane surface and is analogous to the skin effect described in Chapter 1. The simplified skin effect theory given in Chapter 5 is directly applicable and equations (5.19) to (5.21) describe the situation completely.

To calculate the power loss per square metre of conducting plane we may use the surface impedance Z_0 of equation (5.19). If I_T is the total current flowing in the skin layers, per metre width, the power loss per square metre is given by:

$$\begin{aligned} P_L &= I_T^2 \times \text{Real part of surface impedance} \\ &= I_T^2 \times \sqrt{\frac{\omega\mu}{2\sigma}} \\ &= I_T^2/(\delta\sigma) \qquad (5.57) \end{aligned}$$

from equations (5.19) and (5.56).

If the surface value of current density j_1 were known we could integrate equation (5.55) with respect to z in order to determine I_T. This is not necessary however, since the value of $\mathbf{H}_t$ just above the surface is equal to the total current I_T, since I_T would be the surface current in the perfectly conducting case.

Hence if we know the field strength of the wave travelling parallel to the plane the value of I_T can be calculated, thus:

$$\frac{|\mathbf{E}_n|}{377} = |\mathbf{H}_t| = I_T$$

and from (5.57) the power loss per square metre is:

$$P_L = \frac{\mathbf{E}_n^2}{(377)^2} \cdot \frac{1}{\sigma\delta}$$

But $\mathbf{E}_n^2/377$ is the power flux P_T per square metre of the wave parallel to the plane. Therefore we have:

$$P_L = P_T \frac{\rho/\delta}{377} \qquad (5.58)$$

replacing conductivity by resistivity ρ. The factor (ρ/δ) is the resistance of a square metre of surface layer (of thickness equal to the skin depth) measured between opposite edges. Thus the proportion of transmitted power per square metre which is lost in a square metre of plane is a simple ratio of two resistive impedances.

CHAPTER 6

Guided Waves

Introduction

In the parallel-wire transmission line most of the electromagnetic energy travels in the space closely surrounding the parallel wires, but a certain amount does leak away and is lost from the system. The line thus acts partly as a carrier of energy and partly as a radiating aerial. The amount of energy lost is negligible at low frequencies, but increases with increase of frequency, so that frequencies of one or two hundred megacycles per second are the highest at which the parallel-wire line is satisfactory. For frequencies higher than this the loss by radiation is considerable.

In the coaxial line, on the other hand, the energy is guided along the space between the two coaxial conductors and, as it is unable to pass through the walls of the outer conductor, there is no opportunity for any radiation loss to occur at any frequency. There is, however, another source of loss of energy, which lies in the resistance of the conductors themselves. This resistance loss also increases with frequency. There is additional loss caused by the insulating materials necessary to support the inner conductor, and this becomes a major factor when we reach frequencies of the order of 3,000 Mc/s.

Looking at matters from the field viewpoint it seems reasonable to ask why two conductors are necessary, why electromagnetic energy cannot be guided simply by confining it inside a single hollow tube. The answer is that this is perfectly feasible, such hollow tubes, under the name of *waveguides*, being by far the most used type of transmission line for frequencies exceeding about 3,000 Mc/s. This would appear to be quite the most convenient type of transmission line, as simple as a gas or water pipe. Unfortunately it has a serious limitation, that its cross-sectional dimensions must be so related to the frequency of the wave that it is only when the frequency reaches thousands of megacycles per second that the dimensions are small enough to be convenient for use.

For a waveguide transmission line there is no 'flow-and-return' circuit, and it is difficult to talk in terms of current and voltage. Thus the electromagnetic-field concept becomes the only useful one, and most of our subsequent analysis will be in terms of the electric and magnetic field vectors.

The plane wave which we have considered in Chapter 5 was assumed to extend without limit in directions perpendicular to its direction of travel, with its field vectors directed as in Fig. 5.4. The extent of this wave can be limited in the x-direction by placing two plane conducting sheets in the positions shown in Fig. 5.2 so as to form a strip transmission line. In the space between the plates the electric field is normal to the plates and hence satisfies the boundary condition for electric lines at the surfaces. The magnetic field is tangential and hence also satisfies the boundary condition for magnetic lines. Thus the electric lines now terminate on the plates and a plane wave can travel between them, remaining undistorted but now limited to the space between the plates. But the field has been limited only in the x-direction; it still extends without limit in the y-direction. Now let us try to restrict the wave horizontally also by inserting two more conducting plates to form with the original two a hollow rectangular tube, as shown in Fig. 6.1. On applying the boundary conditions we see immediately that the wave cannot exist in its original form, for then on the new boundaries the electric field would be tangential and the magnetic field normal, both of which are inadmissible. Thus a plane wave cannot be propagated in a rectangular tube. If, however, the wave pattern were modified, as shown in Fig. 6.1, it would satisfy the boundary conditions. In this wave the electric field is made to vary with distance along $0y$ so that it has a maximum at the centre of the tube and is zero at its side walls. The magnetic lines are made to curve round

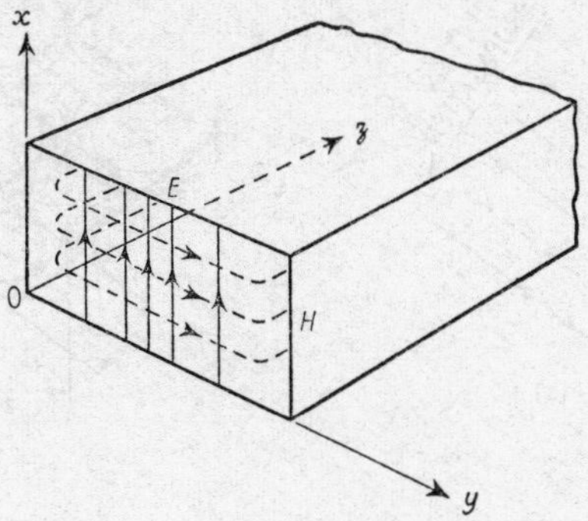

Fig. 6.1. Lines of force in rectangular waveguide.

so that they pass down the tube tangentially to the side walls. Such a re-arrangement seems feasible, but in the next section we must consider in more detail what is involved.

Waveguide transmission lines can be of any cross-section, but almost the only types of practical importance are rectangular and circular guides. The rectangular is by far the more important from a practical point of view, mainly because of the simplicity of the propagation phenomena involved. It is also simple to handle mathematically.

Rectangular Waveguide

We have shown above that the boundary conditions do not permit a rectangular guide to be fitted round a plane wave, but we shall now proceed to show that by superposing two plane free-space waves a new wave pattern is obtained which is of the correct form to satisfy the boundary conditions in a rectangular tube.

Fig. 6.2 (a) represents a section of a plane wave travelling at the usual velocity c in the direction shown by the arrow. The wave is polarized so that the magnetic vector lies in the plane of the paper. The full lines are magnetic field lines drawn at positions of successive maxima and in alternate directions shown by the arrows on them, and correspond to the peaks and troughs of a wave in the sea. The dashed lines midway between them represent positions of zero magnetic field. The distance between two successive maxima is half a wavelength. The electric field is normal to the plane of the paper and in phase with the magnetic field, so that the positions of electric lines of maximum intensity entering and leaving the plane of the paper are as shown by the dots and circles. Fig. 6.2 (b) represents a section of a wave similar to the first in every way except that it is travelling in a different direction.

In Fig. 6.2 (c) these two waves are superposed so that the two points A coincide. At every point the magnetic field of the combination is the resultant of two components, and its direction can be determined by inspection at the points in the diagram where lines cross. These are marked with arrows in Fig. 6.2 (c). At points such as B one of the components, being represented by a dotted line, is zero, so that the resultant is in the direction of the other component. At points such as A or C the resultant will lie on one or other of the bisectors of the two lines such that its direction is between the positive directions

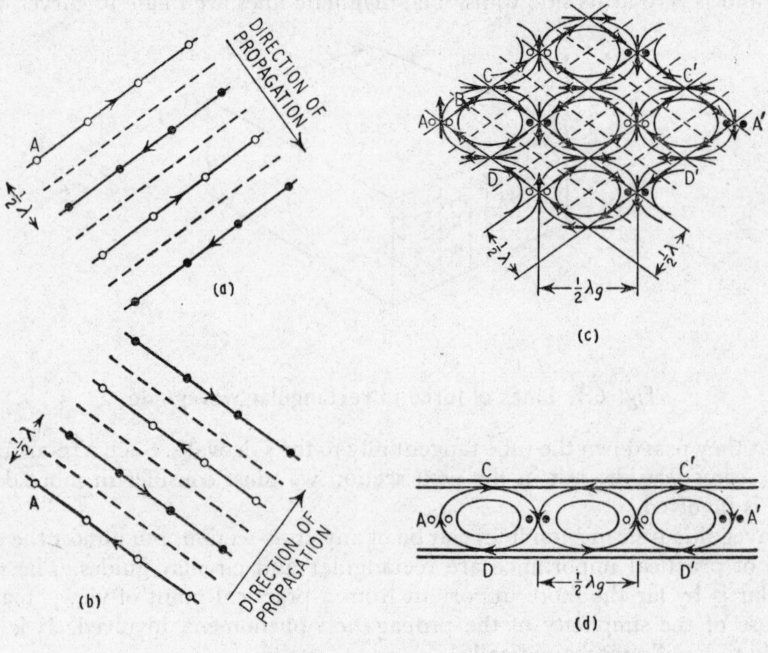

Fig. 6.2. Waveguide mode formed by combining two plane waves.
∘ into paper, • out of paper } electric-field lines.

of the two lines. At points of intersection of dotted lines the resultant magnetic field is zero. These few values serve to indicate the general direction of the field, and it is easy to visualize that the lines of magnetic force of the composite wave will form a set of complete loops as shown in Fig. 6.2 (c).

The electric field in both component waves is normal to the plane of the paper in the sense indicated by a circle or dot. These add or subtract, giving maxima in the composite wave at points such as those marked along the centre line AA′ and falling to zero mid-way between these points. It is also evident that the electric fields cancel all along the lines joining the points C, C′ and D, D′. The wave pattern sketched in Fig. 6.2 (c) is, of course, only a section, and the pattern must be considered as extending in depth above and below the plane of the paper.

At every point on the planes through CC′ and DD′ perpendicular to the paper the magnetic field is tangential and the electric field zero. Thus conducting plates may be placed along these planes without violating boundary conditions, and we then get the wave pattern of Fig. 6.2 (d). Just as in the previous section, we can also insert two conducting plates normal to the electric field, that is, parallel to the plane of the paper, so isolating a section of the wave. Thus it has been possible to build a complete rectangular tube round this composite wave without violating boundary conditions; that is, without disturbing the wave pattern.

This pattern, however, is an instantaneous one, and must move as the two component waves move. A little consideration will show that the composite wave proceeds without change of shape in the direction AA′.

In short, then, a wave pattern of the type formed by combining two plane waves of equal amplitude travelling at an angle to one another can be propagated freely down a rectangular tube. Although for the purposes of the argument the wave pattern has been regarded as composed of two plane waves it is not necessary so to regard it, and in fact it is normally regarded as having an identity of its own, a specific form of wave which can be set up by a particular arrangement of conductors and transmitted in a rectangular waveguide. This wave and all its properties can be derived directly from Maxwell's equations simply by application of the appropriate boundary conditions. This derivation is carried out in Appendix 6.1, but a great deal can be learned from further consideration of its composite aspect.

H_{10} Wave in Rectangular Guide

The wave of Fig. 6.2 (d) is shown in more detail in Fig. 6.3. It will be observed that all the electric lines go directly across from side to side—that is, they are *transverse* to the direction of the wave. The magnetic lines, however, lie partly along the direction of motion—that is, they have a longitudinal component. For this reason the wave is called an H wave, indicating that there is a component of the magnetic field $\mathbf{H}$ in the direction of motion. From the transverse property of the electric field an H wave is also known as a TE wave (Transverse Electric).*

In Fig. 6.3 the co-ordinate system has been changed round so that, in accordance with convention, the x-axis lies along the broad side of the guide. The closeness of spacing of the lines or dots indicates the strength of the field. The end view shows that in passing along $0x$ we cross electric lines which increase in strength to a maximum at the centre and then die away. In going along $0y$ we cross no electric lines. These properties of the field give rise to a simple notation used to indicate this type of field and to distinguish it from other more complex types which can also exist.

In this notation the wave is called an H_{10} wave (or TE_{10}), the subscripts 1 and 0 indicating that there is one field maximum along $0x$ and no maximum along $0y$.

The propagation of an H_{10} wave in a rectangular guide will be discussed in the next section, but the results can be summarized here as follows:

The propagation is to be regarded as a movement of the field pattern of Fig. 6.3 along the guide at a velocity v_p—called the *phase velocity*—which is greater than the velocity of light c.

* Later on we shall meet E waves (or TM waves) so called because they have a component of $\mathbf{E}$ in the direction of motion, but a Transverse Magnetic field.

The wavelength λ_g measured in the guide is the length occupied by a complete cycle of the wave pattern, so that the distance between successive reversals of the field is $\frac{1}{2}\lambda_g$ as marked in the figure. This guide wavelength is always greater than the free-space wavelength λ. The relation between λ_g and λ is also

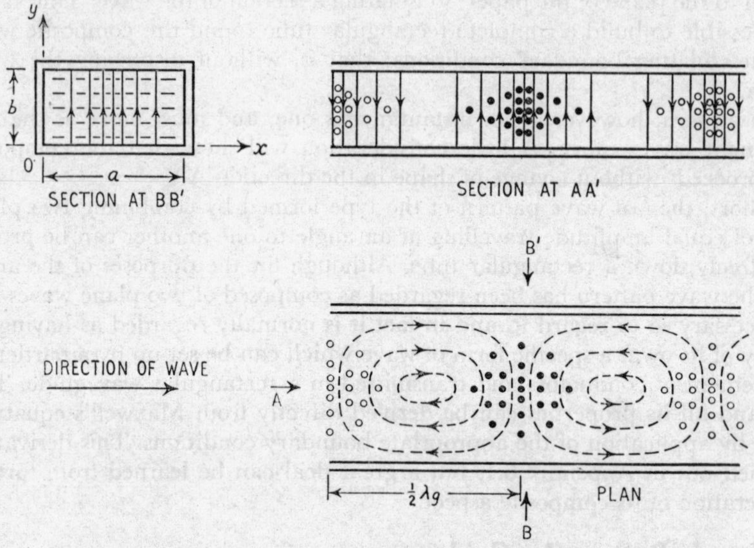

Fig. 6.3. Field pattern of H_{10} wave in rectangular waveguide.
——— electric field lines ∘ into paper
– – – – magnetic field lines • out of paper

dependent upon the length of the side parallel to the magnetic field, that is, the dimension a in Fig. 6.3, and independent of the other dimension b.

The free-space wavelength must always be less than $2a$; otherwise the wave is not propagated. The *critical wavelength*, for which $\lambda = 2a$, is denoted by λ_c. This property can be understood if we remember that the two component waves

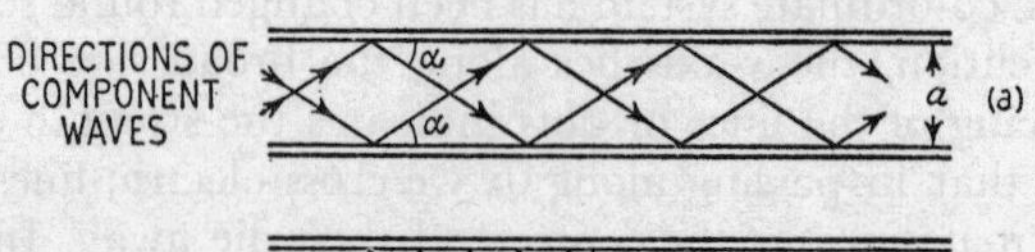

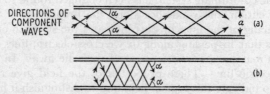

Fig. 6.4. Zigzag path of component waves in rectangular waveguide, (a) $\lambda = 0{\cdot}5\lambda_c$; (b) $\lambda = 0{\cdot}9\lambda_c$.

travel at an angle to the guide and regard them as being reflected from side to side in a zigzag path, as in Fig. 6.4, in the same way as light waves would be successively reflected between two parallel mirrors. The angle α which they make with the walls is determined by λ and the dimension a. If λ is not close to the critical value then α is fairly small as in Fig. 6.4 (a). As λ increases so also does α, and as λ approaches the critical value α approaches 90°, the waves closing up as in Fig. 6.4 (b). In the limit when λ equals the critical value the waves are reflected from side to side without progressing down the tube.

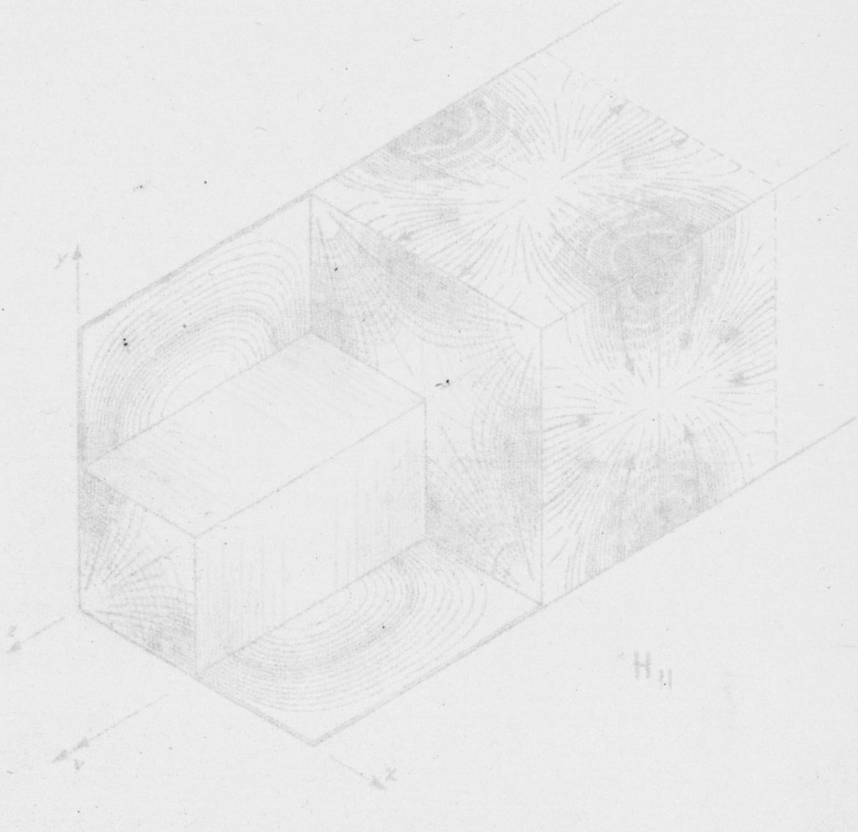

Fig. 6.5. Three-dimensional views of the field configurations of H_{10}, H_{11} and E_{11} modes in rectangular waveguides. The electric field is indicated in red and the magnetic in green, while the current in the waveguide walls is shown in blue.

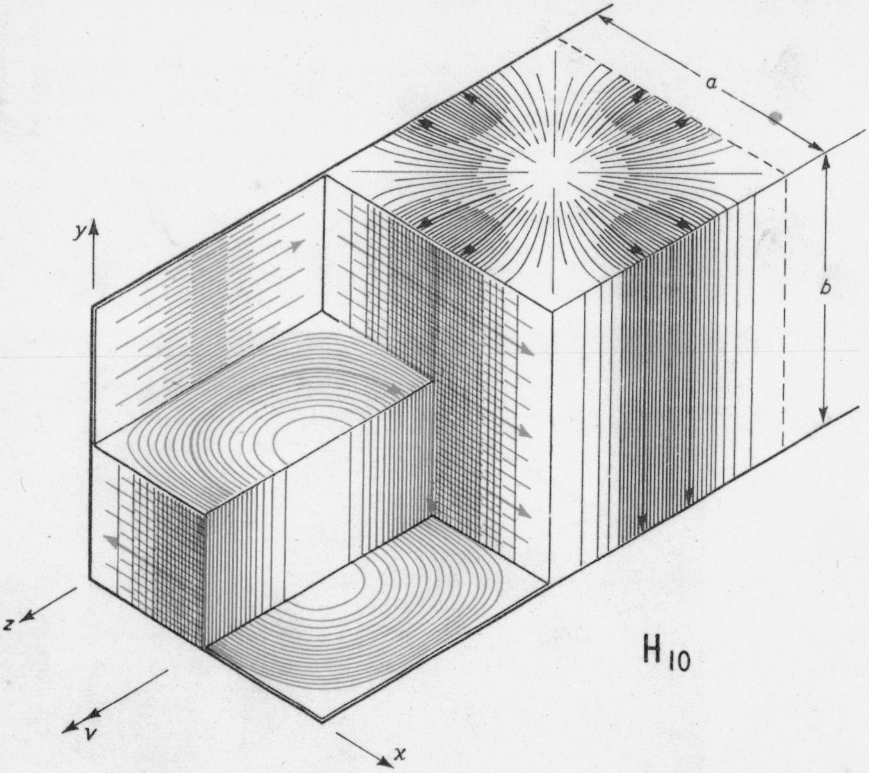

H 10

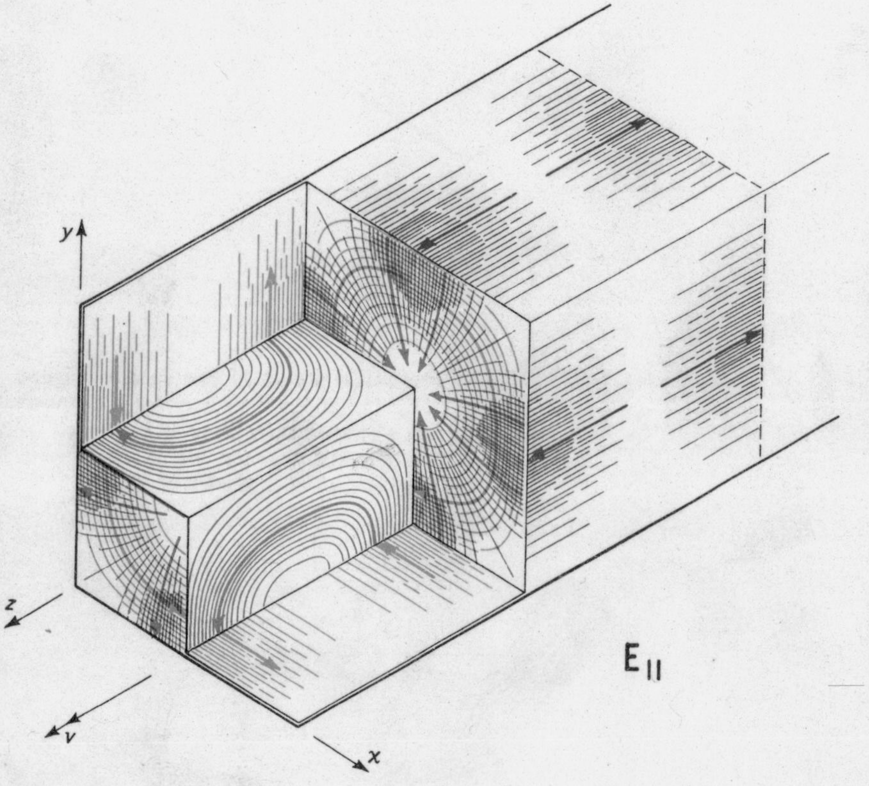

E 11

The distribution of field strength for the H_{10} wave in a rectangular guide is shown pictorially in Fig. 6.5.

Velocity and Wavelength

If we consider the magnetic lines AC and AD of Fig. 6.6 as representative of the wave fronts of the two constituent plane waves of an H_{10} wave, these are both moving at velocity c in directions perpendicular to the wavefronts and given by CE and DE, where AE is the line bisecting the angle CAD. As the wavefronts AC and AD advance parallel to themselves, as shown by the dotted lines in the figure, their point of intersection A moves along the line AE, and

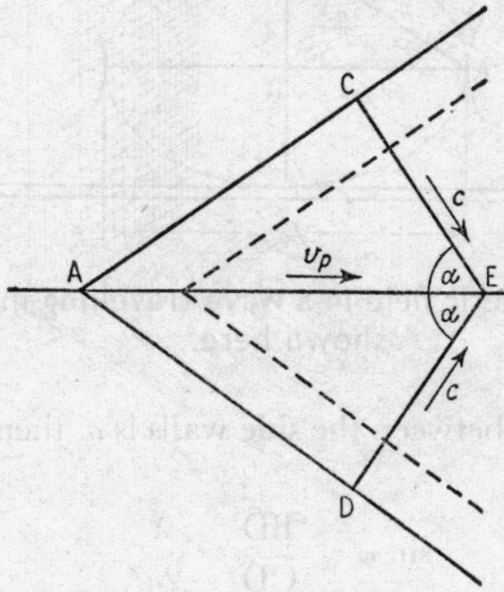

Fig. 6.6. AC and AD represent the wavefronts of two constituent plane waves.

the points C, D and A arrive simultaneously at E. If the velocity of the point A be v_p, then:

$$\frac{c}{v_p} = \frac{\text{CE}}{\text{AE}} = \cos \alpha$$

where 2α is the angle CED between the directions of the two waves. The point A is a typical point on the wavefront of the resultant wave. All such points obviously travel with the same velocity and in the same direction so that the wave pattern of Fig. 6.2 (d) moves along the guide with a velocity v_p given by

$$v_p = \frac{c}{\cos \alpha} \quad . \quad . \quad . \quad . \quad . \quad . \quad . \quad (6.1)$$

Since $\cos \alpha$ is always less than (or equal to) unity, v_p must always be greater than (or equal to) c. That a wave pattern should travel in a waveguide at a velocity greater than the free-space velocity is characteristic of waveguide propagation. This velocity is called the *phase velocity* in the guide, for it is the rate at which a given phase in the resultant wave travels. It will be discussed later in more detail.

For a wave of frequency f in free space the wavelength is defined by the relation $f\lambda = c$. For a guided wave a new wavelength λ_g—the wavelength in the guide—can be defined by the relation

$$f\lambda_g = v_p$$

Since v_p is greater than c, λ_g must be greater than λ.

This guide wavelength is, just as in free space, the distance for one complete cycle measured along the direction of motion. In Fig. 6.2 (d) two of the large loops form a complete cycle, and thus each large loop has a length equal to $\lambda_g/2$. Fig. 6.7 shows one of the loops of magnetic field in a wave travelling in a rectangular guide. AC is a wave front of one of the component waves [like AC in Fig. 6.2 (c)]. In the quarter period which A will take to move the distance $\lambda_g/4$ to D, the point B on the wavefront will move to D. Since AC is a plane wave moving at velocity c, it will in that time cover a distance equal to $\lambda/4$; thus

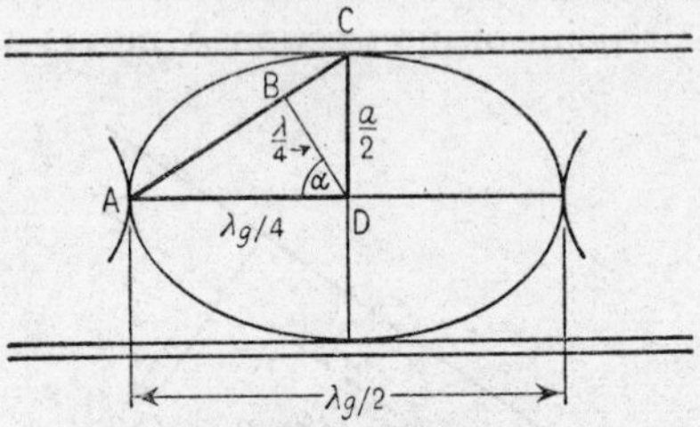

Fig. 6.7. One loop of magnetic field in a wave travelling in a rectangular guide is shown here.

BD $= \lambda/4$. If the distance between the side walls is a, then CD $= a/2$. From the diagram,

$$\sin \alpha = \frac{\text{BD}}{\text{CD}} = \frac{\lambda}{2a} \quad . \quad . \quad . \quad . \quad . \quad . \quad (6.2)$$

and

$$\cos \alpha = \frac{\text{BD}}{\text{AD}} = \frac{\lambda}{\lambda_g} \quad . \quad . \quad . \quad . \quad . \quad . \quad (6.3)$$

Then, since $\sin^2 \alpha + \cos^2 \alpha = 1$,

$$\left(\frac{\lambda}{2a}\right)^2 + \left(\frac{\lambda}{\lambda_g}\right)^2 = 1$$

or

$$\frac{1}{\lambda_g^{\,2}} = \frac{1}{\lambda^2} - \frac{1}{(2a)^2} \quad . \quad . \quad . \quad . \quad . \quad . \quad (6.4)$$

This last formula is a most important expression, giving the guide wavelength of a wave in a rectangular guide in terms of the wavelength in free space of a wave having the same frequency. The treatment in Appendix 6.1 includes a derivation of this equation directly from Maxwell's equations. It should be noted that λ_g is always greater than λ, and that λ_g is dependent also on the cross-sectional dimension in the plane of the magnetic field.

It has been shown that each of the component waves can be considered as following a zigzag path down the tube, being successively reflected at the two side walls of the tube, and always making the angle α with the side walls, as in Fig. 6.4. Equation (6.2) defines α in terms of λ and a. Hence, if we increase λ, $\sin \alpha$ will also increase, and when we reach the wavelength where $\lambda = 2a$ then $\sin \alpha = 1$ and so $\alpha = 90°$. Fig. 6.4 (b) shows the zigzag path when α is nearly $90°$ and it is evident that when α reaches $90°$, the wave will be reflected back and forth between the two sides without advancing down the guide. The wavelength at which this occurs is called the *critical* (or *cut-off*) *wavelength* λ_c. Equation (6.4) can now be put in the form:

$$\frac{1}{\lambda_g^2} = \frac{1}{\lambda^2} - \frac{1}{\lambda_c^2} \quad . \quad . \quad . \quad . \quad . \quad . \quad . \quad (6.5)$$

For free propagation down the guide the free-space wavelength must be less than the critical wavelength, that is, less than $2a$. This corresponds to a critical frequency:

$$f_c = \frac{c}{2a} \quad . \quad . \quad . \quad . \quad . \quad . \quad . \quad . \quad (6.6)$$

A wave of frequency lower than this cannot be transmitted. On the other hand, as λ is made smaller and smaller, α decreases and λ_g becomes more nearly equal

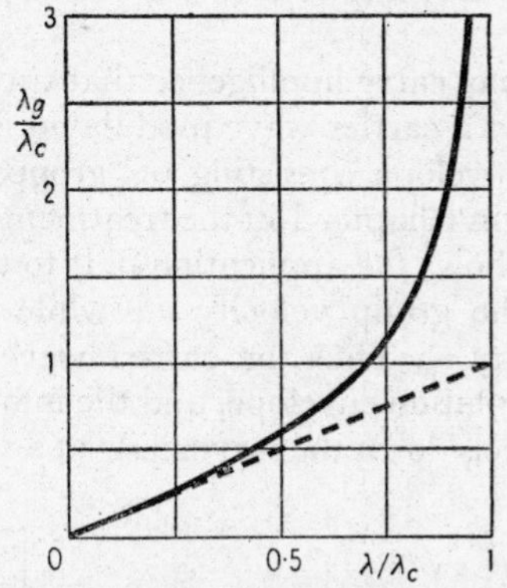

Fig. 6.8. Relationship between λ_g and λ in waveguide.

to λ, approaching it asymptotically. The way in which λ_g varies with λ is shown in the curve of Fig. 6.8.

As an example consider one of the standard waveguides which has internal dimensions of 2·84 in. by 1·34 in. For an H_{10} wave with its magnetic field parallel to the larger dimension, the critical wavelength is $\lambda_c = 2 \times 2{\cdot}84$ in. $= 14{\cdot}4$ cm. Then at a free-space wavelength $\lambda = 10$ cm. the guide wavelength is found by equation (6.5) to be $\lambda_g = 13{\cdot}9$ cm.

Phase and Group Velocities

It has been shown that an H_{10} wave travels at a phase velocity v_p greater than the velocity of light, and given by

$$v_p = \frac{c}{\cos\alpha} = c\frac{\lambda_g}{\lambda} \quad . \quad . \quad . \quad . \quad . \quad . \quad (6.7)$$

Relativity theory states that energy can never be propagated at a speed greater than the velocity of light, so that v_p, although it is the speed of the wave pattern, cannot represent the velocity of energy transmission. That there is another velocity can be seen by considering the zigzag path followed by the two components. From Fig. 6.9 it will be clear that, since the path along the axis is shorter than the zigzag path along which the component waves move with velocity c, the resultant rate of progress of energy along the guide will be less than c, and given by $c \cos \alpha$. This velocity is known as the *group velocity* for a reason which will appear, and, if represented by v_g, then:

$$v_g = c \cos \alpha = c\frac{\lambda}{\lambda_g} \quad . \quad . \quad . \quad . \quad . \quad . \quad (6.8)$$

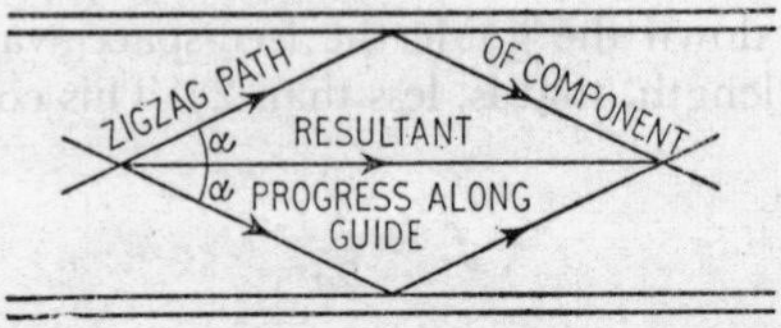

Fig. 6.9. Illustrating the relation between phase and group velocity.

Hence v_g is always less than c, and it is at this velocity that energy and intelligence are propagated.

In order that a wave may carry intelligence that wave must be modulated in some way. Fig. 6.10 shows a carrier wave modulated in amplitude by a speech signal, the modulation envelope consisting of 'groups' of carrier cycles. The same analysis as was used in Chapter 1 in the treatment of group velocity applies here, and Appendix 6.1 shows the application of it to this case. In a waveguide these groups travel at the group velocity v_g, while the carrier wave itself advances at phase velocity v_p. Thus the carrier wave would appear to move forward through the modulation envelope, and the information contained in the modulation envelope travels down the waveguide at a velocity which is less than the free-space velocity.

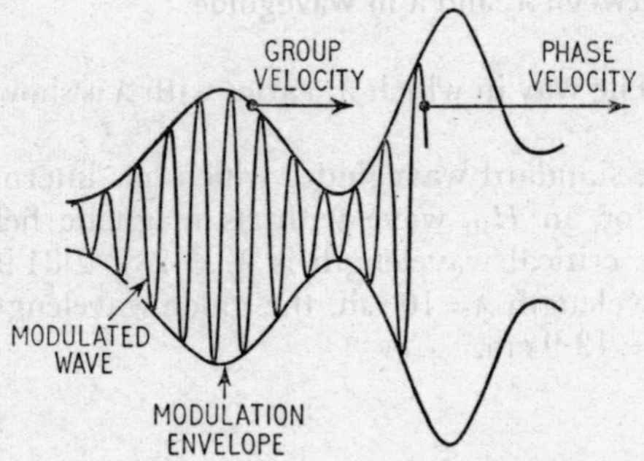

Fig. 6.10. Phase and group velocities in a modulated carrier wave.

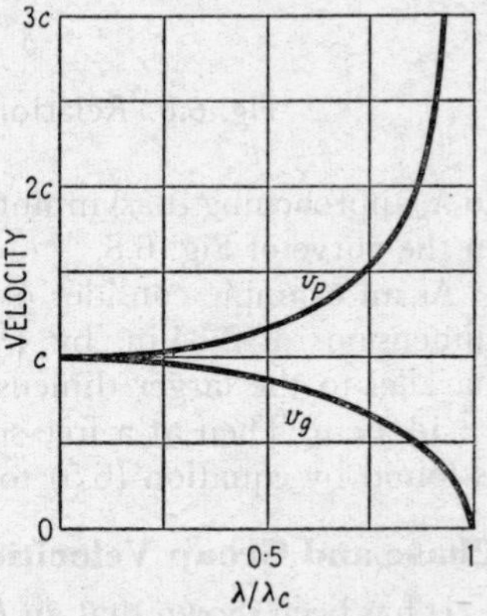

Fig. 6.11. Dependence of phase and group velocities on λ.

That the phase and group velocities have different values is characteristic of a system in which wavelength is not inversely proportional to frequency. The variation is illustrated in Fig. 6.11, and it will be seen that, as λ is reduced and the propagation becomes less and less dependent on the waveguide, v_p and v_g both steadily approach the free-space value c. By equations (6.7) and (6.8) the relation

$$v_p v_g = c^2 \quad . \quad . \quad . \quad . \quad . \quad . \quad (6.9)$$

connects the phase and group velocities.

Higher Modes

H modes. The H_{10} is not the only possible wave type which can be propagated in a rectangular guide; other wave patterns can be derived in the same way as the H_{10} type. When deriving the H_{10} wave we enclosed one row of magnetic-field loops between the side walls. Two or more rows could have been enclosed; in Fig. 6.12 two are shown. This wave satisfies the boundary conditions equally

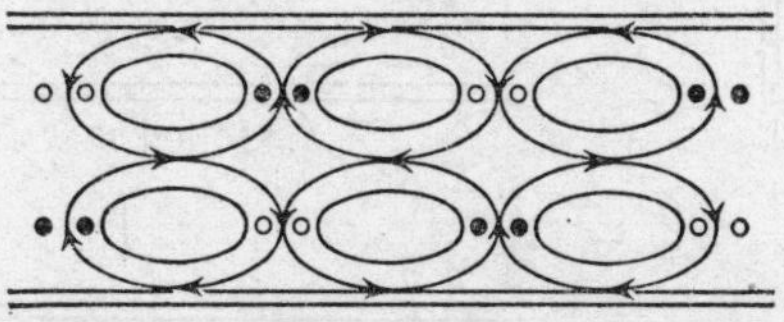

Fig. 6.12. Two rows of magnetic-field loops within a guide

well, but obviously requires a wider guide for its propagation. It is shown in more detail in Fig. 6.13, where it will be seen that the wave pattern has the form of two H_{10} waves placed together. This time two maxima of electric field are encountered in passing along $0x$, and none in passing along $0y$. Thus the wave is called an H_{20} or TE_{20} wave. The H_{30} (TE_{30}) and higher modes can easily be visualized.

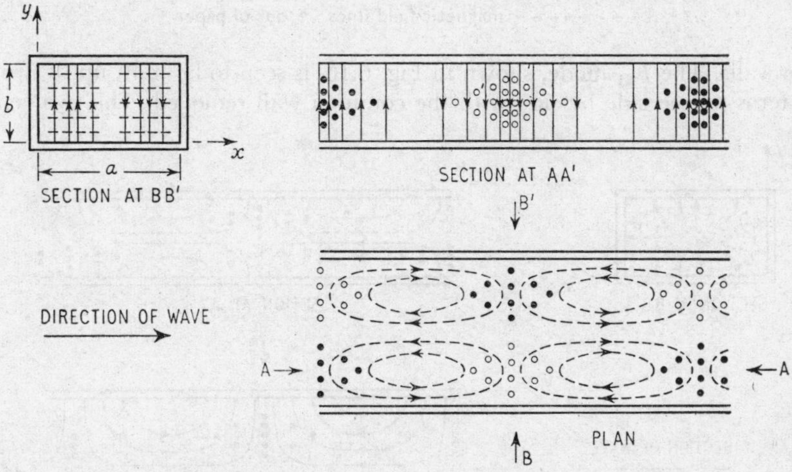

Fig. 6.13. Field pattern of H_{20} wave in rectangular waveguide.
——— electric-field lines ∘ into paper
- - - - - - magnetic-field lines • out of paper

Further modes can exist in which there are maxima of electric field along the $0y$ axis also. Fig. 6.14 shows such a wave, an H_{11}, in which there is one maximum along $0x$ and one along $0y$.

E modes. By superposition of plane waves it can also be shown that another type of wave can exist—an E wave. In this the magnetic field is completely transverse, and the electric field has a component in the direction of propagation. The simplest wave of this type is the E_{11} (or TM_{11}) shown in Fig. 6.15, which has one electric field maximum along each of the sides $0x$ and $0y$. Here the ends of the electric lines shown in the cross-section bend round to form the half-loops in the longitudinal sections, these loops ending normally on the

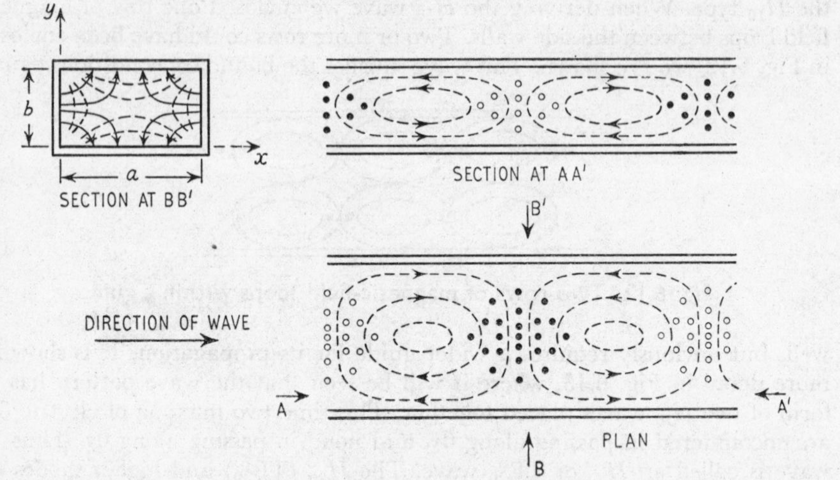

Fig. 6.14. Field pattern of H_{11} wave in rectangular waveguide.
——— electric-field lines ∘ into paper
------ magnetic-field lines • out of paper

side walls. The E_{21} mode, shown in Fig. 6.16, is seen to be built up of two E_{11} patterns placed side by side with the common wall removed. The two central

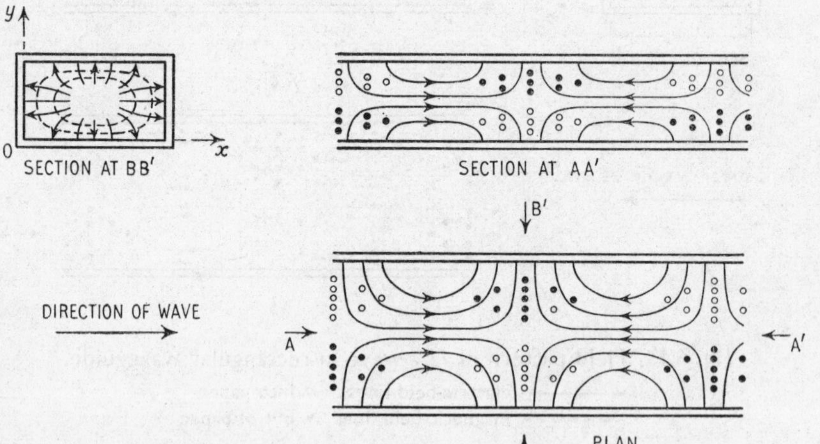

Fig. 6.15. Field pattern of E_{11} wave in rectangular waveguide.
——— electric-field lines ∘ into paper
------ magnetic-field lines • out of paper

sets of electric half-loops instead of terminating on conducting walls now unite to form closed loops.

There are no E waves with a zero index. For example, it is evident that if one tried to construct an E_{10} wave the pattern in a longitudinal section parallel to $0x$ would be as in Fig. 6.15, and this would have to remain the same for any cross-section parallel to $0x$. On the $0x$ plane itself, then, the electric lines would be tangential to the wall, and would thus violate the boundary conditions. Three-dimensional views of the H_{11} and E_{11} modes are given in Fig. 6.5.

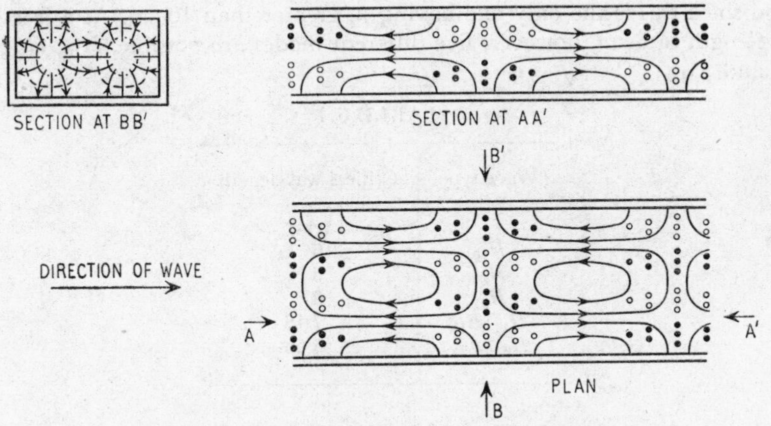

Fig. 6.16. Field pattern of E_{21} wave in rectangular waveguide.
——— electric-field lines o into paper
------- magnetic-field lines • out of paper

Properties of Higher Modes

Each of these modes has its own individual value of critical wavelength, and hence its own guide wavelength and velocity. The H_{10} wave has the longest critical wavelength of all the modes and is called the *fundamental mode*. The bigger a guide is the more modes it will support, but the presence of a multiplicity of modes all travelling with different velocities is clearly undesirable, and indeed the design of anything but the very simplest waveguide system to handle such a range efficiently would be an impossibility. It is usual, therefore, to make the guide large enough to support only the fundamental mode. Thus it follows that a waveguide of given dimensions can be used usefully over only a small frequency range.

Methods of generating the various modes are dealt with in Chapter 7.

▶ It is shown in Appendix 6.2 that in the general case the critical wavelength for an E_{mn} or H_{mn} wave, where m and n have any integral values, is dependent on both dimensions of the cross-section, a and b, and is given by

$$\frac{1}{\lambda_c^2} = \left(\frac{m}{2a}\right)^2 + \left(\frac{n}{2b}\right)^2 \quad . \quad . \quad . \quad . \quad . \qquad (6.10)$$

This reduces to $\lambda_c = 2a$ for the particular case already studied where $m = 1$, $n = 0$, and in this case λ_c is independent of b. The general expression for λ_g is

$$\frac{1}{\lambda_g^2} = \frac{1}{\lambda^2} - \frac{1}{\lambda_c^2} \quad . \quad . \quad . \quad . \quad . \quad . \quad . \quad . \qquad (6.11)$$

where in any particular case λ_c has its appropriate value given by (6.10).

For free propagation in any particular mode the free-space wavelength must be less than λ_c. Since λ_c decreases as m or n is increased, free propagation of only a limited number of modes is possible for a given wavelength and given guide dimensions. Consider, for example, a guide of internal dimensions 8 cm × 4 cm. Critical wavelengths of a few modes, calculated by (6.10), are given in Table 6.1. Thus at a free space wavelength of 10 cm only the H_{10} mode could be propagated since this is the only one having λ_c greater than 10 cm. At a free-space wavelength of 6 cm, however, five different modes are possible, H_{10}, H_{20}, H_{01}, H_{11} and E_{11}.

TABLE 6.1

Wave type	Critical wavelength
	(cm)
H_{10}	16
H_{20}	8
H_{01}	8
H_{11}, E_{11}	7·16
H_{21}, E_{21}	5·66

It is only in very special circumstances that any mode other than the H_{10} is used in a rectangular guide. Nevertheless familiarity with the other simple modes described above is necessary to the understanding of the choice of dimensions for the various guide sizes. The choice of dimensions is also governed largely by the attenuation in the guide, so this will be considered again after the section on attenuation.

Currents in Waveguide Walls

On p. 131 it was stated that a magnetic field parallel to a conducting boundary induces in the conductor a surface current, whose direction of flow is at right-angles to that of the magnetic field. These lines of current flow are

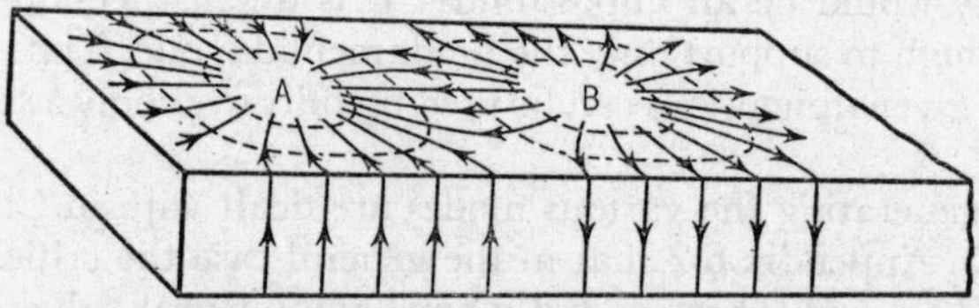

Fig. 6.17. Lines of current flow in waveguide walls for H_{10} wave.

most dense where the magnetic field lines are most dense. Thus the passage of a wave sets up currents in the walls of a waveguide, and their form can be deduced by considering the magnetic field patterns.

The solid lines of Fig. 6.17 give an instantaneous picture of the current flow for an H_{10} wave in a rectangular guide, while the dashed lines indicate the magnetic field close to the walls. It will be seen that on the top face the lines of current flow all converge towards a region A and diverge from a region B, with the reverse effect on the lower face. On the side faces the current flow is always vertical. This pattern of current flow travels with the wave at the phase velocity

v_p. In a perfectly conducting guide it would exist as an infinitely thin current sheet on the inner surfaces of the walls.

Further examples of current flow are shown in Figs. 6.5 and 6.24.

It is important to understand this current distribution, for very useful results can be deduced from it. For example, a narrow slot cut in the wall of a guide will obviously have negligible effect on the propagation of a wave provided the slot does not interrupt the lines of current flow. Thus, with an H_{10} wave, narrow slots cut in positions such as P and Q in Fig. 6.18, P being a slot mid-way across

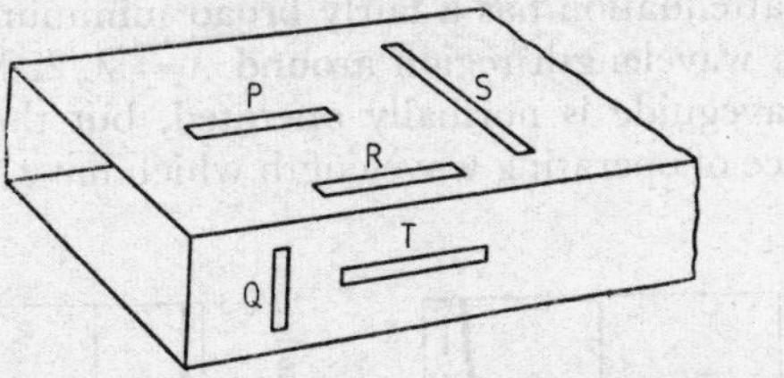

Fig. 6.18. Narrow slots in rectangular waveguide.

the broad face, do not cut across current lines, and so do not affect significantly the propagation of the wave. Slots such as R, S and T, however, always cut current lines and thereby impede the progress of the wave. A slot in the position P is used commonly to enable a probe to be inserted and moved along the guide for investigation of the interior field. The uses of slots will be discussed in more detail in Chapter 7.

Attenuation

Since a current flow is set up in the walls of a guide when a wave is propagated along it, it follows that the resistance of the walls will cause some power loss. This power must come from the wave itself, which is thus progressively attenuated.

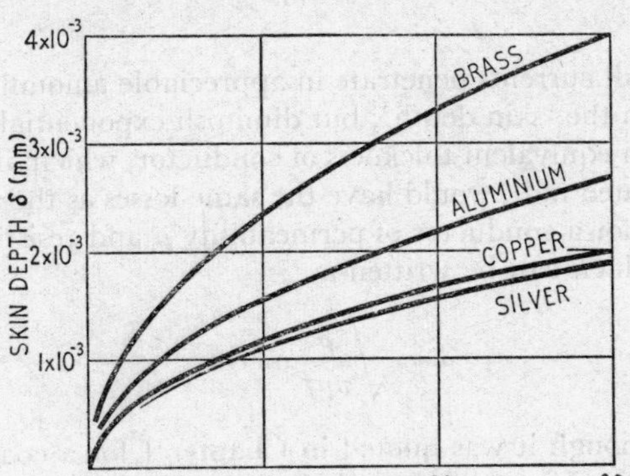

Fig. 6.19. Variation of skin depth with wavelength for different metals.

It has been shown in Chapter 1 that radio-frequency currents do not penetrate far into a good conductor, but are confined to a thin skin on the surface. For purposes of calculation a thickness known as the 'skin depth' is used, which can be regarded as defining for all practical purposes the depth of current penetration. This depth decreases with decrease of wavelength as shown in Fig. 6.19, and is proportional to the square root of the resistivity. For copper at a wavelength of 10 cm it is approximately 0·001 mm.

Thus so far as attenuation is concerned a thick-walled guide is no better than an extremely thin-walled one, and the thickness used in practice can be decided entirely by mechanical considerations. A saving in cost or in weight may be gained by using a composite guide made of a material whose conductivity is unimportant with a thin layer of highly conducting material on its inner surface.

Attenuation curves for copper waveguide are given in Figs. 6.20 and 6.21. In all the curves the attenuation has a fairly broad minimum, which for the H_{10} wave occurs in the wavelength region around $\lambda = \lambda_c/2$. Naturally it is in this region that the waveguide is normally operated, but there are other factors governing the choice of operating wavelength which have still to be considered.

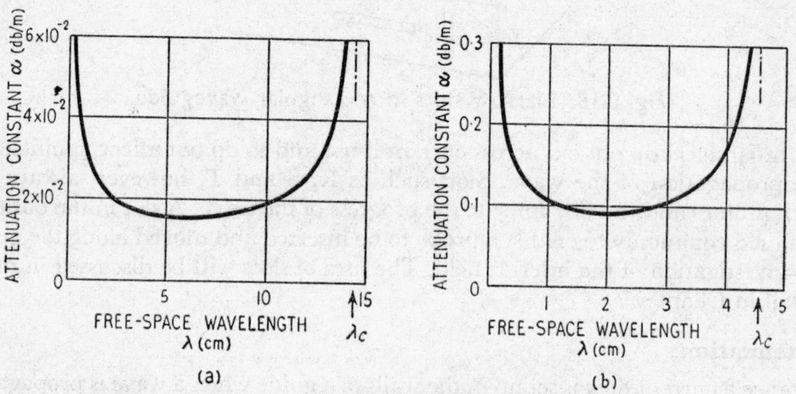

Fig. 6.20. Attenuation constant of H_{10} wave in rectangular copper waveguide (a) of internal dimensions 2·84 × 1·34 in. (b) of internal dimensions 0·9 × 0·4 in.

▶ Actually the wall currents penetrate in appreciable amount to depths several times greater than the 'skin depth', but diminish exponentially. What the skin depth defines is an equivalent thickness of conductor, which, if the current were uniformly distributed in it, would have the same losses as the actual conductor. The skin depth δ for a conductor of permeability μ and resistivity ρ is given in equation (1.6), which can be written as

$$\delta = \sqrt{\frac{\rho}{\pi\mu f}} \text{ metres}$$

This formula, although it was quoted in Chapter 1 for a coaxial line, is quite general for any form of conductor so long as the skin depth is small compared with the radius of curvature. Since the skin depth is so small this limitation is normally unimportant. For copper, with $\mu = \mu_0 = 4\pi \times 10^{-7}$ and $\rho = 1{\cdot}6 \times 10^{-8}$ ohm metre at a wavelength of 10 cm ($f = 3 \times 10^9$ c/s), the skin depth is $\delta = 1{\cdot}2 \times 10^{-6}$ m $= 0{\cdot}0012$ mm. The curves of Fig. 6.19 are calculated from the above formula.

We can now determine the 'surface resistivity' of a conductor at high frequency. This surface resistivity, R_s, is equal to the d.c. resistance of a sheet of the conductor one metre square and of thickness δ, measured between electrodes attached along the length of two opposite edges of the sheet. Thus:

$$R_s = \rho/\delta \text{ ohms} \quad . \quad . \quad . \quad . \quad . \quad . \quad . \qquad (6.12)$$

With the values for copper this becomes $R_s = 8\pi \times 10^{-8} f^{1/2}$ ohms.

If I is the r.m.s. value of the linear current density (or current per metre width), then the power loss per unit area is given by the product I^2R_s.

If a wave has an initial electric field amplitude E_0 and is progressively attenuated, the field amplitude E_z at a distance z along the guide will be given by

$$E_z = E_0 \varepsilon^{-\alpha z}$$

The constant α is called the *attenuation constant*, its value here being in nepers per metre. Magnetic field amplitude, being directly proportional to electric field, is attenuated at the same rate.

The attenuation is most easily calculated by finding expressions for the power flow down the guide and the power absorbed in the walls. The former is calculated from Poynting's theorem, which is given in Appendix 6.3. It is then shown in Appendix 6.4 that the value of α for an H_{10} wave in a rectangular guide of sides a and b (the electric field being parallel to the edge b as in Fig. 6.3) is given by

$$\alpha = \frac{R_s}{120\pi b}\left\{1 + \frac{2b}{a}\left(\frac{\lambda}{2a}\right)^2\right\}\frac{1}{\sqrt{\{1 - (\lambda/2a)^2\}}} \text{ nepers per metre} \qquad (6.13)$$

It will be seen that α varies in a rather complex manner with the size of the tube, the ratio of the cross-sectional dimensions, and the wavelength. The way in which it varies with λ may be seen from Fig. 6.20. In this figure the attenuation is given, not in nepers per metre, but in the more usual unit of decibels per

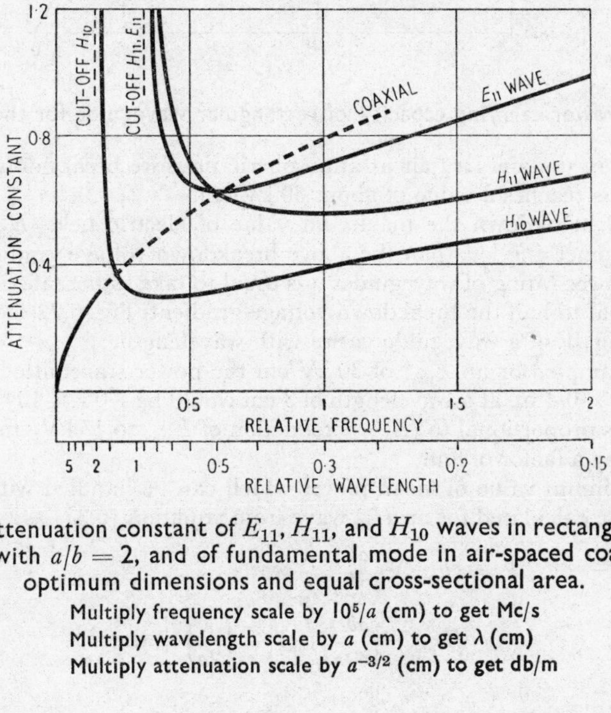

Fig. 6.21. Attenuation constant of E_{11}, H_{11}, and H_{10} waves in rectangular copper waveguide with $a/b = 2$, and of fundamental mode in air-spaced coaxial line of optimum dimensions and equal cross-sectional area.

Multiply frequency scale by $10^5/a$ (cm) to get Mc/s
Multiply wavelength scale by a (cm) to get λ (cm)
Multiply attenuation scale by $a^{-3/2}$ (cm) to get db/m

metre, obtained by multiplying nepers per metre by 8·686 (see Volume 1, Chapter 12). The values are calculated for copper guide; for any other metal the value of R_s and hence of α must be multiplied by a factor $\sqrt{(\rho_{metal}/\rho_{copper})}$.

The attenuation curves for all other modes are similar in form to those of Fig. 6.20, but attenuations are higher in all cases, as can be seen for the E_{11} and H_{11} modes in the curves of Fig. 6.21. The attenuation for any size of guide can be calculated from Fig. 6.21 by multiplying the scales by the factors given in the caption.

Power Carrying Capacity

There is a limit to the power which can be carried by any transmission line. In an air-filled waveguide there is no loss in the air, and the power dissipated in the walls is seldom a limiting factor. The limit is set, however, by voltage

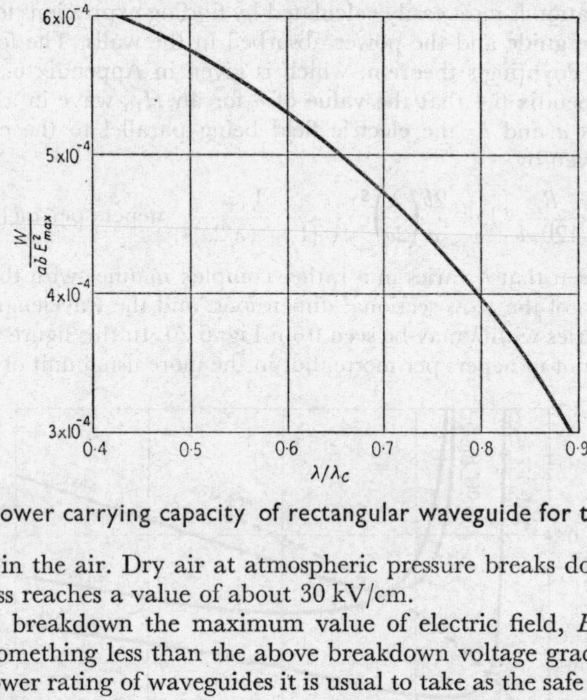

Fig. 6.22. Power carrying capacity of rectangular waveguide for the H_{10} mode.

breakdown in the air. Dry air at atmospheric pressure breaks down when the electric stress reaches a value of about 30 kV/cm.

To avoid breakdown the maximum value of electric field, E_{max}, must be limited to something less than the above breakdown voltage gradient. For the practical power rating of waveguides it is usual to take as the safe limit for E_{max} a value equal to half the breakdown voltage gradient. Fig. 6.22 shows how the power rating W of a waveguide varies with wavelength.

As an example, for an E_{max} of 30 kV/cm the power transmitted by a guide of sides 0·9 × 0·4 in. at a wavelength of 3 cm would be $1{\cdot}05 \times 10^6$ watts. Since the power is proportional to $(E_{max})^2$ reduction of E_{max} to 15 kV/cm will reduce the power by a factor of four.

The maximum value of mean power which can be handled without breakdown can be calculated for an H_{10} wave from equation (6.37) as:

$$P = (E_{max})^2 \frac{ab}{480\pi} \cdot \frac{\lambda}{\lambda_g} \text{ watts}$$

$$= (E_{max})^2 \frac{ab}{480\pi} \sqrt{\left\{1 - \left(\frac{\lambda}{2a}\right)^2\right\}} \text{ watts} \quad . \quad . \quad . \quad (6.14)$$

where E_{max} is the electric field measured halfway across the guide at $x = a/2$, where it has its maximum value.

In the case of a pulsed system P is of course the short-period mean value of the peak power attained during the pulse. With pulses of the order of one microsecond, average pulse powers sufficient to cause voltage breakdown in guides are readily obtainable.

When short r.f. pulses are applied the field at which breakdown occurs is to some extent dependent on the pulse duration and its repetition rate. This is because there is a finite delay between the application of field sufficient to cause breakdown and the actual occurrence of the breakdown, and hence the value of electric field at which breakdown occurs increases as the pulse duration is decreased.

Another important factor influencing breakdown is pressure. The standard figure of 30 kV/cm is for normal atmospheric pressure, but it is found that the breakdown field is approximately proportional to pressure over a wide range. This presents an obvious limitation for airborne equipment. For example, at an altitude of 35,000 ft the air pressure is approximately one-quarter of that at ground level, so that the power-carrying capacity at that altitude is reduced by a factor of about 16. This reduction can be obviated by 'pressurizing' the guide, that is, by sealing off the guide system so that the interior is maintained at or near atmospheric pressure.

Conversely power carrying capacity can be increased above the normal by increasing the pressure inside the guide above atmospheric.

Choice of Waveguide Dimensions

The choice of dimensions for a rectangular guide to be operated at a given wavelength requires consideration of the following factors: (1) desired mode, (2) critical wavelength of this and other modes, (3) attenuation due to conductor loss, (4) power-carrying capacity.

Dimensions are usually chosen so that only the fundamental H_{10} mode can be propagated. In special cases other modes may be chosen, but for all ordinary purposes the H_{10} mode is used. Thus the wavelength range over which a guide of given dimensions may be operated is quite limited, in contrast to a coaxial line, which has a very wide range of operation. If the operating wavelength is λ and the sides of the guide have lengths a and b ($a > b$), then the critical wavelength for the H_{10} mode is $\lambda_c = 2a$. The critical wavelengths for the nearest other modes are: $\lambda_c = a(H_{20})$, $\lambda_c = 2b(H_{01})$. Thus if λ is given and the H_{10} mode alone is to be propagated a must be such that $\lambda/2 < a < \lambda$ and b such that $2b < \lambda$.

For a given dimension a it is usual to define a mean operating wavelength as two-thirds of the H_{10} critical wavelength, so that:

$$\lambda_{\text{mean}} = \tfrac{2}{3}\lambda_c = \tfrac{4}{3}a$$

and to limit the operation to a wavelength band of about 20% on either side of this value. On the short wavelength side this restriction is made in order to exclude the H_{20} mode; on the long wavelength side because the attenuation increases rapidly and the breakdown power decreases rapidly as the cut-off wavelength is approached.

The non-resonant dimension b is usually made roughly equal to $a/2$, this choice giving the lowest attenuation and highest breakdown power compatible with avoidance of the H_{01} mode.

From these considerations a range of standard guides has been developed. Part of this range is given in Table 6.2.

TABLE 6.2

Guide dimensions (in.)				Recommended[1] operating wave-length range (cm)	Attenuation[2] (db/m)	Power[3] rating (MW)
Internal section		External section				
Width	Height	Width	Height			
3·500	1·750	3·660	1·910	14·2 – 9·5	0·013	3·9
2·840	1·340	3·000	1·500	11·5 – 7·7	0·018	2·4
2·372	1·122	2·500	1·250	9·6 – 6·4	0·024	1·7
1·872	0·872	2·000	1·000	7·6 – 5·1	0·034	1·0
1·590	0·795	1·718	0·923	6·5 – 4·3	0·041	0·81
1·372	0·622	1·500	0·750	5·6 – 3·7	0·056	0·54
1·122	0·497	1·250	0·625	4·6 – 3·0	0·077	0·35
0·900	0·400	1·000	0·500	3·6 – 2·4	0·106	0·23

[1] Calculated as $\frac{2}{3}\lambda_c \pm 20\%$.

[2] Calculated from equation (6.13), for $\lambda = \frac{2}{3}\lambda_c$ and copper guide with $\rho = 1{\cdot}62 \times 10^{-8}$ ohm metre.

[3] Calculated from equation (6.14), with $E_{max} = 15$ kV/cm (safety factor of 2).

Comparison between Coaxial Cables and Waveguides

In the consideration of the respective frequency ranges in which coaxial cables and waveguides are most suitable there are a number of relevant factors. The coaxial cable has the advantage in ease of handling, fitting of plugs and sockets, in flexibility, and especially in its freedom from modes over a wide frequency range. Higher modes analogous to waveguide modes do exist, however, and define a lower wavelength limit approximately equal to the mean circumference of the inner and outer conductors multiplied by the square root of the dielectric constant of the insulator. Greater range can be obtained by reducing the diameter, but this increases the attenuation and reduces the power rating of the cable. There is no upper wavelength limit for the coaxial cable.

For purposes of comparison Fig. 6.21 includes a curve of attenuation in an air-spaced coaxial line of optimum dimensions (ratio of radii 3.6) and having the same internal area of cross-section as the waveguide. The solid part of the curve indicates the region over which only the fundamental mode can be propagated. To extend this region to the point where the H_{10} wave has its minimum attenuation would involve halving the coaxial dimensions with a consequent doubling of the attenuation constant.

This illustrates that as regards usable wavelengths there need be no sharp transition from coaxial cables to waveguides. For wavelengths below about 3 cm the dimensions of the coaxial cable become inconveniently small for most uses, if higher modes are to be avoided, and the attenuation is higher than for the waveguide. For wavelengths greater than about 15 cm the superiority of the waveguide as regards attenuation becomes less marked, and its dimensions become inconveniently large. Thus above 15 cm wavelength the coaxial line is generally used; below 3 cm wavelength the waveguide is generally used. In the transition region both may be used, but generally the coaxial cable is used where only low powers are involved and where only short runs are required. Of course these limits are not rigidly set, and in special circumstances may be considerably extended. For example, when very high powers are involved waveguides are sometimes used for wavelengths as long as 50 cm.

Evanescent Waves

Thus far we have assumed that when the free-space wavelength exceeds the critical wavelength for any mode that particular mode is not transmitted. If however a mode is set up at a wavelength greater than its critical value the field is not abruptly cut off, but does penetrate into the tube, its amplitude decaying rapidly with distance. In most circumstances such a mode is negligible except in the immediate neighbourhood of where it has been excited. These rapidly vanishing waves are known as evanescent modes. The rate of decrease of amplitude can readily be shown to follow a calculable exponential law. An evanescent mode is not really a wave in the ordinary sense of the word. It is not a travelling wave, for there is no variation of phase from point to point along the tube; it carries no power, for the electric and magnetic fields are in time quadrature and hence the power is purely reactive. Thus the rapid attenuation of the field is due not to absorption of energy in the walls of the guide but to continuous reflection, all the input power being reflected back to the source. In Chapter 7 the application of this property in an attenuator is described.

▶ Although an evanescent wave is so different from a travelling wave its fields must still satisfy Maxwell's equations, the only mathematical difference being that the form of the solution used for the travelling wave has now ceased to be valid and must be modified to meet the new relation between wavelength and tube dimensions.

It is shown in Appendix 6.1 that in a rectangular guide an H_{10} wave has field components which vary with distance along the guide as $\varepsilon^{-j\beta z}$ (equation (6.28)), where the propagation constant β is equal to $2\pi/\lambda_g$.

Thus, using equation (6.5), we can write:

$$\beta = 2\pi\sqrt{\left(\frac{1}{\lambda^2} - \frac{1}{\lambda_c^2}\right)}$$

When the wavelength is less than the critical wavelength, that is $\lambda < \lambda_c$, the expression under the square root is positive, giving a real value of β. If however the wavelength exceeds the critical value, where $\lambda > \lambda_c$, the expression under the square root is negative, and hence β is imaginary, and can be written as:

$$\beta = \pm j2\pi\sqrt{\left(\frac{1}{\lambda_c^2} - \frac{1}{\lambda^2}\right)}$$

$$= \pm \frac{j2\pi}{\lambda_c}\sqrt{\left\{1 - \left(\frac{\lambda_c}{\lambda}\right)^2\right\}}$$

Thus the factor $\varepsilon^{-j\beta z}$ which represents a change of phase with z when β is real, becomes an exponential change of amplitude with z when β is imaginary. Writing α in place of $j\beta$, and choosing the sign so that the amplitude decreases as z increases, we get the attenuation factor in the form $\varepsilon^{-\alpha z}$, where the attenuation constant α is given by:

$$\alpha = \frac{2\pi}{\lambda_c}\sqrt{\left\{1 - \left(\frac{\lambda_c}{\lambda}\right)^2\right\}}, \quad . \quad . \quad . \quad . \quad (6.15)$$

the unit of α being nepers per unit length of guide. The most important practical case is when λ is much greater than λ_c. The expression under the square root sign in (6.15) is then approximately equal to unity, and (6.15) can be written

$$\alpha \approx \frac{2\pi}{\lambda_c} \text{ nepers per metre} \quad . \quad . \quad . \quad . \quad . \quad (6.16)$$

For example, if $\lambda = 10\lambda_c$ the difference between the values of α given by (6.15) and (6.16) is only 0·5%. For sufficiently large values of λ/λ_c, then, α is practically independent of frequency, and dependent only on tube dimensions. With the appropriate values for λ_c this equation holds for all evanescent wave types.

Propagation in Circular Waveguide

Another simple shape of tube which can be used as a waveguide is one with circular cross-section. This time it is not easy to fit together plane waves in such a way as to satisfy the boundary conditions on a circle. With a knowledge of

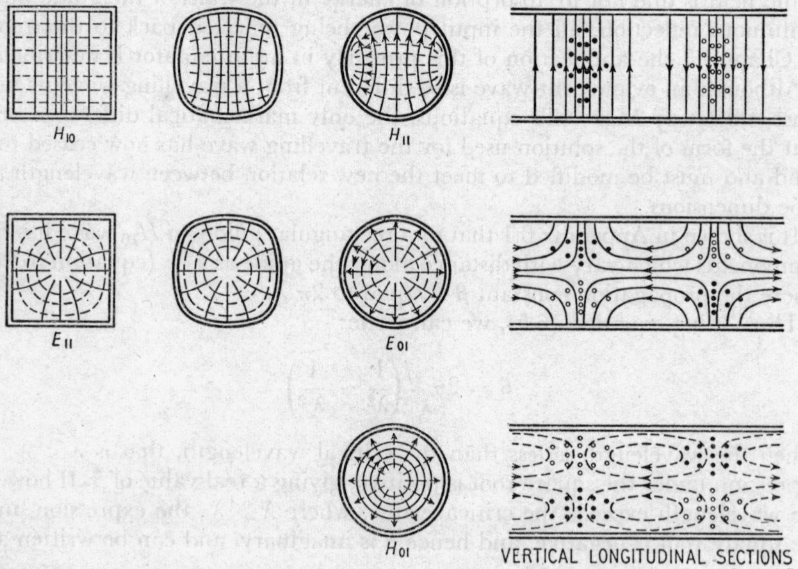

Fig. 6.23. Development of circular waveguide modes from modes in rectangular waveguide.

——— electric-field lines ∘ into paper
- - - - - - magnetic-field lines • out of paper

the modes for a rectangular guide, however, it is not difficult to imagine the changes of shape which would take place in the various field patterns in a square tube when it is gradually deformed into a circle. Fig. 6.23 shows two of the

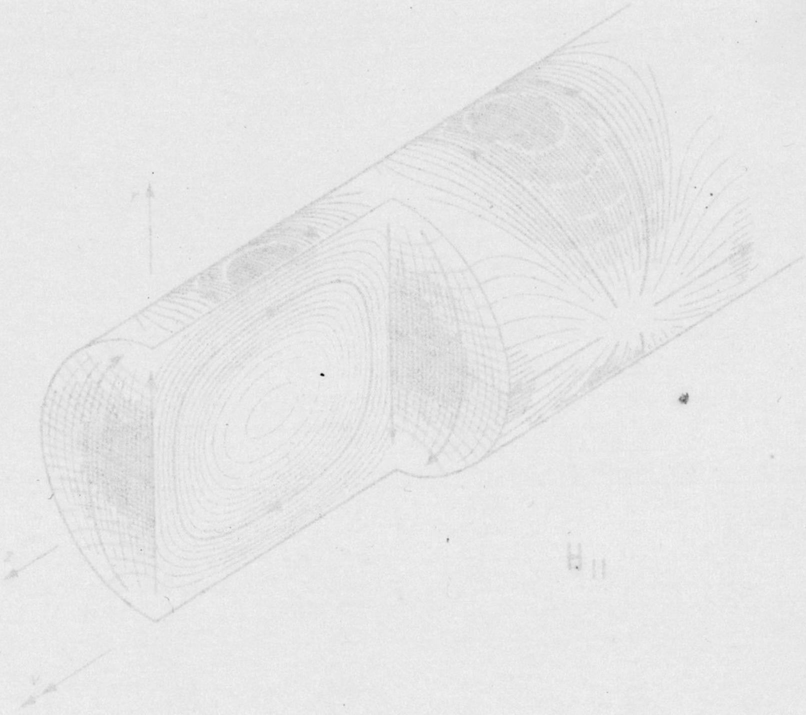

Fig. 6.24. Three-dimensional views of the field configurations of H_{01}, H_{11} and E_{01} modes in circular waveguides. The electric field is indicated in red and the magnetic in green, while the current in the waveguide walls is shown in blue.

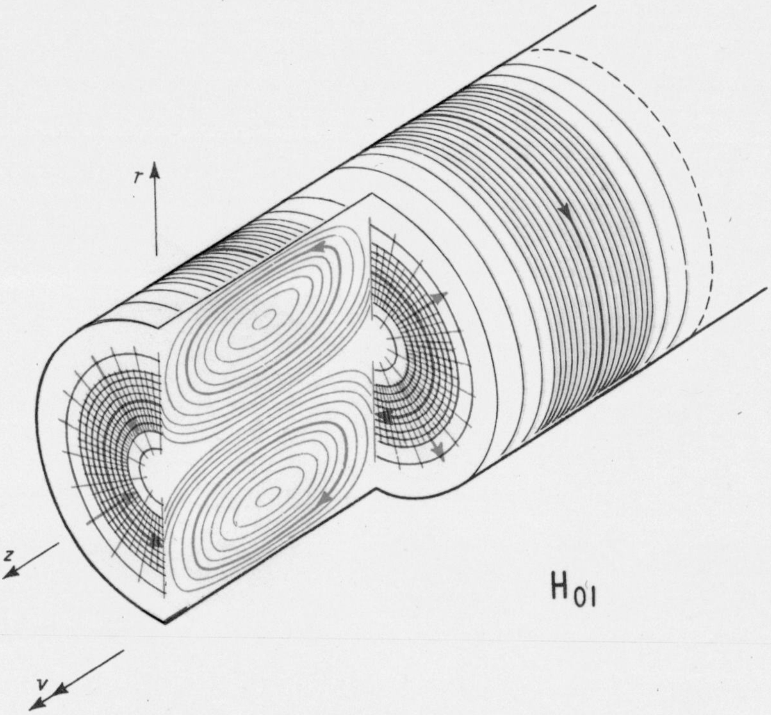

H_{01}

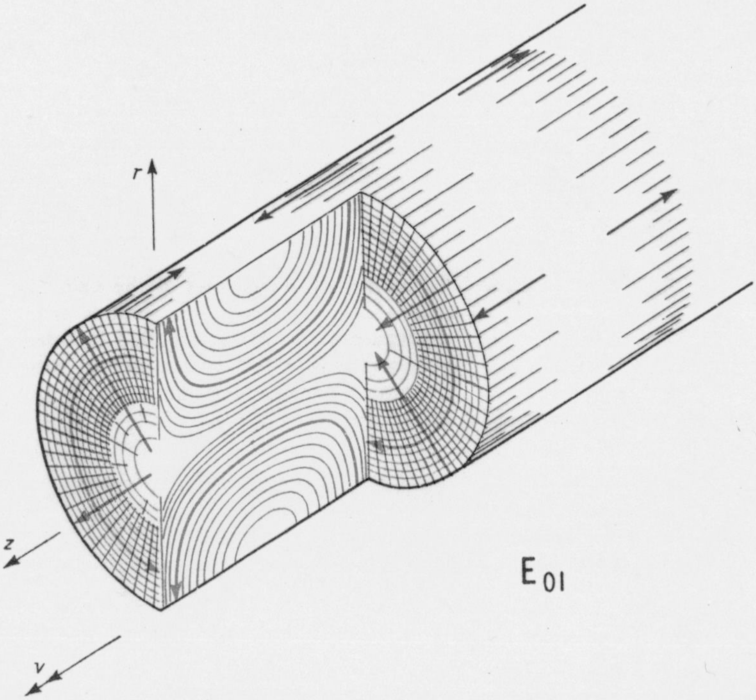

E_{01}

simple modes in a square tube so distorted, and from these it appears that the circular waveguide can also carry E and H types of wave. The field in a longitudinal section is of the same general form in the corresponding modes of rectangular and circular guides, but it will be observed that in Fig. 6.23 different designations have been given to corresponding modes. This is because the subscripts represent values of certain parameters in the field equations, and the field equations for the circular guide are of quite a different form from those of the rectangular guide. This is dealt with in the following section. Fig. 6.23 also shows the third important wave type in a circular guide—the H_{01}, which has no counterpart in the rectangular guide. These three waves are shown in more detail in Fig. 6.24.

The wave types in circular guides have properties very similar to those of the rectangular guide. Here again the wavelength measured in the guide, λ_g, differs from the free-space wavelength λ, and the two are related by the same expression (6.5) as for the rectangular guide,

$$\frac{1}{\lambda_g^2} = \frac{1}{\lambda^2} - \frac{1}{\lambda_c^2}$$

where λ_c, the critical wavelength, is proportional to the tube diameter. We can get an approximate idea of the critical wavelength by considering the rectangular case. For example, in a square tube of side a the H_{10} critical wavelength is $2a$. If we assume that in the circular case the same ratio of critical wavelength to perimeter exists then the H_{11} critical wavelength for a tube of diameter D would be $\lambda_c = \pi D/2$. This is some 8% lower than the value given by theory. The theoretical values are given in Table 6.3.

TABLE 6.3

Mode	Bessel function constant s	Critical wavelength $\lambda_c = \pi D/s$
H_{11}	1·841	1·71D
E_{01}	2·405	1·31D
H_{01}	3·832	0·82D

Modes in Circular Guide

▶ It is shown in Appendix 6.5 that the solution of Maxwell's equation appropriate to a circular tube involves Bessel functions in addition to the simpler trigonometric functions, and it is these which determine the values of critical wavelengths.

We shall consider here only the three simplest modes which have already been introduced. The critical wavelengths for these are dependent on the tube diameter D, and on a Bessel function constant s; values are given in Table 6.3.

The H_{11} is the fundamental mode, having the longest critical wavelength, the counterpart in the circular guide of the fundamental mode in the rectangular guide. The subscript 0 in the E_{01} and H_{01} types indicates that there is no variation of the field in moving round the circumference of the guide. These types are said to be symmetrical. The other type, H_{11}, whose first subscript is 1, has a field whose components vary sinusoidally as one moves round the circumference. This is indicated in Fig. 6.25 where, for the H_{11} wave, the radial electric field is zero at the 0° and 180° positions, with maxima in opposite directions at

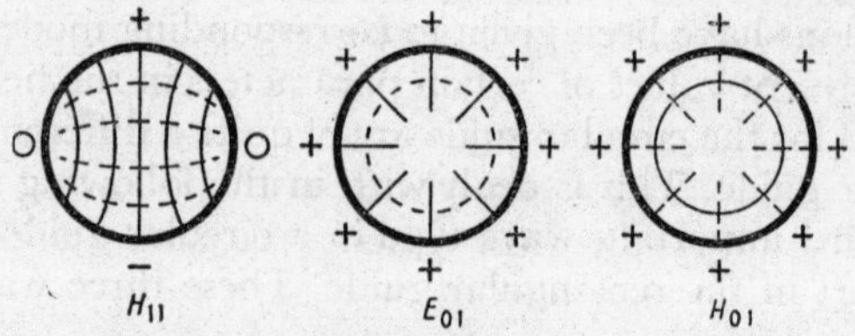

Fig. 6.25. Symmetrical and unsymmetrical modes in circular waveguide.

the 90° and 270° positions. The value of the second subscript determines the complexity of the field variations along the radius; only the simplest cases where this subscript is unity are considered here.

As in the rectangular guide these waves travel with a phase velocity exceeding the velocity of light and have a group velocity less than the velocity of light. The treatment used in Appendix 6.1 for the rectangular guide is equally applicable here, giving,

$$v_p = c\frac{\lambda_g}{\lambda}$$

$$v_g = c\frac{\lambda}{\lambda_g}$$

as before in equations (6.7) and (6.8).

Attenuation in Circular Waveguide

In their progress down the guide these waves will be attenuated because of power dissipated in the resistance of the guide walls. Formulae for the attenuation constants can be derived in the same way as for the rectangular guide. The curves of Fig. 6.26 show the values of attenuation constant for the E_{01} and H_{01}

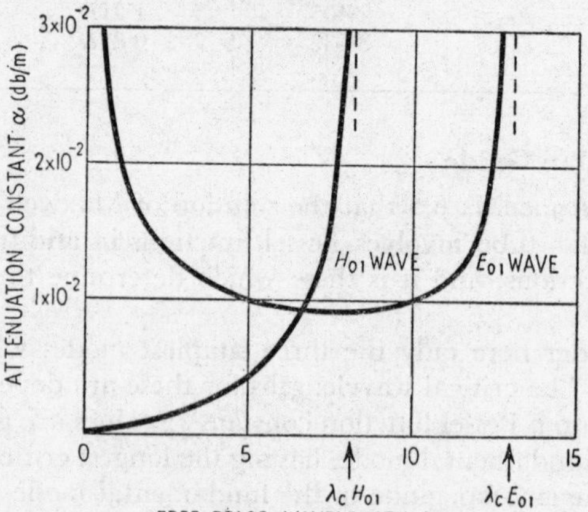

Fig. 6.26. Attenuation constant of E_{01} and H_{01} waves in circular copper waveguide of diameter 10 cm.

waves in a copper guide of 10-cm internal diameter. It will be seen that the two curves are radically different in form. That for E_{01} is of the form discussed previously for wave types in rectangular guides, having a minimum at a wavelength which, in this case, is 0·58 times the critical wavelength. This shape is characteristic of almost all attenuation curves for waveguides. The H_{01} wave in a circular guide is the exception. For this wave the attenuation decreases steadily as the wavelength is decreased, and approaches a zero value.

The mathematical treatment of attenuation gives the following formula for the attenuation of the H_{01} wave in a guide of diameter D:

$$\alpha = \frac{R_s}{60\pi D}\left(\frac{\lambda}{\lambda_c}\right)^2 \frac{1}{\sqrt{\{1-(\lambda/\lambda_c)^2\}}} \text{ nepers per metre} \quad . \quad . \quad (6.17)$$

As before this can be converted to db/m by multiplying by 8·686.

Circular guides are seldom used in long lengths for modes other than the H_{01}, and formulae for the attenuations of these will not be quoted here.

Evanescent Waves in Circular Guide

If the free-space wavelength is greater than the critical wavelength of any particular mode then β for that mode is imaginary, just as in the rectangular guide. The wave is then attenuated with distance according to the factor $\varepsilon^{-\alpha z}$ where the attenuation constant α is given as before by equation (6.15):

$$\alpha = \frac{2\pi}{\lambda_c}\sqrt{\left\{1-\left(\frac{\lambda_c}{\lambda}\right)^2\right\}}$$

or, when λ is considerably longer than λ_c, approximately by equation (6.16):

$$\alpha \approx \frac{2\pi}{\lambda_c}$$

For the H_{11}, E_{01} and H_{01} wave types the values of α, expressed in db/m by equation (6.16), are respectively $32{\cdot}0/D$, $41{\cdot}8/D$ and $66{\cdot}6/D$.

Use of Circular Guides

The circular guide has not the wide application as a transmission line that the rectangular guide has, but has its own special properties which give it important, if limited, applications.

An H_{11} wave in a circular guide has no plane of polarization in the same exact sense as for an H_{10} wave in a rectangular guide, but the plane passing through the axis and coinciding with the straight central line of electric field is normally called the plane of polarization. A wave may be generated with a definite plane of polarization, but in its progress down the tube bends or other discontinuities or a slight ovality may rotate the plane by an unknown and possibly variable amount. This is a severe limitation on the use of the circular guide in its fundamental mode. On the other hand the ability to transmit equally well waves of any polarization may be useful in special cases. Waves of different polarizations will travel without interference and may readily be separated.

The E_{01} mode is important because of its complete circular symmetry. This property is widely used in the design of rotating couplings for use with waveguide systems in which movement is required—for example, for connection to a rotating aerial. The H_{01} mode has similar properties but is not widely used because of the difficulty of generating it in a pure form.

The special form of the attenuation curve of the H_{01} wave indicates important possibilities for transmission over long distances with small loss. This is not so simple as might appear, however. The unusual characteristic is associated with a certain instability in the wave which requires the tube to be perfectly straight and perfectly circular. Imperfections cause energy to be lost into other modes. As the guide must be used with a wavelength very much below its critical wavelength in order to get the advantage of low attenuation these other transmitted modes are numerous and their attenuations are high. With care, however, very low attenuations can be realized.

The problem of transmitting an H_{01} wave round a bend has been partially solved by the discovery, predicted from theory, that there are certain critical angles of bend through which propagation with negligible loss is possible. An H_{01} wave set up in a circular guide bent into a circle of radius large compared with the guide diameter will gradually change into an E_{11} wave as it progresses and then gradually change back into its original form. The length required for

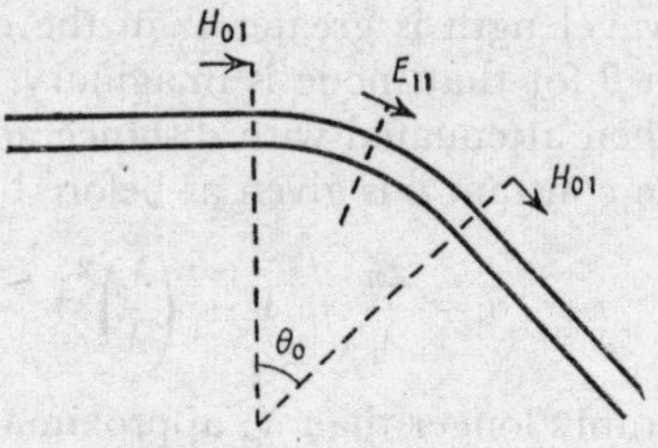

Fig. 6.27. Propagation of H_{10} wave in curved circular waveguide.

this complete cycle defines the critical angle of bend, θ_0 in Fig. 6·27, required to give undisturbed transmission. The critical angle for a guide of diameter D operated at a wavelength λ is given by:

$$\theta_0 = 310° \times \frac{\lambda}{D} \quad . \quad . \quad . \quad . \quad . \quad . \quad (6.18)$$

or by multiples of this angle. It is to be noted that the angle is independent of the radius of curvature of the bend. This of course gives little scope for bends in the design of H_{01} systems. Nevertheless λ/D can be chosen so as to make the critical angle equal to any desired value.

APPENDIX 6.1

H_{10} Wave in Rectangular Waveguide

The direct method of investigating the propagation of waves in any bounded system is to find solutions of Maxwell's equations which satisfy the appropriate boundary conditions. To do this completely for a rectangular guide is not difficult, but it is tedious, since we have six simultaneous differential equations to solve, one for each of the three components of **E** and of **H**.

Let us simplify matters by assuming, as we did for the plane wave, that there is only one component of electric field. This time in accordance with convention we shall choose this component as E_y. The co-ordinate system is fitted to the waveguide as shown in Fig. 6.28, and the lengths of the sides lying along the x- and y-axes are a and b respectively. For the interior of the waveguide it is assumed that $\kappa_r = \mu_r = 1$.

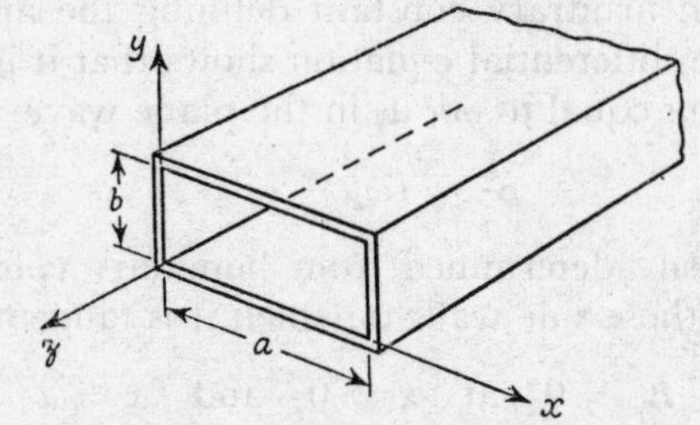

Fig. 6.28. Co-ordinate system for rectangular waveguide.

The equations to be solved are similar to those of equation (5.47), viz.:

$$\left.\begin{aligned} \kappa_0 \frac{\partial E_y}{\partial t} &= \frac{\partial H_x}{\partial z} - \frac{\partial H_z}{\partial x} \\ -\mu_0 \frac{\partial H_x}{\partial t} &= -\frac{\partial E_y}{\partial z} \\ -\mu_0 \frac{\partial H_y}{\partial t} &= 0 \\ -\mu_0 \frac{\partial H_z}{\partial t} &= \frac{\partial E_y}{\partial x} \end{aligned}\right\} \quad . \quad . \quad . \quad . \quad . \quad (6.19)$$

This time, however, we cannot put H_z equal to zero as we did for the plane wave in Appendix 5.2, since the elementary considerations of p. 151 have shown that there must be a magnetic component in the z-direction. To solve the equations (6.19) differentiate the first with respect to t, and substitute for H_x and H_z from the second and fourth, getting:

$$\kappa_0 \frac{\partial^2 E_y}{\partial t^2} = \frac{\partial^2 H_x}{\partial t \partial z} - \frac{\partial^2 H_z}{\partial t \partial x}$$

$$= \frac{1}{\mu_0}\left(\frac{\partial^2 E_y}{\partial z^2} + \frac{\partial^2 E_y}{\partial x^2}\right)$$

Hence:

$$\frac{\partial^2 E_y}{\partial x^2} + \frac{\partial^2 E_y}{\partial z^2} - \kappa_0 \mu_0 \frac{\partial^2 E_y}{\partial t^2} = 0$$

or

$$\frac{\partial^2 E_y}{\partial x^2} + \frac{\partial^2 E_y}{\partial z^2} - \frac{1}{c^2}\frac{\partial^2 E_y}{\partial t^2} = 0 \quad . \quad . \quad . \quad . \quad . \quad (6.20)$$

This is the differential equation to be solved for E_y, and similar equations hold for H_x and H_z. It is a wave equation like (5.49), but complicated by the addition of one more term.

Try as a solution of (6.20) the expression:

$$E_y = A \sin kx \sin (\omega t - \beta z) \quad . \quad . \quad . \quad . \quad . \quad (6.21)$$

where β is the propagation constant, k is for the moment an undetermined constant, and A is an arbitrary constant defining the amplitude of E_y. Substitution of this in the differential equation shows that it is a solution provided that β, instead of being equal to ω/c as in the plane wave, satisfies the equation

$$\beta^2 = (\omega/c)^2 - k^2 \quad . \quad . \quad . \quad . \quad . \quad . \quad (6.22)$$

The constant k is easily determined from boundary conditions. The electric field must be zero at those side walls to which it is tangential, that is:

$$E_y = 0 \quad \text{at} \quad x = 0 \quad \text{and} \quad x = a$$

The form of equation (6.21) satisfies this condition automatically for $x = 0$, but for $x = a$ it requires that:

$$\sin ka = 0$$

whence a number of possible values of k are determined by $ka = \pi, 2\pi, 3\pi, \ldots.$

The first value of k gives the field of what we have called the H_{10} mode. For this value of k (6.21) becomes:

$$E_y = A \sin (\pi x/a) \sin (\omega t - \beta z) \quad . \quad . \quad . \quad . \quad (6.23)$$

with β given, through (6.22), by:

$$\beta^2 = \left(\frac{\omega}{c}\right)^2 - \left(\frac{\pi}{a}\right)^2 \quad . \quad . \quad . \quad . \quad . \quad . \quad (6.24)$$

This value of the phase constant β in the waveguide defines the guide wavelength λ_g by the relation $\beta = 2\pi/\lambda_g$ just as the free-space value of β defines the free-space wavelength λ in equation (5.22). By substituting this in equation (6.24) and dividing through by $4\pi^2$ we get the fundamental relation between λ and λ_g for the H_{10} mode, previously developed from elementary considerations as equation (6.4),

$$\frac{1}{\lambda_g^2} = \frac{1}{\lambda^2} - \frac{1}{(2a)^2} \quad . \quad . \quad . \quad . \quad . \quad . \quad (6.25)$$

Substitution of equation (6.23) into (6.19) enables us to find the following expressions for the field components:

$$\left.\begin{aligned} E_y &= A \sin \frac{\pi x}{a} \sin (\omega t - \beta z) \\ H_x &= -A\frac{\beta}{\omega\mu_0} \sin \frac{\pi x}{a} \sin (\omega t - \beta z) \\ H_z &= A\frac{\pi/a}{\omega\mu_0} \cos \frac{\pi x}{a} \cos (\omega t - \beta z) \\ E_x &= E_z = H_y = 0 \end{aligned}\right\} \quad . \quad . \quad . \quad (6.26)$$

where the phase constant β is given by equation (6.24).

A solution in cos $(\omega t - \beta z)$ could equally well have been used in place of the sine term in equation (6.23), and the two solutions can then be combined in the form:

$$E_y = A \sin \frac{\pi x}{a} \varepsilon^{j(\omega t - \beta z)} \quad . \quad . \quad . \quad . \quad . \quad (6.27)$$

in the same way as was done in the equations for the plane wave equation (5.54). This form of the solution is more convenient for some purposes. It may also be written as:

$$E_y = A \sin \frac{\pi x}{a} \varepsilon^{j\omega t} \varepsilon^{-j\beta z} \quad . \quad . \quad . \quad . \quad . \quad (6.28)$$

The lines of force plotted from the field components give the accurate field distribution whose approximate form was deduced from elementary considerations on pp. 151–3.

The phase and group velocities can now be readily derived. The form $(\omega t - \beta z)$ represents a wave travelling in the positive direction of the z-axis. By equation (1.34):

$$v_p = \frac{\omega}{\beta} = \frac{2\pi c/\lambda}{2\pi/\lambda_g} = c\frac{\lambda_g}{\lambda}$$

as in equation (6.7). By equations (1.38) and (6.24):

$$v_g = \frac{d\omega}{d\beta} = \frac{c^2\beta}{\omega} = \frac{c^2}{v_p} = c\frac{\lambda}{\lambda_g}$$

as in equation (6.8).

A more general solution would be found by taking $ka = m\pi$ (m any integer) as the solution of $\sin ka = 0$ in place of the particular value $ka = \pi$ which gave the H_{10} wave. This gives as the equation for λ_g:

$$\frac{1}{\lambda_g^2} = \frac{1}{\lambda^2} - \left(\frac{m}{2a}\right)^2 \quad . \quad . \quad . \quad . \quad . \quad (6.29)$$

and this value corresponds to the more general H_{m0} wave.

APPENDIX 6.2

General Solution for Rectangular Waveguide

For the most general form of H wave the E_x component must be retained as well as the E_y, but since the wave is transverse electric E_z is still zero. The wave equation for any of the field components is the general one given in equation (5.44). If the expression:

$$E_x = A \cos k_1 x \sin k_2 y \sin (\omega t - \beta z)$$

is substituted in equation (5.44) it is seen to be a solution (for the case where $\kappa_r = \mu_r = 1$) provided that β satisfies the equation:

$$\beta^2 = (\omega/c)^2 - k_1^2 - k_2^2 \quad . \quad . \quad . \quad . \quad . \quad (6.30)$$

By equation (5.42) the component E_y can be found to be proportional to $\sin k_1x \cos k_2y \sin(\omega t - \beta z)$. This time the boundary conditions $E_x = 0$ at $y = 0, y = b$, and $E_y = 0$ at $x = 0$, $x = a$, involve both the dimensions a and b, the values of k_1 and k_2 being thereby determined as $k_1a = m\pi$, $k_2b = n\pi$ with integral values for m and n. This gives as the general expression for λ_g in an H_{mn} wave:

$$\frac{1}{\lambda_g^2} = \frac{1}{\lambda^2} - \left(\frac{m}{2a}\right)^2 - \left(\frac{n}{2b}\right)^2 \quad . \quad . \quad . \quad . \quad (6.31)$$

and hence for the critical wavelength λ_c:

$$\frac{1}{\lambda_c^2} = \left(\frac{m}{2a}\right)^2 + \left(\frac{n}{2b}\right)^2 \quad . \quad . \quad . \quad . \quad . \quad . \quad (6.32)$$

The treatment for the E_{mn} wave is similar, and gives rise to the same equations (6.31) and (6.32) for λ_g and λ_c.

If the expressions for the field components are derived it will be found that for the H wave either m or n may be made zero, but if both are made zero the field vanishes. For the E wave, on the other hand, the field vanishes if either m or n is made zero. Thus, while the fundamental H mode is the H_{10} or H_{01} (depending on whether $a > b$ or $a < b$), the fundamental E mode is the E_{11}.

The expressions (6.7) and (6.8) for phase and group velocity as derived in Appendix 6.1 are quite general, and apply, with appropriate values of λ_g, to any wave type.

APPENDIX 6.3

Power and the Poynting Vector

A travelling wave carries energy with it, and when we are dealing with waves in terms of their electric and magnetic fields it is important to be able to calculate the energy flow in terms of these fields.

Consider an imaginary plane surface in space chosen perpendicular to the direction of motion of a plane wave. There will be a flow of power through this surface, and the power passing through a unit area, in watts per square metre, will be denoted by the symbol **P**. This is a vector quantity, indicating the direction of power flow as well as its magnitude. It is called the Poynting vector after a British physicist who first enunciated an important theorem concerning it. Poynting's theorem states that, if E and H are instantaneous values of the electric and magnetic vectors at a point and θ the angle between them, then there is a power flow in a direction normal to the plane containing E and H of which the instantaneous value per unit area, denoted by P_a, is given* by

$$P_a = EH \sin\theta \text{ webers per square metre} \quad . \quad . \quad . \quad (6.33)$$

The direction of **P** relative to the fields is given by the 'corkscrew rule' (p. 139) and is as shown in Fig. 6.29.

* This relation is most compactly expressed in the notation of vector algebra by the vector product $\mathbf{P} = \mathbf{E} \times \mathbf{H}$. Those familiar with vector methods will see that equation (6.35) follows immediately.

Thus for the plane wave given by equation (5.54) the magnitude of the Poynting vector through a surface coinciding with the plane $z = 0$ at the instant $t = 0$ is:

$$P_a = A^2(\kappa_0/\mu_0)^{1/2} = A^2/120\pi \quad . \quad . \quad . \quad . \quad . \quad . \quad (6.34)$$

and its direction is along the positive z-axis.

In dealing with propagation in a waveguide the power flow is along the guide axis, and so our surface is chosen perpendicular to the axis of the guide. The possible field components in this cross-section are E_x, E_y, H_x and H_y. There will then be two components of **P**, viz.: E_xH_y and E_yH_x, but the direction of the

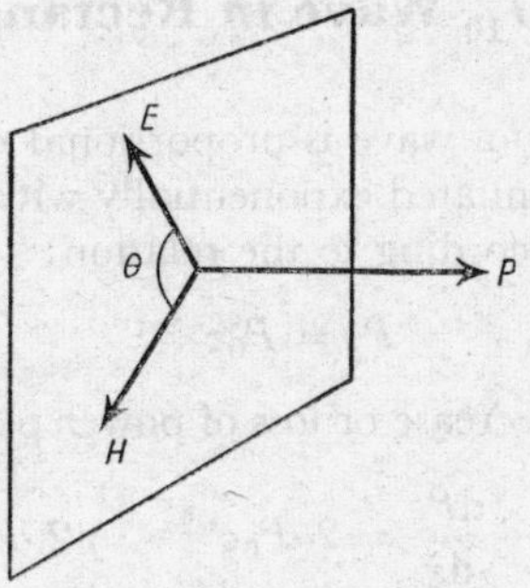

Fig. 6.29. Vector directions in Poynting's theorem.

second is, by the corkscrew rule, along the negative z-axis. Thus the value of **P** at the point (x, y) in the cross-section is given by equation (6.35):

$$P_a = E_xH_y - E_yH_x \quad . \quad . \quad . \quad . \quad . \quad . \quad (6.35)$$

Application of this formula to the equations (6.26) of the H_{10} wave in a rectangular guide at a point in the plane $z = 0$ gives:

$$P_a = \frac{A^2}{120\pi}\frac{\lambda}{\lambda_g}\sin^2\frac{\pi x}{a}\sin^2\omega t$$

This is the instantaneous power flow at one point in the cross-section. To obtain the instantaneous total power P_{inst} this expression must be integrated over the whole area of the waveguide cross-section, and becomes:

$$P_{\text{inst}} = \frac{A^2}{120\pi}\frac{\lambda}{\lambda_g}\int_0^a \sin^2\frac{\pi x}{a}\,dx\int_0^b dy\,\sin^2\omega t$$

$$= \frac{A^2}{120\pi}\frac{\lambda}{\lambda_g}\frac{ab}{2}\sin^2\omega t$$

Usually the mean value P over an interval of time is required, so that $\sin^2 \omega t$ is replaced by its mean value $\frac{1}{2}$, and the mean power is:

$$P = \frac{A^2}{120\pi}\frac{\lambda}{\lambda_g}\frac{ab}{4}\text{ watts} \quad . \quad . \quad . \quad . \quad . \quad (6.36)$$

This expression is used in calculating attenuation in a waveguide.

It is clear from equation (6.26) that the maximum electric field occurs half-way across the guide, at $x = a/2$, and that the maximum value is equal to A. So equation (6.36) can be written as:

$$P = (E_{\text{max}})^2 \frac{ab}{480\pi} \frac{\lambda}{\lambda_g} \text{ watts} \quad . \quad . \quad . \quad . \quad . \quad (6.37)$$

APPENDIX 6.4

Attenuation of H_{10} Wave in Rectangular Waveguide

Since the power carried by a wave is proportional to the product of E and H, then if each of these is attenuated exponentially with an attenuation constant α the power will decrease according to the relation:

$$P_z = P_0 \varepsilon^{-2\alpha z}$$

Hence the rate of power decrease or loss of power per unit length is equal to:

$$-\frac{\mathrm{d}P_z}{\mathrm{d}z} = 2\alpha P_0 \varepsilon^{-2\alpha z} = 2\alpha P_z$$

Thus, if P_{loss} is the power lost in a unit length of guide through which the power flow is P, the attenuation constant is given by:

$$\alpha = \frac{P_{\text{loss}}}{2P} \quad . \quad . \quad . \quad . \quad . \quad . \quad . \quad . \quad (6.38)$$

By the boundary condition equation (5.1) the magnitude of the surface current density is equal to that of the tangential magnetic field at the surface. The current density in the lower surface of the guide (Fig. 6.3) is due to the magnetic field components H_x and H_z, and its mean-square value is given by:

$$I^2 = \tfrac{1}{2}|\mathbf{H}|^2 = \tfrac{1}{2}[|H_z|^2 + |H_x|^2]_{y=0}$$

Multiplication of I^2 by the surface resistivity R_s gives the mean power loss per unit area. Inserting the values for H_z and H_x from equation (6.26) and integrating over the width from $x = 0$ to $x = a$ we get the mean power loss per unit length as:

$$\tfrac{1}{2}R_s \int_0^a \left\{ \left(\frac{A\pi/a}{\omega\mu_0}\right)^2 \cos^2\frac{\pi x}{a} + \left(\frac{A\beta}{\omega\mu_0}\right)^2 \sin^2\frac{\pi x}{a} \right\} \mathrm{d}x$$

which reduces to

$$\tfrac{1}{2}R_s \left(\frac{A}{120\pi}\right)^2 \frac{a}{2}$$

A similar calculation gives the mean power loss per unit length for the side wall $x = 0$ as

$$\tfrac{1}{2}R_s \int_0^b \left(\frac{A\pi/a}{\omega\mu_0}\right)^2 \mathrm{d}y = \tfrac{1}{2}R_s \left(\frac{A}{120\pi} \frac{\lambda}{\lambda_c}\right)^2 b$$

Doubling the sum of these two losses to give the total loss per unit length for all four walls gives:

$$P_{\text{loss}} = R_s\left(\frac{A}{120\pi}\right)^2 \frac{a}{2}\left\{1 + \frac{2b}{a}\left(\frac{\lambda}{\lambda_c}\right)^2\right\}$$

Then, using equations (6.38) and (6.36) and putting $\lambda_c = 2a$, we can calculate the attenuation constant as:

$$\alpha = \frac{R_s}{120\pi b}\left\{1 + \frac{2b}{a}\left(\frac{\lambda}{2a}\right)^2\right\}\frac{1}{\sqrt{\{1 - (\lambda/2a)^2\}}} \text{ nepers per metre} \qquad (6.39)$$

APPENDIX 6.5

Theory of Circular Waveguide

The wave equation (5.44) applies equally to propagation in a circular waveguide, but in that form it is difficult to satisfy the boundary conditions. The equation must be transformed into cylindrical co-ordinates, so that a point

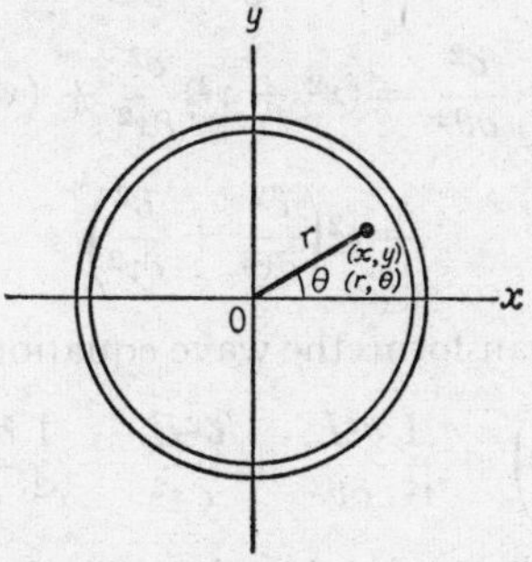

Fig. 6.30. Cylindrical co-ordinate system for circular waveguide.

instead of being represented by the co-ordinates (x, y, z) is represented by (r, θ, z), where r is the radius vector and θ the polar angle, related to x and y, as shown in Fig. 6.30 by:

$$x = r\cos\theta$$
$$y = r\sin\theta$$

The transformation can be carried out most simply by regarding r and θ as two independent variables, in terms of which x and y are defined by the above equations. Thus we can write:

$$\frac{\partial}{\partial r} = \frac{\partial}{\partial x}\frac{\partial x}{\partial r} + \frac{\partial}{\partial y}\frac{\partial y}{dr}$$
$$= \frac{\partial}{\partial x}\cos\theta + \frac{\partial}{\partial y}\sin\theta$$

Whence, after multiplication by r,

$$r\frac{\partial}{\partial r} = x\frac{\partial}{\partial x} + y\frac{\partial}{\partial y}$$

Differentiation with respect to r gives:

$$\frac{\partial}{\partial r}\left(r\frac{\partial}{\partial r}\right) = \left(\frac{\partial}{\partial x} + x\frac{\partial^2}{\partial x^2} + y\frac{\partial^2}{\partial x \partial y}\right)\frac{\partial x}{\partial r} + \left(\frac{\partial}{\partial y} + y\frac{\partial^2}{\partial y^2} + x\frac{\partial^2}{\partial x \partial y}\right)\frac{\partial y}{\partial r},$$

which reduces to:

$$r\frac{\partial}{\partial r}\left(r\frac{\partial}{\partial r}\right) = x^2\frac{\partial^2}{\partial x^2} + y^2\frac{\partial^2}{\partial y^2} + 2xy\frac{\partial^2}{\partial x \partial y} + x\frac{\partial}{\partial x} + y\frac{\partial}{\partial y} \quad . \quad . \quad (6.40)$$

Similarly,

$$\begin{aligned}\frac{\partial}{\partial \theta} &= \frac{\partial}{\partial x}\frac{\partial x}{\partial \theta} + \frac{\partial}{\partial y}\frac{\partial y}{\partial \theta} \\ &= -y\frac{\partial}{\partial x} + x\frac{\partial}{\partial y}\end{aligned}$$

and a second differentiation gives:

$$\frac{\partial^2}{\partial \theta^2} = y^2\frac{\partial^2}{\partial x^2} + x^2\frac{\partial^2}{\partial y^2} - 2xy\frac{\partial^2}{\partial x \partial y} - x\frac{\partial}{\partial x} - y\frac{\partial}{\partial y} \quad . \quad . \quad (6.41)$$

Adding equations (6.40) and (6.41) we get:

$$\begin{aligned}r\frac{\partial}{\partial r}\left(r\frac{\partial}{\partial r}\right) + \frac{\partial^2}{\partial \theta^2} &= (x^2 + y^2)\frac{\partial^2}{\partial x^2} + (x^2 + y^2)\frac{\partial^2}{\partial y^2} \\ &= r^2\left(\frac{\partial^2}{\partial x^2} + \frac{\partial^2}{\partial y^2}\right)\end{aligned}$$

Substitution of this result transforms the wave equation (5.44) into its polar form

$$\frac{1}{r}\frac{\partial}{\partial r}\left(r\frac{\partial E_z}{\partial r}\right) + \frac{1}{r^2}\frac{\partial^2 E_z}{\partial \theta^2} + \frac{\partial^2 E_z}{\partial z^2} - \frac{1}{c^2}\frac{\partial^2 E_z}{\partial t^2} = 0 \quad . \quad . \quad (6.42)$$

κ_r and μ_r being taken equal to unity. We should expect the part of the solution of this equation involving z and t to be of the same form as in previous wave solutions, that is, $\cos(\omega t - \beta z)$ or $\varepsilon^{j(\omega t - \beta z)}$. If the complete solution be written as $E_z = F\varepsilon^{j(\omega t - \beta z)}$ [or $F\cos(\omega t - \beta z)$], where F is that part of the solution involving r and θ, substitution of this in equation (6.42) gives:

$$\frac{1}{r}\frac{\partial}{\partial r}\left(r\frac{\partial F}{\partial r}\right) + \frac{1}{r^2}\frac{\partial^2 F}{\partial \theta^2} + \left(-\beta^2 + \frac{\omega^2}{c^2}\right)F = 0$$

which can be written as:

$$\frac{1}{r}\frac{\partial}{\partial r}\left(r\frac{\partial F}{\partial r}\right) + \frac{1}{r^2}\frac{\partial^2 F}{\partial \theta^2} + k^2 F = 0 \quad . \quad . \quad . \quad . \quad (6.43)$$

Let us consider first the simpler case where E_z and hence F are independent of θ so that (6.43) reduces to

$$\frac{1}{r}\frac{\mathrm{d}}{\mathrm{d}r}\left(r\frac{\mathrm{d}F}{\mathrm{d}r}\right) + k^2 F = 0$$

or

$$\frac{\mathrm{d}^2 F}{\mathrm{d}r^2} + \frac{1}{r}\frac{\mathrm{d}F}{\mathrm{d}r} + k^2 F = 0$$

This equation, which is a special case of what is called *Bessel's Equation*, can only be solved in terms of simple functions by means of an infinite series. Substitution of the series

$$F = 1 - \frac{(kr)^2}{2^2} + \frac{(kr)^4}{(2.4)^2} - \frac{(kr)^6}{(2.4.6)^2} + \ldots \quad (6.44)$$

will show that this satisfies the equation. It is convenient however, to introduce as the solution a new function, which will be defined by this series. The function is called a *Bessel Function* and for it the usual symbol is $J_0(kr)$. In this particular case it is of zero order, indicated by the subscript 0. The full expression for E_z is then

$$E_z = A\, J_0(kr)\,\varepsilon^{j(\omega t - \beta z)}, \quad (6.45)$$

A being as before an arbitrary amplitude constant.

So far k and β are undetermined, but they are readily found by application of a boundary condition. At $r = a$, if a is the radius of the tube, E_z is tangential to the tube wall and must therefore be zero. Hence we have the boundary condition that

$$J_0(ka) = 0$$

Numerical values of $J_0(s)$ for a variable s can be calculated from the series in equation (6.44). When plotted against s these values give the curve shown in

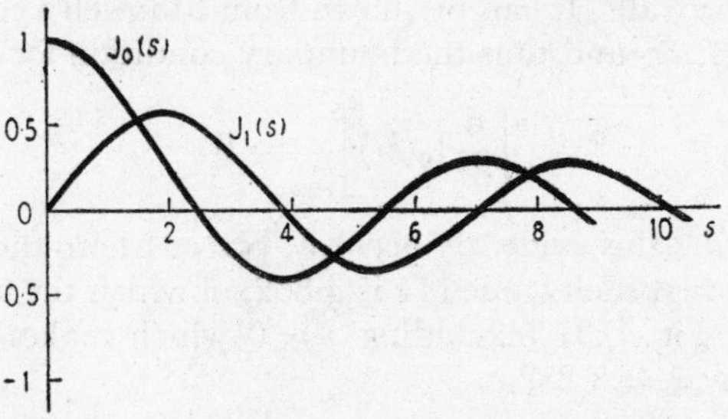

Fig. 6.31. Graph of Bessel functions $J_0(s)$ and $J_1(s)$.

Fig. 6.31. From it we see that $J_0(s)$ is zero for a series of values of s, of which the first, which has the value 2·405, is the only one to be considered here. Thus k is determined as $2{\cdot}405/a$. The propagation constant β, which is given by $k^2 = (\omega/c)^2 - \beta^2$, can now be found to be

$$\beta = \left\{\left(\frac{\omega}{c}\right)^2 - \left(\frac{2{\cdot}405}{a}\right)^2\right\}^{1/2} \quad (6.46)$$

From this the guide wavelength λ_g is determined as

$$\frac{1}{\lambda_g} = \frac{\beta}{2\pi} = \left\{\frac{1}{\lambda^2} - \left(\frac{2{\cdot}405}{2\pi a}\right)^2\right\}^{1/2} \quad (6.47)$$

and then the critical wavelength as $\lambda_c = 2\pi a/2{\cdot}405$. This is an E mode and is known as the E_{01}, the subscript 0 from the Bessel function, and the subscript 1 because the first root of $J_0(s)$ was taken.

Higher order modes involve solutions of (6.43) in which F is not independent of θ. The variation of F with θ must be of period 2π so that there may be no discontinuity in the field. The simplest variation of this type is a sinusoidal one, F being written as $F = R \sin \theta$, where R is a function of r. Substitution of this in (6.43) shows that R must satisfy the equation

$$\frac{\mathrm{d}^2 R}{\mathrm{d}r^2} + \frac{1}{r}\frac{\mathrm{d}R}{\mathrm{d}r} + \left(k^2 - \frac{1}{r^2}\right) R = 0$$

which again has a series solution, this time denoted by the Bessel function of the first order $\mathrm{J}_1(kr)$. The form of this function is shown in Fig. 6.31. Since the complete expression for E_z in this case is given by

$$E_z = A\, \mathrm{J}_1(kr) \sin \theta\, \varepsilon^{\mathrm{j}(\omega t - \beta z)} \quad . \quad . \quad . \quad . \quad . \quad (6.48)$$

the boundary condition will require that

$$\mathrm{J}_1(ka) = 0$$

The smallest value of ka to satisfy this is, from Fig. 6.31, $ka = 3{\cdot}832$. This defines an E_{11} wave, which will not be considered here in any more detail.

For H waves the field components also satisfy equation (6.42). The two simplest modes, the H_{01} and H_{11} have their H_z components given by the same expression as those for E_z in equations (6.45) and (6.48). With H waves, however, the boundary conditions are different, since H_z is not required to vanish at the boundary. There is no E_z, but there is another electric component E_θ tangential to the walls. It can be shown from Maxwell's equations that E_θ is proportional to $\partial H_z / \partial r$, and thus the boundary condition for the H_{01} wave is

$$\left[\frac{\mathrm{d}}{\mathrm{d}r}\mathrm{J}_0(kr)\right]_{r=a} = 0$$

Values of k satisfying this evidently occur at places where the slope of the $\mathrm{J}_0(s)$ curve is zero. The first such value of s is $3{\cdot}832$, of which the approximate value can be seen from Fig. 6.31 (excluding $s = 0$ which makes the field vanish), hence k is given by $k = 3{\cdot}832/a$.

In the case of the H_{11} wave the corresponding boundary condition is

$$\left[\frac{\mathrm{d}}{\mathrm{d}r}\mathrm{J}_1(kr)\right]_{r=a} = 0$$

whence the first solution is $k = 1{\cdot}841/a$.

From these values of k the values of β and λ_g for H_{01} and H_{11} waves can be found as before. The expressions will be the same as those of equations (6.46) and (6.47) with $2{\cdot}405$ replaced by $3{\cdot}832$ and $1{\cdot}841$ respectively.

CHAPTER 7

Waveguide Components and Techniques

THE UNIFORM WAVEGUIDE discussed in the previous chapter forms the basis of waveguide transmission. Its usefulness, however, is greatly extended by the addition of various circuit elements constructed in waveguide form. Examples of these are junctions, terminations, attenuators, and matching and transforming elements. It is these components and their uses which form the subject of this chapter.

Since the use of waveguides is largely limited to the H_{10} mode in a rectangular guide most of the components described are designed for this application. The special applications of other modes and other shapes of waveguide are also included.

Basically a waveguide component is usually a short length of waveguide with one or more planned discontinuities in it. For even the simplest wave type any such discontinuity produces changes in the wave which may be simple to visualize but are seldom simple to deal with mathematically. In fact, advanced mathematical methods have had to be developed to deal with problems involving even the simplest discontinuities. Historically this treatment usually came after the experimental development of the component, the original dimensions of the design being determined by the measurement of field distribution in the waveguide. The aim of most mathematical treatments is to deduce for the waveguide component an equivalent circuit to which the ordinary transmission-line methods can be applied as an aid to the interpretation of the field measurements.

Field measurements play a most important part in the design and adjustment of all waveguide systems, which are much less amenable to precise design by theoretical methods than are the components used at longer wavelengths. Thus our treatment here is often qualitative only.

Formulae and equivalent circuits will sometimes be quoted without proof where the proof is complex but the result can be usefully applied.

Sending and Receiving Guided Waves

A wave is launched in a waveguide by setting up at one end an electromagnetic field which resembles that of the desired mode in the guide. The usual method of doing this is to arrange small radiating aerials in the form of probes or loops inside the guide, the principle being that probes are arranged to lie along the directions of the desired lines of electric force, loops to encircle desired lines of magnetic force.

For the most important wave type, the H_{10} mode in a rectangular guide, the exciting element is usually a single probe passing perpendicularly through the middle of the broad side and hence exciting an electric field perpendicular to the broad side. This arrangement is illustrated in Fig. 7.1 (a). The wave thus generated would be propagated in both directions down the guide, but transmission in the undesired direction is prevented by closing one end of the guide by a metal plate at an appropriate distance behind the probe so that energy initially travelling towards the plate is reflected by it and reinforces the energy travelling in the required direction. For maximum power transfer the probe is approximately $\lambda/4$ long, and the plate approximately $\lambda_g/4$ from the probe. The probe may be fed from a coaxial line, forming an extension of its inner conductor as in Fig. 7.1 (a), or may perhaps be connected directly to a high-frequency oscillator. In the vicinity of the probe the field is very complex, but may be regarded as composed of a large number of different modes. Normally the guide will be so dimensioned that the higher modes are beyond cut-off, and hence are evanescent waves which are rapidly attenuated and become negligible at a short distance from the probe, leaving only the fundamental mode.

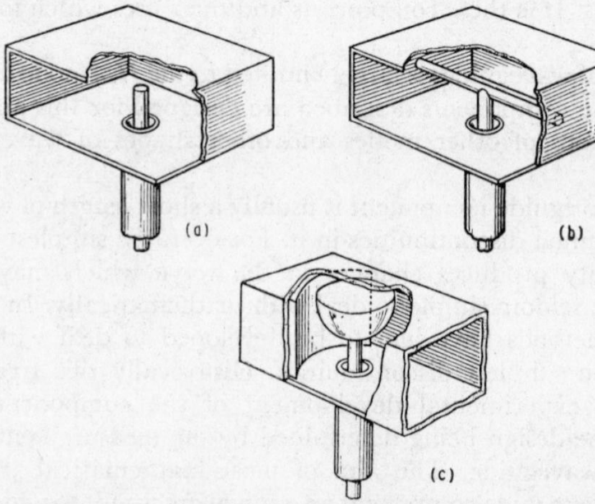

Fig. 7.1. Generation of H_{10} wave from coaxial line by (a) simple probe, (b) crossbar transformer, (c) doorknob transformer.

In practice the distance of penetration of the probe and the position of the reflecting plate are determined experimentally to give the maximum transfer of energy. The values will be correct only for the particular frequency at which they have been adjusted, but the arrangement will operate satisfactorily over a small frequency range.

There are many modifications of this simple arrangement, two of which are illustrated in Figs. 7.1 (b) and (c). In the 'crossbar' type of Fig. 7.1 (b) the probe is given mechanical rigidity by a crossbar which is set perpendicular to the lines of electric field, and hence has little effect on the field. This type has the advantage of operating over a wider frequency range than the simple form. The type of Fig. 7.1(c), with a hemisphere on the end of the probe and a cylindrical reflecting plate, is one which also has a usefully wide operating range. Several forms of this 'doorknob' type are found, specially designed to deal with high powers without breakdown, which in the simple type takes the form of a corona discharge from the end of the probe.

Any means used for launching a wave will be equally effective for receiving at the receiving end of the guide.

Possible methods of generation of higher modes by probes parallel to lines of electric force are shown in Fig. 7.2, and should be self-explanatory. In the case of the E_{21} mode note the use of an extra $\lambda/2$ length of coaxial line in series with one of the probes to provide the necessary 180° phase difference between the probes. It is difficult, however, to generate a mode in a pure form when it is not a fundamental mode and the guide is of such a size that more than one mode can be sustained. Thus the systems of Fig. 7.2, while they would generate

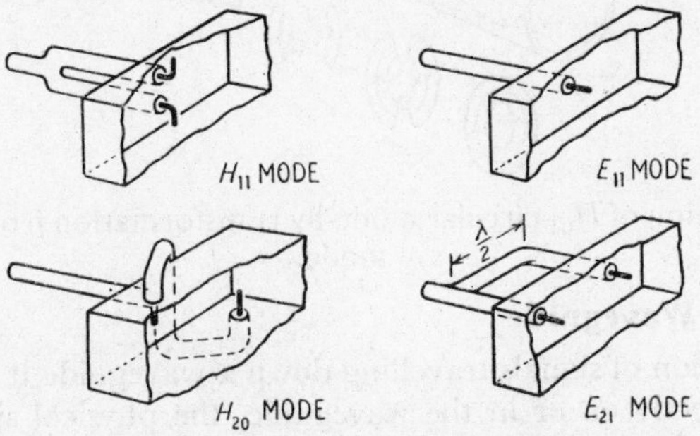

Fig. 7.2. Generation of different modes by arrangements of probes.

predominantly the stated modes, would not generate them exclusively, and further filters would be required.

For a circular guide an arrangement similar to that of Fig. 7.1 (a) would generate an H_{11} wave with its plane of polarization parallel to the probe.

A circular guide capable of supporting an E_{01} wave must also be capable of supporting the H_{11} mode, which has a longer critical wavelength, $1{\cdot}71D$, against $1{\cdot}31D$ for the E_{01} mode. An E_{01} wave, however, has the property of circular symmetry, which the H_{11} mode has not, and can be excited in a pure form by an arrangement having circular symmetry. A probe forming an extension of a

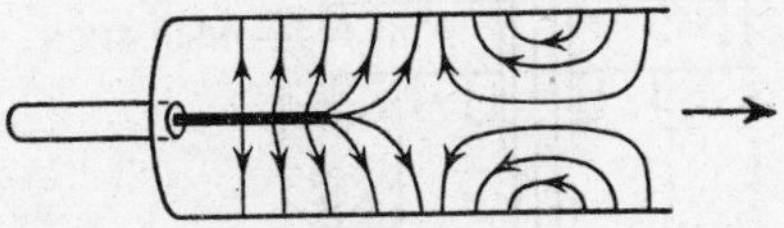

Fig. 7.3. Transformation from coaxial line to E_{01} mode in circular guide.

coaxial line along the axis of the guide is such an arrangement, and Fig. 7.3 shows how the field changes from the coaxial into the waveguide form. A modification of this method of generating the E_{01} mode will be seen in Fig. 7.32 (b).

The foregoing are all examples of what are known as coaxial-to-waveguide transformers. Such methods are not readily applicable to the H_{01} mode in a circular guide, since the circular lines of electric field are not easy to induce by probes or loops. Fig. 7.4 is an example of how it may be done, using a different technique. In this system a rectangular guide carrying an H_{20} mode is transformed to circular shape in such a way that the circular electric field characteristic of the H_{01} mode in a circular guide is gradually produced. This technique of shaping the field by gradual change of the guide shape is an important one of which further examples will be met.

Loops are not often used in the generation of modes in waveguides used as transmission lines, but they are common in waveguides used as resonators. A discussion of these will be found in Chapter 8.

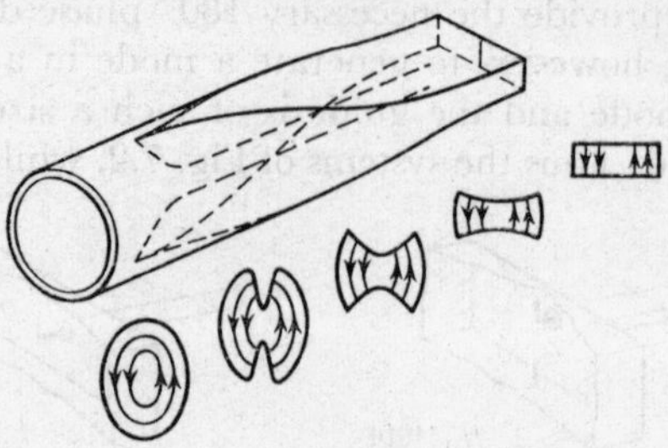

Fig. 7.4. Generation of H_{01} circular mode by transformation from H_{20} rectangular mode.

Detection in a Waveguide

For the detection of signals travelling down a waveguide it is usual to mount the detector directly on or in the waveguide, the physical size of the normal crystal detectors being such that this is readily possible. Fig. 7.5 (a) shows a

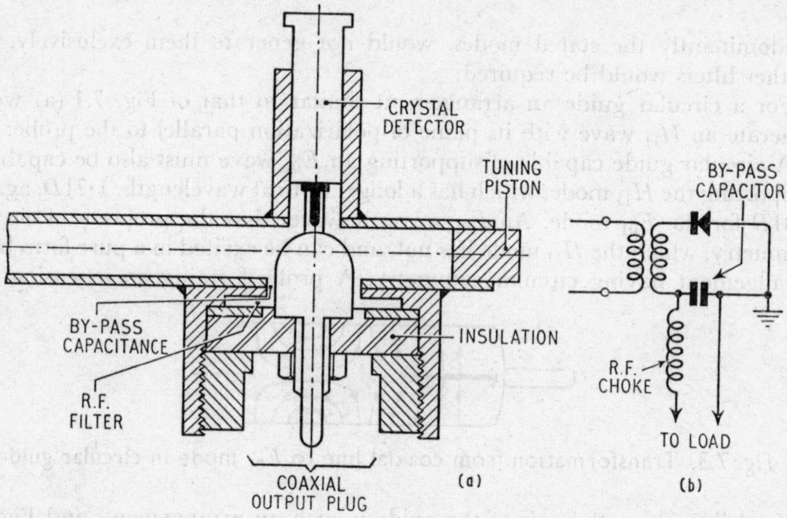

Fig. 7.5. (a) Crystal detector mounted on waveguide; (b) equivalent circuit for (a).

coaxial type crystal mounted on a 'doorknob' transformer acting as detector of an H_{10} wave in a rectangular waveguide.

In order to allow the d.c., a.f. or i.f. components of the crystal current to be used the lower end of the doorknob is connected to the inner conductor of a coaxial plug, the capacitance between doorknob and waveguide being made sufficient to act as a by-pass for the r.f. carrier. Since the frequencies at which waveguides are used are very high an extremely small capacitance is sufficient. The top part of the plug is dimensioned so as to act as a rejection filter at the carrier frequency. Thus the detected signal is separated from the carrier in just the same way as by the circuit of Fig. 7.5 (b) used at lower frequencies, although in the waveguide case the presence of the various components is less obvious.

Here again dimensions must be determined experimentally, and when determined will be satisfactory over only a small frequency range.

Standing Waves

For the transmission lines discussed in Chapter 3 it is shown that a termination which is not equal to the characteristic impedance of the line will cause partial reflection of an incident wave and set up a standing wave in the line. A line having a perfectly absorbing termination is said to be matched. A similar situation occurs for waveguides. Thus, for example, to secure maximum transfer of energy from the waveguide to the detector of Fig. 7.5 (a) this waveguide component must match the waveguide. Furthermore the figure will serve as an example to illustrate that waveguide components are not so readily adjustable as components used at lower frequencies, and have to be built to the correct dimensions. The design procedure is thus to some extent a process of trial and error based on measurements of the standing-wave pattern set up in the waveguide by the component. The measurement of standing-wave patterns, therefore, plays a most important part in the design and adjustment of waveguide systems and components.

It was noted in Chapter 3 that a further reason for keeping the standing-wave ratio as nearly as possible equal to unity was to avoid reducing the power-carrying capacity of the line. At the centimetre wavelengths where waveguides are normally used there is another most important reason. The power output, operating frequency, and frequency stability of most centimetre-wave oscillators, magnetrons in particular, are rather critically dependent on the impedance presented at their output terminals. This impedance depends on the standing-wave ratio in the transmission line connected to the oscillator. It can be shown that the effect is a minimum when the transmission-line system is matched.

In Chapter 3 standing-wave ratio was defined in a two-conductor line as the ratio of the voltage maximum to the voltage minimum on the line [equation (3.14)], or as the corresponding current ratio. In the waveguide, where measurements are made in terms of the field vectors **E** and **H**, the standing wave ratio S is defined as the ratio of maximum to minimum values of the *transverse* components of field, E_t or H_t.

$$S = \frac{(E_t)_{\text{max}}}{(E_t)_{\text{min}}} = \frac{(H_t)_{\text{max}}}{(H_t)_{\text{min}}} \qquad (7.1)$$

As with two-conductor lines, the standing-wave detector is used for the measurement of standing-wave ratio in waveguides. A standing-wave detector consists of a length of waveguide with a narrow longitudinal slot cut down the middle of the broad side, by means of which a detector moving along the outside of the guide may be loosely coupled to the field inside. For the H_{10} wave in a rectangular guide it was shown in Chapter 6 (p. 163) that a narrow slot in this position causes negligible distortion of the wave; no other position of the slot is suitable. Coupling to the field may be by means of a loop or a probe. The latter is almost always used, since it provides coupling to the electric field only, while the loop tends to couple to the electric as well as to the magnetic field, and will then respond in a different manner to forward and reflected waves. In order to disturb the field as little as possible the probe penetrates only a small distance through the slot. It is connected to a detector, usually a crystal detector, mounted on a carriage moving parallel to the slot, and connected to a galvanometer or microammeter. Fig. 7.6 is a diagrammatic sketch of the instrument; compare this with Figs. 3.8 and 3.9.

Although approximate results adequate for some purposes may be obtained with quite a simply constructed instrument, the more accurate measurements necessary in the design of waveguide apparatus require an instrument of high

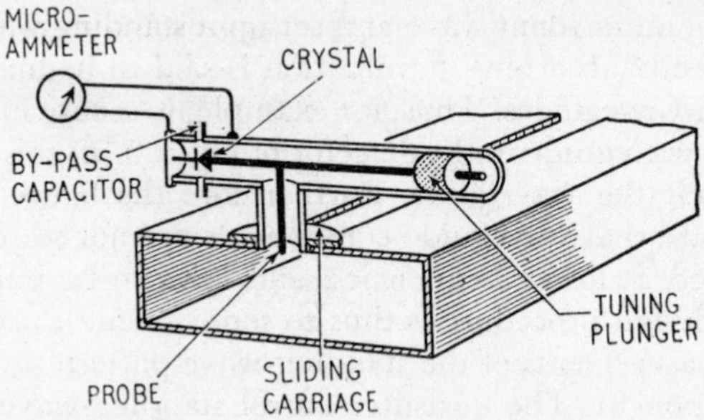

Fig. 7.6. Section through simple form of waveguide standing-wave detector.

mechanical precision designed to avoid any distortion of the guide by the slot and to ensure that the probe moves accurately parallel to the slot and without variation of its coupling to the field.

To measure the standing-wave ratio in a waveguide transmission line the standing-wave detector is inserted in the line, where it must of itself cause the minimum possible discontinuity. Fig. 7.7 shows a typical arrangement of apparatus for the measurement of standing-wave ratio. It is desirable to include a fixed amount of attenuation between the oscillator and the standing-wave detector in order to avoid any possible effect on oscillator frequency of movement of the carriage or of change in the standing-wave ratio. In an unmatched

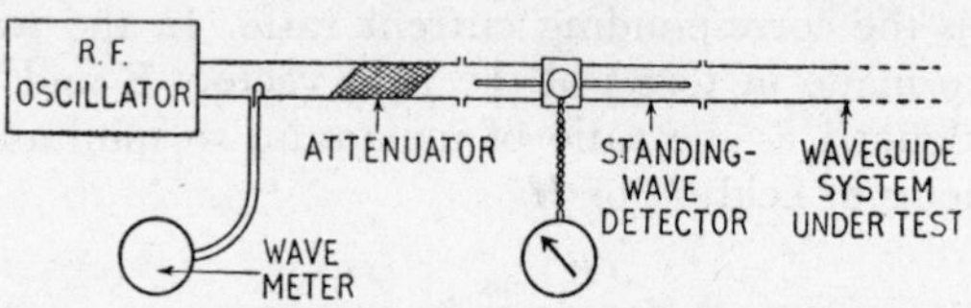

Fig. 7.7. Measurement of standing-wave ratio.

guide the detector current will vary with the position of the carriage, and this variation will be of the general form shown in Fig. 7.8, repeating itself in a distance equal to $\lambda_g/2$. From the maximum and minimum values of current recorded, $I_{\max}$ and $I_{\min}$, the standing-wave ratio is deduced. The law of the detector must, however, be known. For a crystal detector with very small current passing it is usually square law; that is, the current is proportional to the square of the field induced in the probe, and hence to the square of the field in the guide. Thus the standing-wave ratio is given by:

$$S = \frac{(E_t)_{\max}}{(E_t)_{\min}} = \sqrt{\frac{I_{\max}}{I_{\min}}}$$

When there is no reflected wave the standing-wave pattern is a straight line, for which S is unity.

In the interpretation of standing-wave measurements a most useful concept is that of impedance as applied to waveguides. This is dealt with in detail in the following two sections, but here it may be stated that what is called the *wave impedance* at any point in a waveguide is the ratio of the transverse component of electric field to the transverse component of magnetic field at that point. The ratio has the dimensions of impedance and is expressed in ohms. For the H_{10} wave in a rectangular waveguide referred to a co-ordinate system as in Fig. 6.3 the wave impedance Z_W is given by the numerical value of the ratio E_y/H_x, and is equal to 377 λ_g/λ ohms.

The impedance equations used for two-conductor transmission lines can be shown to apply to waveguide systems when this concept of wave impedance is used. It enables waveguide systems to be analysed from standing-wave ratio

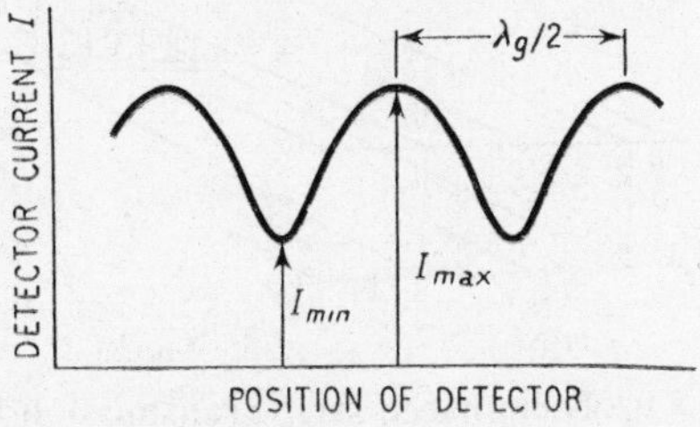

Fig. 7.8. Typical current variation in standing-wave detector.

measurements, and equivalent circuits for them to be drawn in terms of two-conductor transmission lines and components. As an example of the correspondence between the two systems, a twin-wire tranmission line is matched when terminated by a resistance equal to its characteristic impedance; a waveguide is matched when terminated by a resistive film with a surface resistivity equal to the wave impedance.

Impedance Concept for Plane Waves

As an introduction to the concept of wave impedance we shall first consider wave impedance in relation to a plane wave. In the study of transmission lines in Chapter 3 an important parameter was the characteristic impedance, defined as the ratio of voltage to current at any point in an infinite line. For a waveguide there is no precisely measurable voltage or current, still less so for a wave in free space, and all our discussion has been in terms of electric and magnetic fields. For the parallel-strip transmission line in free space, however, it was shown in equation (5.9) that the electric and magnetic field vectors have a ratio which is constant at every point in the space between the strips, and whose value is given by:

$$\frac{E}{H} = \sqrt{\frac{\mu_0}{\kappa_0}} = Z_{fs} \quad . \quad . \quad . \quad . \quad . \quad . \quad . \quad (7.2)$$

where Z_{fs} is a constant which has the value 120π or 377 ohms. Since electric field is expressed in volts/metre, and magnetic field in amperes/metre, the ratio between them is properly expressed in ohms, and thus has the dimensions of a resistance. This ratio is analogous to the characteristic impedance of a transmission line, and is an important extension of the normal concept of impedance to field theory. To avoid confusion impedances expressed in terms of the ratio of electric to magnetic fields are usually called *wave impedances.* It will be shown that the study of wave transmission can be greatly facilitated by the use of wave impedances, and much of the ordinary transmission line theory is applicable.

From equation (5.23) it can be seen that the ratio E/H for a plane wave in free space is also equal to Z_{fs}. This particular wave impedance is termed the *characteristic impedance or intrinsic impedance of free space.*

This concept may be better appreciated by considering the parallel-strip transmission line of Fig. 7.9 terminated in a uniform resistive film of width 1 metre and height a metres, whose surface resistivity [equation (6.12)] is R_s ohms. By equation (5.5) the current I flowing along the line is equal in magnitude to the magnetic field H. If this current flows from one strip to the other through the film it sets up across the film a potential difference V, where:

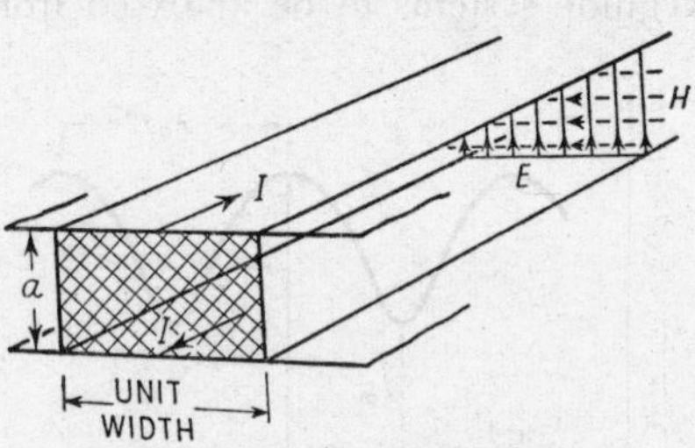

Fig. 7.9. Terminated strip transmission line.

$$V = R_s aI = R_s aH \text{ volts}$$

and consequently the potential gradient is:

$$V/a = R_s H \text{ volts per metre}$$

Thus at the film surface the electric field E, which is numerically equal to the potential gradient, is given by:

$$E = R_s H$$

This expression gives the correct value of E to satisfy equation (7.2) provided that R_s is equal to Z_{fs}. Thus a film of this resistivity is able to absorb the wave with no field discontinuities and thus without reflection.

If R_s has any other value there will be reflection, with an incident wave E_i, H_i, and a reflected wave E_r, H_r. The resultant of these two waves is given by:

$$E = E_i + E_r$$
$$H = H_i + H_r$$

The total current through the termination is now:

$$I = I_i + I_r = H_i + H_r$$

Hence the potential across the termination is $R_s a(H_i + H_r)$, and the potential gradient is $R_s(H_i + H_r)$. If this potential gradient is to be numerically equal to the electric field in the wave then:

$$E_i + E_r = R_s(H_i + H_r)$$

But in addition each wave must satisfy equation (7.2), and hence:

$$\frac{E_i}{H_i} = Z_{fs} \text{ and } \frac{E_r}{H_r} = -Z_{fs}$$

the negative sign for the backward-travelling wave being necessary for the same reason as in equation (3.6). Hence we can write:

$$E_i + E_r = \frac{R_s}{Z_{fs}}(E_i - E_r),$$

from which we find:

$$\frac{E_r}{E_i} = \frac{R_s - Z_{fs}}{R_s + Z_{fs}} \quad . \quad . \quad . \quad . \quad . \quad . \quad (7.3)$$

The ratio E_r/E_i represents the reflection factor ρ of the electric field, and thus by equation (7.3):

$$\rho = \frac{R_s - Z_{fs}}{R_s + Z_{fs}} \quad . \quad . \quad . \quad . \quad . \quad . \quad . \quad (7.4)$$

The standing-wave ratio S, defined in equation (3.17) as*:

$$S = \frac{1 + |\rho|}{1 - |\rho|}$$

is thus given by:

$$S = \frac{R_s}{Z_{fs}}, \quad \text{if } R_s > Z_{fs} \quad . \quad . \quad . \quad . \quad . \quad . \quad (7.5)$$

or

$$S = \frac{Z_{fs}}{R_s}, \quad \text{if } R_s < Z_{fs} \quad . \quad . \quad . \quad . \quad . \quad . \quad (7.6)$$

It is to be noted that these equations correspond exactly with equations (3.18) (3.19), and thus extend the analogy between wave impedances and ordinary impedances.

The same expressions can be used with a plane wave in free space, which has also a wave impedance Z_{fs}. It can thus be completely absorbed by an infinite resistive sheet of surface resistivity Z_{fs} placed perpendicular to the direction of the wave.

Impedance Concept in Rectangular Waveguide

Passing now to an H_{10} wave in a rectangular guide, we see from the field equations (6.26) that the transverse field components E_y and H_x are again in phase, and the numerical value of their ratio, which is constant at every point in the guide, is given by:

$$\left|\frac{E_y}{H_x}\right| = \frac{\omega\mu_0}{\beta} = \frac{(2\pi c/\lambda)\mu_0}{2\pi/\lambda_g}$$

$$= \left(\frac{\mu_0}{\kappa_0}\right)^{1/2} \frac{\lambda_g}{\lambda} = Z_{fs}\frac{\lambda_g}{\lambda}$$

* By this definition S is always greater than or equal to unity. The expression $S = (1 - |\rho|)/(1 + |\rho|)$ is sometimes used instead, in which case S has values varying between 0 and 1.

This ratio defines the wave impedance for the H_{10} wave, and, if it is represented by Z_W, then:

$$Z_W = Z_{fs}\frac{\lambda_g}{\lambda} = 120\pi\frac{\lambda_g}{\lambda} \text{ ohms} \qquad (7.7)$$

Note that the longitudinal component of **H** has no part in this definition. Since λ_g is always greater than λ the wave impedance will always be greater than the intrinsic impedance of free space. Its variation with λ is illustrated in Fig. 7.10.

Since Z_W is constant at every point in a cross-section of the wave then a resistive film of uniform surface resistivity equal to Z_W placed across the end of the guide can absorb all the incident power and thus provide a matched termination for the guide.

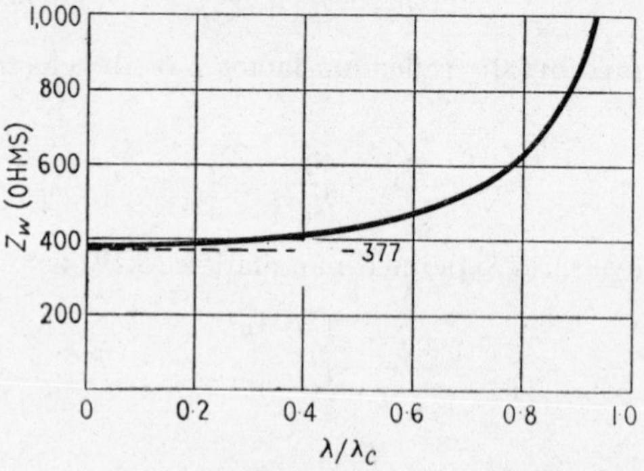

Fig. 7.10. Variation of wave impedance Z_w of H_{10} wave in rectangular guide with λ/λ_c.

▶ If the guide has a termination of surface resistivity Z_T then a treatment similar to that for the plane wave gives the expression for the reflection factor ρ as:

$$\rho = \frac{Z_T - Z_W}{Z_T + Z_W} \qquad (7.8)$$

Thus if ρ is measured Z_T can be found in terms of Z_W. The termination Z_T need not be a pure resistance. It can be regarded more generally as a termination which always has the ratio of transverse field components at its surface equal to Z_T; that is, which has a wave impedance of Z_T. In general Z_T will be complex and the wave will undergo a change of phase on reflection, giving rise to a complex value of reflection factor $\rho = |\rho|\varepsilon^{j\phi}$. If a wave of unit amplitude with phase constant β is incident on this termination, then the amplitude and phase of the reflected wave at a point distant l from the termination are given relative to the incident wave at that point by $\rho\varepsilon^{-2j\beta l}$ or $|\rho|\varepsilon^{j(\phi-2\beta l)}$.

Minimum and maximum values of the combination of incident and reflected waves are $1 - |\rho|$ and $1 + |\rho|$. If the ratio of these two defines the standing-wave ratio S—the quantity measured by the standing-wave detector—then $|\rho|$ is determined by:

$$|\rho| = \frac{S-1}{S+1} \qquad (7.9)$$

If in addition the standing-wave detector is set on a minimum reading and this is at a distance l from the termination, then $\phi - 2\beta l = (2n + 1)\pi$, that is

$$\phi = 4\pi l/\lambda_g + (2n + 1)\pi \qquad (7.10)$$

In determining the phase angle ϕ from this equation it is convenient to adopt the convention that ϕ should lie between π and $-\pi$. Usually the standing-wave detector is placed close to the termination, and the position of the minimum nearest to the termination is taken. The above convention is then met by putting $n = -1$, so that equation (7.10) becomes:

$$\phi = 4\pi l/\lambda_g - \pi \qquad (7.11)$$

Depending on whether the phase angle of the termination is positive or negative two rather different standing-wave patterns are obtained, typical examples of which are shown in Fig. 7.11. Thus ρ is determined in amplitude and phase by (7.9) and (7.11) and hence Z_T is found through (7.8).

In calculations it is convenient to use the ratio Z_T/Z_W rather than Z_T. This is called a normalized impedance, normalized with respect to the wave impedance of the guide. For a perfect termination ρ is zero, and thus $Z_T = Z_W$ or $Z_T/Z_W = 1$.

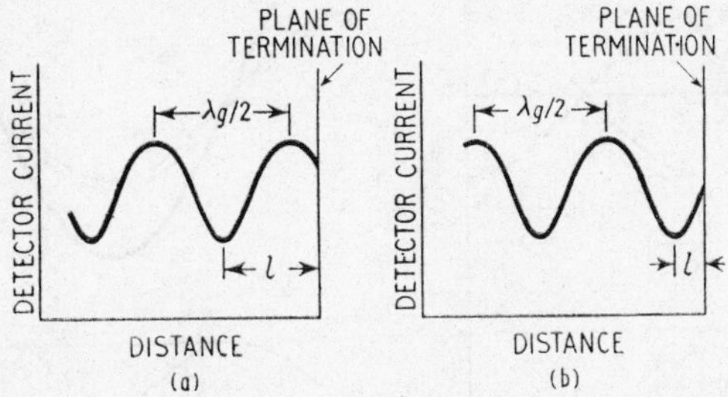

Fig. 7.11. Standing-wave pattern in mismatched guide with reflection factor $|\rho|\varepsilon^{j\phi}$, where (a) $0 < \phi < \pi$, (b) $-\pi < \phi < 0$.

The treatment here has differed somewhat from that used in Chapter 3 for the two-conductor transmission line, but there is complete correspondence between the equations for reflection factor, impedance and standing-wave ratio derived here and those derived in Chapter 3. In the wave treatment used here the emphasis has had to be on the only measurable quantity—standing-wave ratio; in the treatment for the two conductor line the current and voltage distribution were more readily apprehended.

Because of this correspondence the fundamental equation (3.50) of Chapter 3, giving the input impedance of a length of loss-free line terminated in Z_T, applies equally to the waveguide, viz.:

$$Z_S = Z_W \frac{Z_T + jZ_W \tan \beta l}{Z_W + jZ_T \tan \beta l} \qquad (7.12)$$

where all impedances are now wave impedances, and $\beta = 2\pi/\lambda_g$.

As in the case of the two-conductor transmission line there are certain terminations which are of special importance. A particular case is when the remote end is closed by a perfectly conducting plane. In this case the wave impedance of the termination is zero, and thus by (7.12) the input impedance is:

$$Z_S = jZ_W \tan (2\pi l/\lambda_g) \qquad (7.13)$$

This corresponds with equation (3.22), and thus the reactance presented varies with l or λ_g between $+\infty$ and $-\infty$ in the manner shown in Fig. 3.14.

In the following section, where closed and open-ended guides are treated in a more descriptive manner, it is pointed out that the terminating impedance of an open-ended guide is not infinite, and thus the correspondence with equation (3.23) does not hold.

Closed and Open-Ended Waveguides

If a waveguide has a closed end then a wave reaching the end is completely reflected, and the combination of direct and reflected wave constitutes a standing wave. The form of the standing wave can be derived in the same way as was done in Chapter 3 and shown in Fig. 3.3, but the boundary conditions now to be satisfied at the termination are that the resultant electric field component

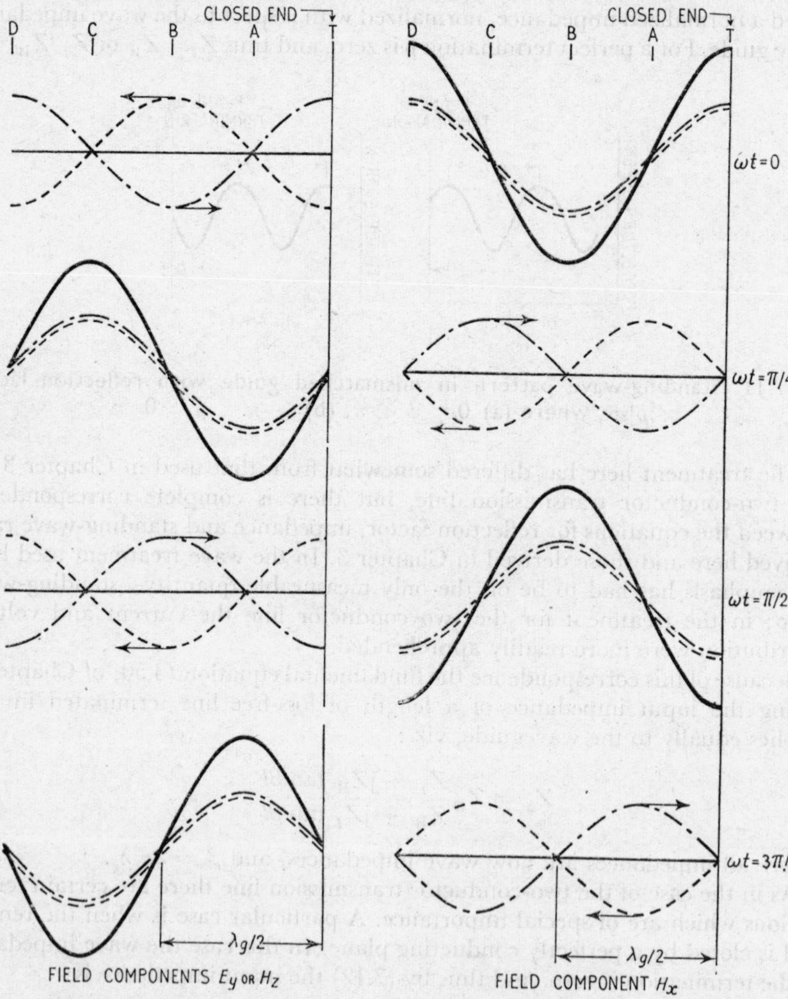

Fig. 7.12. Instantaneous field distribution in closed waveguide.

- - - - - - - - incident wave
— - — - — - — reflected wave
———————— resultant wave

tangential to the closed end and the resultant magnetic field component normal to the closed end must be zero there. For the co-ordinate system of Fig. 6.3 an H_{10} wave has a transverse electric field E_y, and a magnetic field consisting of a transverse component H_x and a component H_z along the axis of the guide. Application of the boundary condition gives the field distribution shown in Fig. 7.12 (to be compared with Fig. 3.3), from which it will be seen that the E_y and H_z components have nodes at T, B and D, that is, at the termination and at multiples of $\lambda_g/2$ from it, while the H_x component has nodes at $\lambda_g/4$, $3\lambda_g/4$, etc. Thus the field in a horizontal cross-section of the tube will be as shown in Fig. 7.13, but, in contrast to the moving pattern of the travelling wave of Fig. 6.3, the fields in this standing-wave pattern oscillate in *time* and are stationary in *position*. Note the space displacement of $\lambda_g/4$ between the positions of the maxima of the electric and magnetic fields in the stationary wave compared with their positions for the travelling wave of Fig. 6.3, and that they also have a time displacement of one-quarter period.

A standing-wave detector coupled to the electric field will read a maximum at the positions of maxima of the electric field, that is, at $\lambda_g/4$, $3\lambda_g/4$, etc., from

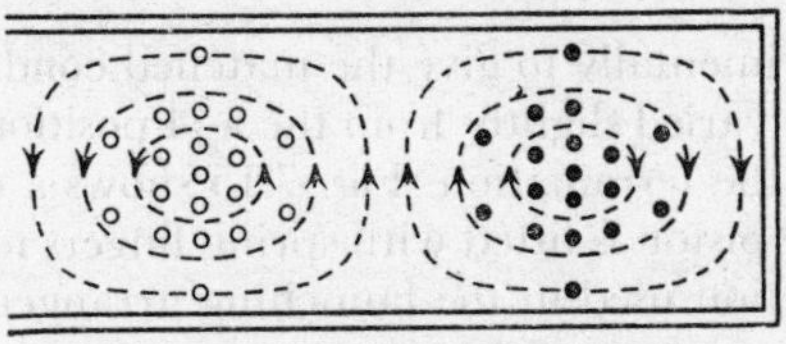

Fig. 7.13. Field pattern of H_{10} standing wave in rectangular waveguide.

------- magnetic field lines
∘ into paper } electric field lines
• out of paper }

the end, and zero at positions mid-way between them. Thus an infinite standing-wave ratio exists in a closed loss-free waveguide. At a distance of $\lambda_g/4$ from the closed end E_y has a maximum and H_x is zero. Thus the ratio of the transverse components E_y/H_x is infinite at this point; and hence the input wave impedance of a $\lambda_g/4$ length of waveguide closed at its far end is infinite. Similarly the input impedance of a $\lambda_g/2$ length is zero. These properties correspond precisely with the results obtained in Chapter 3 for $\lambda/4$ and $\lambda/2$ lengths of short-circuited transmission line. Of course, neither the zero nor infinite values will be actually attained in practice because of small resistive losses in the guide, but it is convenient so to refer to them.

It is important to note, however, that the correspondence breaks down for an open-ended waveguide. This is because radiation of energy takes place from the open end into the surrounding space, which thus appears as a finite terminating impedance across the open end. The radiation is appreciable only when the cross-sectional dimensions of the transmission line are comparable with the wavelength. For that reason it was permissible to neglect it in Chapter 3; it is always appreciable in a waveguide.

The presence of radiation from an open-ended guide affects our previous discussion of a waveguide terminated in a resistive film. The impedance presented by the surrounding space acts in parallel with the terminating impedance and modifies its value. The effect can be obviated by following the termination with a closed $\lambda_g/4$ section of waveguide as in Fig. 7.14, thus placing a true infinite impedance in parallel with the resistive film.

For this purpose and in many other applications a short length of guide with a movable piston, forming a closed end adjustable in position, is much used.

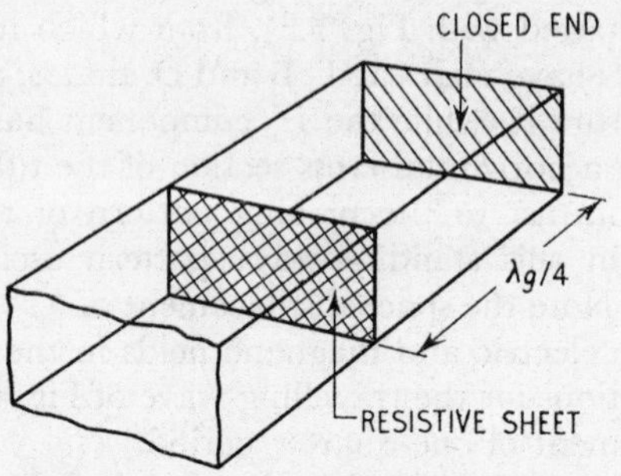

Fig. 7.14. Matched termination of waveguide formed by resistive sheet and short-circuited $\lambda_g/4$ section.

This is adjusted experimentally to give the matched condition, since the tuning piston may have to be varied slightly from the $\lambda_g/4$ position to balance any small residual reactance in the termination. Fig. 7.15 shows a common form of construction in which the piston is fitted with spring fingers to ensure good contact. The quarter-wave section used in the launching arrangements of Figs. 7.1 and

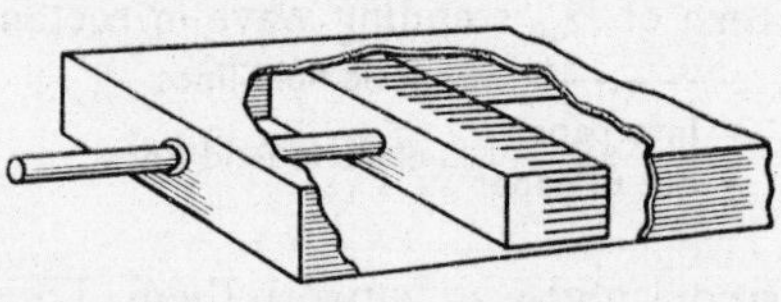

Fig. 7.15. Tuning piston with spring fingers.

7.2 and the detector of Fig. 7.5 performs the same function, although its effect was considered there in a more elementary way.

The variable nature of the contact given by the spring fingers is a disadvantage of this type of tuning piston, and a more satisfactory form is the 'non-contact' type, of which an example is illustrated in Fig. 7.16 (a), the section

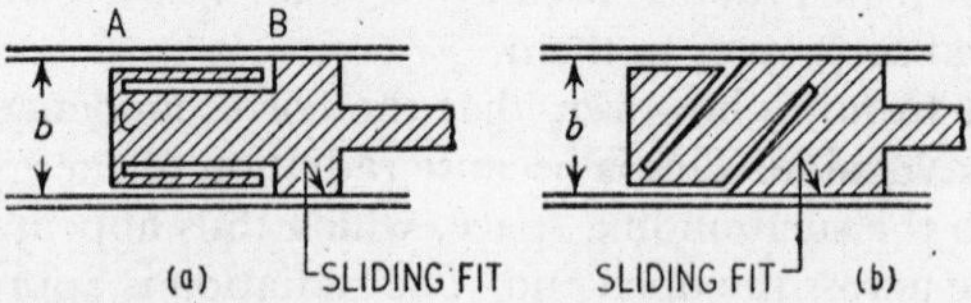

Fig. 7.16. Two types of non-contact tuning piston.

shown being parallel to the narrow dimension of the guide. The part ABC is to be regarded as a narrow waveguide of length $\lambda_g/2$ short-circuited at C and folded at its centre. Thus its input impedance at A is zero, and there is an equivalent short-circuit across both gaps in the piston face. The piston therefore appears as a continuous short-circuit across the guide. The sliding contact, however, now occurs at the quarter-wavelength point B, a high impedance point where the magnetic field, and hence also the wall current, is small. Variations of contact resistance with movement of the piston are now of little importance. This is an example of an important principle by which actual physical short-circuits can be replaced by virtual short-circuits and the physical contact made at a place where poor contact is not harmful.

Fig. 7.16 (b) shows another form of non-contact piston in which the slots are cut diagonally for ease of manufacture.

Couplings

In a system employing waveguides and waveguide components some form of coupling is required to join together the separate pieces. One type of coupling, known as the flange type, is illustrated in Fig. 7.17. Flanges are soldered or

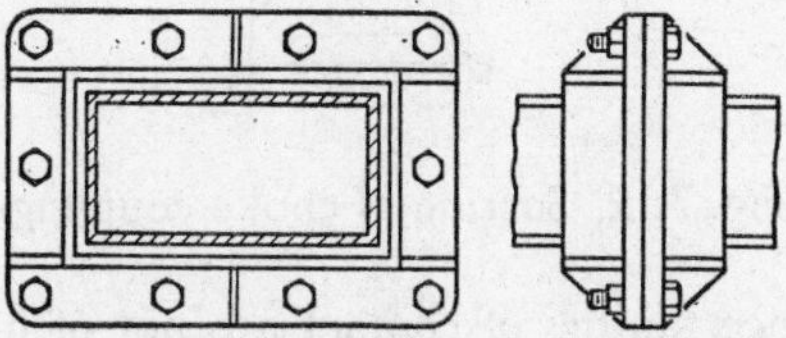

Fig. 7.17. Bolted flange type of waveguide coupling.

brazed on the ends of each length of guide, and these can then be bolted together. It is important that the ends should be plane after finishing so that sections butt together without gaps, as gaps will cause discontinuities in the wall currents and give rise to a reflected wave. The individual lengths must also be correctly aligned so as to avoid a step in the guide at the junction.

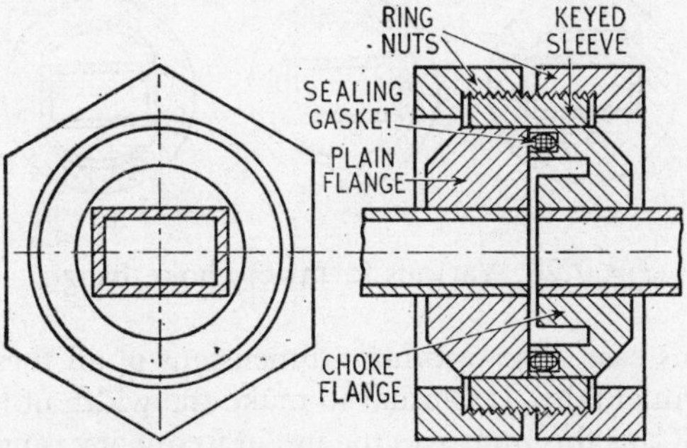

Fig. 7.18. Screwed ring type of waveguide coupling.

The flange coupling is used mainly for the larger guide sizes; for the smaller sizes some form of screwed coupling is preferred on the grounds of convenience and accuracy of alignment. In this type, one form of which is illustrated in Fig. 7.18, the flanges are circular on the outside, and are aligned by a keyed sleeve and clamped by two ring nuts.

As the difficulty of getting good contact increases with decreasing guide size the smaller couplings are usually designed so that a small gap is deliberately left between the guides, as can be seen in Fig. 7.18, and the effect of this is compensated for by a 'choke ring'. Fig. 7.19 illustrates the principle more fully, and shows a section of a joint made up of a plain flange and a choke flange. The L-shaped gap left between the two parts forms a narrow waveguide in which a standing wave is set up. The equivalent length of this transmission line is made equal to $\lambda_g/2$ as in the 'non-contact' piston, so that the definite short-circuit at C, transformed through the half-wave line, is equivalent to a

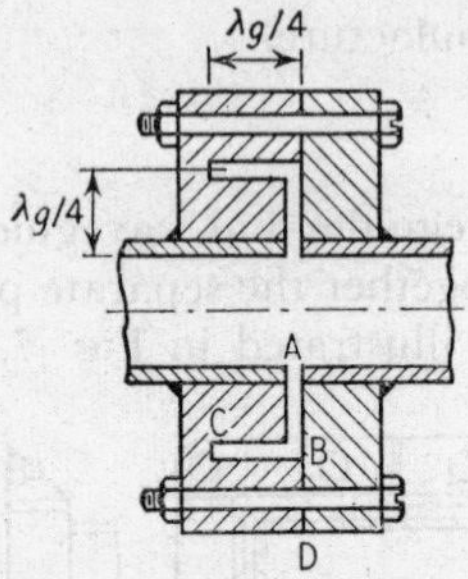

Fig. 7.19. Section of choke coupling.

short-circuit at A. Uncertainties of contact are not of importance, since they occur at the high impedance point B, where the current flow is small.

The choke or 'ditch' BC is necessary only opposite the broad walls of the guide, as shown in Fig. 7.20 (a), since there are no longitudinal currents in the narrow walls (see Fig. 6.17). The most common form, however, is the modification shown in Fig. 7.20 (b), where the chokes have become a complete ring, which is easier to make. With some sizes of guide, however, a ring of the correct size would cut into the corners, so Fig. 7.20 (c) shows another variant which

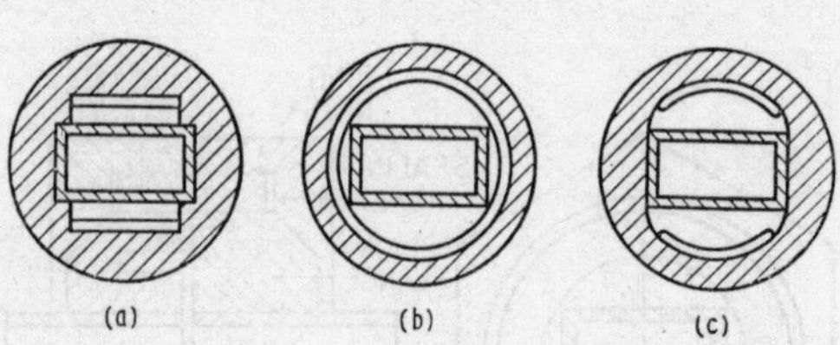

Fig. 7.20. Various forms of choke flange.

can be used in this case. The optimum dimensions of all these chokes are best determined experimentally. It is usual to make the width of the part AB much less than that of BC, as this improves the useful frequency range of the coupling.

As a waveguide system may include quite a number of couplings, the standing-wave ratio of each must be kept very low. For a good coupling the standing-wave ratio is not worse than 1·01 at the design wavelength, and a frequency range of the order of $\pm$ 10% should be obtainable for standing-wave ratios not exceeding 1·05.

Bends, Tapers and Twists

Often a change of direction is necessary in a waveguide run. This can be done simply by the use of a length of guide bent as required. A bend whose plane is parallel to the plane of the magnetic vector is called an *H*-bend, while one whose plane is parallel to the plane of the electric vector is called an E-bend. These are illustrated in Fig. 7.21. As the velocity of propagation in a bent guide differs slightly from that in a straight guide a bend introduces some discontinuity, and

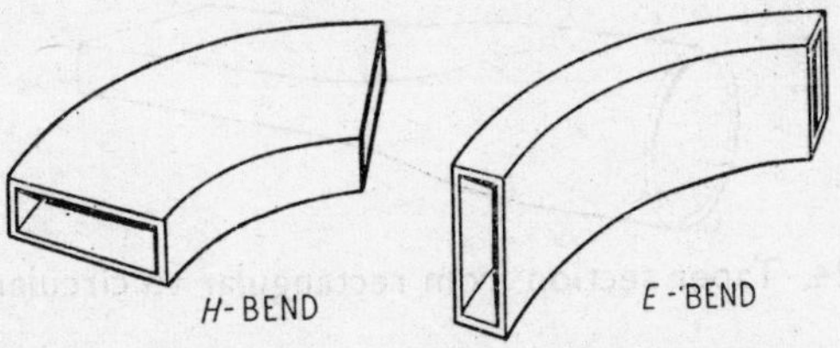

Fig. 7.21. Waveguide bends in E- and H-planes.

hence causes some reflection of energy. This can be minimized by keeping the radius of curvature large compared with the guide dimensions.

Such a bend is clumsy, and it is usually more convenient to use the mitred corner shown in Fig. 7.22. This corner can be made almost reflectionless by a

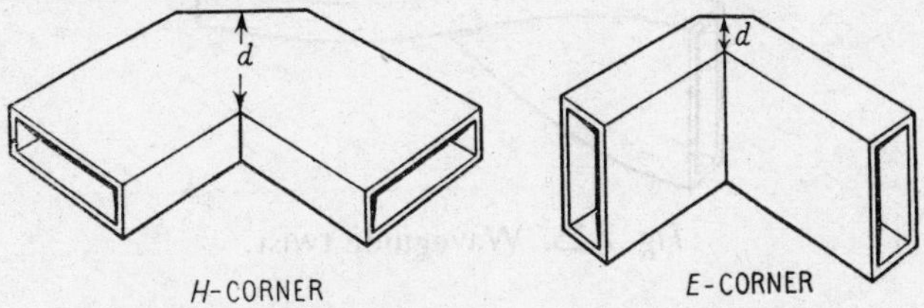

Fig. 7.22. Mitred corners in E- and H-planes.

suitable choice of the dimension d. The value of d depends on the wavelength and guide dimensions, but normal values for d are about $0{\cdot}9a$ for a 90° H-corner and $0{\cdot}85b$ for a 90° E-corner. The double mitred corner of Fig. 7.23 gives a wider frequency range of useful operation than the single type. The length L is

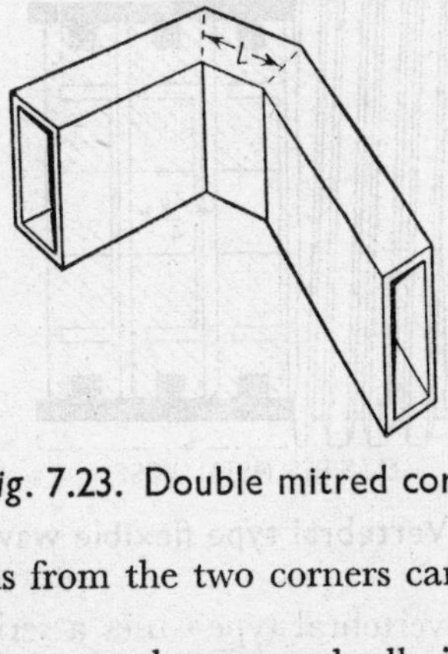

Fig. 7.23. Double mitred corner.

chosen so that reflections from the two corners cancel, the value of L for this being about $\lambda_g/4$.

The principle of making any change gradually in order to avoid reflections is again exemplified in the use of a taper section to join two guides having different dimensions, as may be required in some applications. Little reflection will result if the taper is extended over a distance of one or two guide-wavelengths. Fig. 7.24 shows the form of a taper section joining a rectangular guide carrying an H_{10} wave to a circular guide carrying an H_{11} wave.

Fig. 7.24. Taper section from rectangular to circular guide.

When it is required to change the direction of polarization of a guided wave, usually by 90°, a 'twist' as shown in Fig. 7.25 is used. Again this will cause little reflection if the twist takes place smoothly over a distance of several wavelengths, and imperfections in construction are avoided.

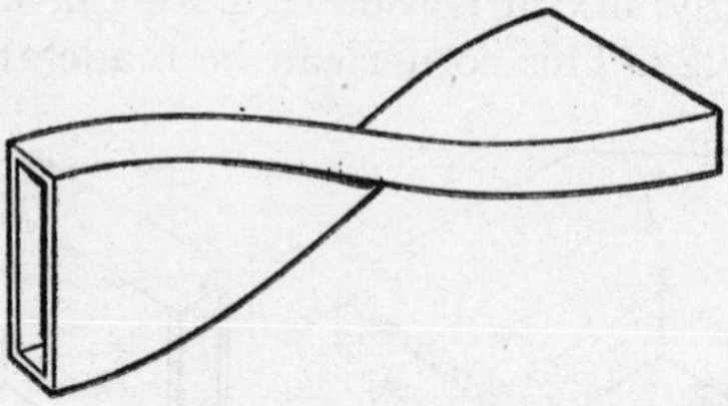

Fig. 7.25. Waveguide twist.

It is often necessary to allow a small amount of relative movement between two guides, and for this a length of flexible guide is used. A common type consists of a continuous spiral of interlocking metal strip formed in the same way as flexible metal hose, of rectangular section and having a moulded rubber

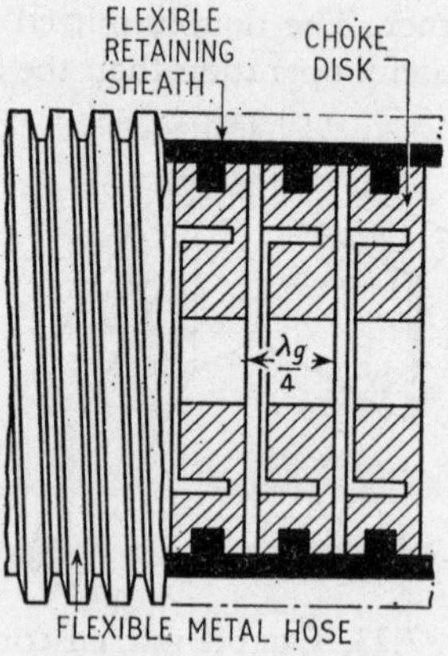

Fig. 7.26. Vertebral type flexible waveguide.

jacket. Another form—the vertebral type—uses a series of discs, each pierced with a rectangular hole of the same size as the waveguide, retained within a ribbed rubber or polythene jacket as shown in Fig. 7.26. The ribs maintain a small spacing between the discs, and each disc has choke grooves in one face, of such dimensions that pairs of discs act as choke couplings. Residual reflections at the faces are minimized by making the combined length of segment and space equal to $\lambda_g/4$. The vertebral type has a greater flexibility than the metal hose type, and is easier to construct for small sizes.

The attenuation of flexible guides is much greater than that of the normal guide, but, as they are used only in short lengths, this is not of great importance.

Rotating Joints

In many radar and communication equipments it is necessary to rotate the aerial with respect to the rest of the equipment, and for this purpose a rotating joint in the waveguide feed must be provided. If the waveguide were a circular one propagating a mode which has circular symmetry, that is an E_{01} or H_{01} wave, rotation of any part of the guide relative to the other parts would in no way affect the propagation. It is not in general satisfactory to use circular guide for a complete waveguide system, but two short lengths of circular guide can be butted together to form a rotating joint, with transformation to the normal rectangular guide at each end. A cross-section of such a joint, with an E_{01} wave in the circular part, is shown in Fig. 7.27. The diameter of the circular tube is

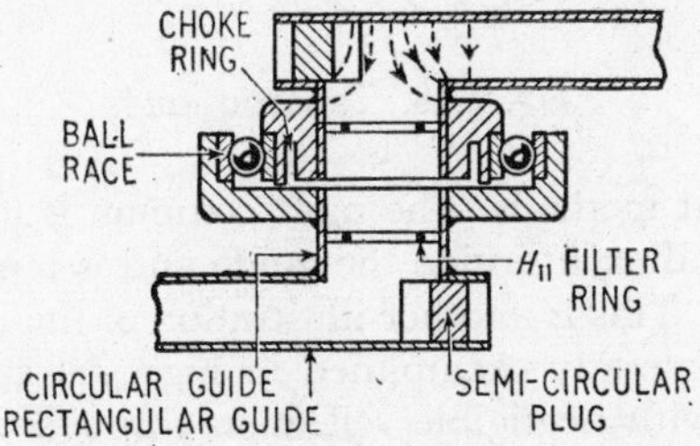

Fig. 7.27. Waveguide rotating joint with H_{10}–E_{01} transformers.

approximately equal to the large dimension of the rectangular guide, and the transition from the H_{10} mode in the rectangular guide to the E_{01} in the circular is assisted by a semi-circular plug fitted at a critical position in the end of the rectangular guide. Consideration of the electric field lines shown in the figure will make it clear that such mode conversion can occur, although it is not particularly obvious that such a simple arrangement will give a reasonably pure E_{01} mode. However, it is found in practice that with suitable choice of dimensions this method does give efficient mode conversion. Inevitably a certain amount of H_{11} wave is set up in the circular guide, and the amount of this unsymmetrical wave which is transferred to the output guide will vary with the angle of rotation and give rise to a variation in output. Various means of suppressing it are in use, a common one being a circular metal ring supported inside the circular guide, as shown in the figure. A ring of the correct diameter acts as a resonant rejector circuit, rejecting the H_{11} mode, while the E_{01} mode is almost unaffected, since its electric field is always perpendicular to the ring. The critical circumference of the ring is slightly greater than the free-space wavelength of the wave. To prevent radiation from the gap between the two circular guides a choke groove is machined as shown.

Another form of rotating joint uses the normal transverse mode in a coaxial line as the circularly symmetric wave. The circular guides are replaced by two short lengths of coaxial line, whose inner conductors are extended to form probe or cross-bar transformers in the two rectangular guides.

Matched Terminations

In making measurements on waveguide components, and in the operation of some of them, it is often desirable to absorb the power propagated down a guide in a matched termination. The matched termination consisting of a resistive film and tuning piston, which has been previously discussed, is not used in practice since it is rather critically dependent on frequency, and there are

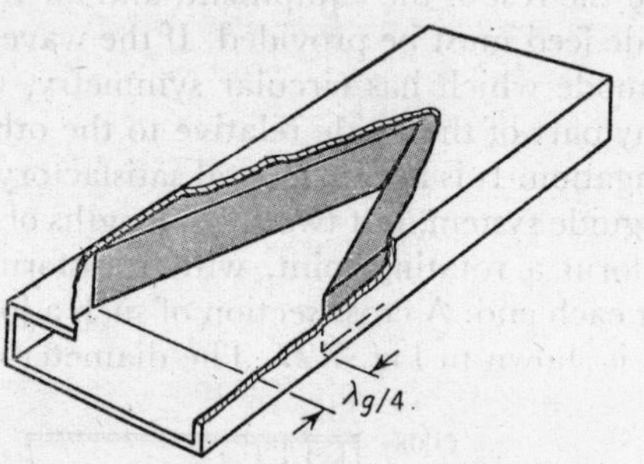

Fig. 7.28. Tapered load.

other more convenient methods. The most common is to use a length of lossy material which is a sliding fit inside the guide and is tapered to a point at the end facing the source. This is another illustration of the important principle in waveguide practice—already exemplified in Figs. 7.4 and 7.24—that a wave can be transformed with negligible reflection through changes of waveguide form if the change is made gradually. The resistivity of the lossy material is not important, but the length must be sufficient to absorb the wave completely. Wood is a convenient material if high powers are not involved, otherwise iron

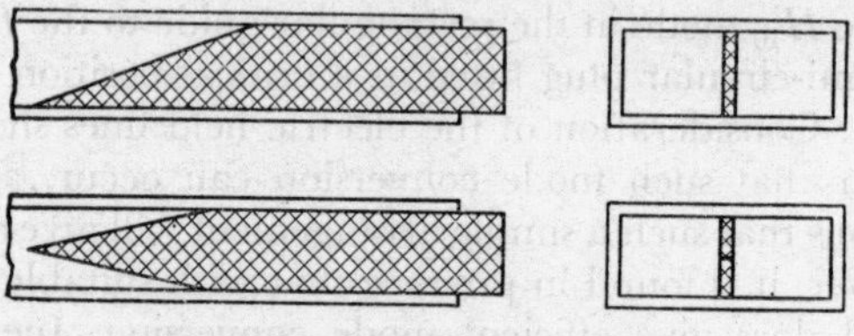

Fig. 7.29. Resistive strip loads

dust or lossy ceramic materials are used. Fig. 7.28 illustrates a good form of the taper, with the points running towards the edges so that they meet the field where it is weakest. One point extends a distance of $\lambda_g/4$ beyond the other so that any residual reflections from the two, being 180° out of phase, will tend to cancel.

Well-matched terminations for rectangular waveguide may also be made from thin resistive strip set longitudinally in the guide and tapered towards the source. As shown in Fig. 7.29 the strip is placed in the centre of the waveguide aligned in the direction of the electric field, and the taper may be a double or a single one. Surface resistivities of about 500 ohms are used, and a total length of approximately $2\lambda_g$ with a taper length of $\lambda_g/2$ is satisfactory. The carbon-coated strip used in the manufacture of potentiometers is very convenient, and is easily cut to shape. A more stable form uses a strip of glass with a thin coating of evaporated metal covered with a film of a protective material such as magnesium fluoride.

Resistive Attenuators

A resistive strip as described in the previous section can be used as an attenuator in a waveguide where it can take the form shown in Fig. 7.30, being tapered to match the waveguide at both ends. The length required to give the desired attenuation must be determined by experiment. This 'tapered vane' attenuator may be made variable by mounting it on two thin rods passing through the guide in the position shown, by which its transverse position in the

Fig. 7.30. Tapered vane variable attenuator.

guide can be altered. The attenuation is a maximum when the vane is in the centre plane of the guide. As the vane is moved towards the guide wall into the steadily decreasing electric field the attenuation decreases steadily to become zero when the vane reaches the guide wall.

In another type of variable attenuator the resistive strip projects through a slot along the centre of the broad side of the waveguide, and its penetration into the guide can be varied. Two forms are shown in section in Fig. 7.31. In the first the vane rotates about a hinge at one end. Because of the simplicity of the construction this type of attenuator is used frequently in experimental apparatus where leakage of radiation from the slot is not of great importance. It is normally used in an uncalibrated form to adjust power output to a desired level.

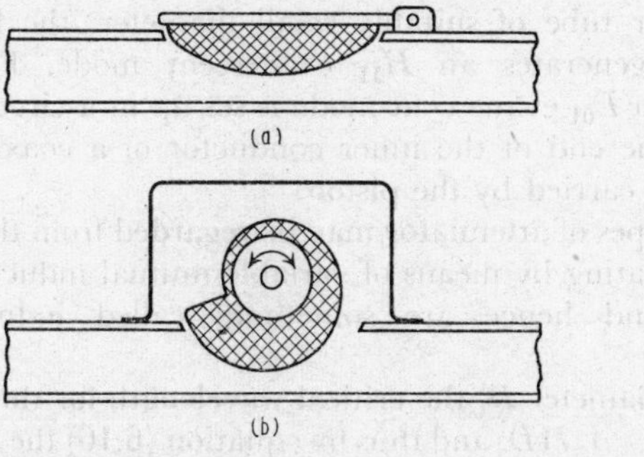

Fig. 7.31. Two forms of variable attenuator using resistive strip.

In the second form, Fig. 7.31 (b), the resistive element is cut in a spiral shape and fixed to a shaft, by means of which it can be rotated. By suitable shaping of the spiral it can be arranged that the attenuation in decibels is proportional to the angular rotation of the shaft. Stray radiation can be prevented by enclosing the moving parts within a metal casing. Values of attenuation up to 40 db are readily obtained, but higher values require very careful design to avoid stray coupling through the slot.

It should be observed that in all these attenuators the vane is shaped so that it enters the field gradually in such a way as to produce minimum reflection at the point of entry. The standing-wave ratio due to the presence of the attenuator can usually be kept below 1·01.

Piston Attenuators

A waveguide operated below cut-off can form the basis of a precision variable attenuator. The essentials of two such attenuators are shown in Fig. 7.32 (a, b). An evanescent wave is set up at one end of a waveguide by a suitable exciting arrangement, that shown in Fig. 7.32 (a) being a wire loop fed from a coaxial line. Inside the guide is a similar loop carried on a movable piston and connected to the output coaxial line. A current is induced in the output loop proportional to the field existing at that position in the guide, and thus as the position of the piston is varied the output varies according to the known law of the

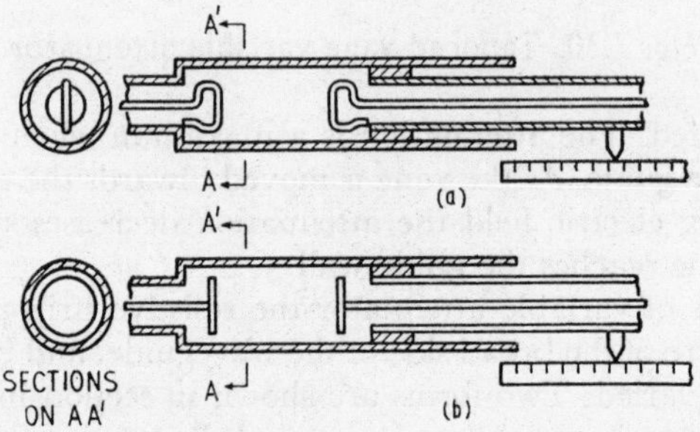

Fig. 7.32. Piston attenuators, (a) H_{11} or inductive type, (b) E_{01} or capacitive type.

evanescent field. The guide may have any shape of cross-section, but is usually circular.

In a circular tube of suitably small diameter, the loop system shown in Fig. 7.32 (a) generates an H_{11} evanescent mode. For the attenuator of Fig. 7.32 (b) an E_{01} evanescent mode is set up in a circular tube by a circular disc fixed to the end of the inner conductor of a coaxial line, and a similar arrangement is carried by the piston.

These two types of attenuator may be regarded from the low-frequency point of view as operating by means of variable mutual inductance and capacitance respectively, and hence are sometimes called inductive and capacitive types.

► For a tube diameter D, the critical wavelength for the H_{11} mode is given by Table 6.3 as $\lambda_c = 1{\cdot}71D$, and thus by equation (6.16) the attenuation constant is

$$\alpha = 2\pi/1{\cdot}71D \text{ nepers per unit length}$$

$$= \frac{32{\cdot}0}{D} \text{ decibels per unit length} \quad . \quad . \quad . \quad . \quad (7.14)$$

Thus with a diameter of 1 cm a piston movement of 1 cm will give a 32-db change in attenuation.

For the E_{01} attenuator the critical wavelength is given by $\lambda_c = 1{\cdot}31D$, and the corresponding value of attenuation constant is

$$\alpha = 2\pi/1{\cdot}31D \text{ nepers per unit length}$$
$$= \frac{41{\cdot}8}{D} \text{ decibels per unit length} \quad . \quad . \quad . \quad . \quad . \quad (7.15)$$

A linear scale attached to the piston can therefore be marked to read directly in decibels. As shown in Chapter 6, the attenuation constant is practically independent of frequency so long as the frequency is well below the critical value. If this condition is not satisfied the exact expression (6.15) must be used.

Obviously the attenuation will have its calculated value only if the evanescent wave is a single pure mode. Thus in the E_{01} attenuator, for instance, it is necessary that the exciting and pick-up discs should be accurately concentric with the tube. Any asymmetry will give rise to a proportion of the H_{11} or other mode.

In all piston attenuators the linear relationship between distance and decibels fails when the input and output couplings are brought close together. Distortion

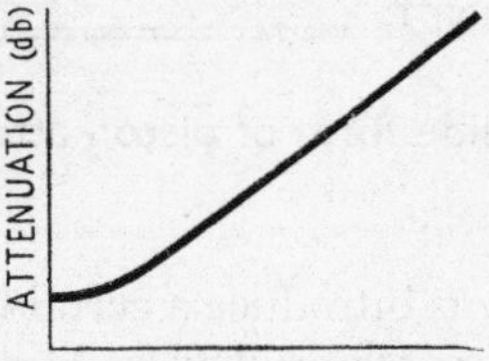

Fig. 7.33. Typical calibration curve of piston attenuator.

of the field then occurs, which produces a curvature in the calibration curve, as shown in Fig. 7.33. This limits the useful operation of a piston attenuator to a minimum attenuation which is dependent on the accuracy required, but is usually in the neighbourhood of 20 db. Thus the rate of change of attenuation with distance can be calculated, but not the absolute value of the attenuation. With a minimum attenuation of the order of 20 db only a small fraction of the available power flows through the attenuator, and thus most of the incident power is reflected at the attenuator input. In other words the input impedance of a piston attenuator is highly reactive; so also is the output impedance. There are two common methods of correcting this. One is to add a length of coaxial cable at each end of the attenuator. An attenuation of about 10 db in each is sufficient to make the overall input and output impedances approximately equal to the cable characteristic impedance. The other method is to incorporate matching resistors in the launching and receiving arrangements. For the inductive attenuator the resistor may be added in series with the loop; for the capacitive type it can take the form of a resistive disc placed across the coaxial line immediately behind the existing disc.

For a well-designed piston attenuator the measured attenuation rate agrees very closely with the calculated rate, and such an attenuator can be a precision instrument.

In the form described the piston attenuator does not fit into a waveguide system, but is applicable to systems using coaxial lines. A form suitable for waveguide use is shown in Fig. 7.34. In this design the circular tube A is the attenuating tube, into which penetrates to a variable extent a thin-walled tube B filled with a dielectric material, for example, polystyrene. A waveguide filled with a dielectric of relative permittivity κ_r has its critical wavelength increased by the factor $\sqrt{\kappa_r}$, so that for the H_{11} mode it is given by $\lambda_c = 1{\cdot}71 D\sqrt{\kappa_r}$. The tube diameter is therefore selected, with reference to the frequency used, so that an H_{11} wave is attenuated in the empty tube, but is freely propagated in the dielectric-filled tube. Alteration of the penetration of B within A thus alters the attenuating length of A. The H_{11} mode in B is excited from a standard rectangular waveguide through a small hole in the broad side, and the bottom end of A is similarly coupled to a second waveguide.

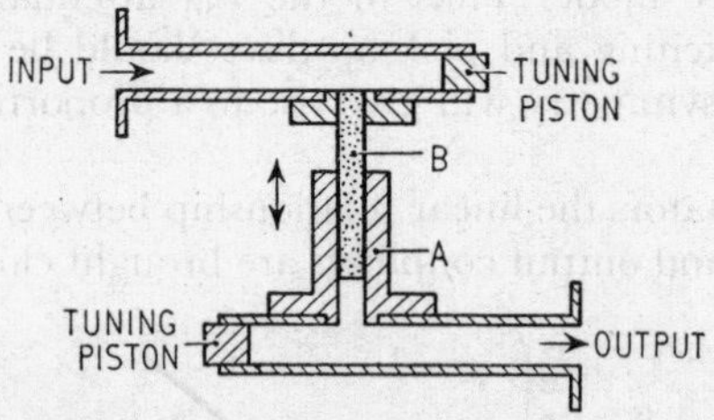

Fig. 7.34. Waveguide form of piston attenuator, H_{11} type.

Matching in Waveguides

Most waveguide components introduce a certain amount of mismatch, which has to be removed by some matching device. Matching can be carried out by means of waveguide stubs of adjustable length, in the same way as matching stubs are used with two-conductor transmission lines, or by means of lumped reactances placed in the waveguide. Stub matching will be considered later on when junctions in waveguides have been dealt with. Lumped reactances take the form of metallic obstacles of various shapes placed in the guide, selected so as to produce effects equivalent to those of lumped inductors and capacitors in two-conductor transmission lines. In the following section we shall consider some types of lumped reactance.

Inductive and Capacitive Irises

The most common form of obstacle used for matching purposes is a thin metal sheet partially obstructing a transverse section of the waveguide, and known as an *iris* or *diaphragm*. The calculation of the effect of such an obstacle is involved, but it is reasonable that, since the iris extends for a negligible distance along the guide and since its resistive losses must be very small, the transverse electric field should have effectively the same value on each side of the discontinuity. The obstacle can consequently be represented as a lumped reactance connected in *shunt* across a transmission line. The iris of the shape shown in Fig. 7.35 (a) can be thought of as collecting charge from the top and bottom walls of the guide and thus storing *electric* energy, so that it is equivalent to a capacitance. The iris of Fig. 7.35 (b), however, provides a partial current path from the top to the bottom wall, thus storing *magnetic* energy, so that it is equivalent to an inductance.

Figs. 7.36 and 7.37 show respectively some other forms of capacitive and inductive iris.

Such iris apertures are usually used as an integral part of a waveguide component to correct a mismatch inherent in the component. From their nature they are not readily adjustable, and their dimensions must be determined by calculation from standing-wave detector measurements or by trial and error. Where high powers are to be carried the inductive type is to be preferred on account of its greater freedom from voltage breakdown.

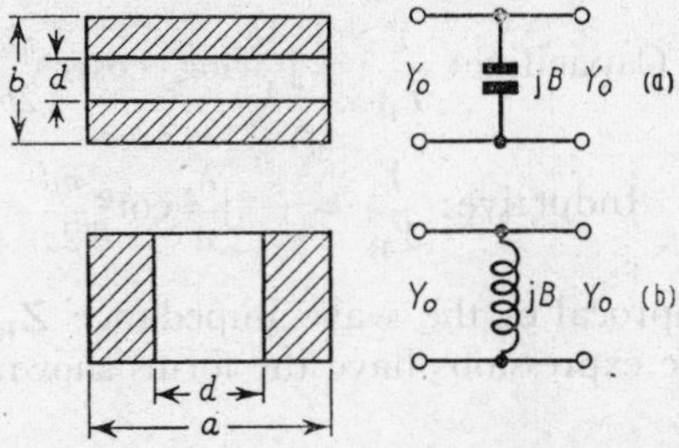

Fig. 7.35. Fundamental types of waveguide iris with their equivalent circuits, (a) capacitive, (b) inductive.

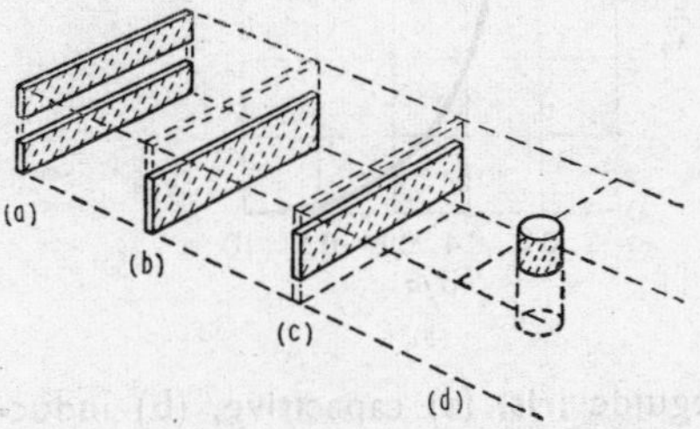

Fig. 7.36. (a)–(c) Various forms of capacitive iris; (d) capacitive post.

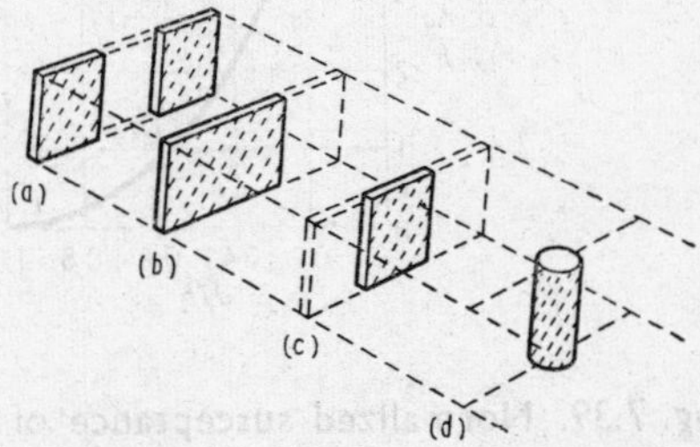

Fig. 7.37. (a)–(c) Various forms of inductive iris; (d) inductive post.

A rod (usually called a post) projecting from the broad face of the guide, as in Fig. 7.36 (d), has a capacitive reactance when its penetration is small. This increases with penetration, but eventually changes sign and becomes inductive, so that the post shown in Fig. 7.37 (d) is inductive. An adjustable form of this

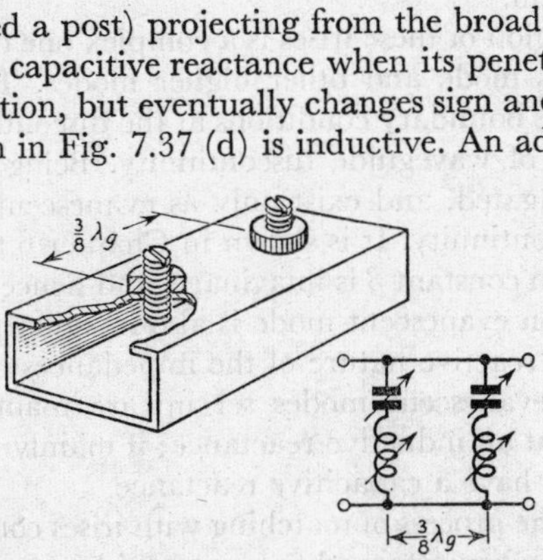

Fig. 7.38. Two-screw waveguide matcher with its equivalent circuit.

reactance consists of a threaded screw secured by a lock-nut, and referred to as a tuning screw. It is often convenient to locate two, or more, such tuners on a short length of guide, as shown in Fig. 7.38, the combination forming a matching unit equivalent to the two-stub tuner shown in Fig. 4.14 (a). Spacing is not critical, but a separation distance of $3\lambda_g/8$ is common.

▶ Since the equivalent inductance or capacitance is in parallel with the line it is more convenient for calculations to have its value in admittance form. The calculations are too involved to be given here, but the normalized admittances for the symmetric irises of Fig. 7.35 can be stated as

$$\text{Capacitive:}\ \frac{Y}{Y_W} = j\frac{4b}{\lambda_g}\log_\varepsilon \operatorname{cosec}\frac{\pi d}{2b} \quad . \quad . \quad . \quad (7.16)$$

$$\text{Inductive:}\ \frac{Y}{Y_W} = -j\frac{\lambda_g}{a}\cot^2\frac{\pi d}{2a} \quad . \quad . \quad . \quad . \quad (7.17)$$

where Y_W is the reciprocal of the wave impedance Z_W of the guide. When plotted against d these expressions have the forms shown in Fig. 7.39. Strictly

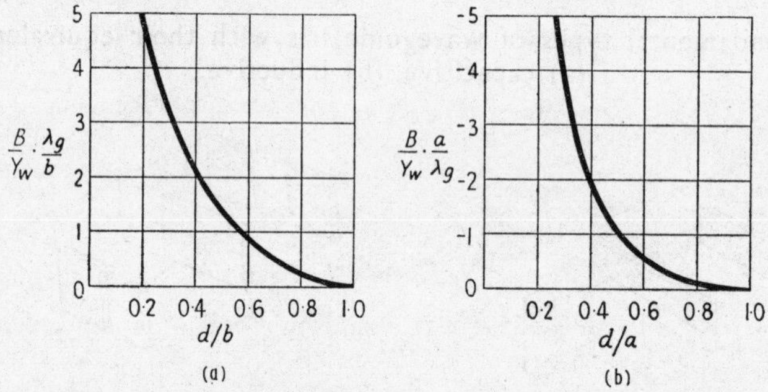

Fig. 7.39. Normalized susceptance of waveguide iris, (a) capacitive, (b) inductive, as a function of iris opening. $Y = jB$.

the formulae refer to very thin irises only, but moderate values of thickness do not greatly affect them.

The field in the region of these irises is a complex one composed of a mixture of the dominant H_{10} mode and other higher modes. The higher modes are required to satisfy the boundary conditions at the discontinuity, and are always set up at any form of waveguide discontinuity. Being beyond cut-off these modes are not propagated, and exist only as evanescent modes in the neighbourhood of the discontinuity. It is shown in Chapter 6 that for an evanescent mode the propagation constant β is imaginary, and hence so also is λ_g. Thus the wave impedance of an evanescent mode is also imaginary, and it is this which is responsible for the reactive nature of the impedances of irises and other discontinuities. If the evanescent modes set up are mainly E modes the discontinuity will present an inductive reactance; if mainly H modes are involved the discontinuity will have a capacitive reactance.

As an example of the process of matching with irises consider the matching of a termination which, when attached to a waveguide, produces a standing-wave ratio of 3·1, with the first minimum at a distance of $0{\cdot}04\lambda_g$ from the termination. Because of the correspondence between expressions for standing-wave ratio in waveguides and two-conductor lines the circle diagram discussed in Chapter 3 can be used in exactly the same way for waveguide-matching problems. Starting from the point A in the circle diagram of Fig. 7.40, which corresponds to the minimum on the standing wave detector where the normalized admittance is 3·1, we move counter clockwise round the circle $S = 3 \cdot 1$ through a distance corresponding to a guide of length $0 \cdot 04\lambda_g$. This brings us to the point B which represents the termination, and shows that it has a normalized admittance $Y/Y_W = 2 \cdot 02 + j1 \cdot 35$. Movement from B clockwise round the same circle

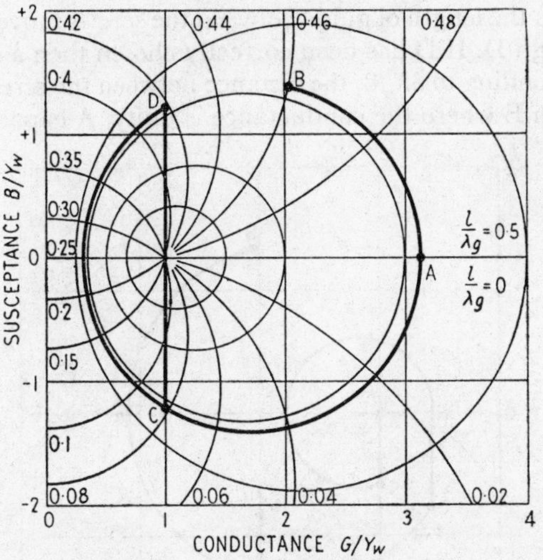

Fig. 7.40. **Circle diagram illustrating matching by a single adjustable iris.**

corresponds to movement along the guide towards the generator. The distance is chosen so as to bring the point to C, where the real part of the normalized admittance is unity, the complex admittance at C being then $1 - j1 \cdot 2$. An iris of normalized admittance $+ j1 \cdot 2$ placed here will move the point to the position $1 + j0$, giving perfect matching. The length of waveguide corresponding to the arc BC is seen from the diagram to be $0 \cdot 122\lambda_g$, and the iris, having a positive

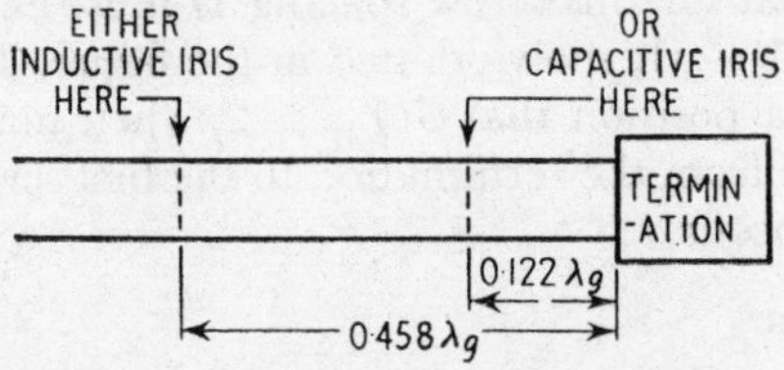

Fig. 7.41. **Positions of matching iris deduced from Fig. 7.40.**

susceptance, must be a capacitive one whose dimensions are calculated from equation (7.16) with $Y/Y_W = j1 \cdot 2$.

An alternative solution is to choose the length of guide so as to bring the point round to D, where the real part of the normalized admittance is again unity, but the complex admittance is now $1 + j1 \cdot 2$. An iris of normalized admittance $- j1 \cdot 2$ placed here will again move the point to $1 + j0$. The length of the arc BD is $0 \cdot 458\lambda_g$, and the negative susceptance now requires an inductive iris whose dimensions are given by (7.17) with $Y/Y_W = - j1 \cdot 2$. The two alternatives are shown in Fig. 7.41.

The process of matching the same termination with the two-screw matcher of Fig. 7.38 is illustrated in Fig. 7.42. The point B again represents the normalized admittance of the termination. Transformation through a length of waveguide will move it round the S-circle on which it lies, $S = 3{\cdot}1$, the arc BC corresponding to the distance from the termination to the first screw. If the first screw is capacitive it will bring the point up to some position such as D. Further transformation through the length of guide between the screws moves the point round the S-circle through D. If D has been correctly chosen then a movement round this circle corresponding to $3\lambda_g/8$, the distance between the screws, will bring the point to a position E where the conductance is unity. A capacitive susceptance

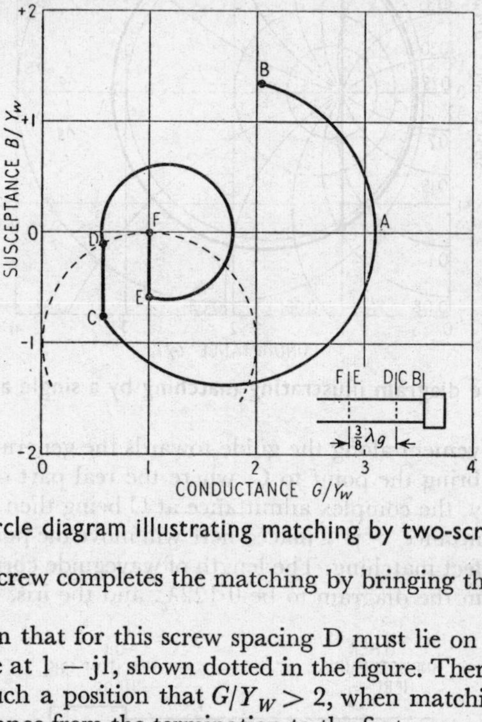

Fig. 7.42. Circle diagram illustrating matching by two-screw matcher.

from the second screw completes the matching by bringing the point to $1 + j0$ at F.

It can be shown that for this screw spacing D must lie on the circle of unit radius with centre at $1 - j1$, shown dotted in the figure. Therefore the point C must not lie in such a position that $G/Y_W > 2$, when matching would be impossible. The distance from the termination to the first screw must be arranged so that this does not occur.

Resonant Apertures

It is evident that for a combination of a capacitive iris and an inductive iris there will be a frequency at which it will exhibit resonance. Thus a thin transverse sheet with a rectangular aperture, as shown Fig. 7.43 (a), will act as a

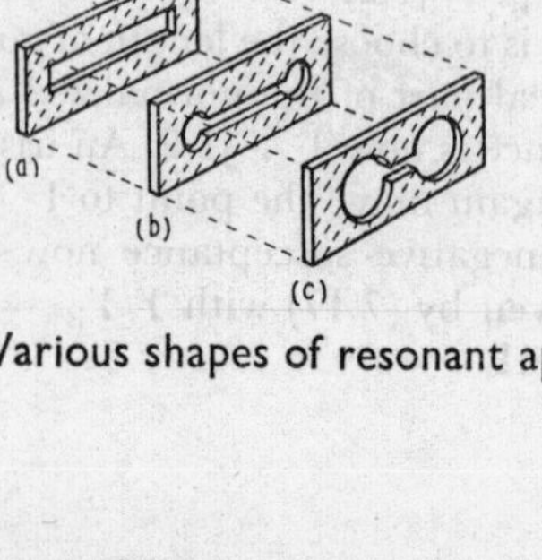

Fig. 7.43. Various shapes of resonant aperture.

parallel resonant circuit. Having a high shunt impedance at resonance, it will at that frequency transmit a wave freely. Such resonant structures have the property of discrimination against frequencies other than the resonance frequency, but as filters they are inefficient, having low Q values. A preferable form of frequency filter is discussed in the next section.

Fig. 7.44 shows the curves upon which the corners of a resonant aperture must lie. It can be seen that if b' is small, then a' should be just greater than the free-space half-wavelength.* Small values of b' give somewhat higher values of Q.

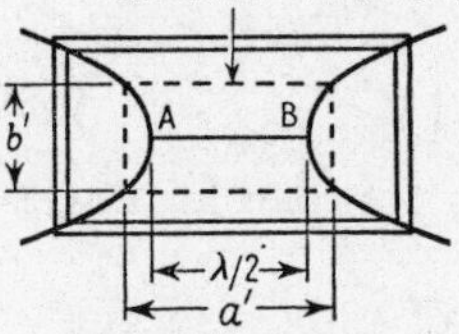

Fig. 7.44. Hyperbolae for determining dimensions of a resonant aperture.

Other shapes of resonant aperture are illustrated in Fig. 7.43 (b) and (c).

An important use of the resonant aperture is in the construction of 'resonant windows'—windows of glass or mica by which a waveguide system can be sealed against moisture or variations in atmospheric pressure without impairing its transmission properties. The presence of the dielectric filling has the effect of adding capacitance. To correct for this the dimension a' of a rectangular aperture should be slightly less than that determined from Fig. 7.44. A practical shape of window is shown in Fig. 7.45.

Fig. 7.45. Resonant window.

▶ Waveguide Frequency Filters

If a length of waveguide, correctly terminated at its far end, has two irises inserted in it then it is possible to find one particular frequency at which the reflections from the two irises will cancel. At that frequency power is freely transmitted along the guide. That this is possible can most easily be seen from a numerical example. Consider the case illustrated in Fig. 7.46 where the irises are inductive, have a separation of $3\lambda_g/8$, and are assumed each to have a normalized admittance $Y/Y_W = -j2$. Beyond the irises the guide is matched and this condition is represented on the circle diagram of Fig. 7.47 by the point $A = 1 + j0$. The insertion of the iris nearest the termination has the effect of moving the point to B, where $B = 1 - j2$. As we pass along the guide towards the generator the admittance changes as specified by points on the standing-wave ratio circle through B. A movement corresponding to $l/\lambda_g = 0{\cdot}375$ brings

* To construct these curves the line AB (= λ/2) is drawn with its centre on the waveguide axis. Then two hyperbolae are drawn with their vertices at A and B respectively, and passing through the corners of the waveguide.

the point around this circle to C, where the admittance is now $1 + j2$. The insertion of the second iris at this position adds an admittance $-j2$ which brings the point back again to the match position A. Thus, when the separation has

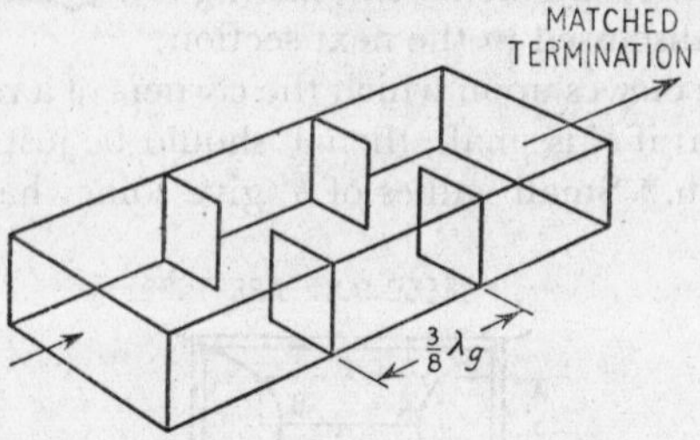

Fig. 7.46. Iris positions for single-cavity filter.

this particular value in terms of λ_g the waveguide appears matched, and power flows freely through the discontinuities.

Variation of the frequency has the effect of changing the value of l/λ_g and hence moves the terminal point along the arc of the circle shown as $A'AA''$, thus moving the input admittance into a region of inductive susceptance on the one side and capacitive susceptance on the other. Since both of these conditions correspond to loss of power by reflection, the section of waveguide with its

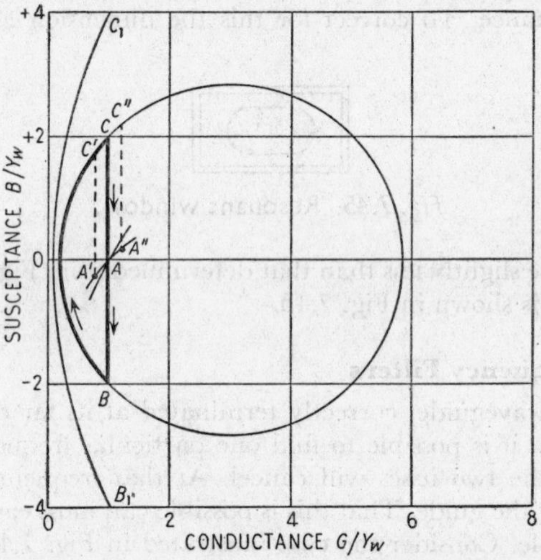

Fig. 7.47. Circle diagram for single-cavity filter.

enclosing irises acts as a filter with a single transmission maximum. To increase the sharpness of the frequency response we look for a means of increasing the angle which $A'AA''$ makes with the conductance axis. This is accomplished by choosing larger normalized susceptances (smaller iris openings), and thereby increasing the radius of the standing-wave circle, as is shown in Fig. 7.47 by the circle B_1C_1 for irises of admittance $-j4$. This increase requires an increase in the separation of the irises to move the point from B_1 to C_1; in this case the length required is $l/\lambda_g = 0{\cdot}426$.

This filter is known as a single-cavity filter, the space between the irises being a resonant cavity. Waveguide cavities will be dealt with in much more detail in the following chapter.

Filters containing three or more irises can be designed to have the properties of band-pass filters. Fig. 7.48 shows a two-cavity filter having irises of susceptances B_1, B_2 and B_3. It can be shown that this filter has properties similar to those of two coupled tuned circuits. Critical coupling is obtained when $B_2 = B_1^2 = B_3^2$, giving the response curve of Fig. 7.48 (a). Values of B_2 greater

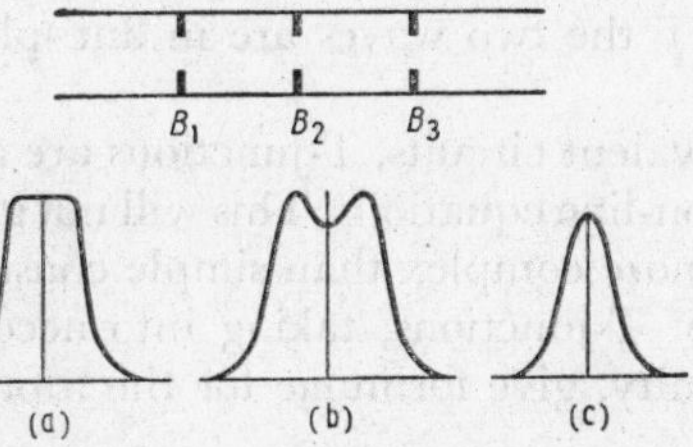

Fig. 7.48. Two-cavity filter and its responses with (a) critical coupling, (b) over-coupling, (c) under-coupling.

than and less than the critical value give respectively the over-coupled and under-coupled responses of Fig. 7.48 (b) and (c).

It will be clear that these are the waveguide analogues of the transmission line filters discussed in Chapter 4, and that many types of waveguide filter are possible. Their detailed design is beyond our scope.

T-Junctions

It is often required to divide a waveguide into two branches, or combine two separate guides into a single one. This is usually done by means of a T-junction, the two forms of which are shown in Fig. 7.49.

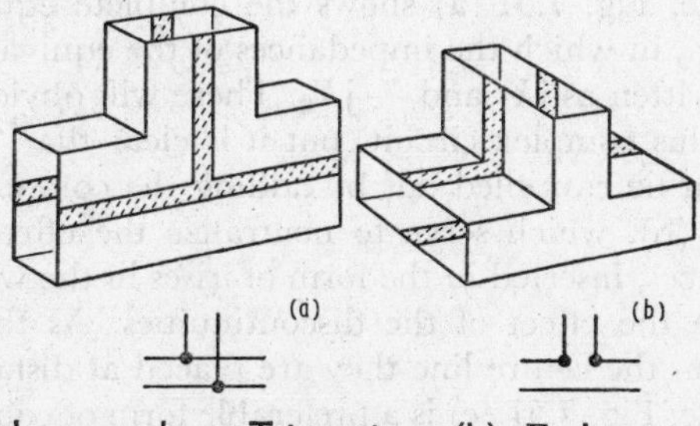

Fig. 7.49. (a) *H*-plane or shunt T-junction; (b) *E*-plane or series T-junction.

That of Fig. 7.49 (a) is called an *H*-plane junction since all three arms lie in the plane of the magnetic vector of the H_{10} mode. The arms of the junction shown in Fig. 7.49 (b) lie in the plane of the electric field, and it is therefore called an *E*-plane junction. From the symmetry it is evident that power fed into the vertical arm will be divided equally between the other two arms, but there are other considerations. In the H_{10} mode in a waveguide the currents in the central portions of the two broad sides flow longitudinally in opposite directions, and the electric field extends across from one broad side to the other. These two central strips thus resemble the two halves of a strip transmission line. The strips are shown hatched in Fig. 7.49, and on this picture it will be clear that the transmission line analogues shown are plausible; that is, the *H*-plane junction has the properties of a shunt junction, while the *E*-plane junction has the properties of a series junction. This important property, which is not apparent from a superficial consideration of the geometry of the junction, gives rise to the nomenclature *shunt* T and *series* T for the *H*- and *E*-plane junctions respectively. It is evident also that the field distributions at the junctions will be as shown in Fig. 7.50. It indicates that in the shunt T the two emergent waves are in phase, whereas in the series T the two waves are in anti-phase at points equidistant from the junction.

Through their equivalent circuits, T-junctions are amenable to treatment by the normal transmission-line equations. This will not give exact results, however, since the problem is more complex than simple considerations indicate.

Detailed analyses of T-junctions, taking into account the distortion of the field by the discontinuity, give formulae for the input impedance of any limb

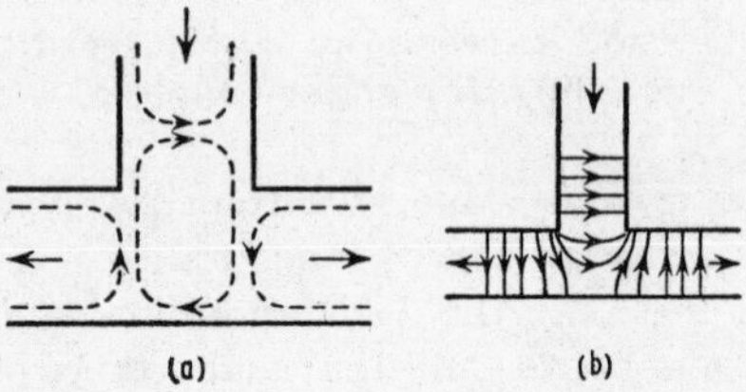

Fig. 7.50. Field distributions in T-junctions (a) shunt, (b) series.
——— electric field
— — — magnetic field

in terms of the terminating impedances in the other two limbs and the guide dimensions. The formulae are complex, but their representations as equivalent circuits are valuable. Fig. 7.51 (a) shows the complete equivalent circuit for the series T-junction, in which the impedances of the equivalent inductors and the capacitor are written as jX_1 and $-jX_2$. There will obviously be reflections at the junction in this complex circuit, but it is clear that, for any particular frequency, these can be cancelled out by adding the compensating reactances shown in Fig. 7.51 (b), which serve to neutralize the effects of jX_1 and jX_2. These extra reactances, inserted in the form of irises in the waveguide junction, will thus neutralize the effect of the discontinuities. As the capacitive irises cannot be located on the centre line they are placed at distances of $\lambda_g/2$ where the effect is the same. Fig. 7.51 (c) is a preferable form of compensated junction using inductive irises, those in the horizontal arms being placed at such a distance that they are transformed through this length of waveguide into capacitive reactances of the required value. Such a compensated junction will transmit freely without reflection at the particular frequency for which the compensation is designed.

T-Junctions as Stub Matchers

As shunt stubs are used for matching in two-conductor transmission lines, so also in waveguides adjustable waveguide stubs may be used. In a waveguide a

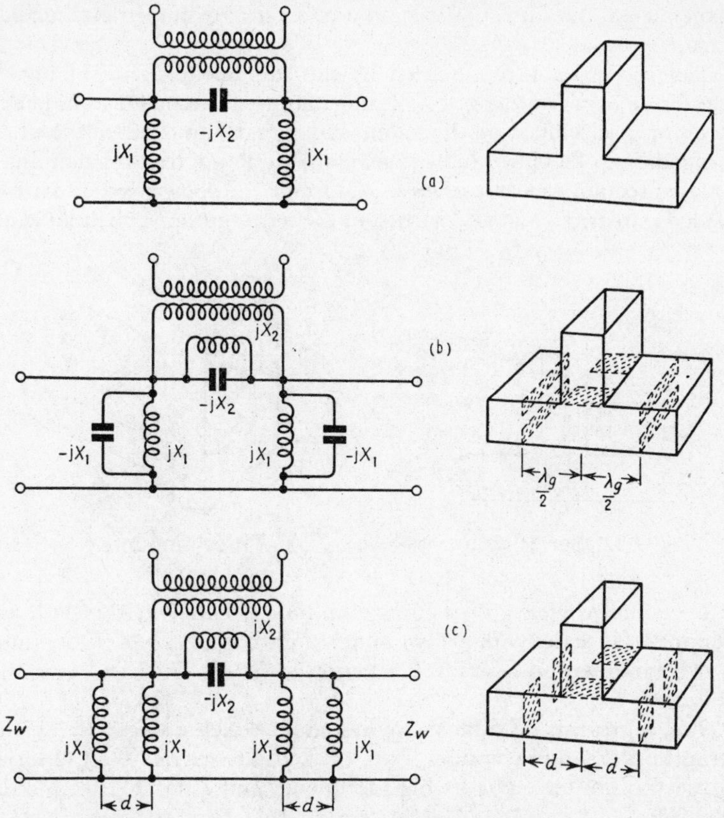

Fig. 7.51. Compensation of series T-junction: (a) uncompensated junction and equivalent circuit; (b) compensation by capacitive reactances; (c) compensation by inductive reactances. Here $d = \frac{\lambda_g}{2\pi} \cot^{-1}\left(\frac{-X_1}{2Z_W}\right)$.

stub can be fitted at either a series or a shunt T-junction in the main guide, and consists of a short length of guide terminated in a movable piston. Movement of the piston gives a reactance varying with the length from a high positive value through zero to a high negative value. This effect is somewhat modified by distortion effects at the junction, so that the impedance range covered in a particular case is best determined by making standing wave measurements for various positions of the tuning piston.

A double-stub tuner, with the stubs separated by a distance of about $3\lambda_g/8$, will match a termination to a guide over a wide range of terminating impedances. A triple-stub tuner can be made to match any terminating impedance.

T-Junctions as Switches

An instructive example of the use of the T-junction is its operation, in conjunction with a TR cell as a switch, in a radar system. The construction and operation of the TR cell is discussed in Chapter 13 of Volume 3; here it is sufficient to regard it as a gas-filled waveguide cell which has a very high impedance when the gas is not ionized and a very low impedance when the gas is ionized.

Consider the series T represented by the equivalent circuit of Fig. 7.52, of which the side arm is of length $\lambda_g/2$ and may be terminated in either a short-circuit or open-circuit, and the main arm has a matched termination. The input impedance of a closed half-wavelength section of transmission line is zero, so the closed section acts as a series short-circuit, and power fed into arm 1 flows unimpeded into arm 3 and is absorbed in the termination. The input impedance

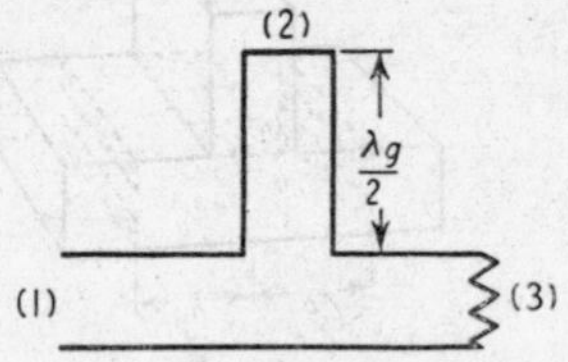

Fig. 7.52. Series stub.

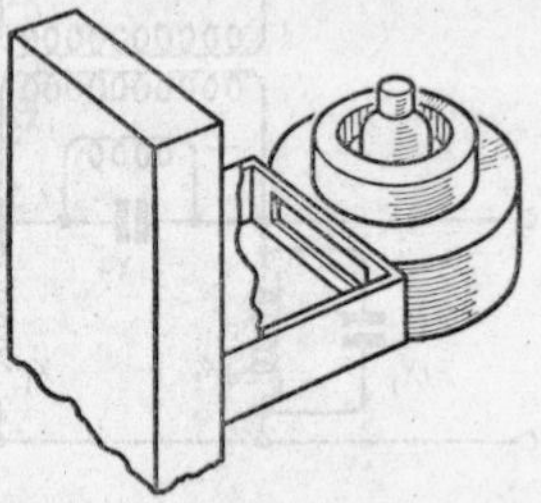

Fig. 7.53. TR cell mounted on series stub.

of the open half-wavelength section is infinite, so that in this case an open-circuit appears in series with arms 1 and 3, and thus no power passes into arm 3. A TR cell mounted on a series T junction as in Fig. 7.53 will give these two conditions.

Fig. 7.54 represents a simple radar system in which a single aerial is used for both transmission and reception. Two TR cells are carried on $\lambda_g/2$ series arms. When the transmitter emits its high-frequency pulse the TR cells ionize. The

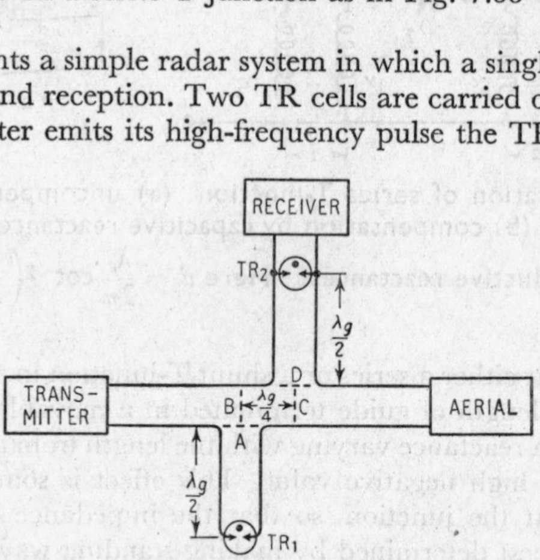

Fig. 7.54. Arrangement of TR cells in simple radar system, series arms.

resulting short circuits in TR_1 and TR_2, transformed through the half-wave-length guides, are equivalent to series short-circuits at the junctions of the two side arms with the main guide, and thus all the transmitter power flows to the aerial. TR_2 effectively protects the sensitive receiver situated beyond it from the damage or paralysis which would result if any substantial fraction of the trans-mitter power reached it. Immediately after the transmitter pulse ceases the cells de-ionize and become open-circuits. When the echo signals return to the aerial and pass back along the main guide they are too weak to ionize the cells. The open circuit at TR_1, transformed through the half-wavelength guide, is now equivalent to a series open circuit at A, which in turn is transformed through the quarter-wavelength of guide BC to become a series short circuit at C. The incoming power is thus directed towards the receiver, passing freely through TR_2, and none is lost by absorption in the transmitter.

It is easy to see that if series junctions are replaced by shunt junctions the

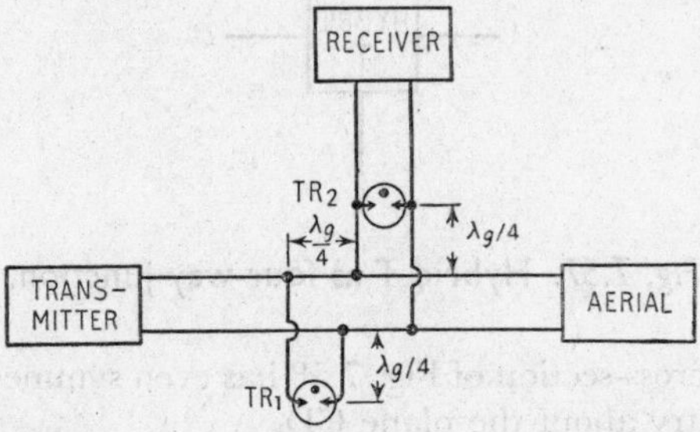

Fig. 7.55. Arrangement of TR cells in simple radar system, shunt arms.

side arms must be $\lambda_g/4$ in length, and the system then becomes that shown in Fig. 7.55.

Hybrid T-Junctions

The superposition of a shunt and a series junction produces the hybrid T-junction shown in Fig. 7.56, which, by reason of its geometric symmetry, has

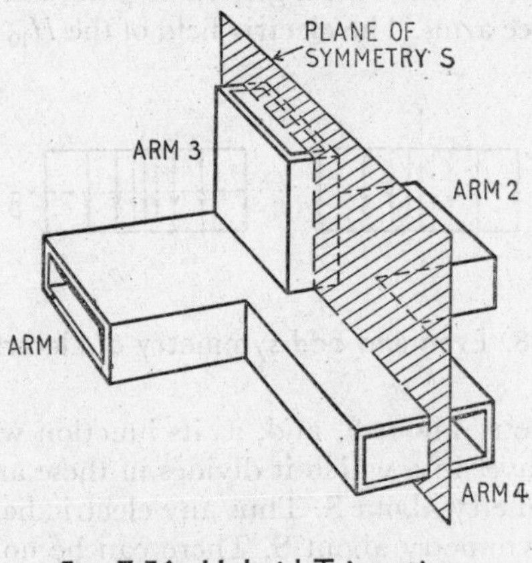

Fig. 7.56. Hybrid T-junction.

additional important properties. In the following paragraphs it will be shown that, if perfectly matched at every arm, a hybrid T acts as a four-way junction, represented diagrammatically in Fig. 7.57, having the property that power incident on any arm divides equally between the two adjacent arms, but no power passes down the opposite arm.

There are a number of other structures with the same property, one of which is the hybrid ring described in a later section.

▶ A field pattern is said to have even symmetry about a plane if the field on one side of the plane is a mirror image of that on the other side. It has odd symmetry if a change of sign is required on one side to produce mirror images. Thus the

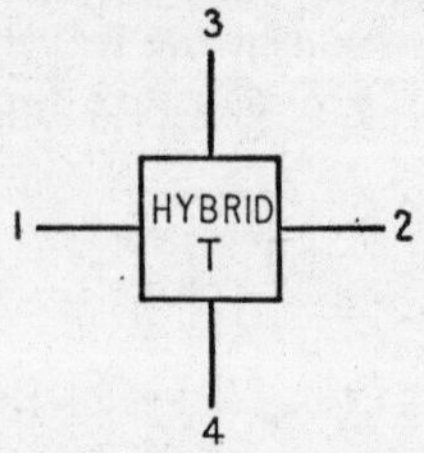

Fig. 7.57. Hybrid T as four-way junction.

electric field in the cross-section of Fig. 7.58 has even symmetry about the plane AB but odd symmetry about the plane CD.

Suppose now that a generator is placed in arm 4 of the hybrid T of Fig. 7.56 and matched terminations on the other three arms. We know that an H_{10} wave entering the shunt junction from the generator divides into two waves in arms 1 and 2, equal in amplitude and phase. The electric field pattern thus has even symmetry about the plane of geometrical symmetry S, and therefore any electric field induced in arm 3 must also have even symmetry about S. But arm 3 cannot support a wave whose electric field has even symmetry about plane S, since the only wave it can support is the H_{10} type, whose electric field has odd symmetry about S. No wave is therefore propagated in arm 3.

A similar state of affairs exists for a generator placed in arm 3, with matched loads on the other three arms. The electric field of the H_{10} wave propagated into

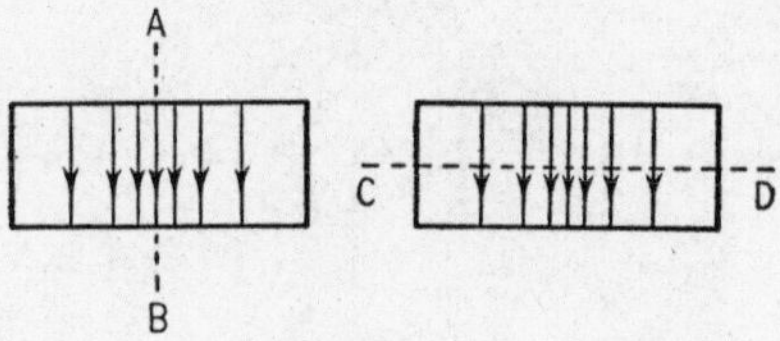

Fig. 7.58. Even and odd symmetry of electric field.

arm 3 has odd symmetry about S, and, as its junction with arms 1 and 2 is a series junction, the waves into which it divides in these arms are in anti-phase, and so have odd symmetry about S. Thus any electric field produced in arm 4 must also have odd symmetry about S. There can be no such wave, since the electric field of the only wave which can be supported by this guide, the H_{10} wave, has even symmetry about S.

It does not follow, however, that the junction will appear as a matched load to a generator placed in arm 3 or arm 4, even when arms 1 and 2 are properly terminated. In each case there will be considerable reflection of power because of the discontinuities introduced. This may be overcome by using matching devices as was done to compensate the simple T-junction, but they must not disturb the geometrical symmetry. A matched form is shown in Fig. 7.59, where the vertical post acts as the matching element for arm 4, and the inductive iris as the matching element for arm 3. In the case when the hybrid T is perfectly matched we can deduce the additional property that a generator in arm 1 will send power equally into arms 3 and 4, and none into arm 2. A similar relation holds for a generator in arm 2.

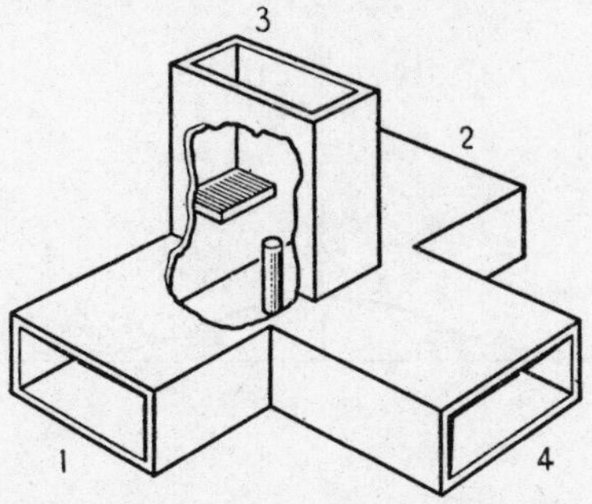

Fig. 7.59. Compensated hybrid T-junction.

Applications of the Hybrid T

An important application of the hybrid T is as a device to keep a transmitter disconnected from a receiver at all times while allowing free connection between each and a common aerial. Fig. 7.60 illustrates the arrangement of the units, including a matched load on one of the arms. The transmitter power divides equally between the aerial and the matched load, and of the received power coming from the aerial one-half passes to the receiver and the remainder is dissipated in the transmitter. This system performs the same function as the arrangements of Figs. 7.54 and 7.55, but with the difference that the transmission path is always open in both directions, and so can be used with a continuously-operating transmitter, for example, in a duplex communication system. This advantage however is gained at the expense of a 3-db loss in each direction, a loss inherent in any system providing such directional properties.

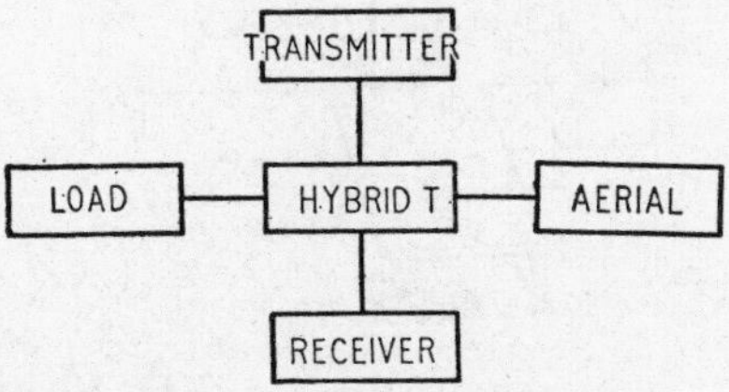

Fig. 7.60. Use of hybrid T for common aerial working.

Another use of the hybrid T is in the reduction of receiver noise by means of a balanced mixer. The simple microwave superheterodyne receiver consists essentially of a crystal-valve mixer terminating a waveguide through which the signal arrives. Power from the local oscillator is loosely coupled into the waveguide near to the crystal, and the i.f. signal is taken from the crystal through an h.f. filter. Every centimetre-wave oscillator generates a band of random noise having an amplitude very small compared with the amplitude of the oscillation but extending over a wide frequency range on either side of the oscillation frequency. This is shown in Fig. 7.61 in relation to the signal frequency. Those noise components falling in the shaded part within the signal acceptance band may, although small, be quite comparable in amplitude with a weak signal, and will be superposed on it. The limiting sensitivity of the receiver may thus be considerably impaired.

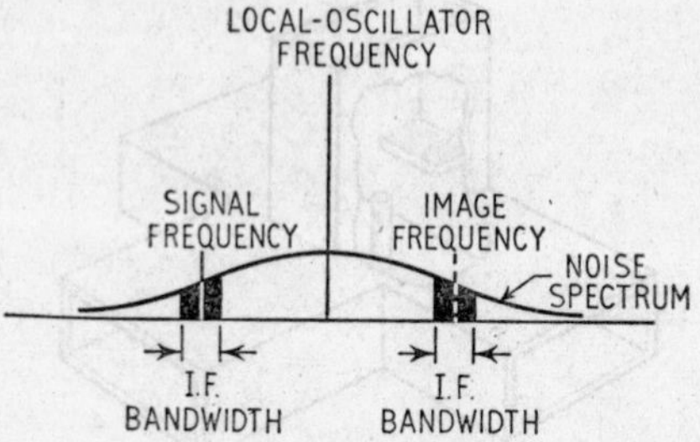

Fig. 7.61. Relation of noise spectrum of local oscillator to other signals.

In the balanced mixer shown in Fig. 7.62 (a) two crystals are used, and are assumed to be identical and to match perfectly the two main arms of a hybrid T. The received signal and the local-oscillator signal are fed into the other two arms respectively. For the arrangement shown the received signals in the two crystals will be in phase, having passed through a shunt junction, while the local-oscillator signals, having passed through a series junction, will be in anti-phase in the two crystals. The i.f. signals coming from the crystals will thus be in anti-phase and are summed in the transformer shown in Fig. 7.62 (b). If we

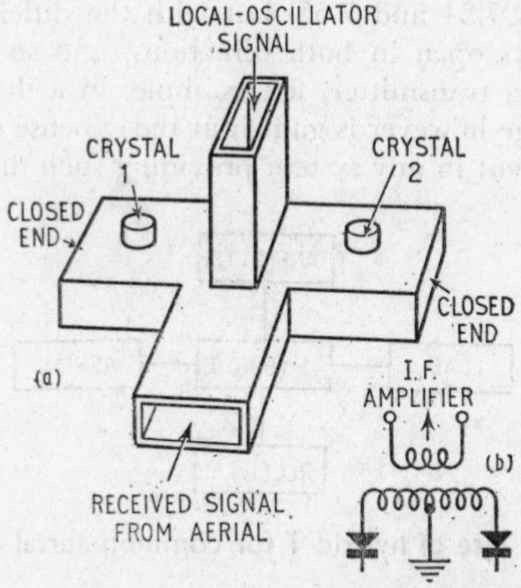

Fig. 7.62. (a) Hybrid T balanced mixer; (b) connections to i.f. amplifier.

consider now an individual pulse of oscillator noise this will divide into two parts which will arrive in anti-phase at the crystals, and will there beat with the main oscillator signals which are also in anti-phase. Thus the i.f. noise signals are in phase and will cancel in the push-pull circuit. In practice balance is never so exact that noise cancellation is complete, but a considerable reduction can be obtained.

Another important property of the balanced mixer is that no signal is lost into the oscillator circuit, however tightly the oscillator is coupled. This is important at the shortest wavelengths where the power available from a local oscillator is too limited to permit loose coupling.

The hybrid T has other important applications. For example, it may be operated as a microwave impedance bridge, and is an essential component in some frequency stabilizing circuits.

Hybrid Ring

The hybrid ring is a further arrangement of four waveguide arms giving the same properties as the hybrid T. It consists of a waveguide in the form of a closed ring of mean circumference equal to $3\lambda_g/2$, with four arms connected in the positions shown in Fig. 7.63. Either shunt or series junctions may be used, but the series form shown is the more usual.

It is clear that a signal entering the ring from arm 1 has two possible paths to any other arm. The two paths to arm 3 differ in length by $\lambda_g/2$, and the two

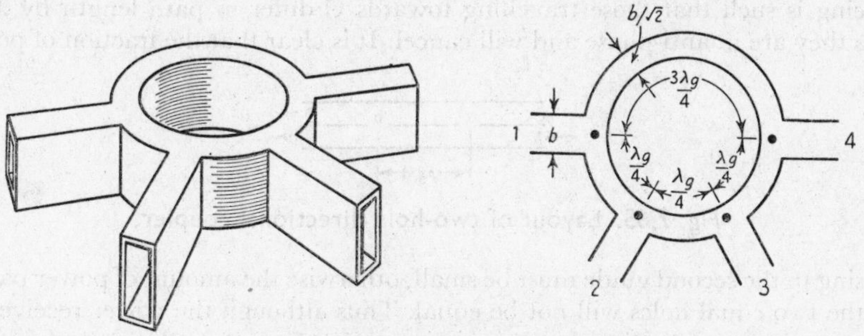

Fig. 7.63. Hybrid ring junction.

equal signals arriving at arm 3 therefore cancel. For arms 2 and 4, however, the paths differ by λ_g and zero respectively, so that the signals arriving there reinforce. The signals emerging from arms 2 and 4 are evidently equal but in antiphase. A signal entering at arm 3 will also be equally divided between arms 2 and 4, but the emergent signals will this time be in phase since the path lengths are now equal. Thus the hybrid ring has the same properties as the hybrid T, the phasing being obtained in the former by adjustment of path length, in the latter by the properties of series and shunt junctions.

For many purposes the hybrid ring and the hybrid T may be used interchangeably. The former is to be preferred for wavelengths below about 3 cm as the constructional tolerances are somewhat less difficult to meet. No difficult matching irises are involved, but it can be shown (see Appendix 7.1), that for matching it is necessary to make the *b*-dimension of the ring smaller than that of the arms in the ratio of $1:\sqrt{2}$.

Directional Couplers

A hybrid of rather a different kind can be made by joining two waveguides side by side with two or more openings connecting them. If the two guides are in contact along their narrow sides and are connected by an opening as shown in

Fig. 7.64, the magnetic field of a travelling wave in the lower guide will be distorted and will induce waves travelling in both directions in the upper guide. If the hole is small the coupling between the two guides will be small, and only a small fraction of the power in the lower guide will be transferred to the upper.

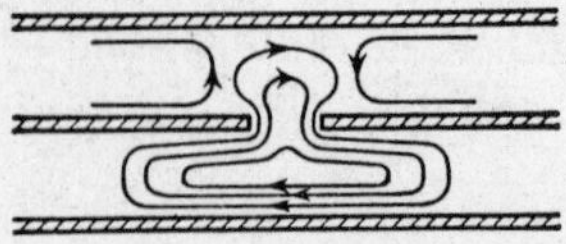

Fig. 7.64. Coupling of guides through small hole.

Consider the arrangement of Fig. 7.65 where there are two equal coupling holes a and b separated longitudinally by a distance of $\lambda_g/4$ and power is fed in at A, the other three ends having matched terminations. Most of the power will pass directly into the load at B. The small amounts of power passing through the coupling holes will each divide equally towards C and D, but the two waves travelling towards D have the same path length and therefore add. The hole spacing is such that those travelling towards C differ in path length by $\lambda_g/2$; thus they are in anti-phase and will cancel. It is clear that the fraction of power

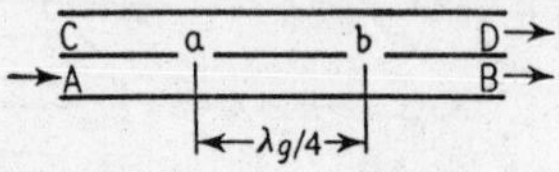

Fig. 7.65. Layout of two-hole directional coupler.

passing to the second guide must be small, otherwise the amount of power passed by the two equal holes will not be equal. Thus although the power received at D is small it is proportional to the power passing from A to B. Similarly power received at C will be proportional to any power passing from B to A.

This latter property allows the arrangement to distinguish between power flow in the two directions in a waveguide, and hence the name *directional coupler.* It can thus distinguish between direct and reflected waves. Matched crystal detectors placed at D and C would give readings proportional to the direct and reflected waves in AB and hence allow a direct determination of the magnitude

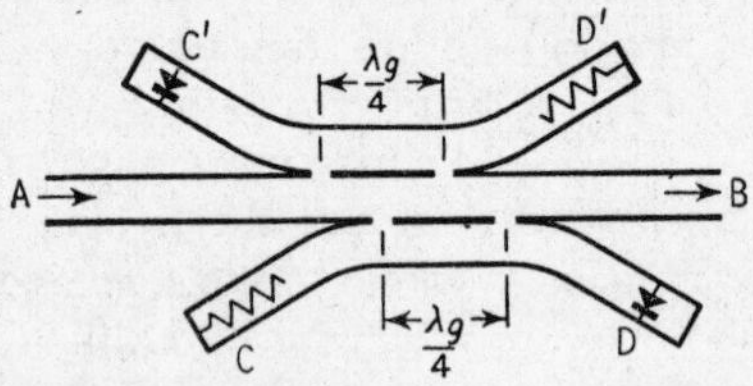

Fig. 7.66. Double directional coupler.

of the reflection factor of the termination at B. Thus the directional coupler may for some purposes replace the standing-wave detector. It does not give information on the phase of the reflection, but in the many cases where knowledge of the magnitude is sufficient it has the great advantages of simplicity and robustness, particularly valuable for field work.

The form of Fig. 7.65 is satisfactory as a one-directional monitor, with a matched crystal detector at D, and a matched load at C. It is, however, less satisfactory as a two-directional monitor with crystals at C and D, since any lack of matching in either crystal produces a reflected wave which is detected directly on the other crystal. A double directional coupler as shown in Fig. 7.66 avoids this difficulty, crystal D detecting the power flow from A to B, and crystal C′ detecting the power flow from B to A.

The operation of the two-hole coupler will obviously be impaired as soon as the frequency of operation departs from the design frequency, there being then incomplete cancellation of the two waves. This impairment is reduced by increasing the number of coupling holes. Fig. 7.67 shows a three-hole coupler in

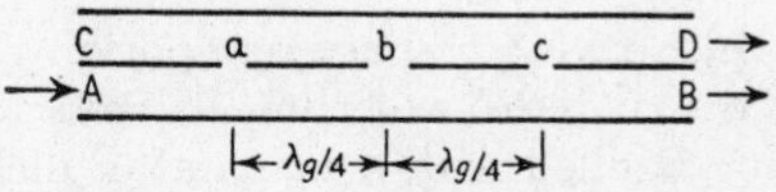

Fig. 7.67. Layout of three-hole directional coupler.

which the amplitude of the wave coupled through the middle hole is twice that of the waves passing through each of the outer holes. With power fed in at A, all waves passing into the second guide in the direction of D have the same phase and therefore add. The waves travelling towards C, however, having relative phases of 0, 180° and 360°, and relative amplitudes of 1, 2 and 1, cancel com-

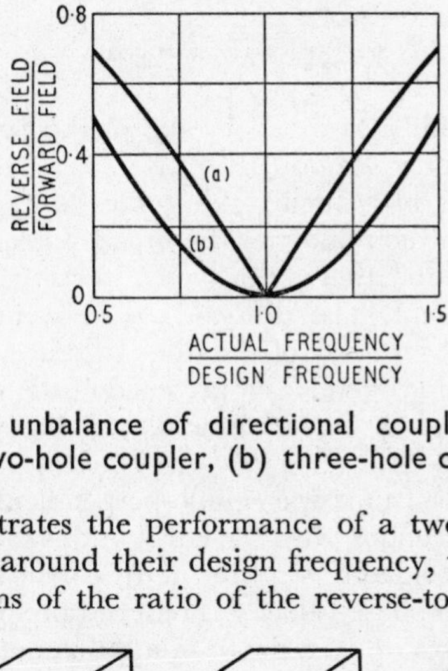

Fig. 7.68. Variation of unbalance of directional coupler with frequency, for (a) two-hole coupler, (b) three-hole coupler.

pletely. Fig. 7.68 illustrates the performance of a two-hole and a three-hole coupler at frequencies around their design frequency, the degree of unbalance being specified in terms of the ratio of the reverse-to-forward voltage in the

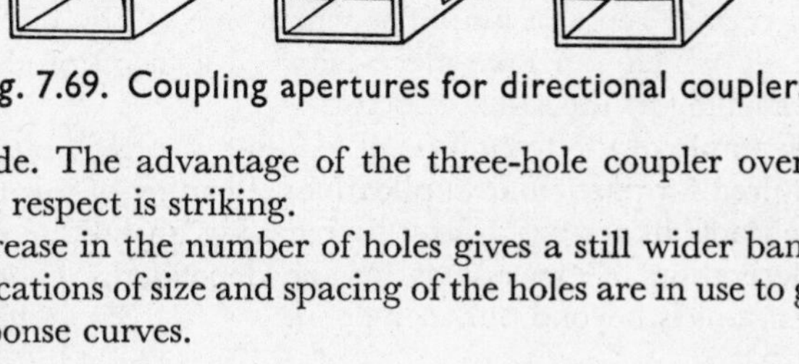

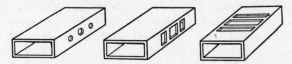

Fig. 7.69. Coupling apertures for directional couplers.

secondary guide. The advantage of the three-hole coupler over the two-hole coupler in this respect is striking.

Further increase in the number of holes gives a still wider bandwidth, while various modifications of size and spacing of the holes are in use to give particular frequency response curves.

Fig. 7.69 shows examples of coupling holes for directional couplers. The circular holes are most appropriate to a coupler in which the power transferred to the secondary guide is less than about one per cent of the main power. Where larger fractions of power are to be transferred rectangular slots are preferable. Guides may be coupled along their broad sides also, in which case the transverse slots shown in Fig. 7.69 are normally used.

In designing directional couplers it is to be noted that the amount of power coupled through a hole is very sensitive to the size of the hole, being proportional to the sixth power of the diameter. ◀

Ridge and Corrugated Waveguides

For applications in which saving of space is important filling of the interior of the guide with a dielectric material will allow its cross-sectional dimensions to be reduced. If the guide is filled with a material of dielectric constant κ_r the critical wavelength for the H_{10} wave is increased from $\lambda_c = 2a$ to

$$\lambda_c = (\kappa_r)^{1/2} 2a \quad . \quad . \quad . \quad . \quad (7.18)$$

Hence the cross-sectional dimensions can be reduced in the ratio $1/\sqrt{\kappa_r}$. In this case the wavelength in the guide changes from the value in equation (6.4) to that given by:

$$\frac{1}{\lambda_g^2} = \frac{\kappa_r}{\lambda^2} - \frac{1}{(2a)^2} \quad . \quad . \quad . \quad . \quad . \quad . \quad (7.19)$$

Both results may be readily obtained by the method of Appendix 6.1, on replacing κ_0 by $\kappa = \kappa_0 \kappa_r$ in equation (6.19).

An alternative means of reducing the guide dimensions is to introduce a longitudinal ridge down the middle of the broad side of the guide. For an H_{10} wave a symmetrical modification of this type distorts the wave without affecting its basic field arrangement. The distortion thereby introduced increases the critical wavelength λ_c. As the size of the ridge increases so does λ_c, but there is no simple formula relating them. The presence of the ridge has, however, the disadvantages of increasing the attenuation of the guide and reducing its power-handling capacity.

If ridges are introduced in a waveguide perpendicular to its axis so that it becomes a corrugated structure then the effect in this case is to reduce the phase velocity of the wave. Provided the spacing of the corrugations is small compared with the wavelength the phase velocity is reduced progressively as the depth of the corrugations increases up to a depth of approximately $\lambda/4$. This technique finds important applications in cases where it is required to reduce the phase velocity to a value less than the velocity of light. Examples are particle accelerators and certain types of amplifier which operate by virtue of the interchange of energy which can take place between a beam of charged particles and a wave travelling at the same velocity.

This is an example of the technique of loading waveguides to give them the properties required for particular applications. Loading of this type produces a structure which acts like a band-pass filter having an infinite number of pass bands. The derivation of expressions for the dependence of velocity on corrugation dimensions is beyond our scope here.

Surface Waves

A limiting case of the corrugated waveguide is the corrugated guiding surface. This takes the form of a plane corrugated conducting sheet. A vertically-polarized plane wave launched over the surface of this sheet in a direction perpendicular to the corrugations can be shown to be distorted in such a way that the energy in the wave is concentrated in a region close to the surface. This is true provided the depth of the corrugations is less than $\lambda/4$, and the amplitude of the wave can be shown to decrease exponentially with distance from the surface. The corrugated surface therefore acts as a guiding surface for the wave, which is known as a surface or Zenneck wave.

Another form of surface which gives the same result is a plane conducting sheet covered with a thin layer of dielectric material. This has the same effect of concentrating the energy in the dielectric and in the space close to the dielectric surface.

The guiding effect is retained if the surface is bent round into a cylinder. Thus a wire coated with a thin layer of dielectric acts as an effective guide for a surface wave. A cylindrical surface wave of this type is called a Sommerfeld-Goubau wave. The energy is carried partly in the dielectric and partly in the surrounding space, the spread of the field into the surrounding space being a complicated function of the dielectric constant and of the ratios of diameter to wavelength. The longer the wavelength the greater is the extent of the surrounding field.

One method of launching this wave is by means of a coaxial line, whose outer conductor is flared at its end into a horn while the inner conductor is continued as the guide wire. The field at the mouth of the horn simulates the required field on the wire, and thus induces a surface wave. With this simple method, however, the losses at the transition are rather high. An efficient transition requires considerable care in design.

The reduction in velocity inherent in surface waves is small, and for a typical surface-wave transmission line the velocity will usually be of the order of 1% less than the velocity of light. The wavelength measured along the wire will consequently be of the order of 1% greater than the free-space wavelength.

Theoretically, the attenuation for the surface-wave transmission line is comparable with that for the waveguide. This, however, takes into consideration only those losses which occur when the wire is perfectly straight and the field is undisturbed by any objects in the vicinity of the wire. It is found in practice that bends, even of large radius, cause appreciable loss, as energy is then no longer trapped but is partly radiated outwards. Even in a straight run of any appreciable length attenuation would be increased by the sag of the wire and the discontinuities at the points of suspension. In a line erected out-of-doors there would be further attenuation from films of dirt and raindrops forming on the dielectric surface. Thus applications of the surface-wave transmission line are greatly limited by practical difficulties.

APPENDIX 7.1

Changes in Waveguide Cross-section

The wave impedance Z_W for a wave in a waveguide has been defined as the ratio of the transverse field components E_y/H_x. Something more nearly corresponding to the characteristic impedance of a two-conductor line can be defined for the H_{10} mode in a rectangular guide as follows. If the field components E_y and H_x of equation (6.26) are rewritten in terms of the maximum electric field amplitude E_{max} and the maximum amplitude of the current density I_{max} induced in the horizontal walls they become

$$E_y = E_{max} \sin \frac{\pi x}{a} \sin (\omega t - \beta z)$$

$$H_x = I_{max} \sin \frac{\pi x}{a} \sin (\omega t - \beta z)$$

The expression (6.36) for the mean power can then be written as

$$P = \frac{E_{max} I_{max} ab}{4}$$

$$= \tfrac{1}{2} . \frac{bE_{max}}{\sqrt{2}} . \frac{aI_{max}}{\sqrt{2}}$$

Taking $bE_{max}/\sqrt{2}$ as representing an average potential difference V between the horizontal walls, and $aI_{max}/\sqrt{2}$ as an average current I flowing along these walls, we obtain the usual power equation:

$$P = \tfrac{1}{2} VI$$

From this a characteristic impedance can be defined as

$$Z_0 = V/I$$

$$= \frac{bE_{max}}{aI_{max}} = \frac{b}{a}\left|\frac{E_y}{H_x}\right|$$

$$= \frac{b}{a} Z_W \quad \text{. . . . . (7.18)}$$

Other equally plausible definitions of V and I may be used, but all result in an expression for Z_0 of the same form, differing only by a numerical factor.

Where there is no change of dimensions in the guide system it does not matter whether Z_0 or Z_W is used in calculations so long as consistency is maintained, since the difference disappears when the impedances are normalized. When changes of dimensions are involved, however, the following examples show that the two definitions of impedance lead to different equivalent circuits, although to the same final result.

Consider Fig. 7.70 (a), which illustrates a junction between two rectangular guides differing in their b-dimensions. These guides have the same wave impedance, but obviously they cannot match each other, since the change in dimensions at the junction must produce an abrupt change in field configuration with consequent reflection. It can be shown that, if in the equivalent circuit the waveguides are represented by two transmission lines of equal characteristic impedance, then the junction can be represented by a transformer of turns ratio $\sqrt{b_2}:\sqrt{b_1}$ and the parallel capacitor shown in Fig. 7.70 (b). If, however, the guide impedance is defined to be proportional to b, as it is in the characteristic impedance definition Z_0 of (7.18), then the two transmission lines of the equivalent circuit have characteristic impedances proportional to b_1 and b_2 and the transformer ratio can be shown to become unity. The effect of the junction can therefore be reduced to the simple shunt capacitor shown in Fig. 7.70 (c). The use of Z_0 rather than Z_W is thus advantageous in simplifying the equivalent circuit. The value of the shunt capacitor is a complex function of the guide dimensions and will not be given here.

This equivalent circuit may now be used to design a waveguide *quarter-wave transformer* to match together the two guides of Fig. 7.70 (a). Neglecting for the

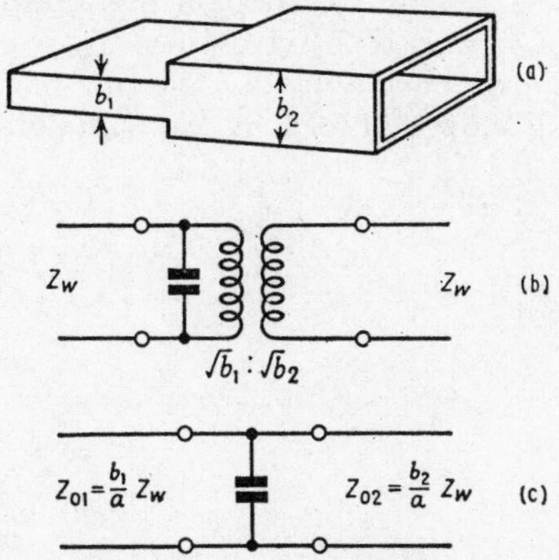

Fig. **7.70.** (a) Junction of two waveguides of different dimensions; (b) equivalent circuit using wave impedance; (c) equivalent circuit using characteristic impedance.

moment the shunt capacitor in the equivalent circuit we remember that, as discussed in Chapter 4, the characteristic impedance Z_0' of a quarter-wave transformer required to match two transmission lines of characteristic impedances Z_{01} and Z_{02} is given by $Z_0' = \sqrt{Z_{01}Z_{02}}$. As Z_{01} and Z_{02} are proportional to b_1 and b_2 respectively, then the b-dimension of the waveguide quarter-wave transformer is given by:

$$b' = \sqrt{b_1 b_2}$$

and the length of the transformer is $\lambda_g/4$. The effect of the capacitor at each of the two junctions can be tuned out by adding suitable inductors as shown in Fig. 7.71 (a). In the waveguide these are provided in the form of an inductive iris at each step. Thus the matched junction takes the form shown in Fig. 7.71 (b).

This impedance concept readily gives the dimensions for the hybrid ring. Arm 1 of the series hybrid of Fig. 7.63 has essentially two outputs connected to it in series through a quarter-wave transformer (the $3\lambda_g/4$ or $5\lambda_g/4$ lengths being equivalent to $\lambda_g/4$). Thus the characteristic impedance of the quarter-wave

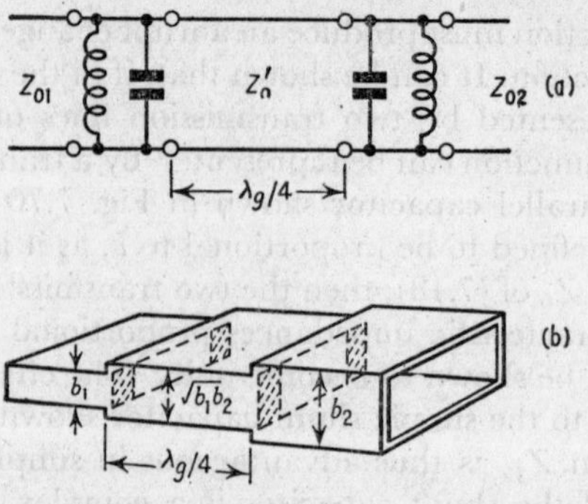

Fig. 7.71. **(a) Equivalent circuit for quarter-wave transformer; (b) matching of waveguides by quarter-wave transformer.**

transformer must be equal to $\sqrt{(Z_0 . 2Z_0)}$. But the transformer consists of two separate paths in series, and thus each path must have a characteristic impedance of $\frac{1}{2}\sqrt{(Z_0 . 2Z_0)}$, that is $Z_0/\sqrt{2}$. Since Z_0 is proportional to the b-dimension, then if the arms have a width b the ring must have a width $b/\sqrt{2}$. A similar argument will show that for a hybrid with parallel junctions the ring must have a width $b\sqrt{2}$.

CHAPTER 8

Cavity Resonators

As a length of two-conductor transmission line with closed ends will resonate at wavelengths which are particular multiples of the line length, so also a length of waveguide closed at both ends will act as a resonator. A wave set up in the waveguide is successively reflected from each end, and a standing-wave system is set up in the bounded space. Such a hollow resonator is known as a *cavity resonator*. Various geometrical shapes are used for different purposes, the shape being usually simple when the resonator is used as a circuit element, for example

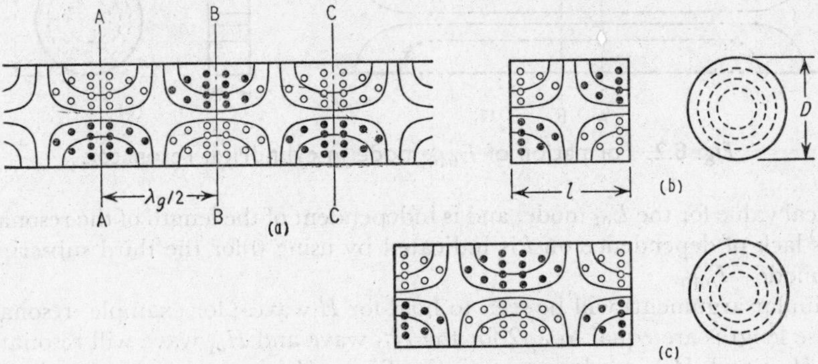

Fig. 8.1. Formation of E_{011} and E_{012} modes in cylindrical resonators; (b) E_{011} mode, (c) E_{012} mode.
——— electric field
— — — — magnetic field

as a wavemeter, more complicated when the resonator forms, as it often does, an integral part of a centimetre-wave valve.

Various modes can occur in the cavity resonator just as they can in the waveguide, and for resonators of rectangular and circular cross-section it is possible to deduce these readily from a consideration of the transmission modes. If we consider, for example, the electric field of an E_{01} wave in a circular guide, as shown in cross-section in Fig. 8.1 (a), and imagine this to be a standing wave set up between direct and reflected waves of equal amplitude, it is clear that end walls could be placed in the positions denoted by AA and BB without disturbing the field, since the lines of electric field would everywhere be perpendicular to those end walls, as required by boundary conditions. This section can then form a cavity resonator with the internal field shown in Fig. 8.1 (b). AA and BB are separated by a distance $\lambda_g/2$, where λ_g is the wavelength in the guide, so that this is the length l of the resonator.

The end walls could equally well have been separated by a greater distance;

for example when placed at AA and CC they give a resonator of length equal to λ_g, with a field as shown in Fig. 8.1 (c). Since both the above resonance modes are derived from an E_{01} wave they are designated respectively the E_{011} and E_{012} modes, the third suffix denoting the number of guide half-wavelengths contained in the length of the resonator. Since the guide half-wavelength is dependent on the frequency and guide diameter, then the different resonance frequencies are thus functions of the length and diameter of the resonator.

There is, however, another important resonance mode, also derived from the E_{01} wave. If an E_{01} stationary wave exists in a circular guide at almost the critical wavelength then λ_g will be very long, as in Fig. 8.2 (a). In the limit when λ_g approaches infinity two plane ends can be inserted to isolate a short section AA, BB without disturbing the wave, whose electric field is perpendicular to these walls at all points. Then the electric field in the resonator is that of Fig. 8.2 (b), where the resonance occurs at a free-space wavelength equal to the

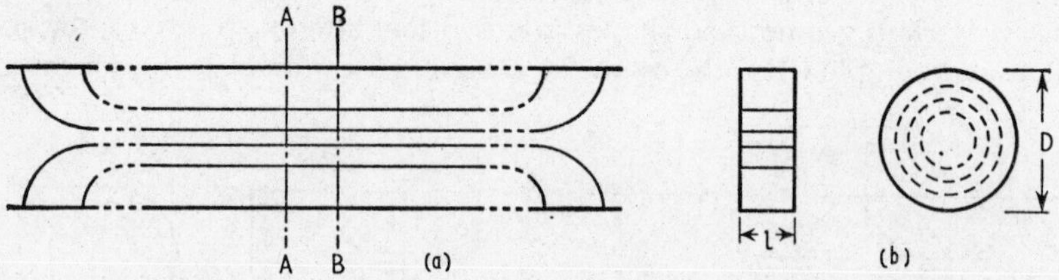

Fig. 8.2. Formation of E_{010} mode in cylindrical resonator.

critical value for the E_{01} mode, and is independent of the length of the resonator. This lack of dependence on l is indicated by using 0 for the third subscript of the mode—E_{010}.

Similar arguments will be seen to hold for H waves; for example, resonators whose lengths are equal to $\lambda_g/2$ for the H_{11} wave and H_{01} wave will resonate in the H_{111} and H_{011} modes respectively. Since H waves have no longitudinal electric field there are no H modes which are independent of resonator length, as in the E_{010}, and hence there are no H modes with the third suffix zero.

The most important resonances in the cylindrical resonator are the E_{010}, H_{011} and H_{111}. The fields of these are shown in more detail in Fig. 8.3, and expressions for their resonance frequencies are included in Table 8.2 (pp. 236-7).

As an example Table 8.1 gives these principal resonance frequencies and the corresponding free-space wavelengths for a cylindrical resonator of diameter 10 cm and length 10 cm:

TABLE 8.1

Properties of a cylindrical copper resonator of length 10 *cm, diameter* 10 *cm.*

Mode	Resonance frequency (Mc/s)	Free-space wavelength (cm)	Q
E_{010}	2,297	13·06	24,600
H_{111}	2,311	12·98	26,100
H_{011}	3,955	7·59	48,400

▶ The value of λ_g for a mode in a circular guide is given by means of equation (6.5) and an appropriate value of λ_c from Table 6.3. Thus for the E_{01} mode in a guide of diameter D it becomes

$$\frac{1}{\lambda_g^2} = \frac{1}{\lambda^2} - \frac{1}{(1{\cdot}31D)^2}$$

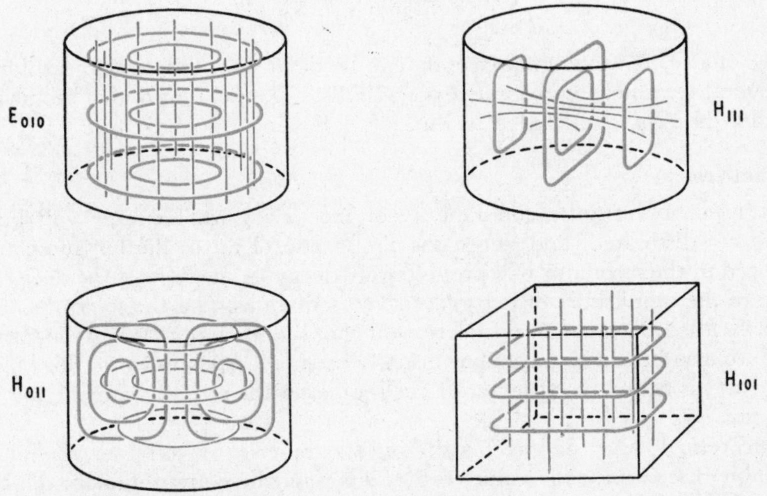

Fig. 8.3. Field patterns in cylindrical and rectangular resonators. The electric field is shown in red and the magnetic in green.

Hence, for resonance in the E_{011} mode with a resonator of length l, the free-space wavelength λ is given by

$$\frac{1}{(2l)^2} = \frac{1}{\lambda^2} - \frac{1}{(1{\cdot}31D)^2}$$

which can be put in the form

$$\frac{1}{\lambda} = \left\{\frac{1}{(1{\cdot}31D)^2} + \frac{1}{(2l)^2}\right\}^{1/2}$$

The resonance frequency, $f = c/\lambda$, is thus:

E_{011} *mode:*
$$f = c\left\{\frac{1}{(1{\cdot}31D)^2} + \frac{1}{(2l)^2}\right\}^{1/2} \quad . \quad . \quad . \quad . \quad . \quad (8.1)$$

Similarly the resonance frequency for the E_{012} mode is given by

E_{012} *mode:*
$$f = c\left\{\frac{1}{(1{\cdot}31D)^2} + \frac{1}{l^2}\right\}^{1/2} \quad . \quad . \quad . \quad . \quad . \quad (8.2)$$

For the E_{010} mode λ_g is infinite, and thus the resonance frequency is:

E_{010} *mode:*
$$f = \frac{c}{1{\cdot}31D} \quad . \quad . \quad . \quad . \quad . \quad . \quad . \quad (8.3)$$

From the values of λ_c in Table 6.3 it is clear that the resonance frequencies for the H_{111} and H_{011} modes are respectively:

H_{111} *mode:*
$$f = c\left\{\frac{1}{(1{\cdot}71D)^2} + \frac{1}{(2l)^2}\right\}^{1/2} \quad . \quad . \quad . \quad . \quad . \qquad (8.4)$$

H_{011} *mode:*
$$f = c\left\{\frac{1}{(0{\cdot}82D)^2} + \frac{1}{(2l)^2}\right\}^{1/2} \quad . \quad . \quad . \quad . \quad . \qquad (8.5)$$

Resonators of rectangular section can be dealt with in a similar fashion, and a general treatment is given in Appendix 8.1. The field for one of the principal modes, the H_{101}, is included in Fig. 8.3, following Appendix 8.1. ◀

Q-factors

Because of the finite conductivity of the cavity walls energy will be continuously dissipated, and hence the amplitude of an oscillation momentarily induced in the resonator will progressively decay. A measure of the decay is the ratio of the amplitudes of two successive oscillations, and the logarithm of this ratio is called the logarithmic decrement Δ of the resonator. When the losses are small so also is Δ. The parameter usually used is the reciprocal of this (actually π/Δ), and is called the Q-factor. Thus the better the resonator the higher is the Q-factor.

Theoretical values of the Q, assuming the material to be copper, are included in Table 8.1. In practice values rather less than these are obtained, the actual values being dependent on the surface finish of the material. It will be seen that the Q for the H_{011} mode is particularly high, corresponding to the low attenuation suffered by the H_{01} mode in a circular waveguide.

▶ It is shown in Appendix 8.2 that the above definition of Q leads to the relation:

$$Q = \frac{\omega \times \text{energy stored in cavity}}{\text{power dissipated in cavity}}$$

For a lumped circuit of L, C and R this relation can be written as:

$$Q = \frac{\omega \times \frac{1}{2}LI^2}{\frac{1}{2}RI^2} = \frac{\omega L}{R} \quad . \quad . \quad . \quad . \quad . \qquad (8.6)$$

Thus the Q defined by equation (8.6) is the same as that given by its more familiar form $\omega L/R$.

The Q for a cavity resonator is thus a measure of its sharpness of tuning, just as it is for an L, C, R tuned circuit. It is shown in Volume 1 that, if a change of frequency Δf away from resonance reduces the amplitude of oscillation to $1/\sqrt{2}$ of its value at the resonance frequency f, then these quantities obey the relation

$$Q = \frac{f}{2\Delta f} \quad . \quad . \quad . \quad . \quad . \quad . \quad . \qquad (8.7)$$

Formulae for the Q-factor may be derived in terms of the resistivity of the material and the dimensions of the cavity in much the same way as values of attenuation constant for the waveguide are calculated. The method is illustrated in Appendix 8.2. The curves of Fig. 8.4, calculated from the expressions quoted in Appendix 8.2, show the variation of Q with the ratio of length to diameter.

It can be shown that the cavity losses reduce the resonant frequencies below those calculated for the loss-free case by an amount Δf given by:

$$\frac{\Delta f}{f} = \frac{8}{Q^2} \qquad (8.8)$$

Since Q-values of cavity resonators are high, this frequency change is usually quite negligible.

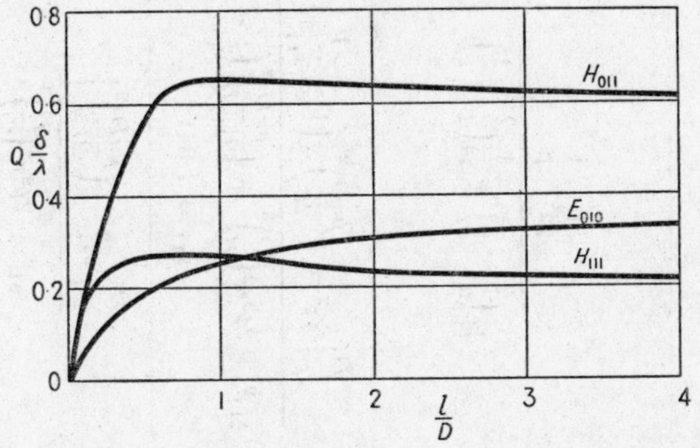

Fig. 8.4. Variation of Q-factor with ratio of length to diameter for cylindrical resonators.

Shunt Resistance

An important parameter in a parallel lumped circuit is its shunt resistance at resonance. A similar concept is valuable for cavity resonators; it can be introduced as follows. If V is the peak voltage measured along a particular path in a resonator and R the equivalent shunt resistance for this path then R can be defined by the relation:

$$\text{Power dissipated at resonance} = \frac{V^2}{2R} \qquad (8.9)$$

This is an important definition, a knowledge of R enabling us to calculate the power input required to maintain a given voltage across the chosen path in the resonator. Usually the path chosen is the one across which the maximum voltage is developed. It is shown in Appendix 8.3 that R is equal to the Q-factor multiplied by a factor dependent on the shape of the cavity, and expressions for R are included in Table 8.2. That the shape factor can be important is illustrated by the case of the E_{010} mode in a cylindrical resonator, where the shunt resistance increases without limit as l is increased, in contrast to the Q, which approaches an asymptotic value as l is increased.

Excitation of Cavity Resonators

For excitation of a resonator it must be coupled to a source of power, and this power is commonly supplied through a coaxial line or a waveguide. If it is by the former then the means of coupling is usually a small loop terminating the cable and projecting into the cavity through a hole in the wall. Current in this loop provides magnetic coupling and the loop must be orientated in such a way as to encircle lines of magnetic flux in the cavity. Fig. 8.5 illustrates how this is done for the three cylindrical modes previously discussed. Note from Fig. 8.5 (b)

TABLE 8.2

Properties of Resonators

Resonator	Mode	Resonance wavelength λ (resonance frequency $f = c/\lambda$)	$Q \times \delta$	Shunt resistance R (ohms)
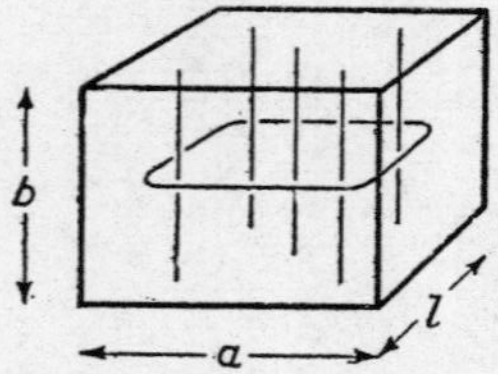	H_{101}	$2\left(\frac{1}{a^2} + \frac{1}{l^2}\right)^{-1/2}$	$\dfrac{\frac{1}{a^2} + \frac{1}{l^2}}{\frac{1}{a^2}\left(\frac{2}{a} + \frac{1}{b}\right) + \frac{1}{l^2}\left(\frac{2}{l} + \frac{1}{b}\right)}$	$480Q \dfrac{b}{(a^2 + l^2)^{1/2}}$
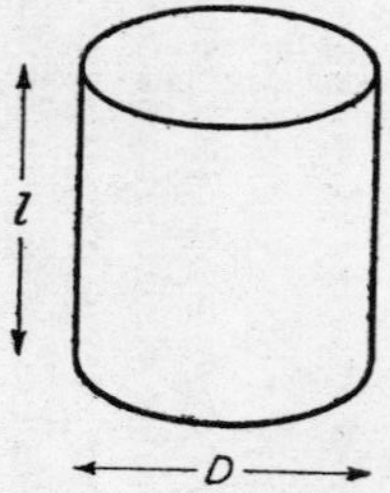	H_{11p} $p \neq 0$	$\left\{\frac{1}{(1{\cdot}71D)^2} + \left(\frac{p}{2l}\right)^2\right\}^{-1/2}$	$\dfrac{\frac{D}{2}\left\{s_{11}^2 + \left(\frac{p\pi D}{2l}\right)^2\right\}\left(1 - \frac{1}{s_{11}^2}\right)}{s_{11}^2 + 2p^2\pi^2\left(\frac{D}{2l}\right)^3 + \left(\frac{p\pi D}{2s_{11}l}\right)^2\left(1 - \frac{D}{l}\right)}$ $s_{11} = 1{\cdot}841$	—
	H_{01p} $p \neq 0$	$\left\{\frac{1}{(0{\cdot}82D)^2} + \left(\frac{p}{2l}\right)^2\right\}^{-1/2}$	$\dfrac{\frac{D}{2}\left\{s_{01}^2 + \left(\frac{p\pi D}{2l}\right)^2\right\}}{s_{01}^2 + 2p^2\pi^2\left(\frac{D}{2l}\right)^3}$ $s_{01} = 3{\cdot}832$	—
	E_{010}	$1{\cdot}31D$	$\left(\frac{2}{D} + \frac{1}{l}\right)^{-1}$	$370Q \dfrac{l}{D}$

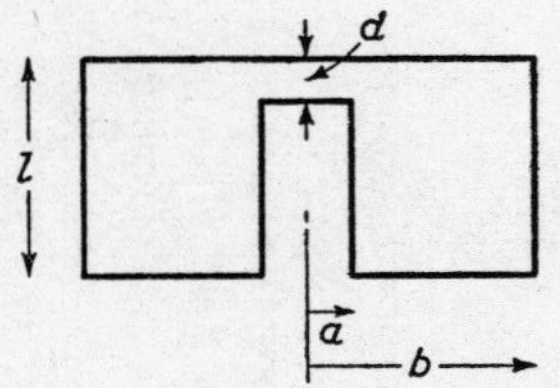	As in Fig. 8.17	$2\pi a\left(\frac{l}{2d}\log_\varepsilon\frac{b}{a}\right)^{1/2}$ approximately.	$\left\{\frac{1}{l}+\frac{1}{2\log_\varepsilon(b/a)}\left(\frac{1}{a}+\frac{1}{b}\right)\right\}^{-1}$	$120\pi Q\frac{l}{\lambda}\log_\varepsilon\frac{b}{a}$
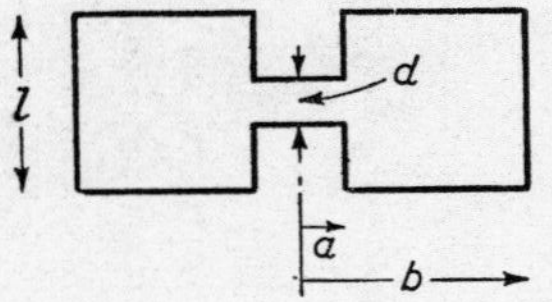	—	$2\pi a\left(\frac{l}{2d}\log_\varepsilon\frac{b}{a}\right)^{1/2}$ approximately.	—	—
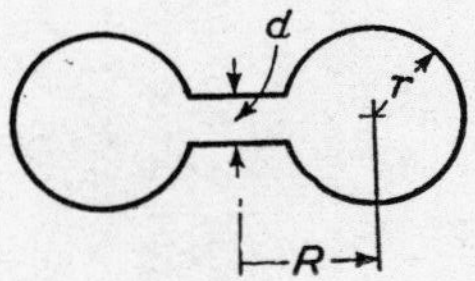	—	$2\pi r\left(\frac{\pi R}{d}\left[1-\sqrt{\left\{1-\left(\frac{r}{R}\right)^2\right\}}\right]\right)^{1/2}$ approximately.	—	—

and (c) that one position of the loop can excite more than one mode. The amplitude of any particular mode, however, is appreciable only when the frequency of the exciting source is at, or very near to, the resonance frequency for that mode.

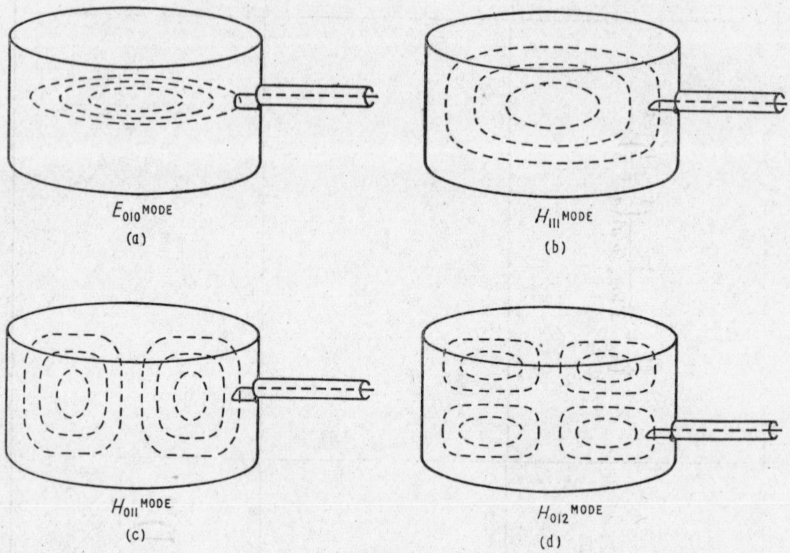

Fig. 8.5. Loop excitation of cavity resonators. Loop is vertical in (a), horizontal in (b)–(d).

Excitation by means of a probe terminating a coaxial line gives electric coupling, but is less common, the probe being arranged to be along lines of electric field in the desired mode. An example is shown in Fig. 8.6.

When a cavity is to be coupled to a waveguide transmission line the coupling is usually made by means of a hole in a common wall between waveguide and

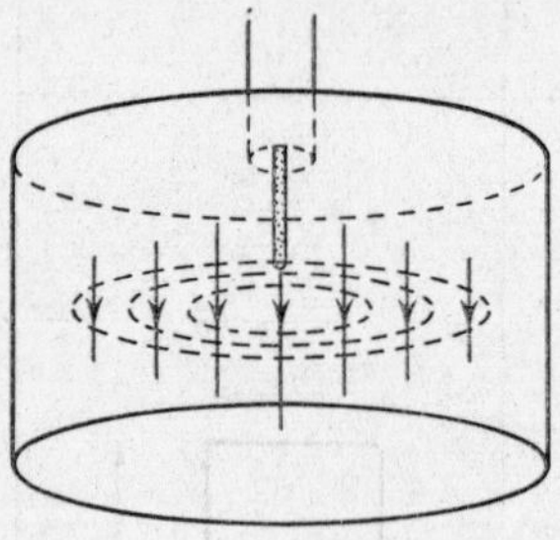

Fig. 8.6. Probe excitation of cavity resonator for E_{010} mode.

cavity. It may be arranged that the magnetic field along the surface of the guide has a component parallel to the required magnetic field along the adjacent surface of the cavity; this gives magnetic coupling. Electric coupling takes place if both cavity and waveguide have electric field components perpendicular to the plane of the hole. Fig. 8.7 illustrates magnetic coupling to a cylindrical cavity.

The introduction of a loop into a cavity must somewhat modify the field pattern, since the electric field must become zero on the conductor. This modification may be considered as provided by the appearance of modes other than the resonance mode. The exciting frequency is generally remote from the resonance frequencies of these additional modes, and they present only reactive impedances to the source. For a given voltage applied to the loop there will be an equal and opposite induced voltage generated by the changing magnetic flux threading the loop from all modes. The effect of all the additional modes can be taken as giving the loop an effective self-inductance L_L.

If H is the amplitude of the magnetic field inside the loop due to the resonance mode, and the loop is so small that H can be considered constant over its area

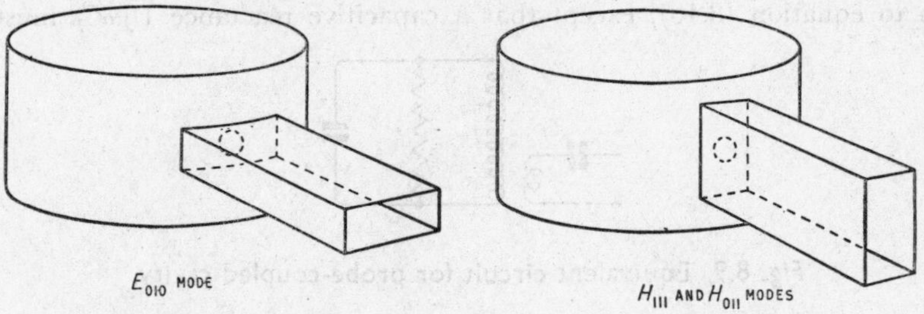

Fig. 8.7. Hole coupling between waveguide and resonator.

Σ then the flux Φ through the loop is $\mu_0 H\Sigma$, and thus the induced voltage in the loop is $-\,\mathrm{d}\Phi/\mathrm{d}t = \mathrm{j}\omega\mu_0 H\Sigma$.

At resonance only the energy supplied to the main resonance mode is real, and thus if R_L is the resistive part of the loop impedance the power supplied to the cavity is $(\omega\mu_0 H\Sigma)^2/2R_L$, and this equals the power loss W in the cavity. Thus the total input impedance of the loop, Z_L, in the cavity at resonance is:

$$Z_L = \frac{(\omega\mu_0 H\Sigma)^2}{2W} + \mathrm{j}\omega L_L \text{ ohms}$$

Using the definition of Q given in equation (8.6) and putting S for the total energy in the cavity, we get:

$$Z_L = \frac{\omega Q(\mu_0 H\Sigma)^2}{2S} + \mathrm{j}\omega L_L \text{ ohms} \qquad . \quad . \quad . \quad . \quad (8.10)$$

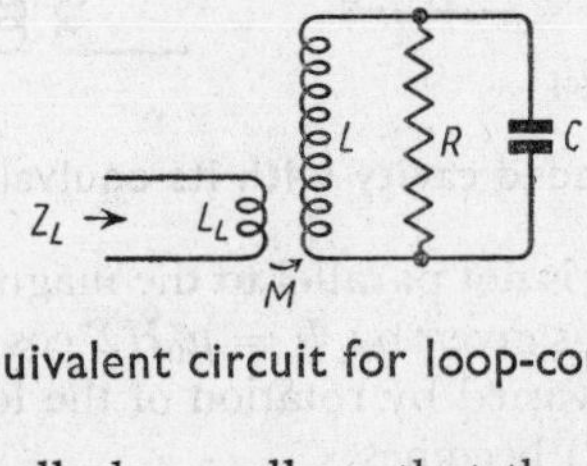

Fig. 8.8. Equivalent circuit for loop-coupled cavity.

The second term will usually be small, so that the impedance at resonance is very nearly a pure resistance.

Based on this equation, the equivalent circuit of Fig. 8.8 for a loop-coupled cavity can now be drawn. The resistance R is the shunt resistance of the cavity discussed in the previous section. This tuned transformer circuit is discussed in Volume 4, where it is shown that the resistance reflected into the primary circuit from the secondary is $\omega Q M^2/L$. This is equivalent to the first term of equation (8.10), and thus the coupling constant M^2/L is given by:

$$\frac{M^2}{L} = \frac{(\mu_0 H \Sigma)^2}{2S} \text{ henrys} \qquad (8.11)$$

Values of this constant are given in Appendix 8.4, but here it can be noted that, for a small loop, the coupling is proportional Σ^2, the square of the area of the loop. Thus the transmission line can be matched to the cavity by adjustment of the area of the loop.

If probe coupling is used the input impedance of the probe is of a similar form to equation (8.10), except that a capacitive reactance $1/j\omega C_P$ must be

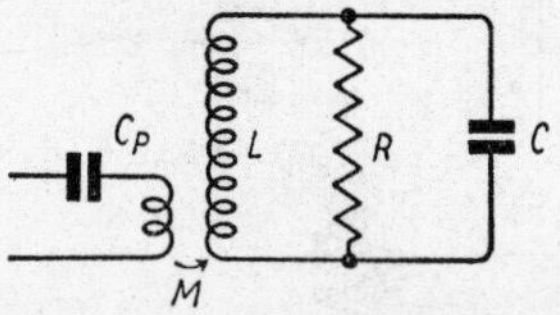

Fig. 8.9. Equivalent circuit for probe-coupled cavity.

added, C_P being the electrostatic capacitance between the probe and cavity walls. The equivalent circuit in this case is that of Fig. 8.9.

The cavities so far discussed have been 'unloaded'; that is, the only losses have been those inherent in the cavity. A cavity with an external load coupled through a second loop is illustrated in Fig. 8.10 (a). If Z_1 is the input impedance, and Z_2 the load impedance measured at the output loop, then:

$$\frac{Z_1}{Z_2} = \left(\frac{H_1 \Sigma_1}{H_2 \Sigma_2}\right)^2 \qquad (8.12)$$

and the cavity acts as a tuned transformer, having the equivalent circuit of Fig. 8.10 (b).

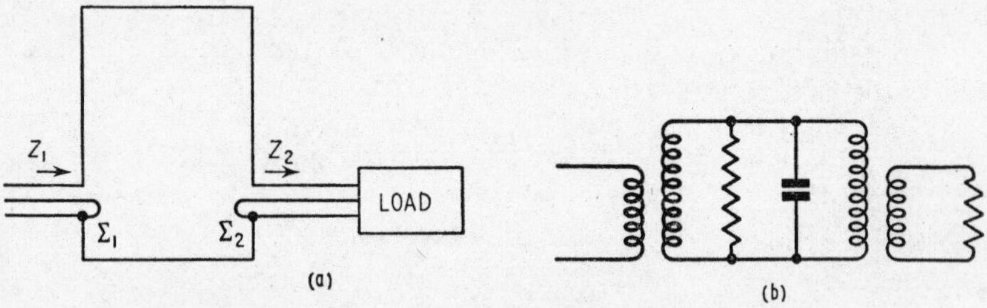

Fig. 8.10. Loaded cavity with its equivalent circuit.

If the normal to the loop is not parallel to the magnetic field, but makes with it an angle θ, then the flux is given by $\Phi = \mu_0 H \Sigma \cos\theta$. The coupling constant of a loop can therefore be varied by rotation of the loop. Thus for loop angles of θ_1 and θ_2 equation (8.12) becomes:

$$\frac{Z_1}{Z_2} = \left(\frac{H_1 \Sigma_1 \cos\theta_1}{H_2 \Sigma_2 \cos\theta_2}\right)^2$$

and the transformation ratio is dependent on the square of the cosine ratio.

Loading on a cavity has the effect of reducing the Q from its unloaded value. The loaded Q-value, Q_L, is defined, in conformity with the definition (8.6) for the unloaded Q, as:

$$Q_L = \frac{\omega \times \text{energy stored in cavity}}{\text{power dissipated in cavity and load}} \quad . \quad . \quad . \quad (8.13)$$

It will be seen that the waveguide frequency filters in Chapter 7 (p. 213) are just cavity resonators treated from a different viewpoint. From the viewpoint of this present chapter the filter of Fig. 7.46 is a rectangular cavity resonator coupled to input and output waveguides by rectangular apertures. It may appear strange that the resonant lengths found in Chapter 7 are not equal to $\lambda_g/2$, but are considerably less. This is explained by the fact that in the examples chosen the coupling apertures are large and have large reactances, which are part of the tuned circuit and hence modify its resonance frequency. As the coupling apertures are reduced in size the resonant length steadily approaches $\lambda_g/2$.

In Chapter 7 it was also shown that smaller apertures give increased sharpness of frequency response. This would be expressed in the language of the present chapter by the statement that a reduction in the amount of coupling increases the loaded Q.

The Cavity as a Wavemeter

One of the chief uses of a resonant cavity is as a wavemeter. A tunable cavity can be used in two ways: as an absorption wavemeter and as a transmission wavemeter. These arrangements are shown diagrammatically in Figs. 8.11 and

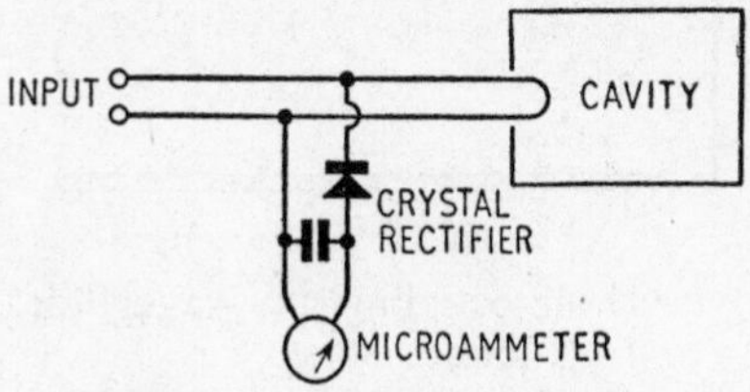

Fig. 8.11. Cavity connected as an absorption wavemeter.

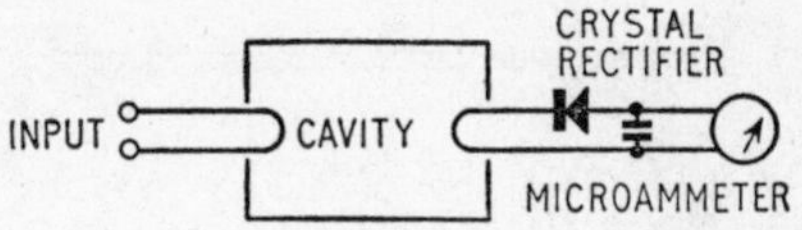

Fig. 8.12. Cavity connected as a transmission wavemeter.

8.12. In the absorption wavemeter the microammeter gives a reading when the cavity is off tune. As the cavity is tuned through resonance a sharp dip in the meter reading occurs through absorption of power in the cavity. In a transmission wavemeter, on the other hand, the meter gives a zero reading except in the neighbourhood of resonance, rising to a sharp maximum at the resonance frequency.

For ease of tuning, wavemeter resonators are usually made in cylindrical form. They commonly use either the H_{111} or H_{011} modes, the length being adjustable by means of a tuning piston. If the range of variation of length is sufficient, two (or more) positions of resonance can be found for any particular frequency, corresponding to the H_{111} and H_{112}, or H_{011} and H_{012}, modes. It is perhaps easier to regard such a wavemeter as a length of circular waveguide closed at each end, resonance occurring when the length is an exact number of half-wavelengths. When the length is n half-wavelengths then the mode will be H_{11n} or H_{01n}.

The length is varied by means of a tuning piston, as shown in Fig. 8.13. In an H_{01n} wavemeter the magnetic field at the surface of the piston is radial, and hence the lines of current flow in the piston, being normal to this, are concentric circles. Thus contact need not be provided between the outside edge of the piston and the side walls; normally a gap is left which is useful in suppressing other modes having radial current flow. The space behind the piston is often damped by a ring of resistive material, to avoid spurious resonances being set up in this space.

For the H_{11n} mode, where there is radial current flow, a non-contact piston is used, designed, as those described in Chapter 7 and shown in Fig. 7.16, to give a low impedance across the gap.

The distance of piston movement L between successive resonances is equal to $\lambda_g/2$, where λ_g is the wavelength in the guide. Using, then, equation (6.5) and

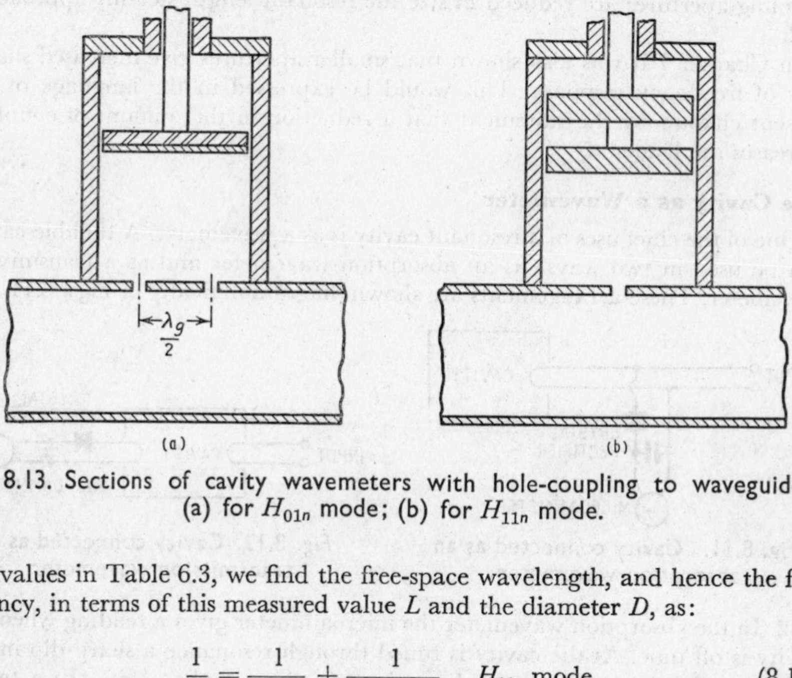

Fig. 8.13. Sections of cavity wavemeters with hole-coupling to waveguides: (a) for H_{01n} mode; (b) for H_{11n} mode.

the values in Table 6.3, we find the free-space wavelength, and hence the frequency, in terms of this measured value L and the diameter D, as:

$$\frac{1}{\lambda^2}=\frac{1}{(2L)^2}+\frac{1}{(1\cdot71D)^2},\quad H_{11n}\text{ mode} \qquad (8.14)$$

$$\frac{1}{\lambda^2}=\frac{1}{(2L)^2}+\frac{1}{(0\cdot82D)^2},\quad H_{01n}\text{ mode} \qquad (8.15)$$

It is difficult to avoid the presence of more than one mode in a tunable resonator, and this either restricts the use of a particular cavity to a small frequency range over which only one mode is present, or requires care in distinguishing between the various possible modes. Fig. 8.14 illustrates the construction of a 'mode chart' for a wavemeter. The maximum range over which this wavemeter can be calibrated to give the frequency from a single reading is indicated.

A form of cavity wavemeter which is free from extraneous modes over a com-

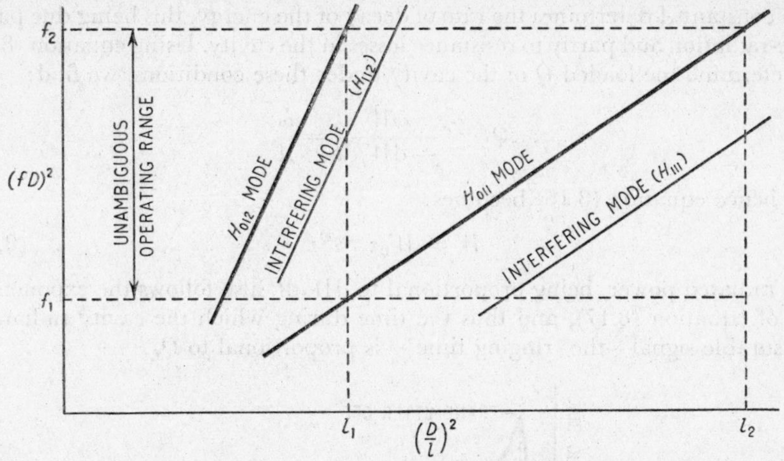

Fig. 8.14. Mode chart for cavity wavemeter, showing range of operation in H_{011} mode without interference from H_{012} mode.

paratively wide range is that shown in Fig. 8.15. It is essentially a cylindrical cavity resonating in the E_{010} mode, the field being distorted by a movable rod along its axis. The resulting field is one which is a hybrid between the E_{010} mode in a waveguide and the normal mode in a coaxial resonator. As there is

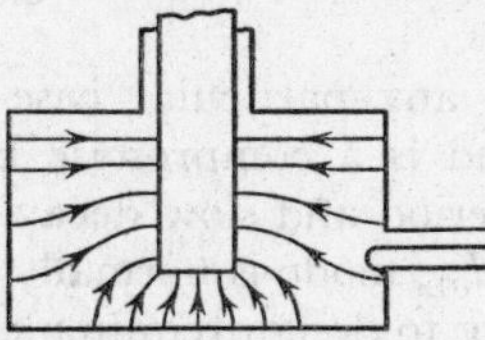

Fig. 8.15. Electric field in E_{010}-hybrid cavity.

no exact expression for the resonant frequency in this case the wavemeter must be calibrated from known frequencies.

The Cavity as an Echo Box

For tests on the operation of a radar equipment a cavity resonator may be used to provide an artificial echo signal. The cavity is provided with a coupling loop connected to a small aerial, or is coupled to outside space through a small hole, and in these forms is known as an echo box.

Placed in the transmitter field, the cavity receives and stores energy during the transmitter pulse, and re-radiates it after the end of the transmitter pulse. The re-radiated energy is picked up by the radar receiver and appears as a sustained echo on the indicator.

▶ The build-up and decay of energy is illustrated in Fig. 8.16. The decay is exponential, so that, if W_0 is the amount of energy stored in the cavity at the end of the build-up period, then the energy W at any subsequent time t is given by:

$$W = W_0 \varepsilon^{-At} \quad . \quad . \quad . \quad . \quad (8.16)$$

The constant A determines the rate of decay of the energy, this being due partly to re-radiation and partly to resistance losses in the cavity. Using equation (8.13) to determine the loaded Q of the cavity under these conditions, we find:

$$Q_L = \frac{\omega W}{-\,\mathrm{d}W/\mathrm{d}t} = \frac{\omega}{A},$$

and hence equation (8.16) becomes:

$$W = W_0 \varepsilon^{-\omega t/Q_L} \quad . \; . \; . \; . \; . \; . \; . \quad (8.17)$$

The radiated power, being proportional to $\mathrm{d}W/\mathrm{d}t$, also follows the exponential law of equation (8.17), and thus the time during which the cavity radiates a measurable signal—the 'ringing time'—is proportional to Q_L.

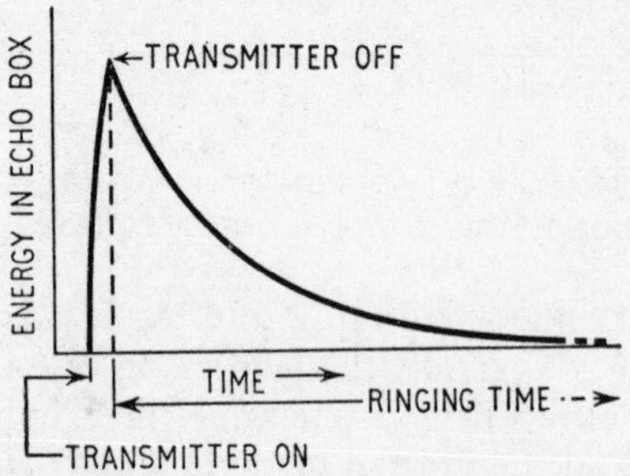

Fig. **8.16. Build-up and decay of energy in echo box.**

The optimum coupling in any particular case is that which makes the ringing time a maximum, and is a compromise between rapid build up of energy during the charging period and slow decay during the ringing period. As a high Q is necessary the H_{01n} mode is normally used. Values of n may vary from 1 to perhaps 50 according to design requirements.

The use of the echo box is dealt with in Volume 7.

Cavities for Klystron Oscillators

A further method of exciting a cavity resonator is by means of a modulated electron beam passing through the resonator. The klystron valve, dealt with in

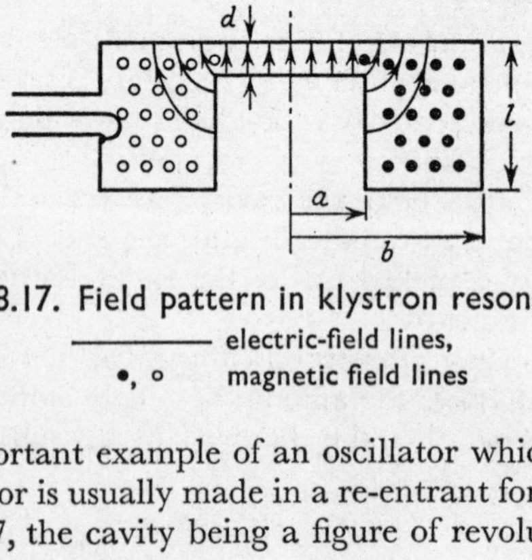

Fig. **8.17. Field pattern in klystron resonator.**
——— electric-field lines,
•, ∘ magnetic field lines

Volume 3, is an important example of an oscillator which uses a resonator in this way. The resonator is usually made in a re-entrant form such as that shown in section in Fig. 8.17, the cavity being a figure of revolution about a vertical axis. In the central part are holes or grids through which the beam passes. Coupling to an external circuit is by means of a loop or an aperture in the side wall of the cavity.

There are two reasons for the use of a re-entrant form of resonator. First, a high electric field can be developed across the small gap, this being necessary for a large interaction between the field and the electron beam; secondly, the small gap gives the short transit time of the electron necessary to the operation of the oscillator.

An important requirement of such a cavity is that it should be tunable. A small tuning range can be accomplished by slight distortion of the cavity dimensions, the effect being best appreciated by visualizing the central part of the cavity as the plates of a capacitor, the remaining part forming a single-turn inductor connected across them. If the top face is made flexible it may be pushed inwards slightly, thus increasing the effective capacitance and hence reducing the resonant frequency. A second method is to insert one or more tuning plugs in the side wall, causing the distortion of the magnetic field shown in Fig. 8.18.

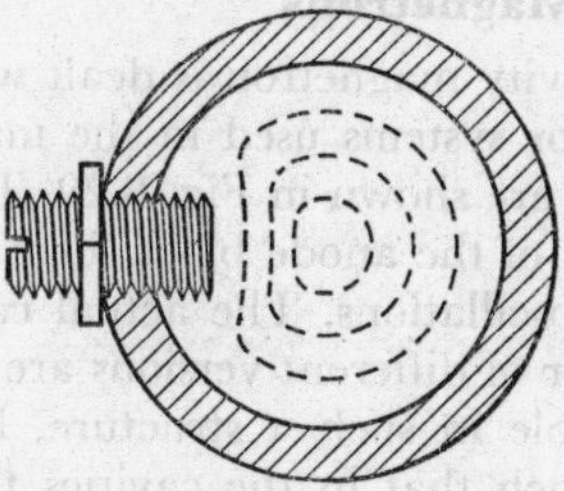

Fig. 8.18. Distortion of magnetic field in cavity by means of a tuning plug.

The effect is to decrease the total magnetic flux in the cavity, which is equivalent to a reduction in the effective inductance, and hence the resonant frequency is increased.

The principles of these tuning methods can be generalized into the following statements. If a cavity wall is pushed inwards at a point of strong electric field the resonant frequency is reduced. If a cavity wall is pushed inwards at a point of strong magnetic field the resonant frequency is increased.

The calculation of the resonant frequency of a cavity of the form which we have been discussing is a difficult matter, and can be done only approximately. For the dimensions given in Fig. 8.17 an approximate expression for the free-space resonant wavelength is:

$$\lambda = 2\pi a\left(\frac{l}{2d}\log_\varepsilon \frac{b}{a}\right)^{1/2} \quad . \quad . \quad . \quad (8.18)$$

The approximations are such that the expression always gives a resonant wavelength which is slightly smaller than the true value.

Two rather similar forms of re-entrant resonator are shown in Fig. 8.19, these being also figures of revolution about a vertical axis. The resonant wavelength of that of Fig. 8.19 (a) is also given approximately by equation (8.18); that of Fig. 8.19 (b) is approximately:

$$\lambda = 2\pi\left(\frac{\pi r^2 R}{d}\left[1 - \sqrt{\left\{1 - \left(\frac{r}{R}\right)^2\right\}}\right]\right)^{1/2} \quad . \quad . \quad . \quad (8.19)$$

Both the Q and the shunt resistance of the re-entrant forms of resonator are less than for the simpler geometrical shapes (see Appendix 8.2). For re-entrant types, however, the shunt resistance is developed across a relatively short path. This is of great importance when the resonator is associated with an electron beam passing along its axis, for it then presents a high impedance to the beam. ◀

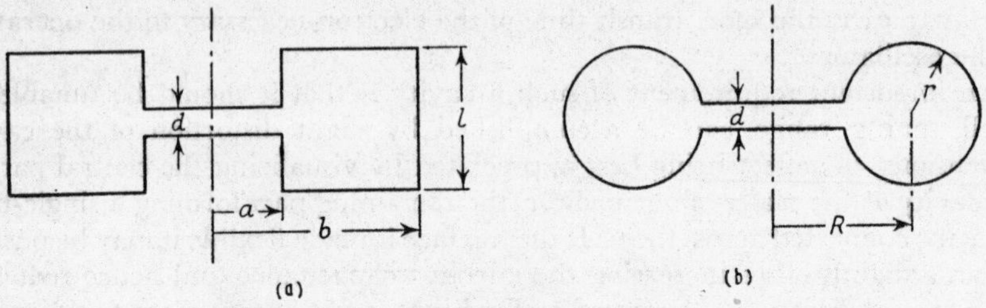

Fig. 8.19. Forms of klystron resonator.

Resonators for Cavity Magnetrons

The operation of the cavity magnetron is dealt with in Volume 3. Here we shall consider the resonator systems used in the magnetron. Cross-sections of typical cavity magnetrons are shown in Fig. 8.20. The anode cavities together with the spaces at the end of the anode block form the resonant system determining the frequency of oscillations. The actual cavity shape is not of great importance, and a number of different versions are in use.

Many modes are possible in such a structure, but the important one for magnetron operation is such that in the cavities the magnetic flux lines are

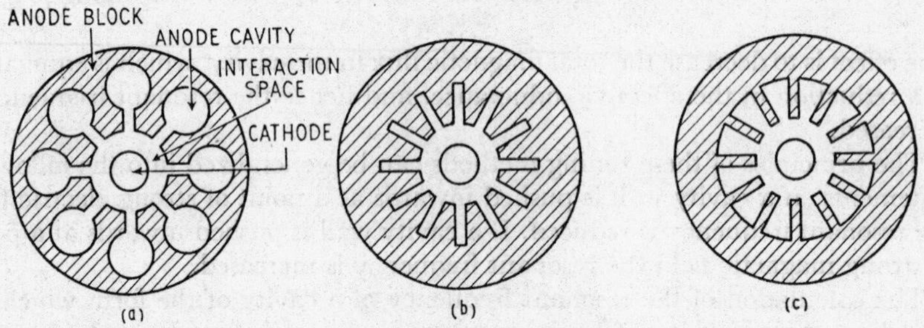

Fig. 8.20. Magnetron anode blocks with cavities consisting of (a) holes and slots, (b) slots, (c) sectors.

parallel to the axis, and the electric field lines pass across the slots, as shown in Fig. 8.21. The significant dimensions of the cavities are those in the plane of Fig. 8.20; the axial length of the anode block and the spaces at its ends affect the resonant frequencies in only a minor degree.

A single anode resonator of the 'hole and slot' type of Fig. 8.21 can be considered, to a first approximation, as a capacitor C, formed by the 'slot' portion, in parallel with an inductor L, formed by the 'hole' portion. For the dimensions given in the figure, C and L can be calculated as:

$$C = \frac{\kappa_0 al}{d}, \quad L = \frac{\mu_0 \pi r^2}{l}$$

Hence the resonant frequency is given approximately by

$$f = \frac{1}{2\pi(LC)^{1/2}} = \frac{c}{2\pi}\sqrt{\frac{d}{\pi r^2 a}} \quad . \quad . \quad . \quad . \quad . \quad . \quad (8.20)$$

Alternative constructions of the block are shown in Fig. 8.20 (b) and (c). In Fig. 8.20 (b) the resonators are parallel sided slots, and as such they can be treated as strip transmission lines, having a resonant length of $\lambda/4$.

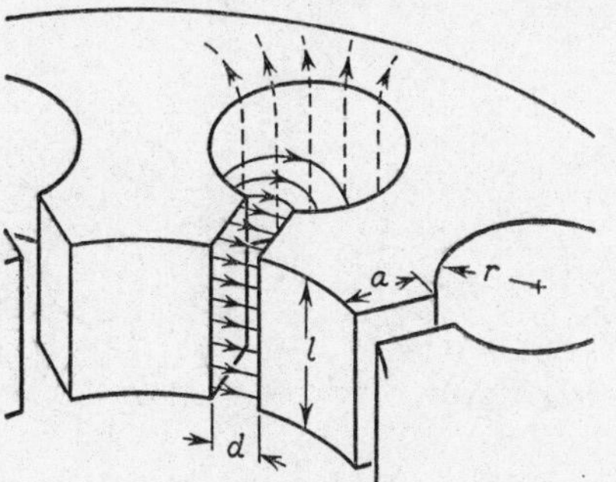

Fig. **8.21. Electric and magnetic fields in hole-and-slot cavity.**

The individual cavities of the magnetron are not isolated from each other, but are mutually coupled through the end spaces and the interaction space. Thus an equivalent circuit of the form shown in Fig. 8.22 can represent the complete resonant system. It is well known that two identical resonant circuits when coupled together have two distinct resonance frequencies; when $2N$ identical circuits are coupled together it can be shown that the system has $N + 1$

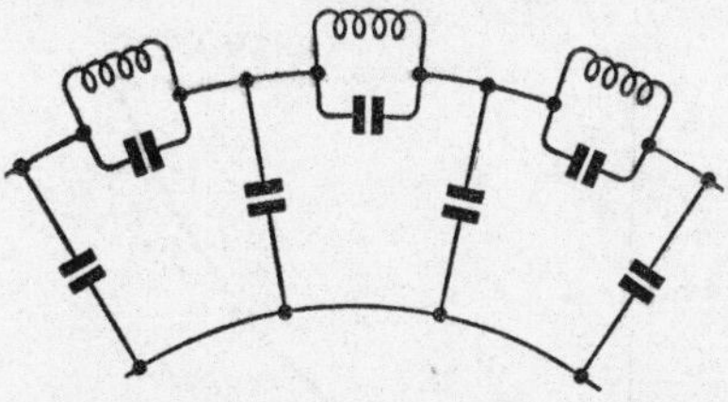

Fig. 8.22. Simple equivalent circuit of magnetron block.

resonance frequencies. Electric field patterns in the interaction space, corresponding to these modes, are shown for an 8-segment magnetron in Fig. 8.23. These are such that phase differences between adjacent segments are respectively $0, \pm \pi/4, \pm 2\pi/4, \pm 3\pi/4, \pi$. The two possible signs correspond to field distributions varying in opposite directions around the block. These modes are called doublets, all modes being doublets with the exception of that in which the phase difference between segments is π (or zero). If the magnetron were perfectly symmetrical the two components of a doublet would have exactly the same resonant frequency. In practice slight asymmetries cause the two components to differ slightly in frequency, causing instability in magnetron operation. A magnetron is therefore always operated in the non-doublet mode, where the phase difference between segments is π. This is known as the π-mode.

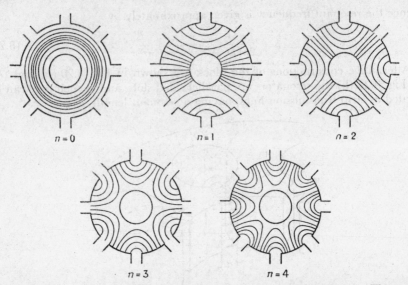

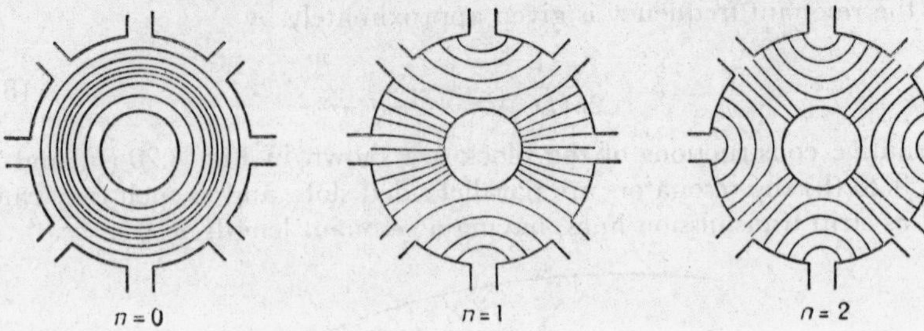

Fig. 8.23. Electric field patterns of modes in 8-segment magnetron. The mode numbers $n = 0, 1, 2, 3, 4$ correspond to phase differences between adjacent segments of 0, $\pi/4$, $2\pi/4$, $3\pi/4$, and π respectively.

Fig. 8.24 illustrates the various resonance frequencies in a magnetron with eight cavities. It will be seen that, in what is termed the 'unstrapped' case, the frequencies of the other modes are close to the π-mode, and with such a system there is the possibility of the magnetron oscillating in one or more of these unwanted modes. It is therefore desirable to modify the construction in order to

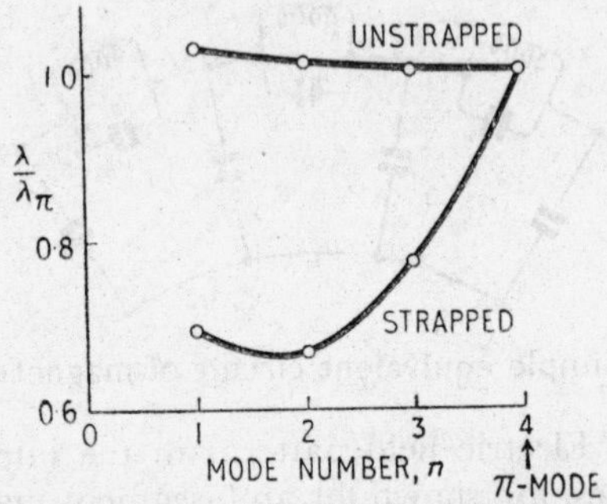

Fig. 8.24. Typical mode spectrum for 8-segment magnetron blocks, strapped and unstrapped, dimensioned to give the same π-mode wavelength, λ_π. Wavelengths of other modes are given relative to λ_π.

increase the frequency difference between the π-mode and the neighbouring modes.

One method of producing this separation is by connecting together those segments which should oscillate in the same phase. Fig. 8.25 shows two such methods of 'strapping'. The straps have an effective inductance for those modes in which the ends of the straps are not at the same potential. This inductance, being in parallel with the inductance of the cavity, increases the frequencies of the unwanted modes relative to the π-mode, as illustrated in Fig. 8.24.

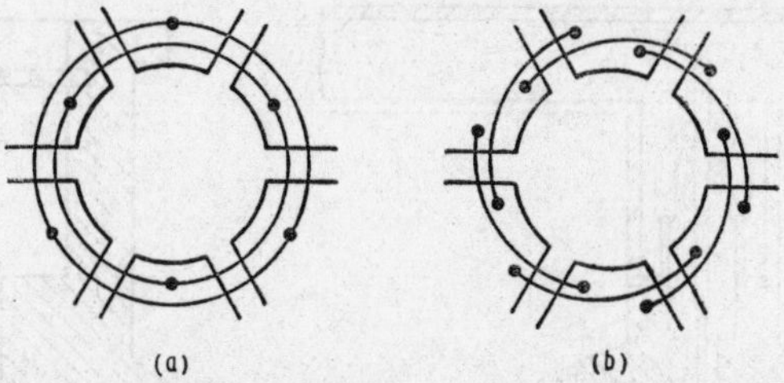

Fig. 8.25. Forms of strapping for magnetron blocks: (a) ring strapping; (b) echelon strapping.

Another method of separating the frequencies is by making alternate cavities of different sizes, the most usual arrangement being the 'rising sun' form shown

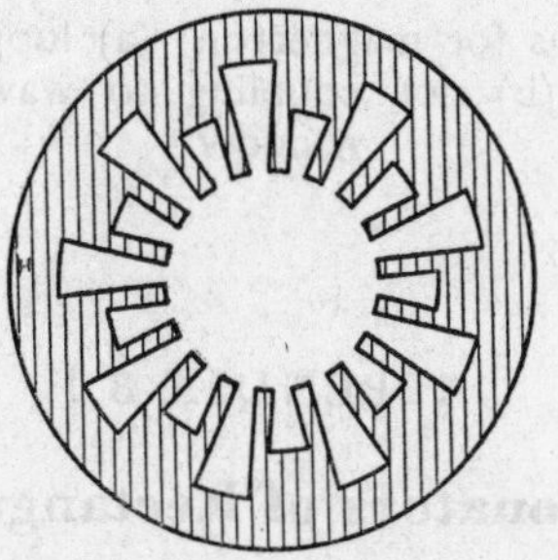

Fig. 8.26. Rising sun magnetron block.

in Fig. 8.26. In this case the frequencies are separated into two groups with the π-mode lying between them, as shown in Fig. 8.27.

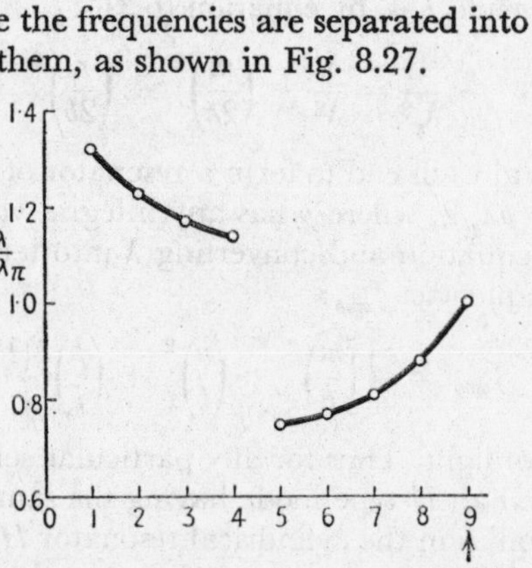

Fig. 8.27. Typical mode spectrum for 18-segment 'rising sun' magnetron block, as in Fig. 8.26. Wavelengths are given relative to λ_π, the wavelength of the π-mode.

Fig. 8.28 illustrates two methods of coupling power out from the magnetron block. The first uses a loop coupled to the magnetic field in one cavity and terminated in a probe which excites a waveguide. In the second a narrow slot acts as a transformer coupling one of the cavities to the output waveguide.

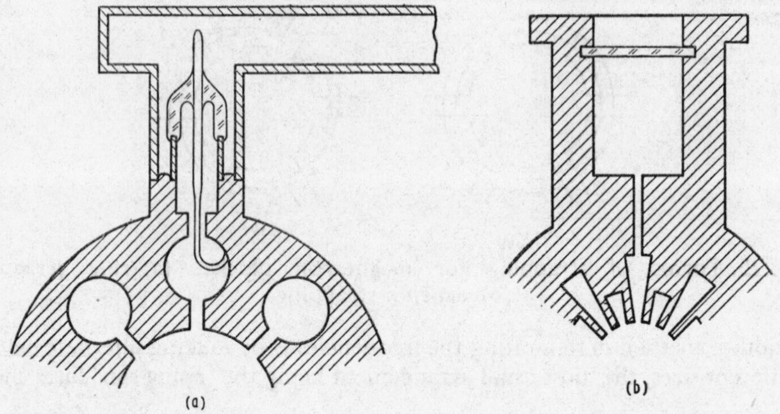

Fig. 8.28. Output couplings for magnetron: (a) loop coupling with coaxial-to-waveguide transformer; (b) slot coupling to waveguide with vacuum-tight window.

APPENDIX 8.1

Cavity Resonators of Rectangular Section

The formula for the guide wavelength of an E_{mn} or H_{mn} wave in a rectangular guide of dimensions a and b is, by equation (6.31):

$$\frac{1}{\lambda_g{}^2} = \frac{1}{\lambda^2} - \left(\frac{m}{2a}\right)^2 - \left(\frac{n}{2b}\right)^2$$

If the guide is closed at each end to form a resonator of length l then resonance will occur when $l = p\lambda_g/2$, where p has any integral value. Inserting this condition in the above equation and converting λ into terms of frequency we get for the resonance frequencies f_{mnp}:

$$f_{mnp} = \frac{c}{2}\left\{\left(\frac{m}{a}\right)^2 + \left(\frac{n}{b}\right)^2 + \left(\frac{p}{l}\right)^2\right\}^{1/2} \quad . \quad . \quad . \quad . \quad (8.21)$$

c being the velocity of light. Thus for any particular set of values of m, n and p there is an E-type and an H-type mode having the same resonance frequency.

For the same reason as in the cylindrical resonator H-type modes with $p = 0$ do not exist; for the E-modes with $p = 0$ the resonance frequencies are independent of l. The most important mode is that corresponding to the H_{10} transmission mode in the guide, the H_{101} mode, whose simple field pattern is shown in Fig. 8.3.

Expressions for the field components of the H_{101} mode are found by adding to those of a forward travelling wave equation (6.26) a set of components representing a backward-travelling wave, formed by changing the sign of the propagation constant β. The resultant of these two gives the required stationary wave in the resonator as:

$$\left.\begin{aligned} E_y &= 2A \sin\frac{\pi x}{a}\cos\frac{\pi z}{l}\sin\omega t \\ H_x &= 2A\frac{\pi/l}{\omega\mu_0}\sin\frac{\pi x}{a}\sin\frac{\pi z}{l}\cos\omega t \\ H_z &= 2A\frac{\pi/a}{\omega\mu_0}\cos\frac{\pi x}{a}\cos\frac{\pi z}{l}\cos\omega t \\ E_x &= E_z = H_y = 0 \end{aligned}\right\} \quad . \quad . \quad . \quad (8.22)$$

In the equations β has been replaced by its value appropriate to the resonator mode, viz. $\beta = 2\pi/\lambda_g = \pi/l$. It is clear from these equations that, in order to satisfy the boundary conditions by making E_y vanish on the end walls, the end walls are situated at $z = \pm l/2$. Note that the above expressions do represent a stationary field in which the position of nodes and loops are not time-dependent.

APPENDIX 8.2

Q-factors

The decrement Δ of a resonant cavity is defined as the natural logarithm of the ratio of the amplitudes of two successive oscillations. Let the electromagnetic energy in the resonator at any instant t be $W(t)$, and $T = 2\pi/\omega$ the period of the oscillation. Then, energy being proportional to the square of the amplitude:

$$\begin{aligned} \Delta &= \log_\varepsilon\left\{\frac{W(t)}{W(t+T)}\right\}^{1/2} \\ &\approx \tfrac{1}{2}\log_\varepsilon\frac{W(t)}{W(t) + T\,\mathrm{d}W(t)/\mathrm{d}t} \\ &\approx \tfrac{1}{2}\log_\varepsilon\left(1 - \frac{T}{W}\frac{\mathrm{d}W}{\mathrm{d}t}\right) \\ &\approx -\frac{T}{2W}\frac{\mathrm{d}W}{\mathrm{d}t} \end{aligned}$$

Putting the rate of dissipation of energy, $-\,\mathrm{d}W/\mathrm{d}t$, equal to P, we get:

$$\Delta = \frac{TP}{2W} = \frac{\pi}{\omega}\frac{P}{W}$$

Q is defined by the relation $Q = \pi/\Delta$, and hence,

$$\begin{aligned} Q &= \frac{\omega W}{P} \quad . \quad . \quad . \quad . \quad . \quad . \quad . \quad . \quad . \quad . \quad (8.23) \\ &= \frac{\omega \times \text{energy stored in cavity}}{\text{power dissipated in cavity}} \end{aligned}$$

The value of P can be calculated in the same way as P_{loss} of Appendix 6.4, as an integral over the surface of the resonator. Thus:

$$P = \tfrac{1}{2}R_s \int_{\text{surface}} |H|^2 \, da \text{ watts} \quad . \quad . \quad . \quad . \quad . \quad (8.24)$$

where da is an element of surface area, and R_s the surface resistivity as in Appendix 6.4.

The instantaneous value of energy density in an electromagnetic field is given by $\frac{1}{2}\kappa E^2 + \frac{1}{2}\mu H^2$ joules/m³, these two terms representing energy in the electric field and in the magnetic field respectively. In a resonator the energy alternates between the electric and magnetic forms, so that the mean energy density can be taken as the peak electric energy $\frac{1}{2}\kappa|E|^2$ or the peak magnetic energy $\frac{1}{2}\mu|H|^2$. Thus for a volume v with $\kappa = \kappa_0$, $\mu = \mu_0$ the total energy in the resonator is given by

$$W = \tfrac{1}{2}\kappa_0 \int_{\text{vol}} |E|^2 \, dv = \tfrac{1}{2}\mu_0 \int_{\text{vol}} |H|^2 \, dv \quad . \quad . \quad . \quad (8.25)$$

Hence:

$$Q = \frac{\omega\mu_0 \int_{\text{vol}} |H|^2 \, dv}{R_s \int_{\text{surface}} |H|^2 \, da} \quad . \quad . \quad . \quad . \quad . \quad . \quad (8.26)$$

As a rough approximation we can replace $|H|^2$ under the integral sign by a mean value. As the magnetic field is a maximum at the surface of the resonator the mean surface value of $|H|^2$ will be roughly twice the mean value throughout the volume, and we can write equation (8.26) as:

$$Q \approx \frac{\omega\mu_0 v}{2R_s a}$$

$$= \frac{1}{\delta} \cdot \frac{v}{a} \quad . \quad . \quad . \quad . \quad . \quad . \quad . \quad . \quad (8.27)$$

using equation (6.12) and the definition of the skin depth $\delta = (\rho/\pi\mu f)^{1/2}$ given on p. 164. A trial of typical values in equation (8.27) will indicate that at centimetre wavelengths Q-values of the order of 10,000 are obtained.

Substitution of the field components (8.22) in equation (8.26) gives the exact value of Q for the H_{101} mode in a rectangular resonator as:

$$Q = \frac{1}{\delta} \cdot \frac{\dfrac{1}{a^2} + \dfrac{1}{l^2}}{\dfrac{1}{a^2}\left(\dfrac{2}{a} + \dfrac{1}{b}\right) + \dfrac{1}{l^2}\left(\dfrac{2}{l} + \dfrac{1}{b}\right)} \quad . \quad . \quad . \quad . \quad (8.28)$$

For a cylindrical resonator of diameter D and length l the same method gives the following expressions:

E_{010} *mode:*

$$Q = \frac{1}{\delta} \cdot \frac{1}{\dfrac{2}{D} + \dfrac{1}{l}} \quad . \quad . \quad . \quad . \quad . \quad . \quad . \quad (8.29)$$

H_{111} *mode:* $$Q = \frac{1}{\delta}\cdot\frac{\frac{D}{2}\left\{s_{11}^2 + \left(\frac{\pi D}{2l}\right)^2\right\}\left(1 - \frac{1}{s_{11}^2}\right)}{s_{11}^2 + 2\pi^2\left(\frac{D}{2l}\right)^3 + \left(\frac{\pi D}{2s_{11}l}\right)^2\left(1 - \frac{D}{l}\right)} \quad . \quad . \quad . \quad (8.30)$$

where $s_{11} = 1{\cdot}841$:

H_{011} *mode:* $$Q = \frac{1}{\delta}\cdot\frac{\frac{D}{2}\left\{s_{01}^2 + \left(\frac{\pi D}{2l}\right)^2\right\}}{s_{01}^2 + 2\pi^2\left(\frac{D}{2l}\right)^3} \quad . \quad . \quad . \quad . \quad . \quad (8.31)$$

where $s_{01} = 3{\cdot}832$.

It is clear from equation (8.27) that the highest Q-values will be obtained from those shapes having a high ratio of volume to surface area. Resonators of the re-entrant type Figs. 8.17 and 8.19 have relatively low volume/surface ratios, and thus have lower Q-values than those of the simple geometrical shapes discussed here.

The quantity $Q\delta/\lambda$ can be seen to be dimensionally independent of length for all modes, and is often useful as a parameter in resonator design, for example, as used in Fig. 8.4. Since δ is proportional to $f^{-1/2}$, the Q values of geometrically similar resonators are inversely proportional to the square roots of their resonance frequencies.

APPENDIX 8.3

Shunt Resistance

By combining equations (8.9) and (8.23), and expressing V as a line integral of the electric field E, we find:

$$R = \frac{V^2}{2P} = \frac{Q\left(\int_\Gamma E\,\mathrm{d}s\right)^2}{2\omega W} \text{ ohms} \quad . \quad . \quad . \quad . \quad (8.32)$$

The value of E in the integral is the amplitude of the component of electric field along the path Γ, $\mathrm{d}s$ being an element of this path. In the H_{101} mode of the rectangular resonator given by equations (8.22) the maximum voltage is developed between the two faces $y = 0$, $y = b$ along a line joining their centre points. In this case the voltage is given by

$$\int_\Gamma E\,\mathrm{d}s = \int_0^b 2A\,\mathrm{d}y = 2Ab$$

and the value for R is found to be:

$$R = 480Q\frac{b}{(a^2 + l^2)^{1/2}} \text{ ohms} \quad . \quad . \quad . \quad . \quad . \quad (8.33)$$

For the E_{010} mode in a cylindrical resonator the maximum voltage is developed along the axis of the cylinder, and with this path the resistance is:

$$R = 370Q\frac{l}{D} \text{ ohms} \quad . \quad . \quad . \quad . \quad . \quad . \quad . \quad (8.34)$$

The shunt resistances of geometrically similar resonators, being proportional to Q, are also inversely proportional to the square root of resonance frequency. The properties of resonators are summarized in Table 8.2.

APPENDIX 8.4

Coupled Cavities

As an example of the calculation of the coupling constant M^2/L of equation (8.11) consider the H_{101} mode in the rectangular resonator, with field components given by equation (8.22), generated by a loop in the position indicated

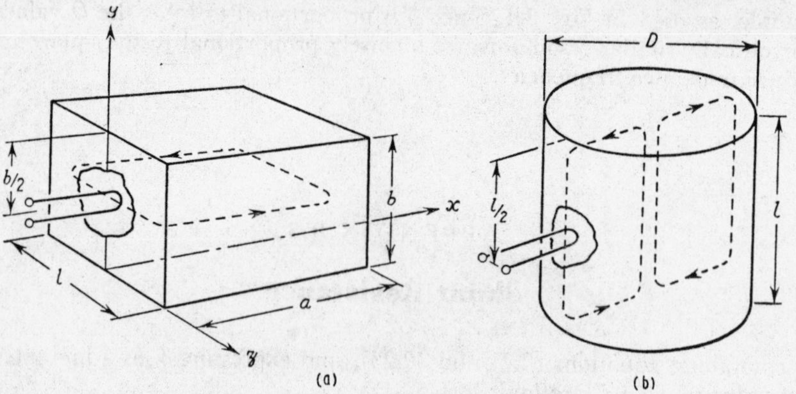

Fig. 8.29. Loop couplings for (a) H_{101} mode in rectangular resonator, (b) H_{011} mode in cylindrical resonator.

in Fig. 8.29 (a). The value of H at the loop is $2\pi A/\omega\mu_0 a$, and the value of W can be calculated by equation (8.25) as $W = \kappa_0 A^2 abl/2$. Hence by equation (8.11) we get:

$$\frac{M^2}{L} = \frac{5{\cdot}02}{10^6}\cdot\frac{l\Sigma^2}{ab(a^2 + l^2)} \text{ henrys} \quad . \quad . \quad . \quad . \quad (8.35)$$

The corresponding expression for the H_{011} mode in the cylindrical resonator of Fig. 8.29 (b) is:

$$\frac{M^2}{L} = \frac{1{\cdot}9}{10^5}\cdot\frac{\Sigma^2}{D^2 l\{(D/l)^2 + 5{\cdot}96\}} \text{ henrys} \quad . \quad . \quad . \quad (8.36)$$

As an example, let us find the area of loop required to match a 75-ohm coaxial line to the H_{011} mode in a cylindrical cavity of length 10 cm and diameter 10 cm, with the loop in the position of Fig. 8.29 (b). From equation (8.36) the value of M^2/L is $2{\cdot}73 \times 10^{-6}\Sigma^2$. By equations (8.10) and (8.11) the impedance at the loop is $\omega QM^2/L$, and thus, with the values of Table 8.1 for Q and ω,

$$75 = 2\pi \times 3955 \times 10^6 \times 48{,}400 \times 2{\cdot}73 \times 10^{-6}\Sigma^2$$

and hence $\quad \Sigma = 1{\cdot}51 \text{ cm}^2$

The coupling to a cavity reduces the Q from its unloaded value Q_U to the loaded value Q_L. Consider the effect of coupling by a matched transmission line of characteristic impedance Z_0 to a cavity. Fig. 8.8 can be put in the equivalent form of Fig. 8.30, with a virtual resonant circuit, consisting of the

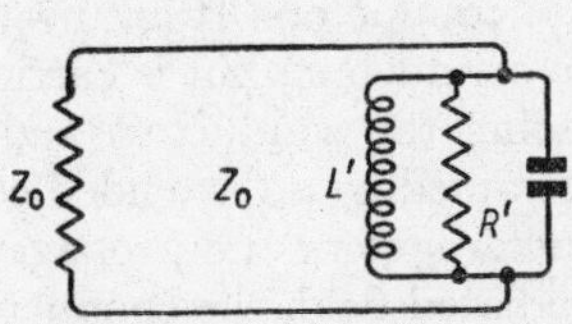

Fig. 8.30. Equivalent circuit for loaded resonator.

elements L', C', R' as shown, placed across the line. If the quantity β is defined by:

$$\beta = \frac{R'}{Z_0}$$

and the loaded Q is defined by equation (8.13) then we can write

$$\frac{1}{Q_L} = \omega L'\left(\frac{1}{R'} + \frac{1}{Z_0}\right) = \frac{\omega L'}{R'}(1 + \beta)$$

$$= \frac{1}{Q_U}(1 + \beta)$$

Hence $\quad Q_L = Q_U/(1 + \beta) \quad . \quad . \quad . \quad . \quad . \quad . \quad . \quad . \quad . \quad (8.37)$

The value of β can be experimentally determined from a measurement of the standing-wave ratio S on the line looking towards the cavity. If $\beta > 1$, S is equal to β and there will be a voltage maximum at the input to the cavity; if $B < 1$, S is equal to $1/\beta$ and a voltage minimum occurs at the cavity input.

If a cavity with both input and output couplings is loaded by these with impedances Z_1 and Z_2 respectively, and β_1, β_2 are defined as above by $\beta_1 = R'Z_1$ and $\beta_2 = R'/Z_2$, then in the same way it can be shown that

$$Q_L = Q_U/(1 + \beta_1 + \beta_2) \quad . \quad . \quad . \quad . \quad . \quad (8.38)$$

If both input and output are matched then it is easy to find the power dissipated in the load impedance. This ratio of this to the power available from the generator line gives the transmission loss function T, which at resonance is:

$$T = \frac{4\beta_1\beta_2}{(1 + \beta_1 + \beta_2)^2} \quad . \quad . \quad . \quad . \quad . \quad (8.39)$$

Thus loading a resonator with $\beta_1 = \beta_2 = \frac{1}{2}$ reduces the loaded Q to one-half of the unloaded Q, and, since $T = \frac{1}{4}$, gives a transmission loss of 6 db.

CHAPTER 9

Principles of Radiation

IN THE PREVIOUS CHAPTERS we have dealt with the guiding of electromagnetic energy by systems of conductors. It has been seen, however, that the energy is not confined to the conductors, but is carried in the moving electric and magnetic fields surrounding the conductors and guided by them. Such moving fields need not be restrained by an extended conductor system but may diverge from a limited conductor system and propagate through the surrounding space. We then have a radiated field, the conductor from which the radiation diverges being the radiator or aerial.* The aerial has the dual function of accepting energy from the transmission line and radiating it into space in desired directions. This latter function of an aerial is determined by its *directional characteristics*.

Conversely, at a receiving station the electric and magnetic fields impinge upon the aerial, and induce in it a voltage, causing a current to flow in the receiving apparatus.

No practical aerial can radiate uniformly in all directions, but such an *omni-directional* or *isotropic radiator* is a useful fiction as a reference standard to which practical aerials can be related.

A further useful fictitious aerial is the *Hertzian dipole*. This is a short linear conductor assumed to carry a uniform oscillatory current, and the magnitude and distribution of the radiation from it can be calculated. Many practical aerials can be regarded as made up of a chain of such short dipoles connected in series, and calculations of their radiation properties can be derived from a knowledge of the radiation properties of the Hertzian dipole.

Consider an aerial, of any form, to be situated at a point O, the centre of a sphere of radius r as in Fig. 9.1. By making measurements over the surface of the

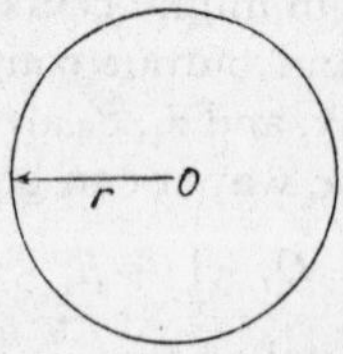

Fig. 9.1. Aerial at the centre O of a sphere of radius *r*.

sphere we can determine the intensity of the radiation in any direction and hence determine the radiating characteristics of the aerial. It is found that for small values of r a field is obtained—the 'near field', which differs in form from that for large values of r—the 'far field'. In this connection r is 'large' if it is

* In the United States the more usual term is 'antenna'.

much greater than the wavelength of the radiation, and so much greater than the dimensions of the aerial that this can be regarded as a point situated at the centre of the sphere. The radiating properties of an aerial are always given in terms of its 'far field'.

Isotropic Radiator

An isotropic radiator is defined as one which radiates uniformly in all directions. The surface area of a sphere of radius r surrounding it is $4\pi r^2$, and since all the power radiated must pass through that sphere (assuming there are no obstacles to absorb power) then the power received per unit area at a distance r for a radiated power P is given by:

$$P_a = \frac{P}{4\pi r^2} \text{ watts per square metre} \quad . \quad . \quad . \quad . \quad (9.1)$$

Such a radiator is quite fictitious, as there is no actual aerial which does produce this uniform radiation of energy. Nevertheless it is a concept which is easy to visualize, and it is convenient to postulate such radiators as reference standards with which, through equation (9.1), other aerials may be compared.

► In Appendix 6.3 it is shown how the power flow through an area can be calculated by means of the Poynting vector. By equation (6.34) the instantaneous power flow for a plane wave in space whose electric field has a peak value E_0 is given by $E_0{}^2/120\pi$, and hence the mean power P_a is:

$$P_a = E_0{}^2/240\pi \text{ watts per metre}^2$$

Equating this to equation (9.1) gives the amplitude of the electric field at a distance r from an isotropic aerial radiating P watts as:

$$E_0 = \frac{(60P)^{1/2}}{r} \text{ volts per metre} \quad . \quad . \quad . \quad . \quad . \quad (9.2)$$

In Chapter 14 further use is made of this equation in determining the variation of field strength with distance, using the r.m.s. value E of field strength to give the expression:

$$E = \frac{(30P)^{1/2}}{r} \text{ volts per metre} \quad . \quad . \quad . \quad . \quad . \quad (9.3)$$ ◄

Hertzian Dipole

The theoretical analysis of a Hertzian dipole of length l carrying a uniform alternating current I shows that at a distance r from the dipole, where r is large, the radiated field has the form and properties of the plane wave discussed in Chapter 5. The wave diverging from the aerial can be thought of as a continually-expanding wave with a spherical wave-front centred at the aerial. To an observer at a very remote point, however, who sees only that part of the spherical wave in his immediate neighbourhood as it passes through his observing point, the wave will appear to all intents and purposes plane. Thus in the far field the radiated field at a point can be considered as that of a plane wave propagated in the direction of a straight line joining the point of observation to the source. The amplitudes of the electric and magnetic field components, which are perpendicular to each other and to the direction of motion of the wave, are proportional to I and to l, and decrease with distance as $1/r$. Hence the power per unit area decreases as $1/r^2$ in the same way as indicated in equation (9.1).

In this case however the energy is not radiated uniformly in all directions. If we consider any plane in which the dipole lies the field strength in different directions in this plane varies in accordance with the length of the arrows in Fig. 9.2 (a), being a maximum in directions at right angles to the dipole, and decreasing to zero in the directions of its axis.

The bounding curves in Fig. 9.2 (a) form the *polar diagram* of the Hertzian dipole in any plane in which the dipole lies. By symmetry the radiation must be uniform in a plane perpendicular to the dipole axis, and therefore the polar diagram in that plane is a circle as in Fig. 9.2 (b). The complete space polar

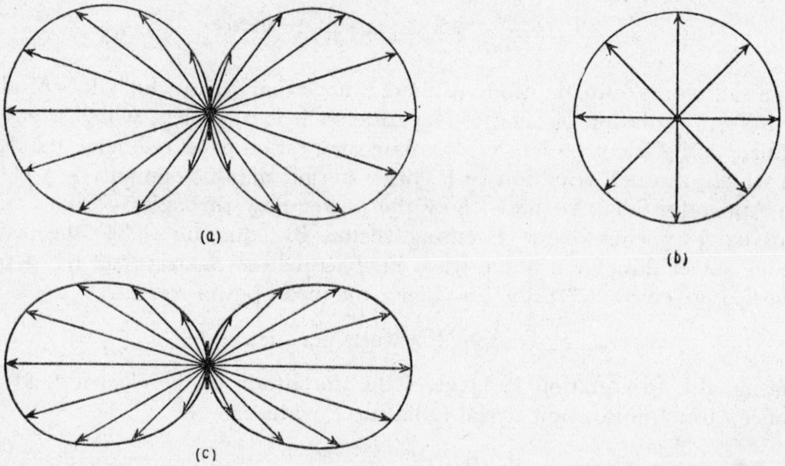

Fig. 9.2. Polar diagram of Hertzian dipole; the amplitudes of the electric or magnetic fields are represented in the plane of the dipole by (a), and in the plane normal to the dipole axis by (b). The power diagram in the plane of the dipole is shown at (c).

diagram of the dipole is the doughnut-shaped surface formed by rotating Fig. 9.2 (a) about the dipole axis.

In contrast the polar diagram of an isotropic radiator is clearly a sphere centred on the point radiator.

The polar diagram may also be drawn in terms of power, as in Fig. 9.2 (c), where the lengths of the arrows determining the polar-diagram curve are proportional to the squares of those of Fig. 9.2 (a).

The Hertzian dipole is also a hypothetical aerial, since it has been defined as a short isolated conductor carrying a uniform alternating current, and this would require a means of accumulating charge at the ends of the element. A physical approximation to it could be made by terminating the dipole in two spheres, as in Fig. 9.3, on which the charges could accumulate, varying in magnitude and sign with the alternations of current. This would give approximately the polar diagram described above, but such a short aerial is not used in practice since it has a highly reactive input impedance and low radiation resistance, and is consequently difficult to excite efficiently. The importance of the Hertzian dipole is more theoretical than practical, since it can be regarded as the element from which larger aerials are constructed and their properties calculated. The isotropic radiator is sometimes even more convenient theoretically although it is even less of a practical proposition.

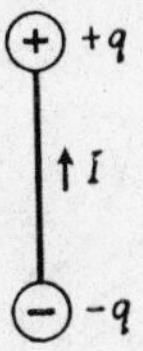

Fig. 9.3. Hertzian dipole.

From the treatment of Appendix 9.1 we find that the field produced by a dipole at a distant point P is such that the electric and magnetic field directions are as illustrated in Fig. 9.4. The electric field is perpendicular to the direction joining P to the dipole and is in the plane containing the dipole.

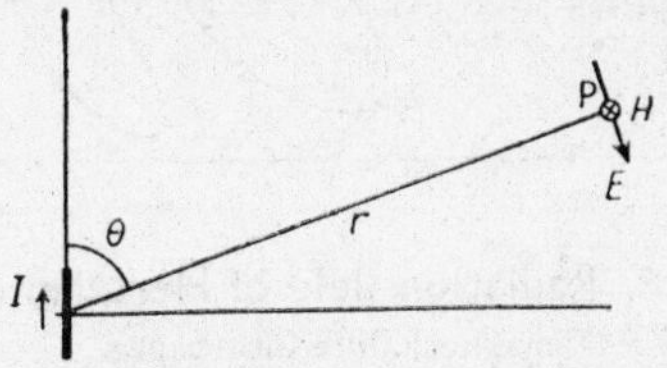

Fig. 9.4. Directions of field vectors of dipole.

Thus in the neighbourhood surrounding P the spherical wave diverging from the dipole will appear as in Fig. 9.5. As before, if P is sufficiently remote from the dipole the field seen by an observer at P will be indistinguishable from that of a plane wave.

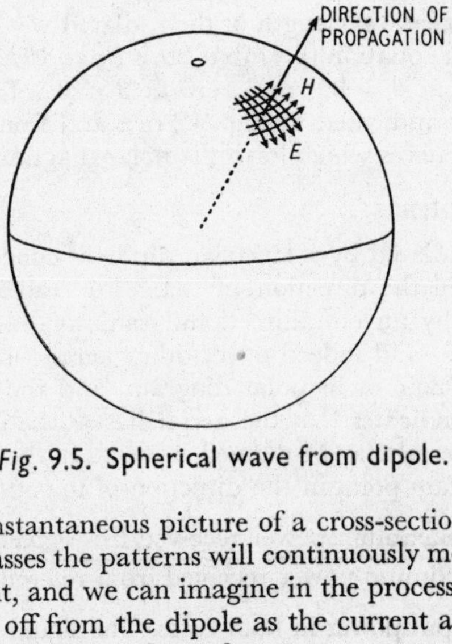

Fig. 9.5. Spherical wave from dipole.

Fig. 9.6 gives an instantaneous picture of a cross-section of the field close to the dipole. As time passes the patterns will continuously move radially outwards with the speed of light, and we can imagine in the process loops of electric field continually breaking off from the dipole as the current alternates and moving outwards to keep up the steady flow of energy.

Appendix 9.1 gives expressions for the radiated field from a dipole of length l, carrying a uniform alternating current of amplitude I_0. It is shown that in the plane of the dipole the electric and magnetic fields at a distant point represented

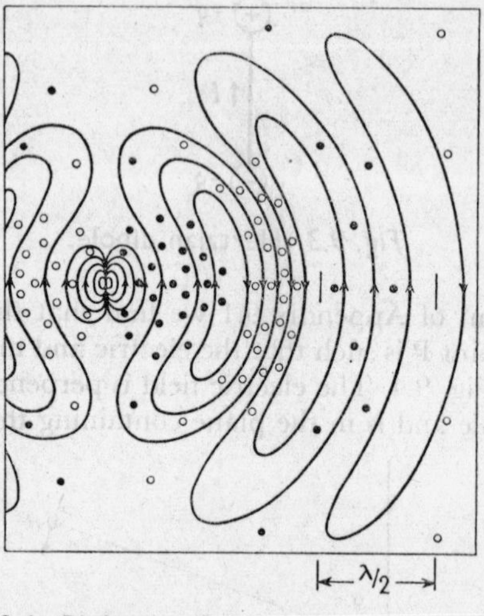

Fig. 9.6. **Radiation field of Hertzian dipole.**
∘ magnetic line into paper
• magnetic line out of paper

by the polar co-ordinates r, θ are directed as in Fig. 9.4 and have amplitudes given by:

$$E_0 = 120\pi H_0 = \frac{60\pi I_0 \sin\theta}{\lambda r} \quad . \quad . \quad . \quad . \quad (9.4)$$

where λ is the free-space wavelength of the radiated wave.

It will be seen from equation (9.4) that both E_0 and H_0 vary as $\sin\theta$ and will thus be a maximum at $\theta = 90°$ and zero at $\theta = 0°$. This is the variation of amplitude with angle indicated in Fig. 9.2 (a), and from the geometry of the figure the bounding curves which form the polar diagram are clearly circles.

Gain and Beam Width

Since the power radiated by a Hertzian dipole is concentrated in particular directions, the field in the direction of maximum radiation must be greater than that produced by an omnidirectional radiator emitting the same total power. Thus a dipole—and indeed every other aerial—has *directivity*, which is represented by the shape of its polar diagram, and the increased signal in a particular direction indicates that the aerial has a *gain* in that direction. The gain G of any given aerial may be defined in terms of the signal power received by a receiver at a distant point in the direction of maximum radiation as:

$$G = \frac{\text{maximum power received from given aerial}}{\text{maximum power received from reference aerial}} \quad . \quad (9.5)$$

assuming the same input power in both cases. The signal power is proportional to the square of the radiation field at the point.

The isotropic radiator is often used as the reference aerial, but it is sometimes convenient to use other reference standards, for example, the Hertzian dipole, and the half-wave dipole discussed later. It is immaterial which is chosen so long as it is clearly stated.

The gain defined by equation (9.5) is the *power gain*, since it is a ratio of two powers. Usually gain is expressed in decibels, and is therefore determined by the relation:

$$\text{db gain} = 10 \log_{10} G \qquad (9.6)$$

The power gain of a Hertzian dipole relative to an isotropic radiator will be shown to be 3/2 or 1·76 db.

A convenient measure of the directivity of an aerial is the angle measured on the polar diagram between points where the radiated power has fallen to half its maximum value. This is known as the *beam width* between half-power points. For an amplitude polar diagram the relevant points are those at which the amplitude of the field has fallen to 0·707 of its maximum. Both cases are illustrated for the Hertzian dipole in Fig. 9.7, showing a beam width of 90°.

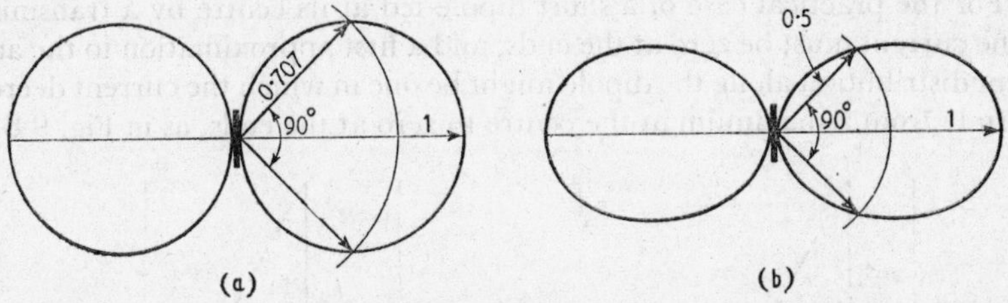

Fig. 9.7. Beam width of Hertzian dipole: (a) in terms of the amplitude of the electric or magnetic field and (b) in terms of power.

In Appendix 9.2 it is shown that the amplitude of the electric field at a distance r from a Hertzian dipole radiating a power P has a value, in the direction of maximum radiation, of $(90P)^{1/2}/r$. Comparing this with equation (9.2) we get the power gain of a Hertzian dipole relative to an isotropic radiator as:

$$G = \left\{\frac{(90P)^{1/2}}{r}\bigg/\frac{(60P)^{1/2}}{r}\right\}^2 = \tfrac{3}{2} \qquad (9.7)$$

Expressed in decibels by means of equation (9.6) this represents a gain of 1·76 db.

By equation (9.4) we see that E_0 has fallen to 0·707 of its maximum when $\theta = 45°$ or 135°. The beam angle included between the half-power points is therefore 90°, as indicated in Fig. 9.7.

Radiation Resistance

In Appendix 9.2 it is shown that a Hertzian dipole of length l carrying an alternating current of amplitude I_0 radiates a power P given by:

$$P = 40\pi^2 I_0^2 \left(\frac{l}{\lambda}\right)^2 \qquad (9.8)$$

where λ is the free-space wavelength of the radiated wave.

Since the power is proportional to I_0^2 and the other quantities are constant this suggests rewriting equation (9.8) as the power dissipated in a fictitious resistance R_{rad} of such as value that:

$$\tfrac{1}{2}I_0^2 R_{rad} = 40\pi^2 I_0^2\left(\frac{l}{\lambda}\right)^2$$

whence

$$R_{rad} = 80\pi^2\left(\frac{l}{\lambda}\right)^2 \text{ ohms} \quad . \quad . \quad . \quad . \quad . \quad (9.9)$$

R_{rad} is known as the *radiation resistance.* Equation (9.9) is not of general application to aerials other than the Hertzian dipole where l is much smaller than λ, but the concept of radiation resistance is applicable to all types of aerial. It will be shown later that for a loss-free aerial this radiation resistance is the resistive component of the input impedance of an aerial.

Short Linear Aerials

The hypothetical constant current element which we have discussed in the Hertzian dipole is useful theoretically but does not represent a practical situation. For the practical case of a short dipole fed at its centre by a transmission line the current must be zero at the ends, and a first approximation to the actual current distribution along the dipole might be one in which the current decreases uniformly from a maximum at the centre to zero at the ends, as in Fig. 9.8 (a).

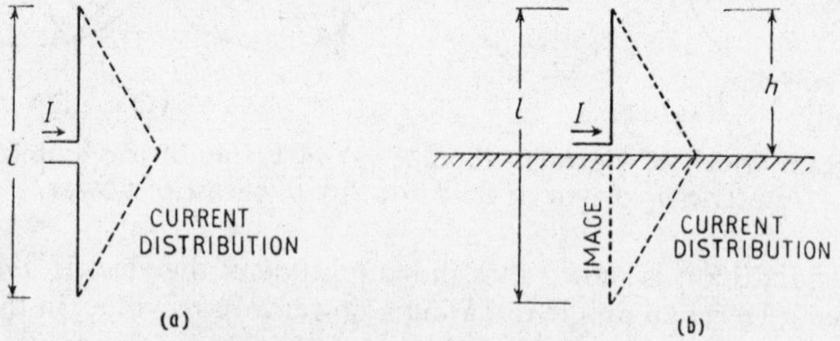

Fig. 9.8. (a) Short dipole with linear current distribution; (b) Short unipole with linear current distribution.

Let the current at the centre terminals have the same value as the uniform current assumed in the Hertzian dipole. For the above current distribution the average current along the dipole is clearly one-half of the maximum, and thus the radiated field intensities are reduced to one-half, and the radiated power to one-quarter. Therefore the radiation resistance (referred to the current at the terminals) is one-quarter that of the constant current element of the same length, as given in equation (9.9). In this case, then,

$$R_{rad} \text{ (short dipole)} = 20\pi^2\left(\frac{l}{\lambda}\right)^2 \text{ ohms} \quad . \quad . \quad . \quad (9.10)$$

Although the assumption of current distribution has been an arbitrary one, the expression proves to be a good approximation for short aerials, and is useful up to $l = \lambda/4$.

Consider now the case of Fig. 9.8 (b), which represents a short aerial of length h, with linear current distribution, mounted on a reflecting plane. Such an aerial is called a *unipole*. The effect of the reflecting plane can be represented by an image of the unipole, as shown in Fig. 9.8 (b), and thus the unipole and reflector produce the same field above the plane as does a dipole of length $l = 2h$ when both have the same current flowing. Since, however, the unipole radiates only into the space above the plane, its total radiated power is only half that of the dipole. Thus its radiation resistance is only half that of the dipole, and by equation (9.10):

$$R_{\text{rad}}\ (\text{unipole}) = 40\pi^2\left(\frac{h}{\lambda}\right)^2 \text{ ohms} \quad . \quad . \quad . \quad . \quad (9.11)$$

This approximation holds good for values of h up to $\lambda/8$.

On the assumption of uniform current distribution the gain of a short dipole, as given by equation (9.7), is 3/2. By the above argument the power gain of a unipole relative to an isotropic radiator is twice that of a dipole and therefore equal to 3.

The Half-Wave Dipole

In order to calculate the radiated field of a longer aerial it is necessary to know the current distribution in the aerial. The calculation of the actual current distribution is a difficult matter and the result is usually a very complicated mathematical expression. It is common practice, therefore, to assume that the current distribution has some form which is approximately the same as the real distribution but which can be represented by some simple expression. The linear current distribution assumed in the last section is useful only for short aerials.

A very commonly used aerial is the *half-wave dipole*, one whose length is approximately one-half of the free-space wavelength of the radiated wave. A linear current distribution is quite unsuitable for this aerial but, when fed at its centre by means of a transmission line, it is found to have a current distribution which is approximately sinusoidal, with a maximum at the centre and zero at

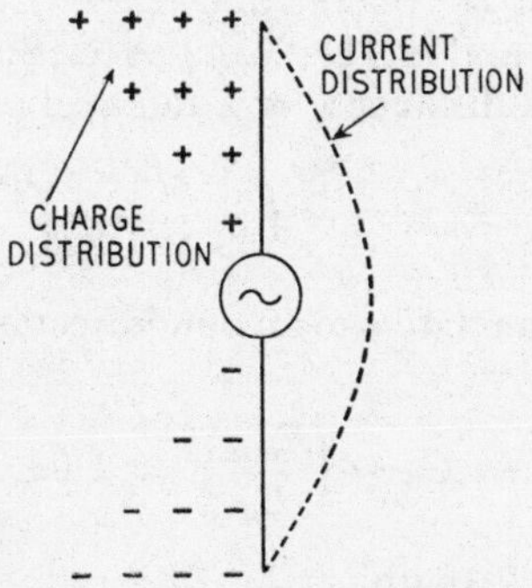

Fig. 9.9. Sinusoidal current and charge distribution on dipole.

the ends. In the u.h.f. and v.h.f. regions the dimensions of the half-wave dipole make it very convenient as an aerial or as an element in aerial systems.

The half-wave dipole is dealt with theoretically as a chain of Hertzian dipoles. If the current were uniform the positive charge at the end of one Hertzian dipole would be just cancelled by an equal negative charge at the opposite end of the adjacent dipole. When the current distribution is not constant—sinusoidal is assumed here—successive dipoles of the chain have slightly different current amplitudes. In this case there is incomplete cancellation of adjacent charges, and charges are built up on the surface of the dipole, as in Fig. 9.9. The form of the polar diagram of the half-wave dipole in the plane of the dipole has the form shown in Fig. 9.10, the beam width between half-power points being 78°. This pattern will clearly be symmetrical about the axis of the dipole, giving a circular polar diagram in the plane perpendicular to the axis.

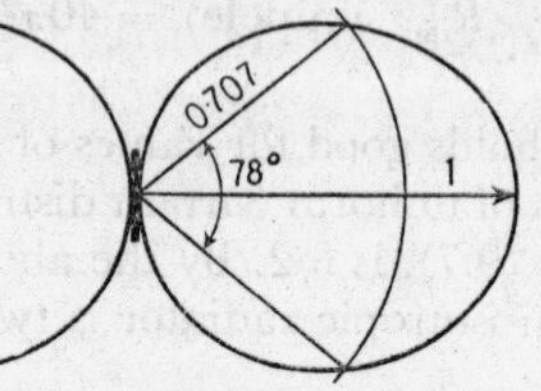

Fig. 9.10. Amplitude polar diagram of half-wave dipole.

It is shown in Appendix 9.3 that the radiation resistance of the half-wave dipole is 73 ohms. It may be noted that this is appreciably higher than the value which would have been obtained by the substitution of $l = \lambda/2$ in equation (9.10).

In Appendix 9.3 it is shown that the amplitude polar diagram in the plane of the axis is determined by the function

$$\frac{\cos\left(\frac{\pi}{2}\cos\theta\right)}{\sin\theta}$$

where θ is the angle measured from the dipole axis. It is easy to show that this function falls to 0·707 of its maximum value of unity at angles of 51° and 129°, giving the beam width of 78° quoted above.

From equations (9.40) and (9.41) it can be seen that the maximum amplitude of the radiation field at a distance r for a radiated power P is given by

$$E_{\max} = \frac{60}{r}\left(\frac{P}{30 \times 1{\cdot}22}\right)^{1/2}$$

and hence the power gain relative to an omnidirectional radiator is, by equation (9.2):

$$G_0 = \left(\frac{E_{\max}}{E_0}\right)^2 = 1{\cdot}64 \quad . \quad . \quad . \quad . \quad . \quad (9.12)$$

or, expressed in decibels, 2·16 db.

The r.m.s. field strength E at a distance r will be given by $E = E_{\max}/\sqrt{2}$, and hence the value for a half-wave dipole, corresponding to equation (9.3) for the isotropic radiator, is:

$$E = \frac{60}{r}\left(\frac{P}{60 \times 1{\cdot}22}\right)^{1/2}$$

$$\approx \frac{7\sqrt{P}}{r} \quad . \quad . \quad . \quad . \quad . \quad . \quad . \quad . \quad . \quad . \quad (9.13)$$

Since the half-wave dipole is a practical aerial its impedance as a terminating load on the transmission line from which it is fed can be measured. If this is done it is found that the reactive and resistive parts of the impedance vary with aerial length as shown in Figs. 9.11 and 9.12, from which it can be seen that the impedance is also dependent on the diameter of the rods of the dipole. The important regions of the curves are those corresponding to a length of approximately $\lambda/2$, which represents a half-wave dipole. If the length is exactly one half-wavelength the terminal impedance includes a small series inductance. If however the dipole length is made such that the reactance is zero then the input impedance is a pure resistance and can be readily matched to the transmission

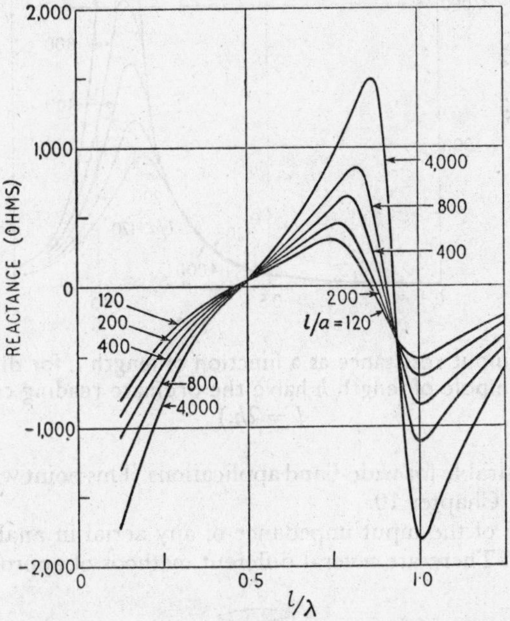

Fig. 9.11. Dipole input reactance as a function of length *l*, for different values of radius *a*. (For a unipole of length *h* halve the ordinate reading corresponding to $l = 2h$.)

line. It will be seen from the figures that the actual length in this case is slightly less than $\lambda/2$, the difference becoming greater as the thickness is increased. At this *resonant length* the current distribution in the aerial is very nearly sinusoidal, and the input impedance is then equal to the radiation resistance, whose value has already been quoted as 73 ohms. Strictly the input resistance will also include the conductor resistance, but this is usually negligible in comparison with the radiation resistance.

The reason for the practical importance of the half-wave dipole operated in the resonance condition is now clear; the input impedance is purely resistive, and is thus readily matched to a transmission line, for which 73 ohms is a convenient value.

Normally an aerial is required to operate over a band of frequencies, and if this band is at all large it is desirable that the change of aerial impedance with frequency should be as small as possible. It will be seen from Figs. 9.11 and 9.12

that in the region of the $\lambda/2$ resonance point the resistance is not significantly dependent on the diameter of the aerial but the reactance is, and increase of the diameter will reduce the rate of change of reactance with frequency. Thus a

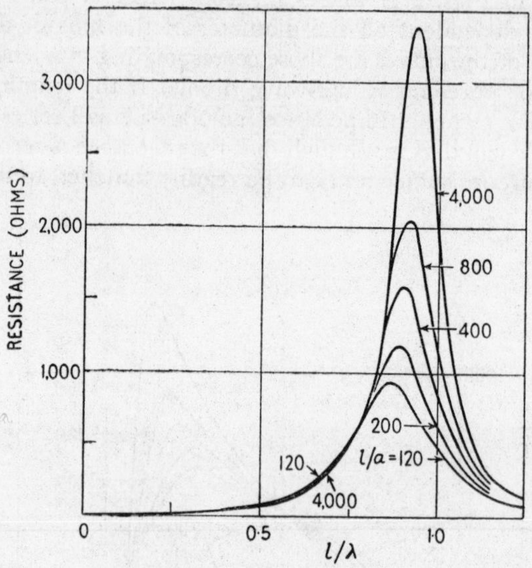

Fig. 9.12. Dipole input resistance as a function of length l, for different values of radius a. (For a unipole of length h halve the ordinate reading corresponding to $l = 2h$.)

thick dipole is desirable for wide-band applications. This point will be considered in more detail in Chapter 10.

The expression of the input impedance of any aerial in analytical form is a difficult problem. There are several different methods of approach, but all are

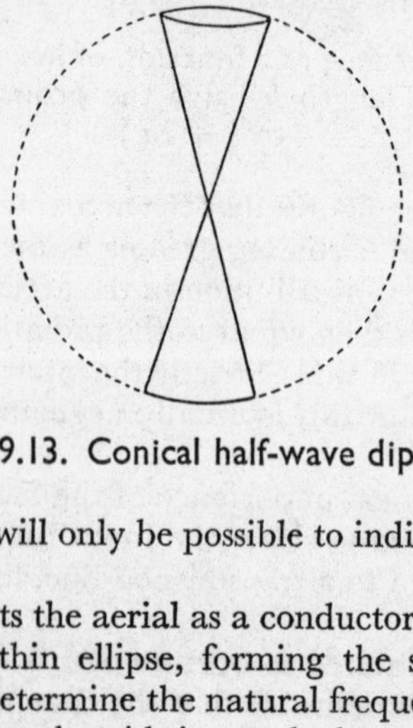

Fig. 9.13. Conical half-wave dipole.

beyond our scope here. It will only be possible to indicate the nature of some of the methods used.

One of the methods treats the aerial as a conductor whose longitudinal cross-section is that of a long thin ellipse, forming the solid known as a prolate spheroid. It is possible to determine the natural frequencies of free oscillation of charges on the surface of a spheroid, in much the same way as the oscillation frequencies of a cavity resonator are found. When the aerial is fed from a transmission line the current flow can be determined in terms of an infinite series of free-oscillation modes, and hence an expression for the input impedance found. The solution cannot be extended to the circular cylinder, which is the common shape of a dipole, so with this method the actual aerial is replaced by an 'equivalent' thin prolate spheroid. Within its limitations the method gives useful results.

In another method the dipole is regarded as two cones of narrow angle set apex to apex as in Fig. 9.13. This can now be treated as a conical waveguide, for which propagation equations can be found in a rather similar manner to those for the cylindrical waveguide.

The curves of Figs. 9.11 and 9.12 are obtained from a more recent method due to Hallén, which enables the cylindrical aerial to be treated directly.

Small Loop Aerial

The next type of aerial to be considered is a small loop. This will be taken in the form of a conductor bent into a rectangle of side l, as in Fig. 9.14 (a), such

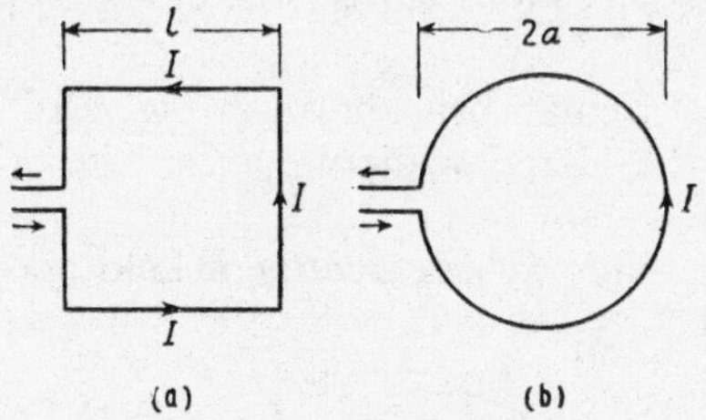

Fig. 9.14. Loop aerials.

that the length l is small in comparison with the free-space wavelength λ of the radiated wave. The current can then be considered constant in amplitude and phase around the loop. The radiation from this can be determined by treating it as a chain of four Hertzian dipoles.

The polar diagram of the loop (shown in Fig. 9.16) is found to be identical with that of a Hertzian dipole whose axis is perpendicular to the plane of the loop. The directions of the field vectors are interchanged, however, the electric field for the loop being always parallel to the plane of the loop, as in Fig. 9.15. It is found also that the radiation pattern is independent of the shape of the loop, provided that the area remains small.

The treatment is given in Appendix 9.4, and shows that the field components at the point P in Fig. 9.15 are directed as shown there, and have amplitudes given by:

$$E_0 = 120\pi H_0 = \frac{120\pi^2 I_0 \sin\theta}{r} \frac{A}{\lambda^2} \quad . \quad . \quad . \quad . \quad (9.14)$$

where A is the area of the loop and I_0 the current amplitude. Although the loop is rectangular the far field is symmetrical about the axis of the loop (i.e., independent of ϕ) and thus the polar diagram in the plane of the loop is a circle.

A more usual form of loop is the circular one of Fig. 9.14 (b). In view of the form of equation (9.14) and the symmetry of the polar diagram it is reasonable to assume that a circular loop of area equal to the square loop will give the same radiated field pattern. An exact analysis confirms this.

From equation (9.14) we find that the amplitude polar diagram, for a square or circular loop, in any plane through the axis of the loop is determined by sin θ,

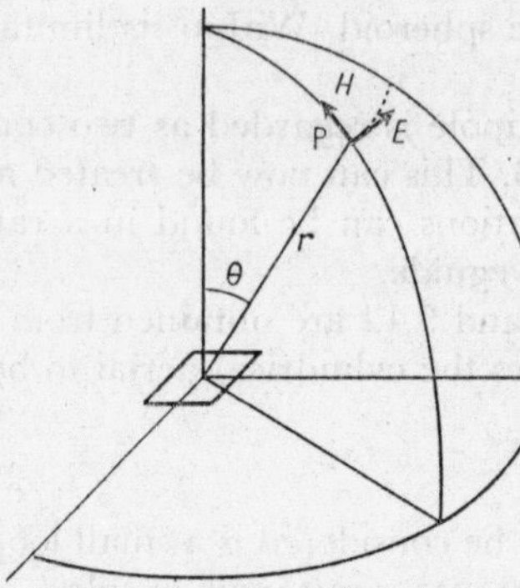

Fig. 9.15. Directions of field vectors of loop aerial.

and therefore takes the circular form shown in Fig. 9.16. This is identical with the polar diagram of the Hertzian dipole, as in Fig. 9.7 (a), having a beam angle of 90°.

The approximations made in this treatment hold good for diameters up to about 1/10 wavelength.

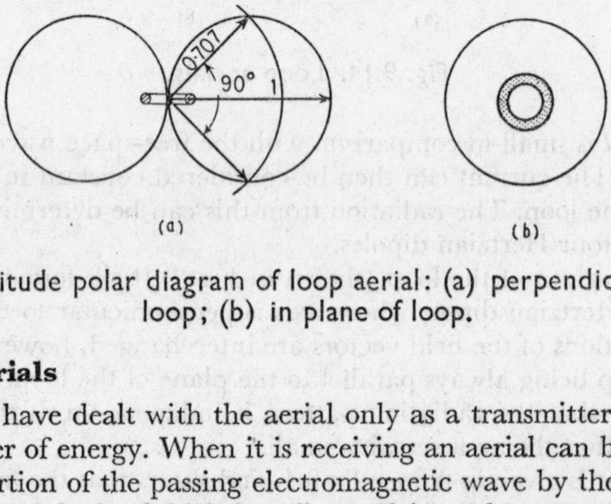

Fig. 9.16. Amplitude polar diagram of loop aerial: (a) perpendicular to plane of loop; (b) in plane of loop.

Receiving Aerials

Thus far we have dealt with the aerial only as a transmitter of energy, and not as a receiver of energy. When it is receiving an aerial can be considered as causing a distortion of the passing electromagnetic wave by the presence of its conducting material, the field being distorted in such a way as to satisfy the boundary conditions at the surface of the conductor. As a result current flows in the conductor, and charges are produced on its surface of such magnitudes as are required by the boundary conditions.

Fortunately the properties of an aerial acting as a receiver are similar in nearly all respects to its corresponding properties as a transmitter. This depends on a theorem known as the Reciprocity Theorem, which may be stated as follows: *If an e.m.f. applied to the terminals of an aerial A produces a current at the terminals of another aerial B, then the same e.m.f. applied to the terminals of aerial B will produce the same current at the terminals of aerial A.*

An immediate consequence of this theorem is that *the polar diagram of a receiving aerial is the same as its polar diagram when used as a transmitting aerial.*

In other words the relative response of an aerial to waves arriving from different directions is the same as the relative field produced in these directions by the aerial used as a transmitter.

Hence the gain of an aerial is also the same whether it is used for transmitting or receiving.

A further deduction from the Reciprocity Theorem is that the impedance of an aerial referred to the terminals is the same for receiving as for transmitting.

The Reciprocity Theorem has wider applications in electrical engineering, but its proof and the deductions from it will not be given in detail here.

With so many reciprocal relationships existing between transmitting and receiving aerials it must be emphasized that the current distributions along an aerial are usually very different in the two cases. A plane wave incident on a receiving aerial induces a current in it. The aerial then acts as a transmitter and re-radiates with a field pattern characteristic of the current distribution.

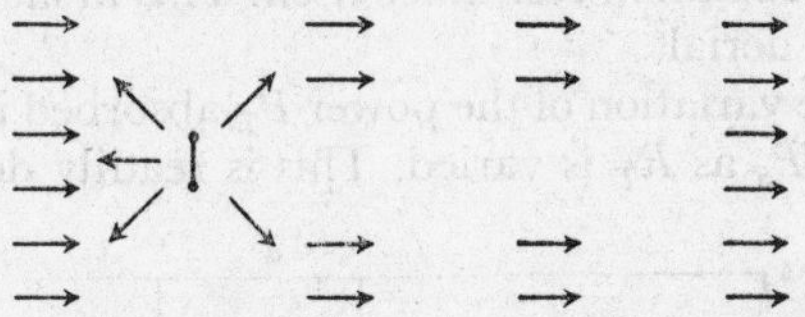

Fig. 9.17. Shadow behind receiving aerial.

The combination of the incident and re-radiated fields gives the polar diagram of the receiving aerial. Theory shows and experiment confirms that the result is such that the receiving and transmitting polar diagrams are the same.

The relationship of the re-radiated or scattered field to the incident field is represented diagrammatically in Fig. 9.17. In the direction to the right of the aerial the phase of the scattered wave is such as partially to cancel the incident wave, so that a shadow region is produced. This is not, of course, a sharply defined geometrical shadow, but does indicate the manner in which energy absorbed by the aerial is removed from the incident beam.

Consider an aerial of terminal impedance equal to its radiation resistance

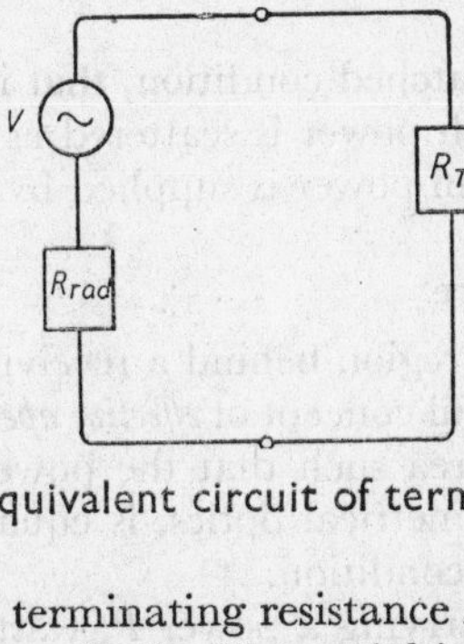

Fig. 9.18. Equivalent circuit of terminated aerial.

R_{rad}, delivering power to a terminating resistance R_T, and let an incident wave induce a voltage V at the terminals. The aerial is equivalent to a generator of r.m.s. voltage V and internal impedance R_{rad}, and the complete arrangement can therefore be represented by the equivalent circuit of Fig. 9.18. The power P_T absorbed in the terminating resistance is:

$$P_T = \frac{V^2 R_T}{(R_T + R_{\text{rad}})^2} \quad . \quad . \quad . \quad . \quad . \quad . \quad . \quad (9.15)$$

and this power is clearly a maximum when $R_T = R_{\text{rad}}$. In this condition the load is matched to the aerial. The power absorbed in the termination is then given by:

$$P_T = \frac{V^2}{4R_{\text{rad}}} \quad . \quad . \quad . \quad . \quad . \quad . \quad . \quad . \quad (9.16)$$

Note that a power P_S given by:

$$P_S = \frac{V^2 R_{\text{rad}}}{(R_T + R_{\text{rad}})^2} \quad . \quad . \quad . \quad . \quad . \quad . \quad . \quad (9.17)$$

is 'dissipated' in the radiation resistance itself. This in fact represents the power re-radiated from the aerial.

Fig. 9.19 shows the variation of the power P_T absorbed in the termination and the scattered power P_S as R_T is varied. This is readily derived from equations

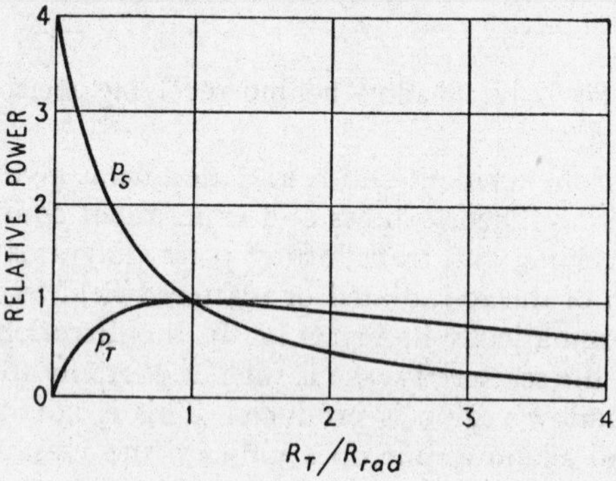

Fig. 9.19. Variation of power absorbed P_S and power scattered P_T as terminating resistance is varied.

(9.15) and (9.17). In the matched condition, that is, when the load equals the radiation resistance, as much power is scattered as is absorbed, and this is the condition in which maximum power is supplied by the aerial to the load.

▶ The Aerial as an Aperture

The concept of a shadow region behind a receiving aerial, introduced in the last section, suggests the useful concept of *effective aperture*. An aerial can be given a fictitious cross-sectional area such that the power absorbed by this area, if calculated according to geometrical optics, is equal to that actually absorbed by the aerial in its matched condition.

Consider a plane wave carrying a power P_a watts per square metre. This is the energy passing per second through a unit area normal to the direction of propagation. Its value in terms of the electric field has been discussed in

Appendix 6.3. If an aperture of area A_e, placed normal to the direction of propagation, is able to absorb all the power which passes through it then the total power P absorbed would be:

$$P = P_a A_e \text{ watts} \qquad (9.18)$$

The maximum power actually delivered by the aerial to the load is given by equation (9.16), and hence, if P_a is known, the effective aperture A_e of the aerial can be calculated. Values of effective aperture for the Hertzian dipole and half-wave dipole are calculated in Appendix 9.5. The values are:

Hertzian dipole:

$$A_e = \frac{3}{8\pi}\lambda^2 = 0{\cdot}12\lambda^2 \qquad (9.19)$$

Half-wave dipole:

$$A_e = \frac{30}{73\pi}\lambda^2 = 0{\cdot}13\lambda^2 \qquad (9.20)$$

These values of A_e neglect any resistive losses and assume that the load is matched to the aerial and the aerial directed to receive the maximum signal.

It will be noted that the effective aperture of a short dipole is independent of its length. A useful picture of the effective aperture of a half-wave dipole is of a rectangular area approximately $\lambda/2$ by $\lambda/4$ as shown in Fig. 9.20.

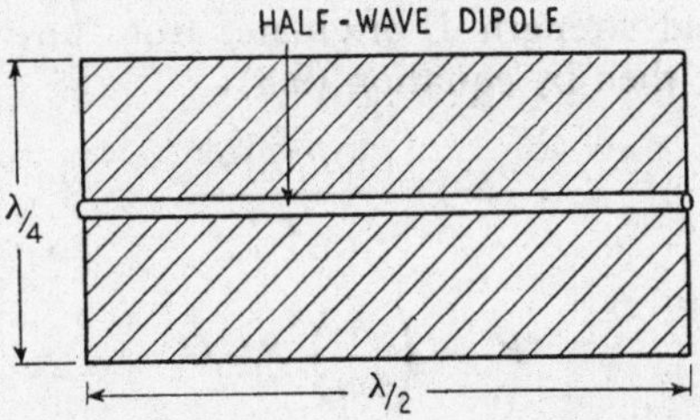

Fig. **9.20. Approximate representation of effective aperture of half-wave dipole.**

Relation of Aperture to Gain

Since gain is a power ratio it follows from the definition that the gain of a receiving aerial is proportional to its effective aperture. By equation (9.7) the gain of a Hertzian dipole relative to an isotropic radiator is 3/2, and therefore by equation (9.19) the effective aperture of an isotropic radiator is:

$$A_e = \frac{1}{4\pi}\lambda^2 \qquad (9.21)$$

It follows that the gain (relative to an isotropic radiator) of any aerial of effective aperture A_e is:

$$G_0 = \frac{4\pi}{\lambda^2}A_e \qquad (9.22)$$

Values of aperture and gain for the three fundamental aerials studied are collected in Table 9.1.

TABLE 9.1

Aerial	Effective aperture	Gain (ratio)	Gain (db)
Isotropic	$\lambda^2/4\pi = 0{\cdot}080\lambda^2$	1	0
Hertzian dipole	$3\lambda^2/8\pi = 0{\cdot}120\lambda^2$	1·5	1·76
Half-wave dipole	$30\lambda^2/73\pi = 0{\cdot}131\lambda^2$	1·64	2·16

Power Received by an Aerial

The concept of equivalent aperture allows us to develop simply an expression for the power P_r received by any aerial situated in a radiated field of r.m.s. electric field strength E. If A_{er} is the effective aperture of the receiving aerial and G_r its gain, then, by equation (9.18):

$$P_r = P_a A_{er} \quad . \quad . \quad . \quad . \quad . \quad . \quad . \quad (9.23)$$

where P_a, the power density, is by Appendix 6.3:

$$P_a = \frac{E^2}{120\pi}$$

Hence by equation (9.21):

$$P_r = \frac{1}{30}\left(\frac{\lambda E}{4\pi}\right)^2 G_r \quad . \quad . \quad . \quad . \quad . \quad . \quad (9.24)$$

If the received field strength E originates from an aerial with a gain G_t radiating a power P_t, then by equation (9.3):

$$E = \frac{(30P_tG_t)^{1/2}}{r}$$

and thus:

$$P_r = \left(\frac{\lambda}{4\pi r}\right)^2 P_tG_tG_r \quad . \quad . \quad . \quad . \quad . \quad . \quad (9.25)$$

If both G_t and G_r are replaced by values of equivalent aperture equation (9.24) becomes:

$$P_r = \frac{1}{\lambda^2 r^2} P_t A_{et} A_{er} \quad . \quad . \quad . \quad . \quad . \quad . \quad (9.26)$$

The expressions (9.25) and (9.26) are important for calculations of received power, but are valid only in free-space. In Chapter 14 it will be seen how different from this actual radio propagation conditions usually are.

Re-Radiation—the Radar Equation

Obstacles lying in the path of a radiated beam will cause partial scattering of the energy. The amount of energy scattered will clearly depend on the shape and size of the obstacle, and in general it will be scattered in all directions. Examples of this scattering by the earth and the atmosphere will be dealt with in the chapter on Wave Propagation. Here we shall deal with the particular case of the energy scattered back, or reflected, along the beam towards the transmitter. It is on this that the operation of radar depends, targets being detected by means of the echo formed by the energy scattered back along the radar beam. The reflecting power of a target is defined as an area, which is known as the *effective echoing area* or *radar cross-section,* and denoted by the symbol σ. This is the area which would have to absorb all the energy incident on it and subsequently re-radiate it uniformly in all directions, in order to produce the same signal at the radar receiver as does the actual target.

Real targets are generally of complex shape, and their effective echoing areas vary in a complicated way with both the wavelength and the angle from which the radar views the target—that is upon the *aspect* of the target. It is seldom possible to calculate σ, which must normally be determined from actual radar measurement, and corresponds only in a general way with the actual target size.

If P_a is the power density reaching the target and P_a' the power density of the echo signal at the receiver, then by the above definition of effective echoing area:

$$P_a' = \frac{\sigma P_a}{4\pi r^2}$$

r being the distance between radar and target. We can therefore replace equation (9.23) by:

$$P_r = P_a' A_{er}$$

$$= P_a \frac{\sigma}{4\pi r^2} A_{er}$$

and hence the equation (9.26) for the received power becomes in the radar case:

$$P_r = \frac{1}{4\pi\lambda^2 r^4} P_t \sigma A_{er} A_{et} \quad . \quad . \quad . \quad (9.27)$$

This is known as the *Radar Equation.* It should be noted that in this case the received power is inversely proportional to the fourth power of the range.

Effective Echoing Area of Targets

As an illustration of how rapidly effective echoing area may alter with wavelength the curve of Fig. 9.21 shows the value of σ for a metal sphere. This is

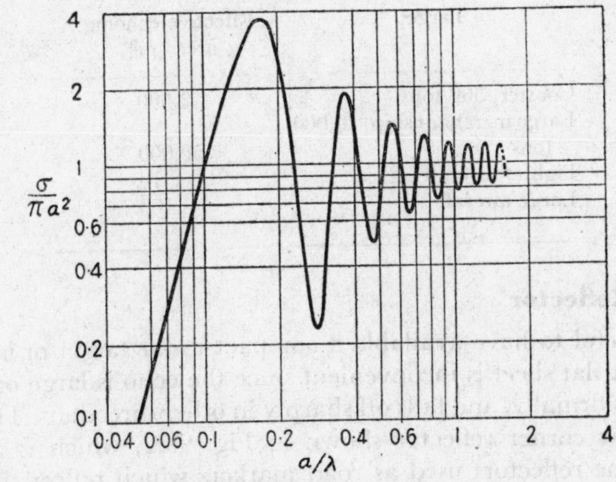

Fig. 9.21. Effective echoing area σ of sphere, radius a, as a function of wavelength.

one of the few cases where calculation is possible, but the result cannot be quoted in simple form. However it can be seen that as the ratio of radius to wavelength increases the effective echoing area approaches the geometrical cross sectional area πa^2. By reason of the symmetry of the sphere σ is independent of aspect.

The theoretical values of echoing area for a number of simple geometrical shapes are given in Table 9.2. In all these, with the obvious exception of the sphere, σ decreases rapidly as the aspect departs from the normal to the surface.

TABLE 9.2

Effective Echoing Area σ of Geometrical Shapes

Object	Aspect	Validity	σ
$\lambda/2$ dipole	parallel to electric vector	—	$0{\cdot}88\lambda^2$
Sphere (radius a)	any	$a \gg \lambda$	πa^2
Flat sheet (area A)	normal to ray	dimensions $\gg \lambda$	$\dfrac{4\pi A^2}{\lambda^2}$
Cylinder (length l, radius a)	axis normal to ray	dimensions $\gg \lambda$	$\dfrac{2\pi a l^2}{\lambda}$

Such simple shapes seldom occur in practice, and the echo received from a ship or an aircraft, for example, is the integrated effect of a large number of waves scattered from the different parts of the structure. It is therefore a very sensitive function of aspect.

The figures in Table 9.3 gives a rough indication of the order of the effective echoing area of targets at centimetre wavelengths.

TABLE 9.3

Effective Echoing Area of Targets

Target	Effective echoing area (m^2)
Coaster, 500 tons	2,500
Large merchant ship, 10,000 tons	50,000
Fighter aircraft	10
Large aircraft	100

The Corner Reflector

It is often useful to have available a compact radar target of large effective echoing area. A flat sheet is inconvenient since the echo is large only when the sheet is viewed normally, and falls off sharply in other directions. The best shape is the triangular corner reflector shown in Fig. 9.22, which is a large scale equivalent of the reflectors used as road markers which reflect the light from motor-car headlamps. The fundamental optical property of the corner reflector is that, within certain limits of inclination, a ray entering the corner is reflected back in exactly the opposite direction, as in Fig. 9.22.

The optical law does not hold precisely at radio wavelengths, since they are comparable in dimensions with the size of the reflector, and scattering occurs

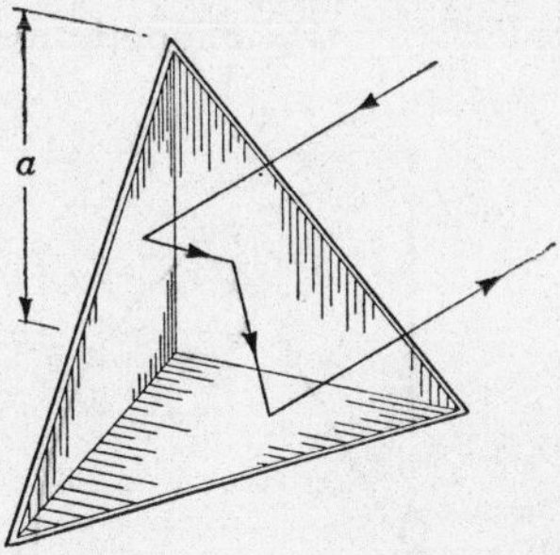

Fig. 9.22. Triangular corner reflector.

as with all other shapes. It can be calculated that a corner reflector of side a has a maximum effective echoing area given by

$$\sigma_{\max} = \frac{4}{3}\frac{\pi a^4}{\lambda^2} \quad . \quad . \quad . \quad . \quad . \quad . \quad . \quad . \quad (9.28)$$

This maximum occurs when the ray is incident at the same angle on all three faces (this angle may be shown to be 35°), but it is still large for directions over most of the octant for which rays can enter the corner.

All directions can be covered by making a cluster of eight such corners, as shown in Fig. 9.23.

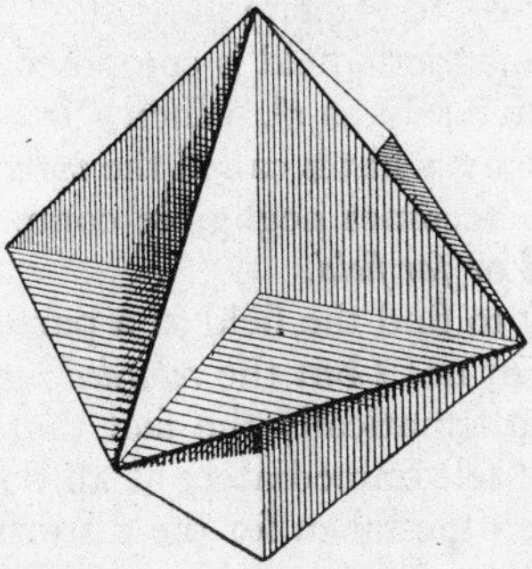

Fig. 9.23. Octahedral cluster of corner reflectors.

APPENDIX 9.1

Radiation from a Hertzian Dipole

The calculation of the field radiated from even such a simple structure as a Hertzian dipole is a complicated procedure, and the detailed analysis is beyond our scope here. We can, however, discuss the form of the result.

Let the dipole be a thin conductor of length l, carrying a uniform alternating current which, in this case, is most conveniently represented in its complex form $I_0\varepsilon^{j\omega t}$. Its radiation field at a distance r is conveniently expressed in terms of the spherical co-ordinate system (r, θ, ϕ) of Fig. 9.24. At the point P the electric field vector can be expressed in terms of the three mutually-perpendicular components E_r, E_θ, E_ϕ, and similarly for the magnetic-field components H_r, H_θ, H_ϕ.

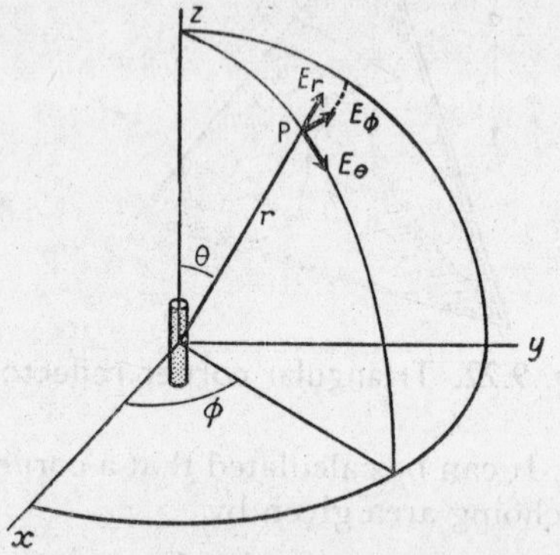

Fig. 9.24. Co-ordinate system for Hertzian dipole.

It can be shown that $H_r = H_\theta = 0$, and that the expression for H_ϕ in free space is:

$$H_\phi = \frac{I_0 l \sin\theta\, \varepsilon^{j\omega[t]}}{4\pi}\left(\frac{j\omega}{cr} + \frac{1}{r^2}\right) \quad . \quad . \quad . \quad . \quad . \quad (9.29)$$

where $[t] = t - r/c$, and c is the velocity of light.

It will be seen that the magnetic field is composed of two terms, one varying inversely as r, the other inversely as r^2. When r is small the second term will predominate, and it represents what is called the *induction field* or *near field.* When r is large the second term becomes negligible compared with the first, which represents the *radiation field* or *far field.*

In using equation (9.29) to find the field at a particular time t, one must use in the exponential argument not t but the *retarded time* $t - r/c$, usually denoted by $[t]$. This represents mathematically the fact that the effect of a change in current at the source is not felt immediately at all points in space, but after an interval determined by the time taken for the disturbance, travelling outwards with the velocity of light, to reach the observer.

If we consider only the radiation field, which is the effective one in radio communication, equation (9.29) reduces to

$$H_\phi = \frac{jI_0 l \sin\theta\, \varepsilon^{j\omega[t]}}{2\lambda r} \quad . \quad . \quad . \quad . \quad . \quad . \quad (9.30)$$

where ω has now been expressed in terms of the wavelength λ.

In the general case the electric field is more complex than the magnetic field, but for the radiation field it reduces also to a single component E_θ (E_r and E_ϕ being zero) given by:

$$E_\theta = \frac{j60\pi I_0 l \sin\theta\, \varepsilon^{j\omega[t]}}{\lambda r} \quad . \quad . \quad . \quad . \quad . \quad . \quad (9.31)$$

Using the notation $[I]$ to represent a useful fiction known as the *retarded current* $I_0 \varepsilon^{j\omega[t]}$ we can write the above equations compactly as :

$$H_\phi = \frac{j[I]l \sin \theta}{2\lambda r} \quad . \quad . \quad . \quad . \quad . \quad . \quad . \quad (9.32)$$

$$E_\phi = \frac{j60\pi[I]l \sin \theta}{\lambda r} \quad . \quad . \quad . \quad . \quad . \quad . \quad . \quad (9.33)$$

H_ϕ and E_θ are mutually perpendicular and both are perpendicular to the direction of r. The ratio E_θ/H_ϕ gives the value:

$$\frac{E_\theta}{H_\phi} = 120\pi \text{ ohms} \quad . \quad . \quad . \quad . \quad . \quad . \quad . \quad (9.34)$$

This ratio gives the wave impedance at the point P, and it will be seen that it is equal to the intrinsic impedance of a plane wave in free space as dealt with in Chapter 5. At P the field components are tangential to the surface of the sphere, and thus in the vicinity of a point such as P the radiated wave in the far field can be regarded as a plane wave which has travelled in a straight line from the source with a velocity c.

Since the expressions are independent of ϕ the dipole axis is an axis of symmetry of the field.

APPENDIX 9.2

Power Radiated from a Hertzian Dipole

To find the total power radiated from a Hertzian dipole use the Poynting theorem equation (6.33) to get the power flowing through a small element of area and integrate over the surface of a sphere. The element of area on a sphere as in Fig. 9.25 is $r\,d\theta . r \sin \theta \, d\phi$, and thus the instantaneous value of the total radiated power is:

$$P_{\text{inst}} = \int_0^\pi \int_0^{2\pi} E_\theta H_\phi r^2 \sin \theta \, d\theta d\phi \quad . \quad . \quad . \quad . \quad (9.35)$$

By means of equations (9.31) and (9.34) we can write:

$$120\pi H_\phi = E_\theta = jE_{\text{max}} \sin \theta \; \varepsilon^{j\omega[t]} \quad . \quad . \quad . \quad . \quad (9.36)$$

where E_{max} is the electric-field amplitude in the direction of maximum radiation. The expression for the mean power P then becomes:

$$P = \tfrac{1}{2}\frac{E_{\text{max}}{}^2}{120\pi} 2\pi r^2 \int_0^\pi \sin^3 \theta \, d\theta$$

$$= \frac{E_{\text{max}}{}^2 r^2}{90} \quad . \quad . \quad . \quad . \quad . \quad . \quad . \quad . \quad (9.37)$$

Hence

$$E_{\text{max}} = \frac{(90P)^{1/2}}{r} \quad . \quad . \quad . \quad . \quad . \quad . \quad . \quad (9.38)$$

Substituting in equation (9.37) for E_{max} from equations (9.36) and (9.31) we get the value of radiated power in terms of the peak value I_0 of the aerial current:

$$P = 40\pi^2 I_0^2 (l/\lambda)^2 \quad \ldots \ldots \quad (9.39)$$

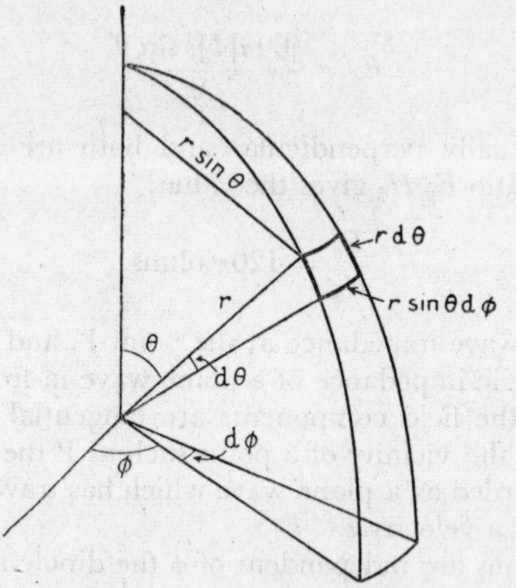

Fig. 9.25. Element of surface area on sphere.

APPENDIX 9.3

Half-Wave Dipole

Consider a thin linear aerial of length l equal to $\lambda/2$ carrying a sinusoidal current distribution such that the current I at a distance z from the centre is given by $I = I_0 \cos(2\pi z/\lambda)\varepsilon^{j\omega t}$. The aerial can be considered as composed of a

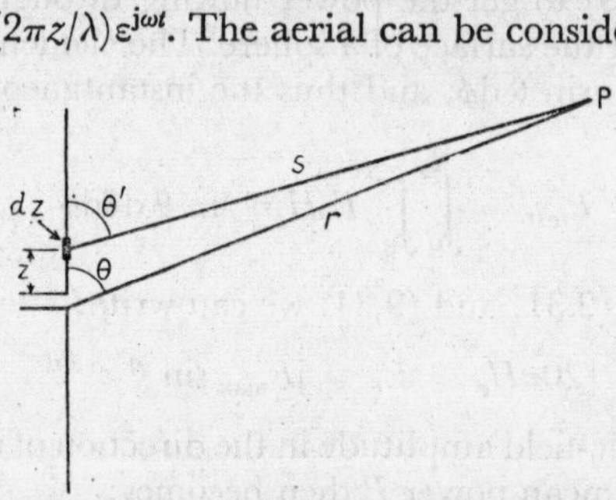

Fig. 9.26. Representation of half-wave dipole.

chain of Hertzian dipoles each of length dz and the radiated field is then an integral of the contributions of these Hertzian dipoles.

Using the notation of Fig. 9.26 and the expression (9.31) we get for the electric field in the far zone:

$$E_\theta = \int_{-\lambda/4}^{\lambda/4} \frac{j60\pi I_0 \cos(2\pi z/\lambda) \sin\theta' \varepsilon^{j\omega(t-s/c)}}{\lambda s} dz$$

Because the distance is large it is possible to make some simplifying approximations in this integral. We can put $\theta = \theta'$, and $s = r$ in the denominator. For the s in the exponential, however, small changes in s may cause important changes in phase, so we write approximately, $s = r - z \cos \theta$. The integral then reduces to:

$$E_\theta = \frac{j60\pi I_0 \sin \theta}{\lambda r} \int_{-\lambda/4}^{\lambda/4} \cos \frac{2\pi z}{\lambda} \exp \left\{ j\omega \left(t - \frac{r - z \cos \theta}{c} \right) \right\} dz$$

which becomes, after a somewhat lengthy but straightforward evaluation:

$$E_\theta = \frac{j60 I_0 \varepsilon^{j\omega[t]}}{r} \cdot \frac{\cos \{(\pi/2) \cos \theta\}}{\sin \theta} \quad . \quad . \quad . \quad . \quad (9.40)$$

where $[t]$ is the retarded time $t - r/c$, referred to the centre of the dipole.

The factor $\cos \{(\pi/2) \cos \theta\}/\sin \theta$ determines the polar diagram in the plane of the dipole.

As before H_ϕ has a value such that $E_\theta/H_\phi = 120\pi$.

From equation (9.40) we can calculate the radiated power by means of equation (9.35) and get:

$$P = 30 I_0^2 \int_0^\pi \frac{\cos^2 \{(\pi/2) \cos \theta\}}{\sin \theta} d\theta \quad . \quad . \quad . \quad . \quad (9.41)$$

To get the radiation resistance equate the power to $\frac{1}{2} I_0^2 R_{\text{rad}}$, and hence find:

$$R_{\text{rad}} = 60 \int_0^\pi \frac{\cos^2 \{(\pi/2) \cos \theta\}}{\sin \theta} d\theta \quad . \quad . \quad . \quad . \quad (9.42)$$

This integral cannot be evaluated in terms of common functions. Numerical evaluation gives its value as:

$$R_{\text{rad}} = 60 \times 1{\cdot}22 = 73 \text{ ohms} \quad . \quad . \quad . \quad . \quad . \quad (9.43)$$

Note that this value of radiation resistance is referred to the current at the centre terminals.

APPENDIX 9.4

Radiation from Rectangular Loop

For the radiation pattern of the group of four Hertzian dipoles forming the rectangular loop of Fig. 9.27 we shall consider the far field in the xy-plane (i.e., with $\theta = 90°$).

Dipoles 2 and 4 are symmetrically placed on either side of the xy-plane and the currents in them are in opposite phase. Their effects therefore cancel out at all points in the xy-plane. Dipoles 1 and 3 will produce field components E_θ and H_ϕ in this plane. The cross-section of the loop in the xy-plane is shown in Fig. 9.28. The difference in path length between the two dipoles measured from a distant point is AC $= l \sin \phi$, and hence the phase difference ψ is $(2\pi l/\lambda) \sin \phi$. Thus the electric field at the distant point is given by:

$$E_\theta = - E_{\theta 0} \varepsilon^{j\psi/2} + E_{\theta 0} \varepsilon^{-j\psi/2}$$

$$= - 2j E_{\theta 0} \sin \left(\frac{\pi l}{\lambda} \sin \phi \right),$$

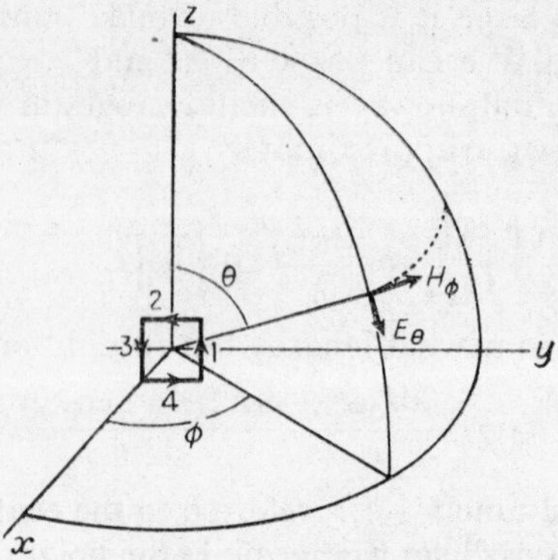

Fig. 9.27. Co-ordinate system for loop aerial.

where $E_{\theta 0}$ is the field which would be produced by a parallel dipole situated at the origin 0.

Where $l \ll \lambda$ this can be written to a first approximation as:

$$E_\theta = -2jE_{\theta 0}\frac{\pi l}{\lambda}\sin\phi$$

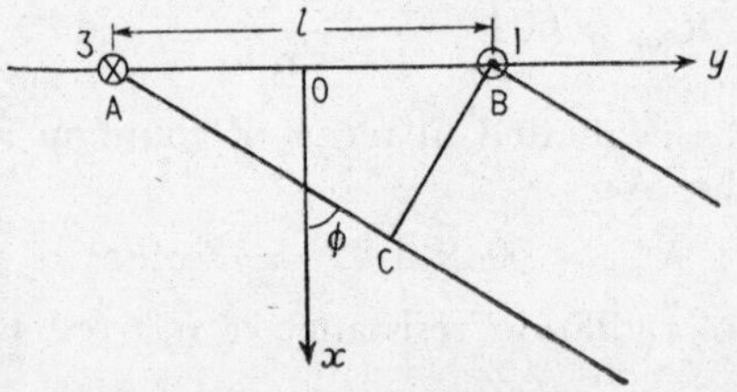

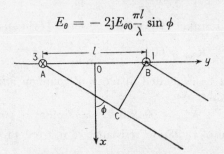

Fig. 9.28. The cross-section of a loop in the *xy*-plane is represented by I and 3.

For $E_{\theta 0}$ we substitute equation (9.33), putting $\theta = 90°$, and get:

$$E_\theta = \frac{120\pi^2[I]\sin\phi}{r}\frac{l^2}{\lambda^2}$$

$$= \frac{120\pi^2[I]\sin\phi}{r}\frac{A}{\lambda^2} \quad (9.44)$$

where A is the area of the loop.

The only magnetic field component is H_ϕ, and is given as before by $H_\phi = E_\theta/120\pi$.

Although we have dealt with the field in one plane only it can be shown that this far field is the same in any plane through the z-axis and is thus symmetrical about the axis of the loop.

Thus by exactly the same method as in Appendix 9.2 the total radiated power from the loop can be calculated as:

$$W = 160\pi^4 I_0^2 (A/\lambda^2)^2 \quad (9.45)$$

from which can be deduced the value of the radiation resistance of the loop:

$$R_{\text{rad}} = 320\pi^4 (A/\lambda^2)^2 \quad (9.46)$$

APPENDIX 9.5

Effective Aperture

To find the effective aperture of an aerial substitute in equation (9.18) the value of P given by equation (9.16), and $P_a = E^2/120\pi$, as derived in Appendix 6.3, E being the r.m.s. value of the electric field in the incident plane wave. Thus:

$$\frac{V^2}{4R_{\text{rad}}} = \frac{E^2 A_e}{120\pi} \quad . \quad . \quad . \quad . \quad . \quad . \quad . \quad . \quad (9.47)$$

For a Hertzian dipole, since the current distribution is uniform, the effective value of the induced voltage V is the product of the effective electric field at the dipole and its length, so that $V = El$. Substituting this and the value in equation (9.9) for R_{rad} we get:

$$A_e = \frac{3}{8\pi}\lambda^2 \quad . \quad . \quad . \quad . \quad . \quad . \quad . \quad . \quad (9.48)$$

For a half-wave dipole with a current distribution $I_0 \cos (2\pi z/\lambda)$ we assume that the voltage induced in an infinitesimal element is proportional to the current in the element, and thus:

$$V = \int_{-\lambda/4}^{\lambda/4} E \cos \frac{2\pi z}{\lambda}\, dz$$

$$= \frac{E\lambda}{\pi}$$

With the radiation resistance taken as 73 ohms the effective aperture becomes:

$$A_e = \frac{30}{73\pi}\lambda^2 \quad . \quad . \quad . \quad . \quad . \quad . \quad . \quad . \quad (9.49)$$

CHAPTER 10

Basic Theory of Aerial Elements and Arrays

Introduction

Before the principles of radiation established in the previous chapter can be applied to practical aerials of all frequencies and types, it is necessary to consider a number of fundamental factors concerning single aerial elements and groups or arrays of such elements. The method followed will be a study of various arrangements of two aerial elements, and the procedures developed will be extended to arrays of many unit aerials. The approach is mainly from the viewpoint of transmitting aerials, but it will be shown at the end of the chapter that the results are easily applied to receiving aerials.

In this chapter we shall be mostly concerned with polar diagrams and aerial gain. However, the many other characteristics of aerials such as input impedance, radiation resistance and change of properties with frequency, which are all closely related, must be kept in mind.

Since the radiation from an aerial flows outwards in all directions, a complete description of the intensity in any direction involves solid geometry. However, sufficient accuracy is usually obtained by considering the polar diagrams of field intensity or power density in two or more suitably chosen planes. In what follows polar diagrams representing electric field intensity will be employed. If the field strength in a direction which does not fall in one of these planes is required, it can usually be determined by a suitable combination of the known field strength in the chosen planes.

A further complication is that sometimes the electric field vector lies in the plane of the polar diagram and sometimes it is at right angles to that plane. To avoid any confusion on this account the direction of the field vector will be shown when it lies in the plane of the polar diagram. When it is at right angles to the plane it will be shown as a circle with a cross.

For convenience, in referring to the planes associated with dipoles the plane through the centre of the dipole, but at right angles to it, is called the equatorial plane, while planes containing the dipole are meridian planes. The field strength at a distance r from a particular aerial in the plane where the polar diagram is of interest may be expressed as the product of three factors:

(a) The field strength on the equatorial plane (at right angles to the plane) at a distance r from a half-wave dipole radiating a power P. From equation (9.13) the r.m.s. field strength is given approximately by:

$$E = \frac{7\sqrt{P}}{r} \text{ volts per metre}$$

(Alternatively the formula $E = 60I_0/r$ may be used where I_0 is the r.m.s. value of the input current.)

(b) A field-strength gain factor which gives the field strength gain in the direction of maximum radiation in the plane concerned.

(c) A polar-diagram factor, which is a trigonometric function of θ the angle made by the axis of a radiating element or array with the direction in which the field strength is required. This factor must be normalized to have a maximum value of unity.

Polar diagrams will be plotted as the product of the last two factors; i.e., they are diagrams of field-strength gain (or loss) relative to the maximum field strength from a half-wave dipole radiating the same power.

In this chapter we shall be mainly concerned with idealized aerials. The manner in which practical aerials deviate from the ideal will be treated in Chapter 11.

Half-wave Dipole as the Basic Radiating Element

The half-wave dipole is the basic radiating element of many types of aerial array. It is, therefore, necessary to have a full knowledge of its properties, not only at its resonant frequency but also at frequencies slightly removed from resonance. Such dipoles are usually constructed from stranded copper wire or tubing, depending upon the wavelength and physical dimensions.

In Chapter 9 the polar diagram and the impedance of a half-wave dipole were deduced for the actual frequency of resonance. An appreciation of the

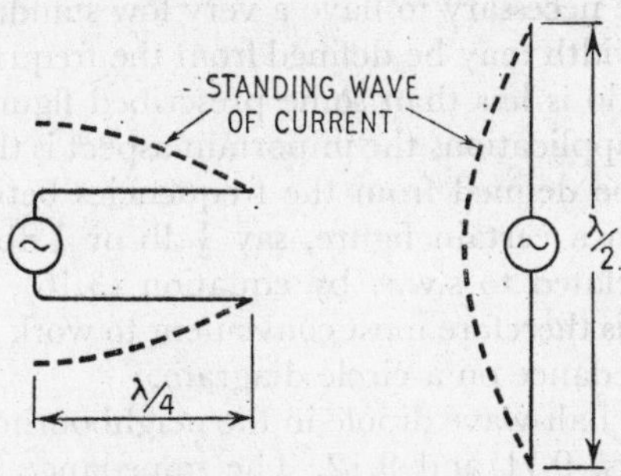

Fig. 10.1. Comparison of the quarter-wave open-circuited line and the half-wave dipole.

properties at frequencies slightly away from resonance, can be obtained by analogy with transmission-line theory. In Chapter 3 the standing waves which occur on an open-circuited twin-conductor line were described. Very similar standing waves occur if the two conductors are separated at the open ends. In the limit, when each conductor has turned through a right angle, the conductors are collinear. If we had started with a quarter-wave line, a half-wave dipole would have resulted. The current distributions for these two cases are compared in Fig. 10.1.

It may be objected that during the opening out process the capacitance per unit length would no longer be uniform so that the current distribution would change. This is perfectly true but, in fact, the tapering off of capacitance per unit length is quite small, and the ends of the conductors will have capacitance.

Furthermore, as the wires are opened the loss of power due to radiation will modify the current distribution. The net effect, however, is that the current distribution of the half-wave dipole remains very close to a sinusoid, as assumed in Chapter 9.

During the opening out process there will be a gradual increase in power lost due to radiation, so that, although the reactance at the input terminals will vary in much the same manner as the corresponding transmission line, there will be an appreciable resistive term to account for these losses. A comparison of Figs. 3.11 and 9.11 demonstrates the general similarity of the reactance versus length curves. (In Fig. 3.11 the origin is on the right, and in Fig. 9.11 a half-wave dipole corresponds to a quarter-wave line.) It should also be noted that for lines of low characteristic impedance the reactance in the neighbourhood of a quarter wavelength is low, while in the case of dipole aerials near a half wavelength the reactance is low for small values of length to radius ratio; i.e., for thick aerials.

The equivalent circuit for this situation was shown in Chapter 3 to be a series inductor and capacitor; in this case a series resistance must be added to account for the radiation, although the value of this resistance changes with frequency. From the above argument it can be concluded that thin wires cut as a half-wave dipole will have a high reactance to resistance ratio or a high Q, while thick tube dipoles will have a lower Q. From this it follows that single-wire aerials have a narrower bandwidth than thick aerials.

There is no generally accepted definition for the bandwidth of an aerial, because different types of signal require different bandwidths. For some applications it may be necessary to have a very low standing-wave ratio on the feeder, and the bandwidth may be defined from the frequencies between which the standing-wave ratio is less than some prescribed figure; often the figure is 1·1 or 1·2. For other applications the important aspect is the mismatch loss, and the bandwidth may be defined from the frequencies between which the mismatch loss is less than a certain figure, say $\frac{1}{2}$ db or 1 db. However, the mismatch loss may be related to s.w.r. by equation (3.16), typical values being given in Table 3.1. It is therefore most convenient to work in terms of s.w.r. and to plot the aerial impedance on a circle diagram.

The impedance of a half-wave dipole in the neighbourhood of resonance may be obtained from Figs. 9.11 and 9.12. The impedance is replotted in circle diagram form in Fig. 10.2 for two dipoles, one a thick dipole with a ratio of length to radius of cross-section l/a of 120, and the other a thin dipole (e.g. one constructed from a single wire) for which l/a is 4,000. The impedances at points removed $\pm$ 5% and $\pm$ 10% from the resonance frequency are marked by points on the curves.

Assuming that the feeder has an impedance of 70 ohms the standing-wave circles for say 1·2, 2 and 3 may be drawn in as shown. It will be observed that the thin dipole has an impedance of about 70 ohms at resonance, and that resonance takes place when the length is a few per cent less than a half wavelength. The thick dipole has an impedance at resonance which is a little lower than 70 ohms, so that for small standing-wave ratios it would be necessary to use a cable of lower impedance. Thus for a standing-wave ratio of 1·2, the thin dipole would have a bandwidth of about $\pm \frac{3}{4}$%, while the thick dipole, if matched to about 65 ohms, would have a bandwidth of about $\pm 1\frac{1}{2}$%. For a standing-wave ratio of 2 and a feeder of about 70 ohms, corresponding to a mismatch loss of $\frac{1}{2}$ db, the following general deductions can be made. The thin dipole has a bandwidth of about $\pm 2\frac{1}{2}\%$, while the thick dipole has a bandwidth of about $\pm 5\%$. If a somewhat larger s.w.r. of 3 is taken as the criterion, the figures are roughly $\pm 5\%$ and $\pm 10\%$ respectively. Thus the thick dipole has about twice the bandwidth of the thin dipole. It will be noted that the length for self-resonance for a thick dipole is a little shorter again than for the thin dipole. This is due to the capacitance of the ends of the dipole. Owing to conductor loss and radiation, the actual velocity of a wave along a conductor is always a little less than the free-space velocity. The geometry of the feed

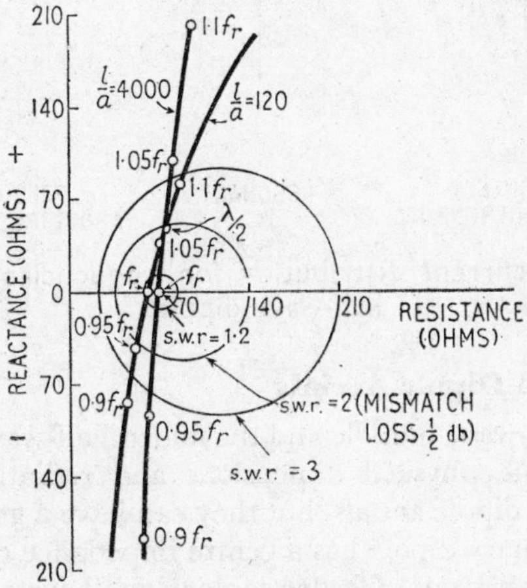

Fig. 10.2. Impedance of half-wave dipoles in neighbourhood of resonance.

point can also affect the aerial input impedance to a small extent. The actual physical length at which a nominal half-wave dipole comes into tune must therefore be found by experiment, but it always turns out to be a few per cent shorter than a half wavelength in free space.

Another definition that is sometimes used for the bandwidth of a half-wave aerial is the frequency range over which the magnitude of the reactance falls within the limits of $\pm$ 73 ohms. The ratio of the mid-band frequency to this total bandwidth may be taken to be roughly the Q of the aerial.

It is not always convenient to use thick dipoles. In such cases the same effect can be obtained by arranging a number of wires axially on the surface of a cylinder so as to form a cylindrical cage. The effective radius of the cage is somewhat less than the actual radius by a factor which depends upon the number and size of the wires. The greater the number of wires in the cage the more nearly does the cage approach a metallic cylinder. A more detailed discussion of wideband dipoles is given in Chapter 12.

The effect on the radiation pattern due to frequency changes of a few per cent is generally negligible. The current distribution will change slightly in a manner which can be appreciated from Fig. 10.3.

The shorter the aerial becomes the more nearly does the current distribution approximate to the triangular form. For lengths above the resonant length the dipole input current falls or the radiation resistance increases. The properties of longer dipoles can be appreciated more readily after a study of linear arrays.

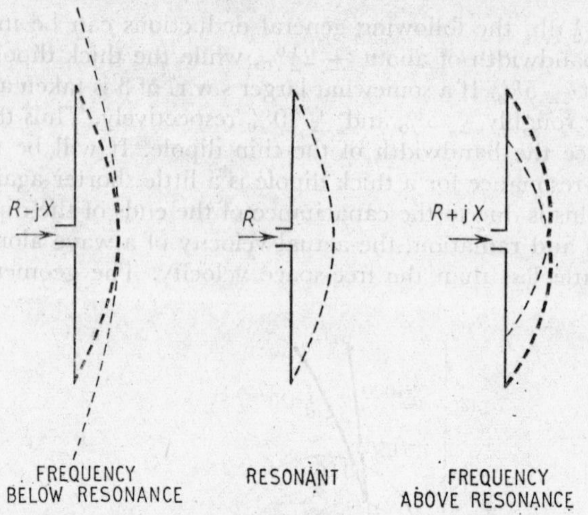

Fig. 10.3. Change of current distribution for frequencies near resonance of a half-wave dipole.

Folded Unipole and Dipole Aerials

The folded quarter-wave unipole and the folded half-wave dipole aerials have substantially the same physical dimensions and radiation diagrams as the ordinary unipole and dipole aerials, but they can have a good deal higher input impedance. The ordinary dipole has a centre impedance of about 73 ohms and is a good match to most kinds of feeder cable which have a solid dielectric. Both coaxial cable and twin-wire feeder of the kind having polyethylene dielectric usually have an impedance of 70–80 ohms.

When the radiation characteristics of a dipole are suitable, therefore, it is usually employed because no special matching device is needed to couple it to the feeder. The unipole, however, is not often used in its simple form because its impedance, 36·5 ohms, is too low to match a feeder directly.

When either type of aerial is used with parasitic elements, in the manner described later in this chapter, the centre impedance is altered and may be considerably less than its normal value. A dipole, for instance, may then have an impedance of 10–20 ohms only. This makes matching between the aerial and its feeder difficult and it is often desirable to replace the simple unipole or dipole by an arrangement having a higher impedance. The folded elements provide this higher impedance and, in their most usual form, they have an impedance of four times their simple counterparts. They also have some mechanical advantages, and they have a greater bandwidth than simple elements.

In its simplest form, the folded quarter-wave unipole is a length of tubing which is bent to form two limbs, each a quarter-wavelength long, as shown in Fig. 10.4 (a). One end of one limb is earthed and the other is fed from the centre conductor of a coaxial cable, the outer of which is earthed. The cable preferably approaches the aerial underneath the earth plane. The aerial can be depicted diagrammatically as in (b), where the generator V represents the voltage supplied by the feeder.

Suppose now that we modify this to the form (c) in which three generators each of $V/2$ are included. It can be seen that this is equivalent to (b); generators

1 and 2 are in the same phase and, acting together, still provide the voltage V to drive the right-hand limb of the aerial. Generators 1 and 3 are in antiphase and so add to zero; the conditions are thus exactly the same as if the right-hand limb were earthed directly.

Generators 2 and 3 act in phase around the closed loop in Fig. 10.4 (c). However, this loop is a quarter-wave line short-circuited at its far end, the top of the aerial. It, therefore, has a very high impedance at the generator end, and the current is very small.

Now consider generator 1 alone. It feeds in parallel the two limbs of the aerial which can, therefore, be regarded from the point of view of this generator as an

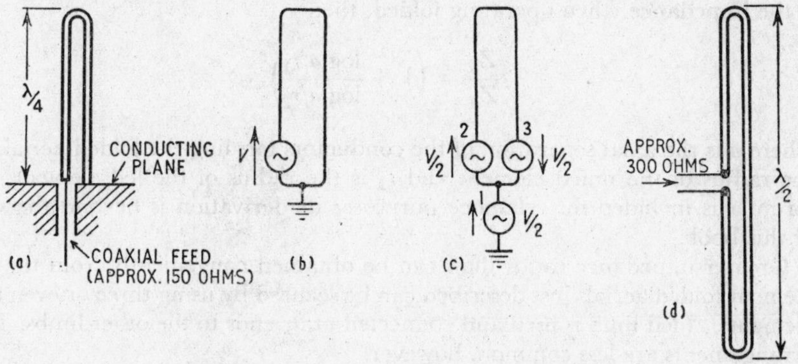

Fig. 10.4. (a), (b) and (c) the folded quarter-wave unipole; (d) the folded half-wave dipole.

ordinary simple unipole fed from a generator of $V/2$ and with an impedance of 36·5 ohms. The total aerial current is thus $(V/2)/36{\cdot}5$ and, by symmetry, is divided equally between the two limbs.

The current I in one limb, say the left-hand one, is therefore one-half the total or:

$$I = \frac{V}{4 \times 36{\cdot}5}$$

Now this current is the input current to the aerial, for it is the current flowing in the fed limb, and so the input impedance is:

$$Z = \frac{V}{I} = 4 \times 3{\cdot}65 = 146 \text{ ohms}$$

or approximately 150 ohms.

A folded dipole, Fig. 10.4 (d), can be regarded as two unipoles end to end, and by similar reasoning its centre impedance turns out to be:

$$Z = 4 \times 73 = 292 \quad . \quad . \quad . \quad . \quad . \quad (10.1)$$

or approximately 300 ohms.

This fourfold increase of impedance obtained by folding the aerial is obtained only when both conductors have the same diameter. A greater ratio can be obtained by making the unfed limb of greater diameter than the fed or a smaller ratio by making it smaller than the fed limb.

The impedance ratio is unaffected by the spacing of the limbs within normal limits, when both are of the same diameter. In practice, when the aerial is built from tubing, it is common to space the limbs about four times the tube diameter, but, when the aerial is constructed from parallel wires, the spacing is relatively much greater, being usually about $\lambda/50$.

The impedance ratio obtained holds not only for the unipole and dipole as discussed here but also for the aerials when used in conjunction with parasitic elements. The folding is then particularly valuable.

▶ If Z_A is the impedance of a dipole operating in the unfolded manner and if Z is the impedance when operating folded, then

$$\frac{Z_F}{Z_A} = \left(1 + \frac{\log a/r_1}{\log a/r_2}\right)^2$$

where a is the axial separation of the conductors forming the folded aerial, r_1 is the radius of the unfed element and r_2 is the radius of the fed element. This formula is included for reference purposes; its derivation is beyond the scope of this book. ◀

Greater impedance ratios than can be obtained conveniently from the two-element folded aerials just described can be secured by using three or even more elements. A fed limb is used and connected at its ends to the other limbs. These arrangements are less common, however.

The bandwidth of folded elements is usually at least twice that of unfolded elements using similar sized tubing. This is partly a consequence of the greater effective radius of two tubes in parallel, but it is mainly due to the susceptance compensation provided by the folding. Reverting to Fig. 10.4 (a), the impedance of the short-circuited quarter-wave line provided by the bent conductor is in shunt with the aerial input impedance. At frequencies just off resonance this provides the correct type of compensation for the aerial reactance. At frequencies just below resonance the aerial is capacitive while the shunting impedance is inductive. Just above resonance these reactances both change sign. Similar remarks apply for folded dipoles.

The mechanical advantages of these aerials are obvious when aerials made of tubing are considered.

Shunt-Fed Dipoles

In a simple half-wave dipole the feed voltage at the centre is effectively in series with the aerial. Although the 73-ohm impedance of such an aerial is suitable for feeding by means of cable of similar impedance, it is too low for feeding by open-wire lines. Another device for making the aerial present a higher impedance is the shunt method of excitation. This is illustrated in Fig. 10.5 (a). The aerial dipole itself is unbroken, but it is fed with a shunt voltage at points CD.

Its method of operation can best be understood by analogy with the tapped resonant line shown in Fig. 4.8. There it was shown that the reactance at the tapping point was zero and that the tapping impedance increased as the distance from the short-circuit was increased. The balanced line equivalent of Fig. 4.8 is shown in Fig. 10.5 (b). The reactances X_A and X_B are again equal and opposite and the impedance at the tapping is similar to a parallel resonant circuit. If such a line is opened out to make a half-wave dipole we get Fig. 10.5 (a). The radiation loss causes the equivalent parallel circuit to be rather lossy. Values of impedance can be found to suit most transmission lines. If CD is about one-eighth of a wavelength the impedance is about 600 ohms. This method of matching is sometimes called the delta match.

The quarter wave monopole version of this device is shown in Fig. 10.5 (c).

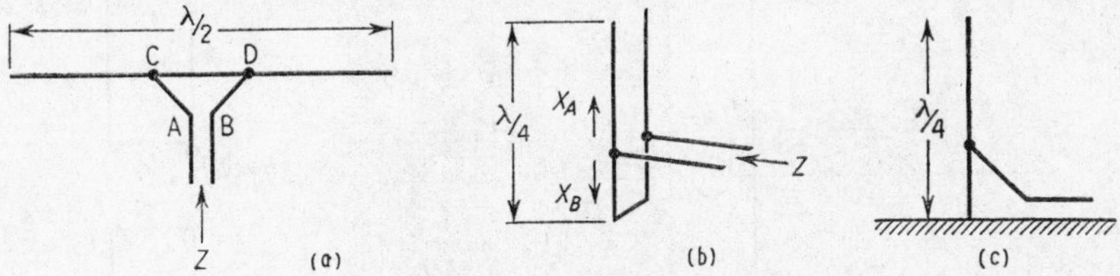

Fig. 10.5. (a) and (b) the shunt-fed dipole and its tapped resonant-line equivalent; (c) the quarter-wave shunt-fed unipole.

Short Dipoles

At the lower frequencies, the dimensions of half-wave dipoles and quarter-wave unipoles are so large that it is often impracticable to employ conductors of such lengths. It is, therefore, often necessary to use short dipoles and unipoles. If such short radiating elements are free from copper loss, they can be as efficient as resonant elements provided it is possible to match the generator to them without loss. A short dipole will have a radiation resistance of perhaps a few ohms, and a relatively high negative reactance. To match a generator to such a load will, therefore, generally require a large positive tuning reactance and a step-down transformer. Provided these components are loss-free the generator can be matched to the radiation resistance of the short aerial. We have already seen that the polar diagram of a short aerial is not much different from that for a resonant dipole or unipole. It will also be shown at the end of the chapter that a short aerial is as efficient as a resonant aerial under receiving conditions, provided that matching can be carried out efficiently. The practical aspects of short aerials will be considered in more detail in the next chapter in connection with low-frequency aerials. However, it is important to realize that although the half-wave dipole is considered as the basic radiating element in this chapter, it is not necessarily the only efficient aerial element for transmission and reception.

If the current distribution on a short aerial is known, the effective length is found by determining the area under the curve of current against distance along the aerial. This area is then divided by the maximum current which occurs at the feed point. The effective length is then the length of the Hertzian dipole, carrying the same feed current, which would produce the same field at a distance as the actual aerial. In the case of unipoles it is often called the effective height. This topic will also be considered in greater detail in the next chapter.

For a half-wave dipole with a sinusoidal current distribution, the effective length is $2/\pi$ times the actual length. This follows because the area under a sine curve from 0° to 180° is $2/\pi$ times the area of the rectangle which bounds the portion of the sine wave. The effective height of a quarter-wave unipole is thus also $2/\pi$ or 0·636 of the actual height.

Slot Aerials

A narrow rectangular slot in an infinite conducting sheet will radiate like an aerial, if fed with radio-frequency energy between opposite sides of the slot.

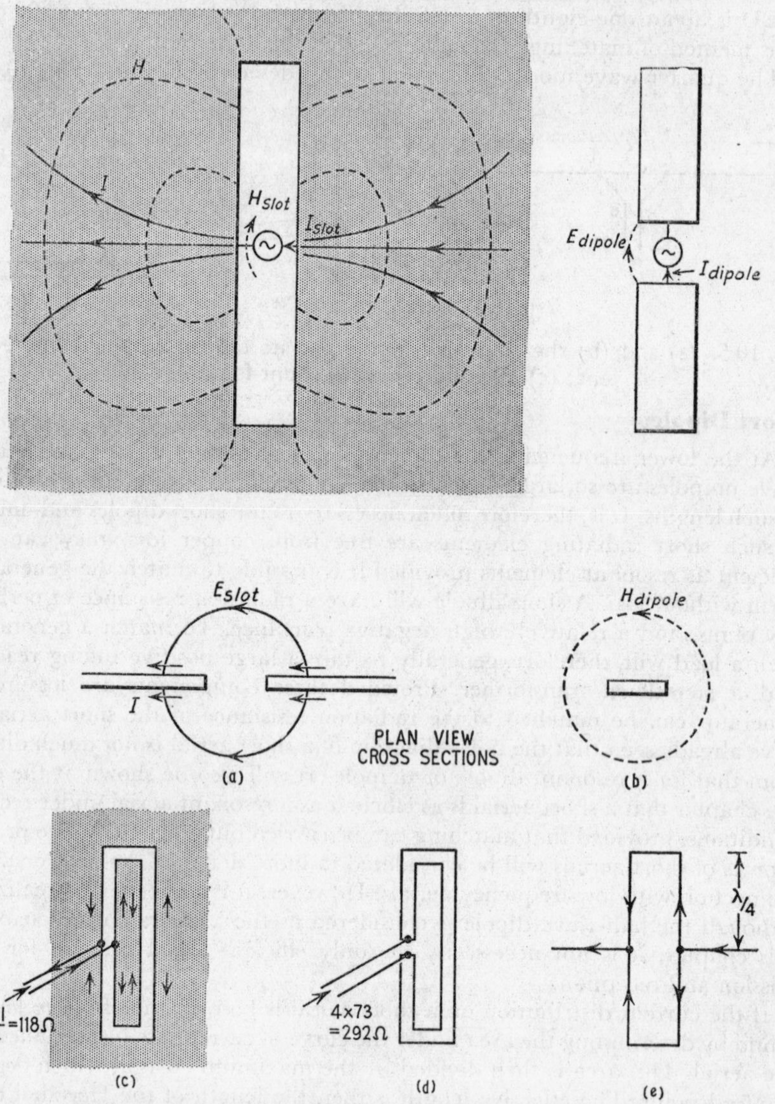

Fig. 10.6. Babinet's theorem: (a) slot in infinite sheet; (b) equivalent dipole; (c) folded slot; (d) equivalent folded dipole; (e) wire model showing reactance variation of slot.

Such an aerial is known as a slot aerial and the basic type is shown in Fig. 10.6 (a). If the sheet were perfectly conducting, the flow of current in the sheet could be deduced and hence the radiation. However, the radiating properties of such a slot can be deduced by an application of Babinet's Theorem in a much simpler manner. By this theorem, the field distribution round the slot and the radiation from it can be shown to be the same as for an electric dipole which would just fill the slot, but with the following modifications:

(1) As compared with the electric dipole the **E** and **H** field and radiation vectors are interchanged. The electric field from the slot is related to the magnetic field from the dipole (at corresponding points in space) by the impedance of free space. Thus at any point:

$$\mathbf{E}_{\text{slot}} = Z_{fs}\mathbf{H}_{\text{dipole}}$$

Similarly:

$$\mathbf{H}_{\text{slot}} = \mathbf{E}_{\text{dipole}}/Z_{fs}$$

where $Z_{fs} = 120\pi$ or 377 ohms.

(2) The electric field in the equatorial plane of the slot changes sign as we pass from one side of the conducting sheet to the other.

In Fig. 10.6 (b) the electric dipole which would just fill the slot is shown. If the dipole and the slot are a half-wavelength long, they will both be resonant when fed at the middle. In the equatorial plane of the dipole the radiation field is *magnetic* and may be represented by circles round the dipole. In a meridian plane of the dipole the field is *electric* and the field strength is given by equation (9.40), the polar diagram being of the form shown in Fig. 9.10.

Hence we may deduce that the radiation field in the equatorial plane of the slot is *electric* and that in a meridian plane is *magnetic*. Applying modification (2) above, if a plan-view section of the slot is drawn the direction of the electric field at an instant is as shown in Fig. 10.6 (a). This reversal of field as we pass from one side of the sheet to the other is an obvious condition of symmetry when the flow of current in the sheet is considered. The magnetic field at the surface of the sheet is similar in form to the electric field from a dipole. Hence we may deduce the current in the sheet from boundary condition (4) of equation (5.1) in Chapter 5. The current at an instant in the vicinity of the slot is shown in Fig. 10.6 (a) by drawing lines at right angles to the magnetic field.

The radiation from a double-sided slot aerial in an infinite sheet is in many respects similar to the radiation from a magnetic dipole. A comparison of the radiation from an electric dipole, a magnetic dipole, and a slot aerial is shown in Fig. 10.7 (a), (b) and (c). The fields of (b) and (c) are similar, but with the following exceptions:

(a) The magnetic dipole has a polar diagram of H in the zx plane consisting of two circles, whereas for the slot the polar diagram is of the form:

$$\frac{\cos(\pi/2 . \cos\theta)}{\sin\theta}$$

by analogy with a half-wave dipole. The half-wave slot thus has slightly more gain (0·40 db) than the magnetic dipole.

(b) The electric field in the equatorial plane of the slot changes sign on passing from one side of the sheet to the other.

The impedance at the feed point of a half-wave slot may be deduced in a qualitative manner from the known dipole impedance of 73 ohms. If the magnetic field which encircles the feed current of the slot in Fig. 10.6 (a) is considered we have:

$$I_{\text{slot}} = |\mathbf{H}_{\text{slot}}| \times 2\pi r$$

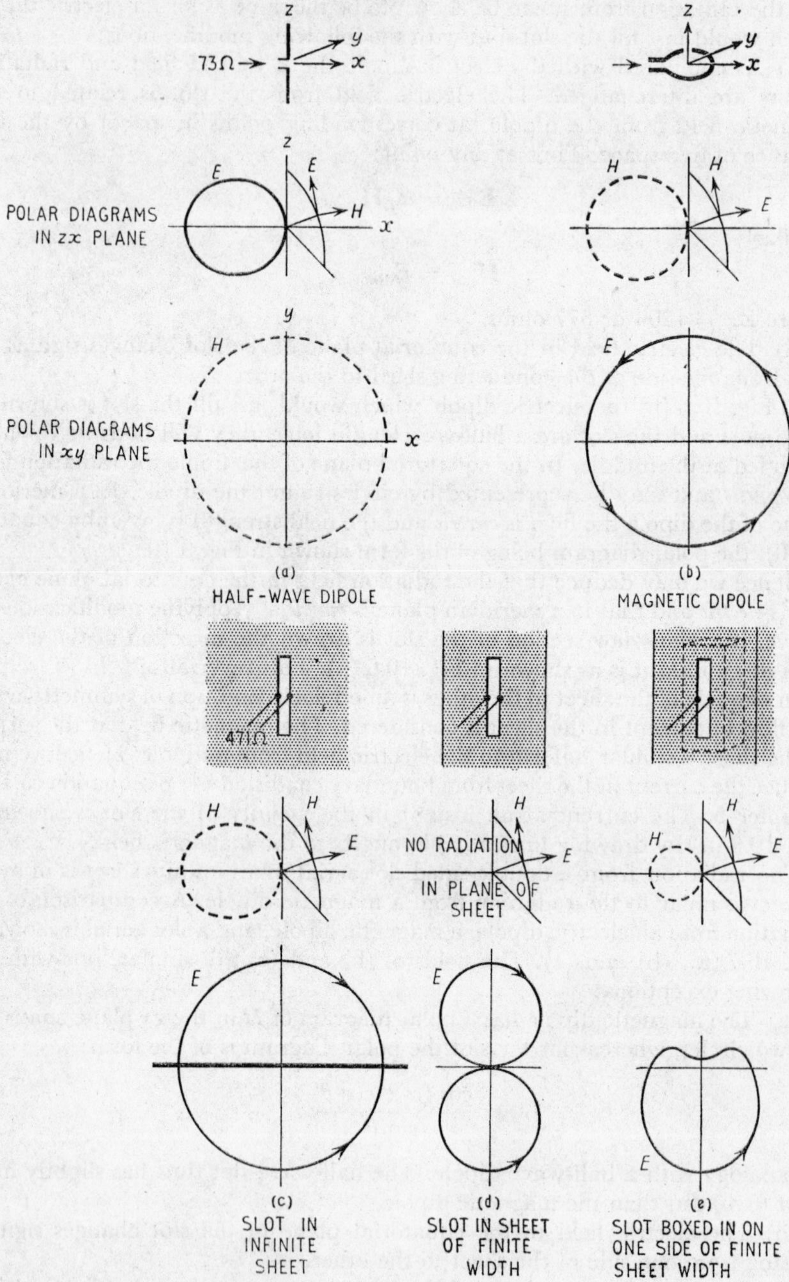

Fig. 10.7. Comparison of basic aerial elements.

where r is the radius of the path considered. Substituting for $\mathbf{H}_{slot}$ from Babinet's Theorem, we get

$$I_{slot} = \frac{|\mathbf{E}_{dipole}|}{Z_{fs}} \times 2\pi r$$

But $|\mathbf{E}_{dipole}| \times \pi r$ is the voltage V_{dipole} applied to the electric dipole of Fig. 10.6 (b). Therefore

$$I_{slot} = 2 \times \frac{V_{dipole}}{Z_{fs}} \quad . \quad . \quad . \quad . \quad . \quad . \quad (10.2)$$

If the slot and the dipole radiate the same power we have:

$$I^2_{slot} Z_{slot} = \frac{V^2_{dipole}}{Z_{dipole}} \quad . \quad . \quad . \quad . \quad . \quad . \quad . \quad (10.3)$$

where Z_{slot} is the impedance between the edges of the slot; i.e., the impedance between A and B presented to the generator. Z_{dipole} is the dipole impedance, assumed to be 73 ohms for the resonant condition.

Substituting for I_{slot} from equation (10.2) in equation (10.3) we get:

$$4 \times \frac{V^2_{dipole}}{Z_{fs}{}^2} \times Z_{slot} = \frac{V^2_{dipole}}{73}$$

$$Z_{slot} = \frac{377^2}{4 \times 73}$$

$$= 471 \text{ ohms} \quad . \quad . \quad . \quad . \quad (10.4)$$

The same result would have been obtained if we had started with the dipole current. Thus the slot has a rather high impedance. This may be reduced by using what is known as the folded slot shown in Fig. 10.6 (c). The electric dipole of Fig. 10.6 (d) which would fill the slot is recognizable as the folded dipole. It follows again from Babinet's Theorem that the impedance at the drive point of the folded slot is $471/4 = 118$ ohms.

If a slot is shorter than a half-wavelength it will have positive reactance associated with the radiation resistance, whereas a short dipole has negative reactance. This follows intuitively from the resonant slot if it is imagined as two quarter-wave lines in parallel as in Fig. 10.6 (e). It also follows from the reciprocal relationship between the slot and the dipole. A slot longer than a half-wavelength will have negative reactance.

The sheet surrounding a slot must in practice be of finite size. This will modify the distant field as shown in Fig. 10.7 (d). Clearly the fields cancel out in the plane of the sheet. However, it is not often that radiation is required on both sides of the slot, and the more usual slot aerial has one side boxed in, so as to suppress one half of the radiation as in Fig. 10.7 (e). The equatorial polar diagram cannot be obtained by simple analysis, but the general shape of the polar diagram in the xy plane is as shown. The field at the back of the slot is due to diffraction of the waves from the front.

It is possible to have arrays of slot aerials. The properties of arrays of slots are very similar to the properties of arrays of electric dipoles. However, in the remainder of this chapter attention will be confined to arrays of dipoles, leaving the special problems of arrays of slots to Chapters 12 and 13.

Arrays of Two Driven Aerials

A single aerial element does not normally exhibit any great directivity, and therefore, it does not have a high gain. In order to obtain greater directivity and gain, it is common practice to employ two or more aerials in an array. As an introduction to this subject we consider arrangements having two equal-strength aerials, which are oriented in the same direction. In order to determine

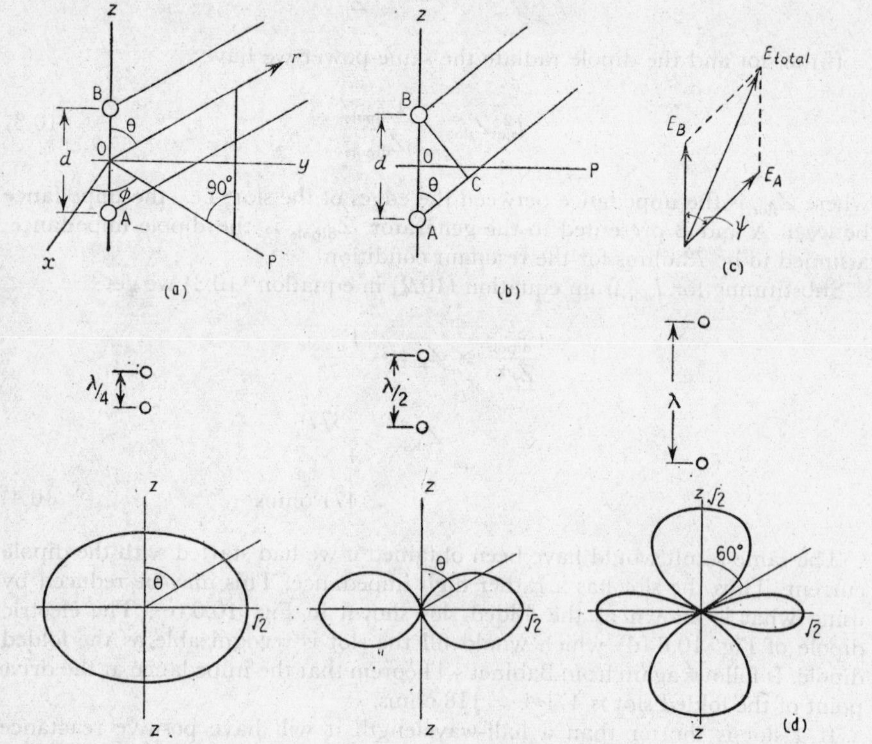

Fig. 10.8. Group patterns for a pair of equal strength cophased isotropic radiators: (a) and (b) geometry for calculating patterns; (c) vector diagram for adding field from A and B at a distance; (d) group patterns for λ/4, λ/2 and λ spacing (solids of revolution about *zz*). Maximum voltage gain $\sqrt{2}$ times one element.

the radiation pattern and gain of such an arrangement it is necessary to sum the radiations from the two elements of the array having due regard to the relative phase.

The case to be considered is shown in Fig. 10.8 (a), the spacing between the two radiators being *d* metres. For the moment the actual characteristics of the radiators are not specified but they are assumed to be identical, similarly oriented and excited in phase. It is further assumed that there are no interaction effects; i.e., the field of one radiator is unaffected by the presence of the other. In the direction (θ, ϕ) in the figure, at a large distance r metres, let $E(r, \theta, \phi)$ be the electric field strength due to a power P radiated from one element alone. If the power P is now shared between the two elements A and B the field strength due to A alone is given by:

$$E_A = \frac{E(r, \theta, \phi)}{\sqrt{2}}$$

The field strength due to B alone has a similar value if the distance r is very large compared with the spacing d. Since the aerials are similarly oriented, the polarizations of these two fields are the same, but the field vectors will not necessarily be in time phase with one another. In some directions it may be that the two fields are in phase; for example in the direction OP in Fig. 10.8 (b) the two fields will obviously add in phase since all points on this line are equidistant from the two aerials. In the direction (θ, ϕ), at a distant point, the field from A will lag behind that from B owing to the greater distance which the radiation from A has to travel. If we take the plane in which the rays from A and B lie as in Fig. 10.8 (b), the field from A will lag behind that from B by a phase angle dependent upon the distance AC where BC is perpendicular to AC.

Now
$$\begin{aligned} AC &= d \cos\theta \text{ metres} \\ &= \frac{d}{\lambda} \cos\theta \text{ wavelengths} \\ \therefore\ \psi &= \frac{2\pi d}{\lambda} \cos\theta \text{ radians} \end{aligned} \qquad (10.5)$$

where ψ is the phase angle by which the field from A lags behind that from B. To obtain the resultant field strength at a distance in the direction θ, two vectors of equal magnitude but having the angle ψ between them, must be added together. From the geometry of the vector diagram in Fig. 10.8 (c) we have for the resultant field strength:

$$\begin{aligned} E_{\text{total}} &= 2E_A \cos\psi/2 \\ &= 2\frac{E(r, \theta, \phi)}{\sqrt{2}} \cos\left(\frac{\pi d}{\lambda}\cos\theta\right) \\ &= E(r, \theta, \phi) \times \sqrt{2}\cos\left(\frac{\pi d}{\lambda}\cos\theta\right) \\ &= E(r, \theta, \phi) \times \text{array factor} \end{aligned} \qquad (10.6)$$

where array factor $= \sqrt{2}\cos\left(\frac{\pi d}{\lambda}\cos\theta\right)$

This equation gives the field strength in any direction due to the array as the product of the field strength due to a single aerial radiating the same total power and an array factor which accounts for the modification of the radiation pattern due to radiating power from the two elements of the array. In this case the array factor has the maximum value of $\sqrt{2}$, when $\theta = \pi/2$, although there may be other directions of similar value depending upon the precise relationship between d and λ. In this direction the field strength is increased by the factor $\sqrt{2}$, or the power density is increased by the factor 2. By the definition of aerial gain given in Chapter 9 this means that in the direction concerned the power gain due to the array as compared with a single element is 2, or expressed logarithmically 3 db. Since there is a gain in some directions there must be a loss in certain other directions. The trigonometric part of the array factor has a maximum value of unity, and it enables the voltage gain or loss in any direction to be obtained.

In general equation (10.6) may be interpreted as the product, taken in the desired direction, of the radii of two solid radiation patterns. One is the pattern of the single radiation element (e.g., a dipole) radiating the same total power, and the other is the pattern represented by the array factor, sometimes called the group or space pattern. The latter may be imagined to be the radiation pattern that would result if the individual elements were uniform radiators; i.e., if they radiated the same power density in all directions. No physical electrical radiator can in fact produce such radiation, although in acoustics a pulsating sphere produces uniform radiation of longitudinal acoustic waves. This fictitious uniform electrical radiator is called an isotropic radiator. In Chapter 9 the isotropic radiator was found to be a convenient standard of reference for the gain of an aerial element. There it was not necessary to visualize the field radiated. In the present connection it is not possible to visualize the field but we can assume that at a distant point the polarizations from the two radiators are in the same direction, although it is not necessary to specify that direction. When the isotropic radiators are replaced by similarly oriented aerial elements, the polarization is immediately determined. If the aerial elements are not oriented in the same direction equation (10.6) is not appropriate and there is then no alternative but to carry out a direct summation. However, most cases in practice consist of arrays of similarly oriented aerial elements.

Polar plots of the array factor for two radiators are given in Fig. 10.8 (d) for three spacings, quarter-wave, half-wave, and full-wave. The directions of zero field can easily be verified as the direction in which AC is a half-wavelength, so that the two fields cancel. The complete space polar diagram in these three cases is a solid of revolution about the axis of symmetry corresponding to the axis through the radiators. These are not, of course, the polar diagrams of practical aerials, because they refer to uniform or isotropic radiators. They are the group or space patterns.

The polar diagrams resulting when actual aerial elements replace the isotropic radiators can easily be deduced by the application of the above product rule. To illustrate this rule, two types of aerial are considered. The first is an array of two collinear cophased half-wave dipoles and the second is two parallel half-wave dipoles excited in phase.

The first case is illustrated in Fig. 10.9 (a). With two collinear dipoles, with their centres half a wavelength apart, the array factor which determines the group pattern is given by:

$$\sqrt{2}\cos\left(\frac{\pi d}{\lambda}\cos\theta\right) \quad \text{where} \quad d = \frac{\lambda}{2}$$

and the dipole element pattern by:

$$\frac{\cos\{(\pi/2)\cos\theta\}}{\sin\theta} \quad \text{from equation (9.40)}$$

In any direction θ to the axis the resultant pattern is the product of these two factors:

$$\sqrt{2}\cos\left(\frac{\pi d}{\lambda}\cos\theta\right) \times \frac{\cos\{(\pi/2)\cos\theta\}}{\sin\theta} \quad . \quad . \quad . \quad (10.7)$$

In Fig. 10.9 (a) the first two patterns are combined to give the final pattern. The method of combination is to multiply the radii OA and OE together to give OF. To signify this operation we may say that the patterns are multiplied together.

Fig. 10.9 (b) shows the same process carried out for two dipoles in line but

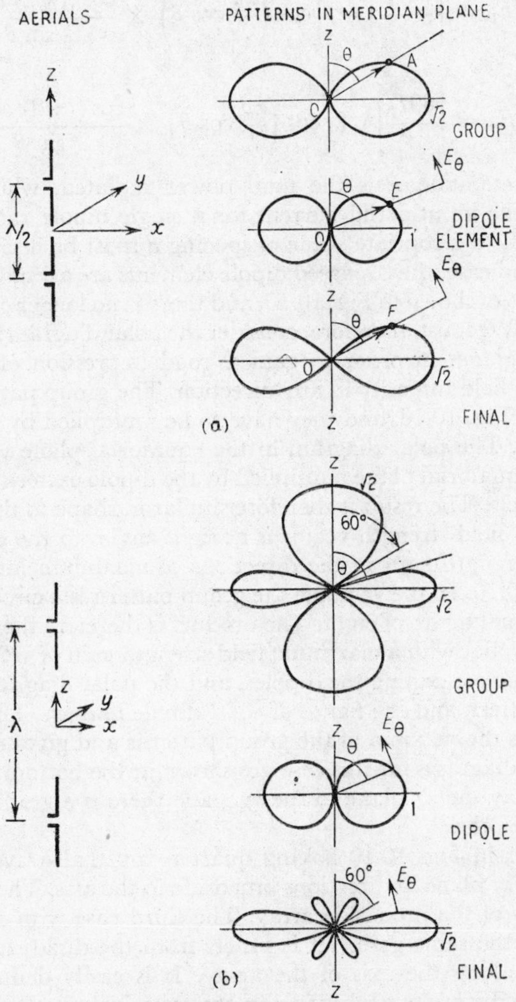

Fig. 10.9. Polar diagrams for a pair of collinear cophased dipoles. The complete diagrams are solids of revolution about *zz*. Maximum voltage gain $\sqrt{2}$ times dipole gain.

one wavelength apart. In this case the null from the dipole element pattern causes a null along the axis of the final pattern but minor lobes exist as shown. All the polar diagrams in Fig. 10.9 are sections through solids of revolution. Thus the polar diagram for E_θ in the equatorial plane is a circle in each case. Dipoles arranged vertically and above one another thus give all round coverage and gain in a horizontal direction. They are thus suitable for some forms of broadcasting and are sometimes called broadcast arrays.

The equation for determining the field strength due to the array at a distance r metres is the product of the maximum field strength from a single dipole radiating the same total power, and equation (10.7). Thus:

$$E_\theta = \left[\frac{7\sqrt{P}}{r}\right]\sqrt{2}\left[\cos\left(\frac{\pi d}{\lambda}\cos\theta\right) \times \frac{\cos\{(\pi/2)\cos\theta\}}{\sin\theta}\right]$$

or

$$E_\theta = \left[\frac{60I_0}{r}\right]\sqrt{2}\left[\cos\left(\frac{\pi d}{\lambda}\cos\theta\right) \times \frac{\cos\{(\pi/2)\cos\theta\}}{\sin\theta}\right] \quad . \quad (10.8)$$

In the first equation P is the total power radiated, while in the second equation I_0 is the input aerial current for a single dipole radiating the same total power. The appropriate value of spacing d must be inserted.

For the second case, the cophased dipole elements are arranged at right angles to the array axis as shown in Fig. 10.10, and there is no longer circular symmetry about this axis. We must, therefore, consider the polar diagram in three mutually perpendicular planes in order to gain a good impression of the solid figure which gives the field intensity in any direction. The group patterns of Fig. 10.8 are repeated in Fig. 10.10, and they have to be multiplied by suitably oriented dipole patterns. The polar diagram in the equatorial plane will be the group pattern in the equatorial plane multiplied by the dipole pattern in the equatorial plane; i.e. a circle. The result is therefore similar in shape to the group pattern. In this case the field strength vector is at right angles to the equatorial plane, and the field strength gain in the directions of maximum intensity is $\sqrt{2}$, as shown in Fig. 10.10. In the yz plane the group pattern is a circle and the dipole pattern is the usual figure of eight. The product is therefore the same as a dipole pattern in shape, but with a maximum field strength gain of $\sqrt{2}$. The remaining plane is the plane containing the dipoles, and the polar diagram is the product of the group pattern and the figure of eight dipole pattern. The null along the dipole axis splits the maxima of the group patterns and gives nulls along the z axis. The polar diagrams for this case are shown at the bottom of the figure. As we move from say the xz plane to the xy plane there is a gradual change from one shape to the other.

The two cases in Fig. 10.10 having quarter- and half-wave spacings show 3-db gain in the xy plane in directions broadside to the axis. They are, therefore, simple examples of the broadside array. The third case with a spacing of one wavelength has the same gain but it suffers from the disadvantage that there are large lobes along the axis of the array. It is easily deduced that larger spacings will produce more lobes in the equatorial plane. For example if the spacing were increased to 10 wavelengths there would be 10 nulls in a right angle between the x axis and the y axis. Unless required for special purposes these wide spacings do not provide useful polar diagrams. The aerials of Fig. 10.10 do not have great practical importance, but they are of value in illustrating the method of obtaining polar diagrams for arrays.

So far, consideration has been given to arrays of two aerials in which the elements are excited in phase. If the elements are excited with the same radio frequency but with a phase displacement between the signals fed to them, a new range of possible polar diagrams exists. In equation (10.5) we must add the

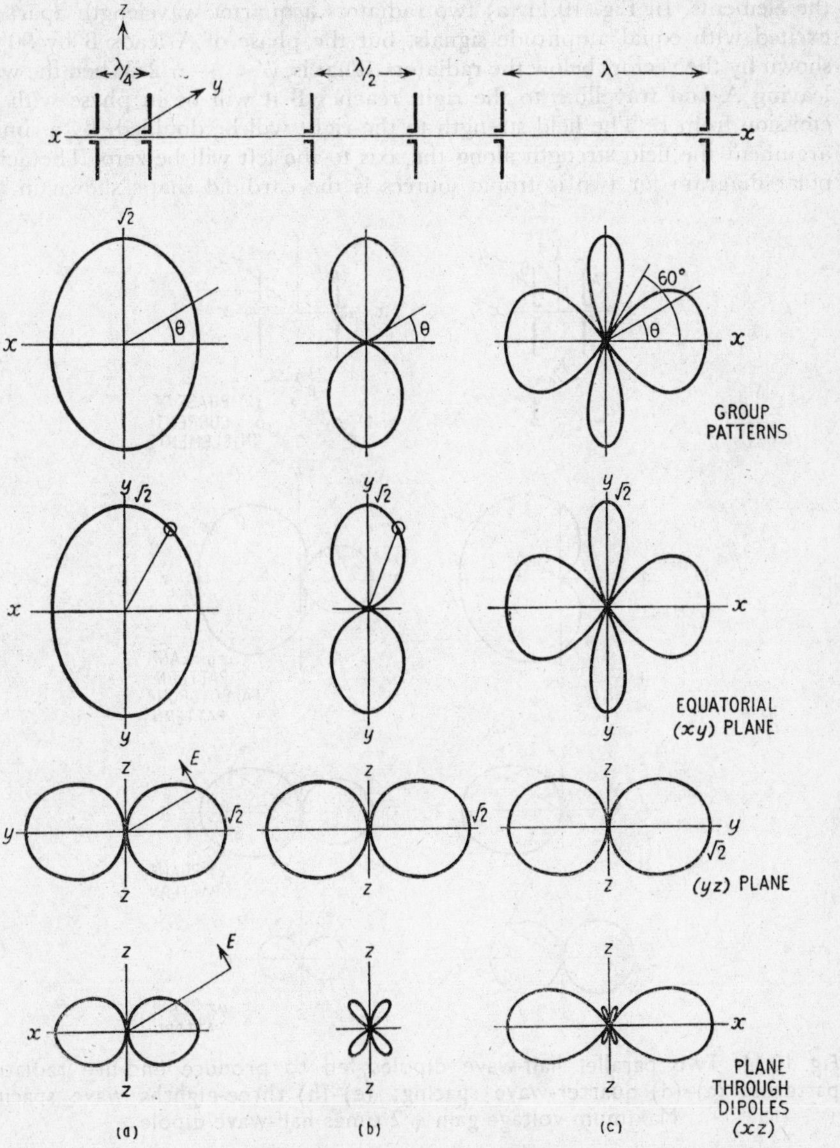

Fig. 10.10. Polar diagrams for a pair of equal strength cophased dipoles arranged for broadside operation.

phase ψ' by which the signal in A lags that in B of Fig. 10.8 (a). Instead of equation (10.5) we then get:

$$\psi = \frac{2\pi}{\lambda} d \cos\theta + \psi' \quad . \quad . \quad . \quad . \quad . \quad (10.9)$$

Generally speaking there is only one value for ψ' which gives polar diagrams of interest. This value is the phase shift corresponding to the distance between the elements. In Fig. 10.11 (a) two radiators a quarter wavelength apart are excited with equal amplitude signals, but the phase of A leads B by 90° as shown by the vectors below the radiators. That is, $\psi' = -\pi/2$. When the wave leaving A and travelling to the right reaches B it will be in phase with the emission from B. The field strength to the right will be doubled. By a similar argument the field strength along the axis to the left will be zero. The actual polar diagram for two isotropic sources is the cardioid shape shown in (b),

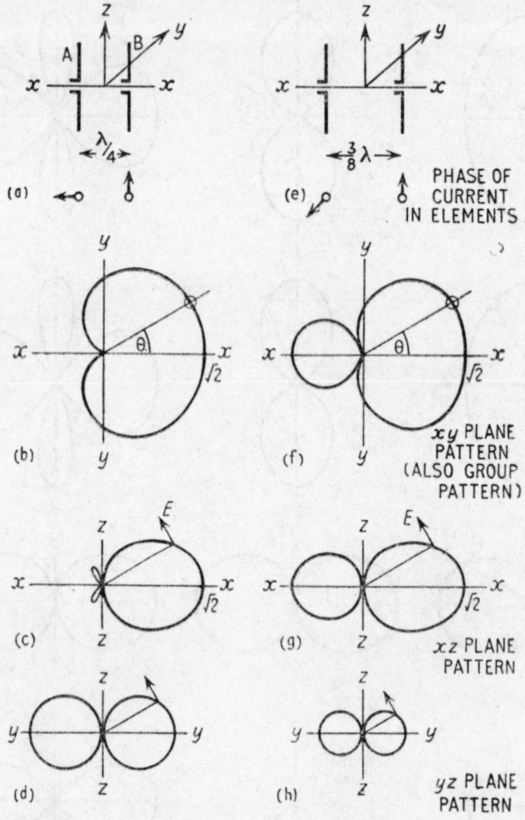

Fig. 10.11. Two parallel half-wave dipoles fed to produce end-fire radiation patterns: (a)–(d) quarter-wave spacing; (e)–(h) three-eighths wave spacing. Maximum voltage gain $\sqrt{2}$ times half-wave dipole.

which is a section of a solid of revolution. By the previous argument the array factor consisting of voltage gain and polar diagram factors, is given by:

$$F = \sqrt{2}\cos\left(\frac{\pi d}{\lambda}\cos\theta - \frac{\pi}{4}\right) \quad \text{where } d = \frac{\lambda}{4}$$

or

$$F = \sqrt{2}\cos\frac{\pi}{4}(1 - \cos\theta) \quad . \quad . \quad . \quad . \quad . \quad . \quad . \quad (10.10)$$

The energy from the two radiators is thus directed mainly into the hemisphere to the right.

So far the radiators of Fig. 10.11 (a) have been considered isotropic; if they are replaced by two half-wave dipoles at right angles to the axis there are again three planes to consider. The first is the equatorial plane since this contains the direction of maximum radiation. Since the dipole diagram for this plane is a circle the array pattern is still the cardioid of Fig. 10.11 (b), with a field strength gain of $\sqrt{2}$. In the plane containing the dipoles the cardioid must be multiplied by the figure of eight pattern. The result is the large forward lobe with the two small backward lobes, as shown at (c). The polar diagram in the remaining plane is deduced in like manner and shown at (d). In Fig. 10.11 (e) to (h) the process has been repeated for a dipole spacing of $3\lambda/8$ with a phase displacement between signals of $2\pi \times 3/8$ radians. Arrangements of aerials spaced and phased in this way are known as end-fire arrays. With a spacing of half a wavelength, however, the array fires in both directions along the x axis and is not strictly an end-fire array. Spacings of less than half a wavelength are, therefore, normally employed.

Throughout this section interaction effects between aerial elements have been neglected. This assumption is not always justified so that the results are only approximately correct. A qualitative discussion of these effects is given when the mutual impedance between two dipoles is considered.

Aerials above a Conducting Plane

In Chapter 9 a unipole mounted on a reflecting plane was shown to produce a field above the plane similar to half of the field produced by a dipole. Fig. 9.8 is a special case of the method of images which is very useful in determining to a first order the performance of aerials above the ground.

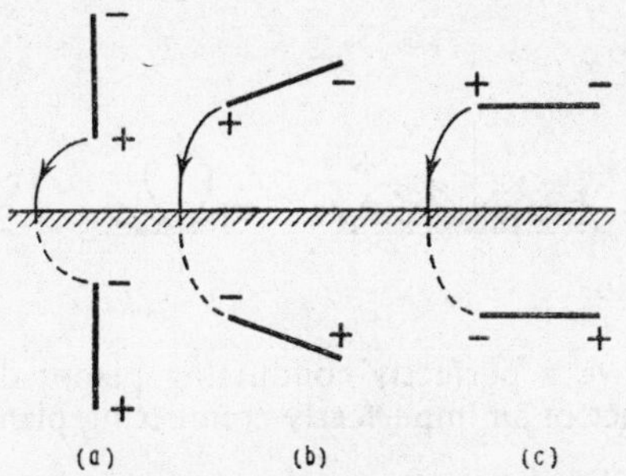

Fig. 10.12. The images of radiating elements: (a) is positive image; (c) is negative image.

If the plane is perfectly conducting there can be no tangential electric field; i.e., all lines of electric force must meet the plane normally. Referring to Fig. 10.12 and applying this condition, we can assign polarities to the respective images for an assumed polarity on the aerial elements above the plane. Notice that the image of the vertical element has the same polarity as itself (known as a positive image) while the horizontal element and its image have opposite polarities (known as a negative image).

By analogy with optics the aerial element and its image behave as an array of two elements. In Fig. 10.13 (a), which refers to the positive image case, the angle of incidence θ is equal to the angle of reflection. Since the aerial and its image are excited in phase, the results of the previous section apply. If the height h above ground is $\lambda/4$ or $\lambda/2$ and the elements are half-wave dipoles, the polar diagram shapes in Fig. 10.9 will apply, and the field strength will be reinforced along the plane and at low angles of elevation. These results are reproduced in Fig. 10.13 (b). However, it should be noticed that the field strength gain along the plane is 2 (or 6 db) as compared with $\sqrt{2}$ for two driven collinear dipoles. This extra gain only applies if the plane is a perfect conductor, and also if the effect of the plane on the dipole impedance is neglected. The latter effect causes a slight loss of gain at low heights. Where the reflecting plane is a

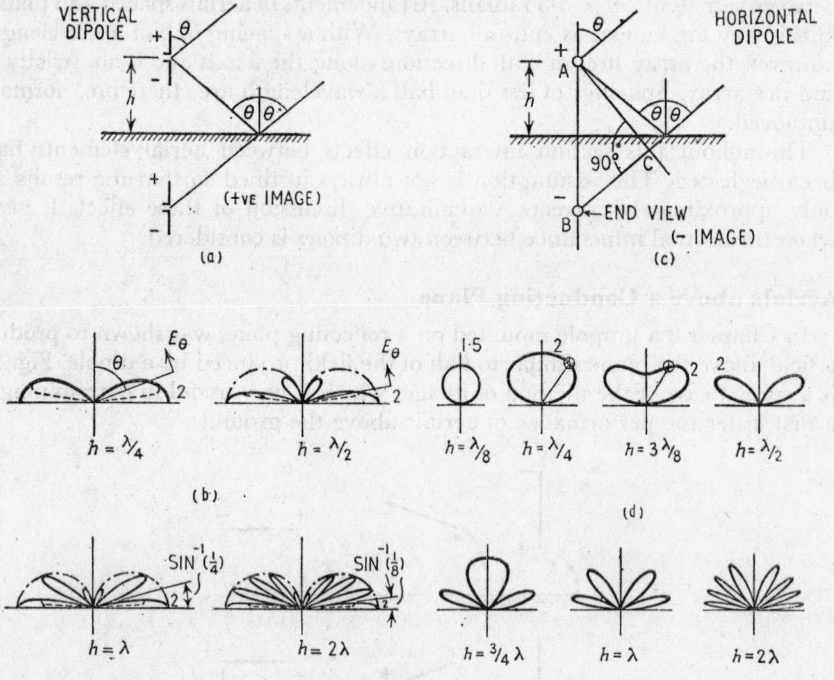

Fig. 10.13. Aerials above a perfectly conducting plane; dotted lines show the approximate effect of an imperfectly conducting plane; e.g., soil.

conducting screen or suitable mesh, the gains quoted are nearly achieved, but where the plane is normal soil, the gain along the ground is not realized. In fact, the field strength along the surface of the ground for fields which vary inversely as the distance is zero, as shown by the dotted lines in Fig. 10.13 (b). There is also a smaller loss of gain at other angles of elevation. The modifications which arise from imperfect reflectors are considered in more detail in the next section.

At a height of one wavelength the polar diagram is the product of a group pattern due to two cophased isotropic elements two wavelengths apart, and a dipole pattern. The result is also shown in Fig. 10.13 (b). The first null will be at an angle to the axis of $\cos^{-1}\left(\frac{\lambda/2}{2\lambda}\right)$ or at an elevation of $\sin^{-1}(1/4)$. The polar diagram for a height of two wavelengths is also shown.

If the aerial is a horizontal dipole above a conducting plane, then its image is excited in anti-phase. An end view of such a dipole is shown in Fig. 10.13 (c). In a direction θ to the vertical in the plane of the paper, the image will provide a signal lagging the aerial signal by a phase of:

$$\left(\frac{2\pi 2h}{\lambda}\cos\theta + \pi\right) \text{ radians}$$

The factor by which the resultant field strength at a distance will be greater than that from a dipole in free space is therefore given by:

$$F = 2\cos\left(\frac{2\pi h}{\lambda}\cos\theta + \frac{\pi}{2}\right)$$

$$= -\,2\sin\left(\frac{2\pi h}{\lambda}\cos\theta\right) \quad . \quad . \quad . \quad . \quad . \quad . \quad (10.11)$$

This assumes that the dipole current is unchanged by the presence of the plane. The effect of the plane on the dipole impedance is considerable at heights below about half a wavelength. This is discussed later in connection with mutual impedance. For a height of a quarter wavelength the field strength gain in the upwards direction is 2. In this case the image is phased and placed to give an end-fire effect in the upward direction. If the conducting plane is metallic or a suitable metallic curtain or mesh this gain is in fact realized, but if the plane is normal soil, the gain is usually only about 3 db. This aspect is considered in greater detail in the next section.

The polar diagrams assuming a perfectly conducting plane are shown in Fig. 10.13 (d) for various heights. Owing to the antiphase image there is no radiation along the ground. The diagrams for heights of about one wavelength are of interest in connection with aerial arrays which are designed to give low angle of elevation lobes which are often required for directing a beam on to the ionospheric layers (See Chapter 14). If an array produces a horizontal beam when far removed from the earth, when it is mounted about a wavelength above the earth the beam will be deflected upwards. The free-space pattern of the array is multiplied by one of the patterns in Fig. 10.13 (d). The angle to the vertical of the lowest lobe can be obtained directly, since it is the direction in which BC is half a wavelength. This follows because the image is excited in antiphase to the aerial and the extra half-wave delay of BC causes the signal to be reinforced by the image. Thus the angle at which this occurs is given by:

$$\theta = \cos^{-1}\frac{\lambda/2}{2h}$$

or the angle of elevation is:

$$\alpha = \sin^{-1}\frac{\lambda}{4h} \quad . \quad . \quad . \quad . \quad . \quad . \quad (10.12)$$

A common requirement is to produce a lobe at about 10° or 15° to the horizontal, where $\sin\alpha = 0{\cdot}2$. Thus a height of about 1·25 wavelengths is often used for arrays which have a negative image. The higher angle lobes due to the group pattern arising from the reflector are reduced because the array in free space has very little high-angle radiation. An example of this type of aerial is the rhombic aerial described in Chapter 11.

Aerials above the Surface of Soil or Sea Water

In almost all practical radio problems it is necessary to take account of the effect of the surface of the earth or sea on aerials and propagation. The conductivity and relative permittivity of soils and sea water are given in Table 5.1. It will be observed that the conductivity of soil is very low, and it is clear that the results of the previous section cannot be applied to the reflection of radio waves by the earth and sea without closer investigation. If a radio wave is incident upon the surface of the earth or sea, most of the energy will in general be reflected, but a small amount is transmitted into the dense medium, and is soon dissipated as shown by Table 5.1. The reflection factor for the reflected wave is therefore generally less than unity, although for two very important cases it is very close to unity. The calculation of the reflection factors for given conductivity and dielectric properties is beyond the present scope, but typical results are summarized in Fig. 10.14. Actually the reflection factor depends

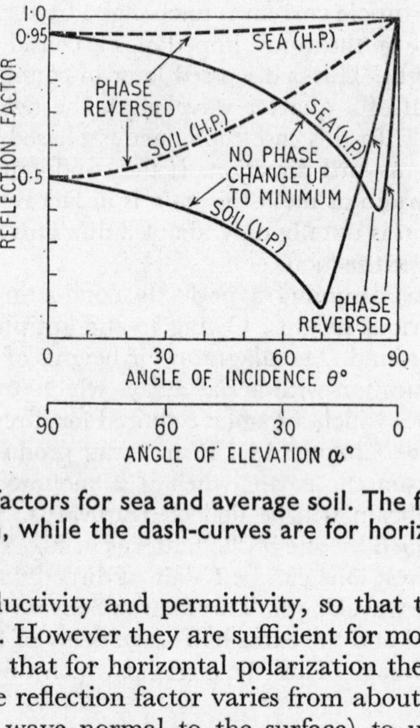

Fig. **10.14. Reflection factors for sea and average soil. The full-line curves are for vertical polarization, while the dash-curves are for horizontal polarization.**

upon frequency, conductivity and permittivity, so that the curves shown are rather rough averages. However they are sufficient for most practical purposes.

It will be observed that for horizontal polarization the phase is reversed on reflection and that the reflection factor varies from about 0·5 for zero angle of incidence (i.e., for a wave normal to the surface) to unity for an angle of incidence of 90° (i.e., a wave grazing the surface). The phase reversal corresponds to the negative image deduced in the previous section. For horizontal polarization the results of the previous section can be applied to poorly conducting reflectors, with but slight modification. At grazing incidence the reflection factor is unity, the earth or sea behaving as a perfect reflector, due to its dielectric properties. For normal incidence, such as occurs with the vertically-reflected radiation from a horizontal dipole above the earth, the polar diagrams of Fig. 10.13 (d) apply except that the maximum voltage gain is rather less than 2. Generally speaking the gain is 3 or 4 db. Summarizing, for horizontal polarization the sea can be considered to be a perfect reflector, and the earth behaves as a perfect reflector for grazing incidences. For normal or nearly normal incidence on soil, there is a loss on reflection, the reflection factor varying between 0·4 and 0·8 depending upon frequency and soil properties.

For vertical polarization the situation is a little more complicated. At normal or nearly normal incidence (θ small) the reflection factor for sea is good while that for soil may be as low as 0·5 depending upon frequency, conductivity and permittivity. There is no phase change on reflection, a situation which corresponds to the positive image deduced in the previous section. Thus Fig. 10.13 (b) can be applied for values of θ up to at least 60° for sea reflections with no great error, but for soil even at small values of θ the field strength will be less than indicated. However, the situation at large angles of incidence (i.e., grazing incidence) is usually of more importance. It will be observed from Fig. 10.14 that at angles of incidence corresponding to a wave grazing the soil or sea, the reflection factor rapidly approaches unity and the phase on reflection is reversed. That is, the image has changed to a negative image. In the horizontal directions of the polar diagrams in Fig. 10.13 (b) there can be no field strength of the type which varies inversely with distance because the aerial and its image cancel one another. These polar diagrams cannot be applied to imperfect reflectors without modification. The dotted curves shown on the lower lobes of the polar diagrams indicate roughly the way in which the field strength varies at low angles of elevation with a vertical dipole above soil or sea. This phase reversal on reflection causes vertically-polarized radiation to behave in a similar manner to horizontally-polarized radiation at grazing incidence, and accounts for the fact that there is little difference between the propagation conditions for the two types of polarization.

Fig. 10.14 also shows that there are certain angles of incidence with vertical polarization, for which the reflection factor is very small. The angle above the horizontal at which this occurs is known as the Brewster angle, and it marks the point at which the image changes its sign. For soil the angle is about 20°. For radiation striking the ground at this angle to the horizontal there is very little reflected energy, the radiation being absorbed in the soil. Thus at this angle in Fig. 10.13 (a) the field strength is determined by the vertical dipole alone, there being no image. For sea water, the angle is considerably less, only a few degrees to the horizontal, and the reflection factor only falls to about 0·4. It may be concluded that the polar diagrams of vertical aerials above soil or sea water are highly dependent upon the properties of the reflector, and it would not be possible to obtain accurate polar diagrams with this polarization.

▶ Mutual Impedance Effects

Up to this point the interaction between closely spaced aerials has been neglected. This is an inaccurate assumption for aerials a small fraction of a wavelength apart. For suppose we have two half-wave dipoles side by side nearly touching one another. The impedance of the two aerials driven in parallel would be 73 ohms, because as we have seen from Fig. 9.12 the diameter of the conductors has little effect on the radiation resistance. Therefore the impedance of each dipole alone would be 146 ohms. If one of the aerials were removed to a large distance this impedance of 146 ohms would fall to 73 ohms. The difference is accounted for by the mutual impedance. Mutual impedance effects are negligible at distances greater than a few wavelengths, because the power received by one dipole is a very small fraction of the power radiated from the other dipole. The received voltage and current are thus small compared with the transmitting values. The impedance of one dipole is virtually unaffected by the presence of the other at large spacings.

In the case of the two dipoles considered above, when they are very close together aerial 1 will cause a voltage in aerial 2 which tends to oppose its driving voltage. As compared with a single dipole in free space, the voltage applied to aerial 2 will have to be increased in order to maintain a fixed current. The ratio of driving voltage to resultant current is therefore higher than for an isolated dipole; i.e., the impedance is greater than 73 ohms. As the dipoles are gradually separated the impedance falls from the value of 146 ohms found above, owing to the rapid reduction of field strength at short distances.

Aerial number 2 will react back upon aerial number 1 in a similar way. By symmetry the impedances of the two aerials will be equal.

At a spacing of about half a wavelength the voltage in aerial 2 due to aerial 1 will be changing from opposing the driving voltage to assisting it, because of the retardation of phase as we move from aerial 1. We may conclude that at this spacing the mutual effects are not so great. At a slightly greater spacing the voltage in aerial 2 due to aerial 1 will tend to assist the driving current and the apparent impedance of each aerial will be less than 73 ohms. At about one wavelength spacing, it will return to approximately 73 ohms and increase again. Thus as the spacing increases the apparent impedance of each aerial fluctuates about 73 ohms but the amplitude of the fluctuations diminishes rapidly and beyond 2 wavelengths the effect is small.

The above simple argument neglects the actual phase relationship between the driving voltage and the induced voltage due to the other aerial. When these effects are taken into account it is found that the apparent impedance also includes a series reactance which is positive at small spacings and then changes to negative and thereafter alternates and diminishes. The actual calculation of mutual impedance effects presents considerable difficulty, particularly at small spacings when one aerial is in the induction field of the other. At large spacings it may be deduced from radiation or propagation theory. All that can be attempted here is a definition of mutual impedance itself.

Consider two adjacent aerials the first being open-circuited and the second carrying a current I_2. This current in aerial 2 will cause a voltage V to appear at the terminals of aerial 1. The ratio of V to I_2 is termed the mutual impedance Z_{12} between the two aerials. (By the reciprocal theorem, a current I_2 in aerial 1 would produce a voltage V in aerial 2, so that the mutual impedance is the same for either direction of transmission.) The self impedance Z_{11} of aerial 1 is the ratio of its driving voltage to resultant current when aerial 2 is open-circuited. In practice Z_{11} is very close to the impedance of aerial 1, when aerial 2 is removed to a distance. If now the two aerials carry currents I_1 and I_2 flowing in the same sense, we have for the input voltage to aerial 1:

$$V_1 = Z_{11}I_1 + Z_{12}I_2 \qquad (10.13)$$

and for aerial 2:

$$V_2 = Z_{22}I_2 + Z_{12}I_1 \qquad (10.14)$$

Hence the apparent impedance of aerial 1 is:

$$Z_{a1} = \frac{V_1}{I_1} = Z_{11} + Z_{12}\frac{I_2}{I_1}$$

and of aerial 2:

$$Z_{a2} = \frac{V_2}{I_2} = Z_{22} + Z_{12}\frac{I_1}{I_2}$$

The mutual impedance Z_{12} is, in general, a vector which can be in any quadrant. The current ratios can also be in any quadrant, so that the self-impedance is liable to have a vector added to it which can be in any quadrant.

Returning to the case of two dipoles side by side fed with the same current and in phase, we have:

$$\frac{I_2}{I_1} = 1$$

and

$$Z_{a1} = Z_{a2} = Z_{11} + Z_{12} \quad . \quad . \quad . \quad . \quad (10.15)$$

For this case Z_{11} is 73 ohms and Z_{12} is given by the curves of Fig. 10.15. It

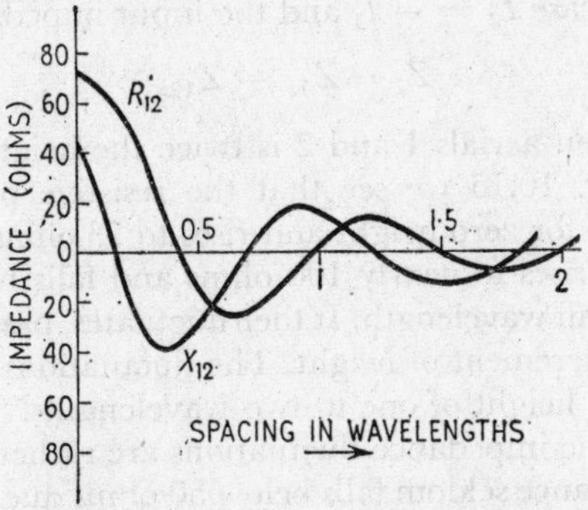

Fig. 10.15. Mutual impedance curves for two parallel half-wave dipoles.

can be checked that at very small spacings the apparent impedance is 146 ohms resistance plus a reactance.

If the two dipoles are spaced a quarter wavelength and fed for end fire operation, we have:

$$I_2 = jI_1$$

where I_1 is the current in the forward element of the array and I_2 the equal magnitude current in the back element. The apparent impedance of the forward element is then:

$$Z_{a1} = Z_{11} + jZ_{12} \quad . \quad . \quad . \quad . \quad . \quad (10.16)$$

Now $Z_{12} = 40 - j27$ at this spacing which gives an input impedance of of $100 + j40$ for the forward element. The impedance of the back element is given by:

$$Z_{a2} = Z_{22} - jZ_{12} \quad . \quad . \quad . \quad . \quad . \quad (10.17)$$

which gives a value of $46 - j40$. Thus the power radiated from the forward element is greater than that from a single dipole carrying the same current, while the back element radiates correspondingly less power.

The mutual impedance effects between two collinear dipoles are almost negligible for anything except quite small spacings between the ends of the two dipoles. This can be understood because one dipole is in the radiation null of the other. It is usual therefore to neglect the mutual impedance effects when considering arrays of collinear dipoles.

Another important case is the impedance of a half-wave dipole above a conducting plane. For a vertical dipole above a horizontal plane the modification to the free-space impedance is not very great (a few ohms) except when one end of the dipole is nearer to the plane than a quarter wavelength. When one end is nearly touching the plane the impedance rises to about 100 ohms.

For a horizontal dipole above a conducting plane the modification to the free-space impedance is rather greater and does not become negligible until the dipole is more than one wavelength above the plane. At very low heights it can be appreciated that the impedance will be very low if the plane is a good conductor, e.g., a metal, because the negative image will nearly cancel the radiation from the dipole. An approximate value of the input impedance for various heights can be obtained by making an allowance for the mutual impedance due to the image. In this case $I_2 = -I_1$ and the input impedance is given by:

$$Z_i = Z_{11} - Z_{12} \qquad (10.18)$$

The spacing between aerials 1 and 2 is twice the height of the aerial above the plane. Using Fig. 10.15 we see that the resistive part of the input impedance starts at zero for zero height and rises to 73 ohms at nearly a quarter-wave height. It then rises to nearly 100 ohms and falls to 73 ohms again at a height just short of a half wavelength. It then fluctuates, passing through 73 ohms every quarter-wave increment of height. The fluctuations drop to within a few ohms of 73 ohms at a height of one to two wavelengths.

With typical soils the impedance fluctuations are rather smaller, and at very low heights the impedance seldom falls below 50 ohms due to the relatively poor conductivity of soil.

Dipoles with Parasitic Elements

The gain of two parallel half-wave dipoles spaced a quarter wavelength and driven in end-fire fashion has been found to be 3 db. The gain of a half-wave dipole parallel to a conducting plane and spaced a quarter-wavelength from it has been found to be 6 db. Apart from the fact that a conducting plane can be simulated by a curtain of suitably spaced wires, the question arises as to whether it is possible to achieve similar gains by any simpler arrangement. By using an undriven reflector rod or wire parallel to the dipole, and suitably spaced from it, gains of about 3 db or a little more can in fact be realized. However, the impedance of this rod, which is called a parasitic element, must be adjusted to achieve the desired effect. This can be obtained at spacings of about one-eighth to one-quarter of a wavelength from the driven element. The parasitic element may be behind the driven aerial in relation to the desired direction of maximum gain, in which case it is called a reflector, or it may be in front of the driven aerial in which case it is called a director. A reflector and a director may both be used to obtain even more gain. These principles form the basis of the Yagi aerial described in Chapter 12.

The two cases are shown in Fig. 10.16, where A is the driven aerial, and B is the parasitic element with an adjustable impedance Z connected to its terminals. This impedance is always made reactive, and the parasite will have a very small resistance loss, so to a first approximation the parasite cannot waste any power as heat. It merely accepts power from the driven element and re-radiates it. The problem is to choose the spacing, and phase the current in the parasite, so that the desired directivity is obtained. To calculate this information proves to be almost insuperable and it is always determined experimentally. The fact that the parasite is in the induction and radiation field of the dipole is a severe complication. However, an impression of the method by which the parasite functions can be obtained from a vector diagram. At a spacing of 0·15 wavelength the mutual impedance between two dipoles has zero angle.

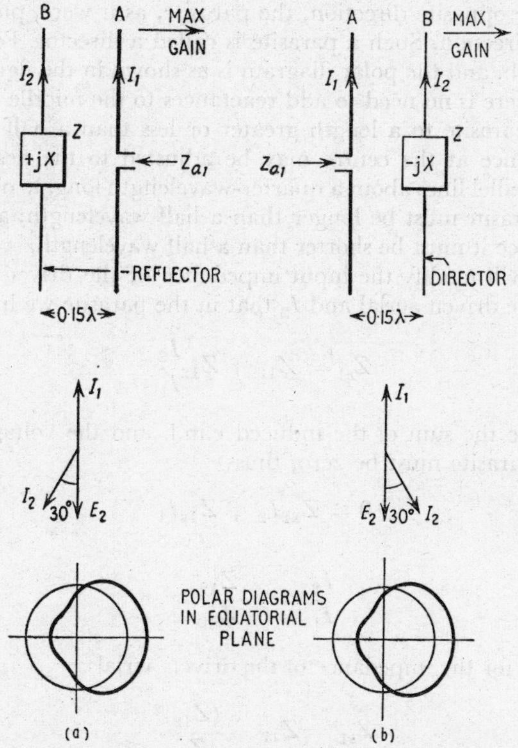

Fig. 10.16. Dipole aerials with parasites: (a) dipole and reflector; (b) dipole and director.

In Fig. 10.16 (a), which refers to this spacing, I_1 is the current in the driven element and E_2 is the voltage induced in the parasite. This is a voltage which can be imagined to exist at the centre of the parasite, and which is equivalent to the distributed voltages acting in the parasite. Because the mutual impedance has zero angle, and because a positive current in the driven element results in an oppositely directed voltage in the parasite (by consideration of a line of force and the close spacing) the voltage E_2 is in antiphase with I_1. If the impedance of the parasite is a positive reactance of sufficiently large value, it will have a current I_2 lagging E_2 by perhaps 30°. The current I_2 thus leads I_1 by 150°. It is thus phased to produce an end-fire effect in the direction shown; i.e., the parasite is behaving as a reflector. The actual angle of lead of I_2 does not correspond to the spacing of the elements (54°) so that the end-fire effect is not ideal, and complete cancellation does not occur in the reverse direction. Nevertheless the parasite produces a field at the driven element which is only about 90° out of phase with the field from the driven element. The current in the parasite is usually about 0·9 times that in the driven element, so that the gain in the forward direction is of the order of 3 db. The polar diagram is shown in Fig. 10.16 (a).

If the effective impedance of the parasite measured at the centre is phased by additional reactances to have a leading angle of 30° (i.e., the net reactance is capacitive) the vector diagram of Fig. 10.16 (b) applies. The end-fire effect is this time in the opposite direction, the parasite, as it were, pulling the polar diagram in its direction. Such a parasite is called a director. For this case the gain is about 3 db, and the polar diagram is as shown in the figure.

In practice, there is no need to add reactances to the middle of the parasite. By cutting the parasite to a length greater or less than a half wavelength its effective impedance at the centre may be adjusted to the desired value. By analogy with parallel lines about a quarter-wavelength long, to obtain a positive reactance the parasite must be longer than a half wavelength, and to obtain a negative reactance it must be shorter than a half wavelength.

▶ The parasite will modify the input impedance of the driven aerial. If I_1 is the current in the driven aerial and I_2 that in the parasite we have:

$$Z_{a1} = Z_{11} + Z_{12}\frac{I_2}{I_1}$$

In the parasite the sum of the induced e.m.f. and the voltage to drive the current in the parasite must be zero, thus:

$$0 = Z_{22}I_2 + Z_{12}I_1$$

or

$$\frac{I_2}{I_1} = -\frac{Z_{12}}{Z_{22}}$$

Thus we have for the impedance of the driven aerial:

$$Z_{a1} = Z_{11} - \frac{(Z_{12})^2}{Z_{22}} \quad . \quad . \quad . \quad . \quad . \quad . \quad (10.19)$$

For the spacing just considered $Z_{12} = 60$ ohms. For a reflector phased to have a current lagging 30° the value of Z_{22} would be about $73 + j42$. If Z_{11} is assumed to be 73 ohms this gives a resultant impedance of:

$$Z_{a1} = 36 + j21$$

Notice that the resistive part of the input impedance is considerably reduced. This is typical of most aerials with parasites although it is not an essential feature. The input impedance also has a considerable reactive term, which should be taken into account during matching. This is usually effected by a slight length adjustment on the driven element. ◀

Although the spacing above is that for achieving gains near the maximum, it requires rather critical adjustments, and the aerial impedance is somewhat low. For the reflector it is usual to adopt a spacing of about a quarter wavelength. For this spacing the field-strength gain is also about 1·4, or 3 db, but the aerial impedance is about 60 ohms or even more, depending upon the angle of lag in the reflector. The quarter-wave spacing is less effective in the case of a director parasite and the spacing of 0·15 wavelength is commonly adopted. In practice, the determination of spacing and lengths of parasite and driven aerial is carried out experimentally using adjustable elements. Field strengths are measured and adjustments are made to achieve a nearly resistive impedance at the driven element.

Linear Arrays

The method of determining the field pattern of two aerials is easily extended to a number of aerials equally spaced along a straight line. This is known as a linear array. As before we assume that all the aerials produce fields of equal strength, and interaction between elements is neglected. In the first case to be considered the aerials are excited in phase. To obtain the group pattern, consider n isotropic radiators spaced at a distance of d metres as in Fig. 10.17 (a).

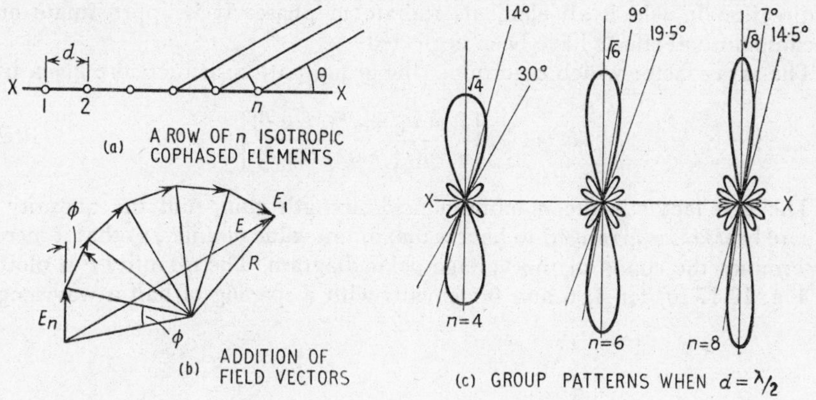

Fig. 10.17. Group patterns for linear array of n isotropic elements.

At a distance large compared with d the field strengths from the separate radiators will be substantially equal. If E_n is the vector representing the field from the nth radiator, the field from the $(n - 1)$th radiator will be represented by E_{n-1} lagging E_n by the angle:

$$\phi = \frac{2\pi}{\lambda} d \cos \theta$$

The field from the next radiator to the left will be represented by a vector lagging by the same angle behind E_{n-1}. The other radiators will provide field vectors lagging progressively until the vector E_1 corresponding to the first radiator is reached. The field strength at the distant point is given by the sum of these vectors. From the geometry of the vector diagram in Fig. 10.17 (b) the sum E is given by:

$$E = 2R \sin n\phi/2$$

and

$$E_1 = 2R \sin \phi/2$$

Eliminating the radius R we get:

$$E = E_1 \frac{\sin n\phi/2}{\sin \phi/2}$$

$$= E_1 \frac{\sin \{(n\pi d/\lambda) \cos \theta\}}{\sin \{(\pi d/\lambda) \cos \theta\}} \quad . \quad . \quad . \quad . \quad (10.20)$$

In the broadside direction $\theta = \pi/2$ and we get:

$$E = nE_1$$

since all radiators are radiating in phase. If the same total power were concentrated in one radiator the field strength would be $E_1\sqrt{(n)}$. The field strength gain of the array is therefore $\sqrt{n}$ in the direction of maximum radiation, as compared with a single radiator. The power density gain in the direction of maximum radiation is therefore n times that for a single radiator. This simple result is approximately true for all arrays of aerials which are designed to have a direction in which all elements radiate in phase. It is approximate only because mutual effects have been neglected.

The array factor which determines the group pattern is therefore given by:

$$F = \sqrt{n}\left[\frac{1}{n}.\frac{\sin \{(n\pi d/\lambda) \cos \theta\}}{\sin \{(\pi d/\lambda) \cos \theta\}}\right] \quad . \quad . \quad . \quad . \quad (10.21)$$

The first factor is the maximum field strength gain, and the quantity in square brackets is arranged to have a maximum value of unity, so that it merely determines the shape of the voltage polar diagram. The quantity F is plotted in Fig. 10.17 (c) for 4, 6 and 8 elements with a spacing of half a wavelength

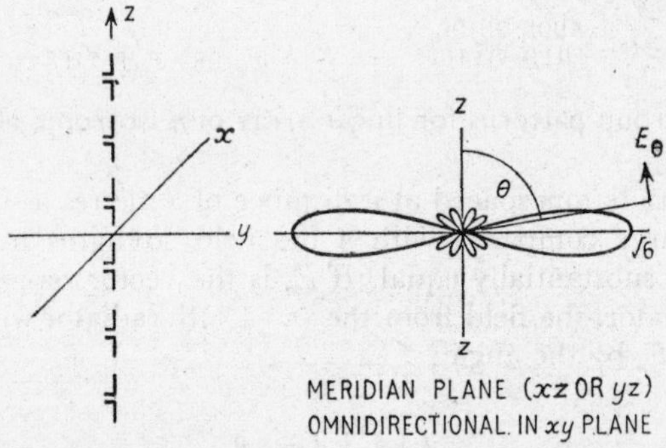

Fig. **10.18. Linear array of collinear half-wave dipole elements.**

between elements. The voltage gain figures are marked, and the beam half widths both to 3 db decrease of field strength and to the first nulls. The complete polar diagrams are solids of revolution about XX.

The two practical cases arising from the linear-array group pattern are the collinear array of dipoles and the broadside array. The collinear array will have a polar diagram given by the product of the group pattern and the meridian-plane dipole pattern as in Fig. 10.18. The broadside array will have a polar diagram given by the product of the group pattern and the appropriate patterns of a dipole as in Fig. 10.19. It will be observed that this array is capable of forming in the equatorial plane a narrow forward and a similar backward

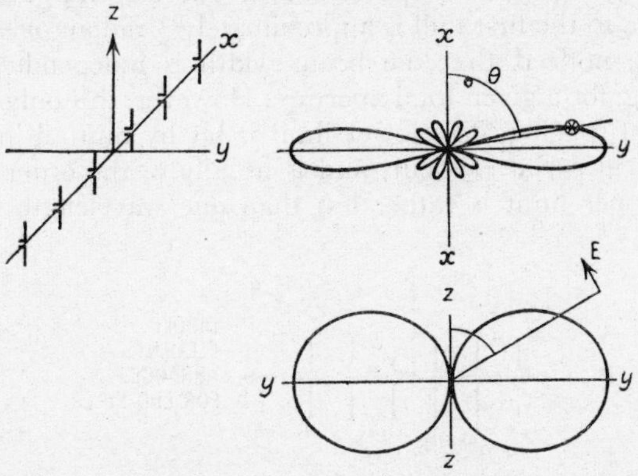

Fig. **10.19. Linear broadside array of half-wave dipoles.**

beam. In the vertical plane through the main beams the polar diagram is still that of a dipole. Methods of narrowing the beam in this plane and of eliminating backward radiation are given in the next section.

For broadside arrays with a large number of elements an important rule can be deduced for the beam width. Since the beam width is small, cos θ in equation (10.21) can be replaced by θ' radians, where $\theta' = (\pi/2) - \theta$. The angles out to the first nulls are then given by:

$$\frac{\sin\left(\frac{n\pi d}{\lambda}\theta'\right)}{\sin\left(\frac{\pi d}{\lambda}\theta'\right)} \approx 0$$

or

$$\frac{n\pi d}{\lambda}\theta' \approx \pm\pi$$

or

$$\theta' \approx \pm\frac{\lambda}{nd} \text{ radians} \quad . \quad . \quad . \quad . \quad . \quad (10.22)$$

The denominator is the length of the array plus one spacing, and may be

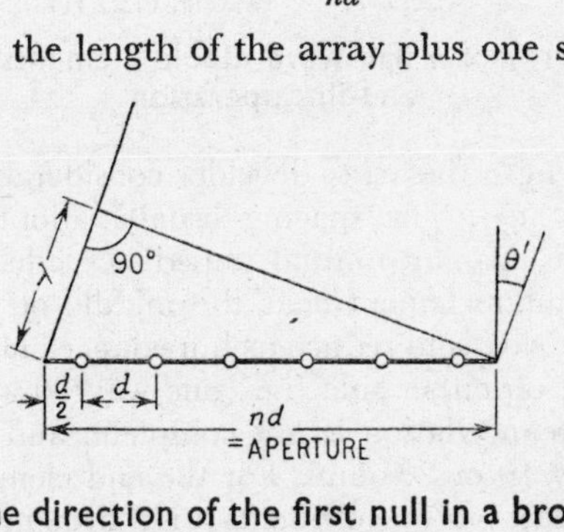

Fig. **10.20. The direction of the first null in a broadside array.**

regarded as the aperture of the array. The direction of the first null is therefore that shown in Fig. 10.20. The angle θ′ is also the 3-db beam width.

Alternatively the direction θ' in radians is the reciprocal of the aperture expressed in wavelengths, a very convenient rule. For example a broadside array of 8 half-wave elements spaced half a wavelength apart, has a beam in which the angle to the first null is approximately $\frac{1}{4}$ radian or nearly 15°.

It should be noticed that the beam width is independent of the actual element spacing, for a given total aperture. However, this only applies between certain limits of spacing. The lower limit is set by mutual impedance effects between practical aerial elements and is usually of the order of half a wavelength. The upper limit is rather less than one wavelength, because with a

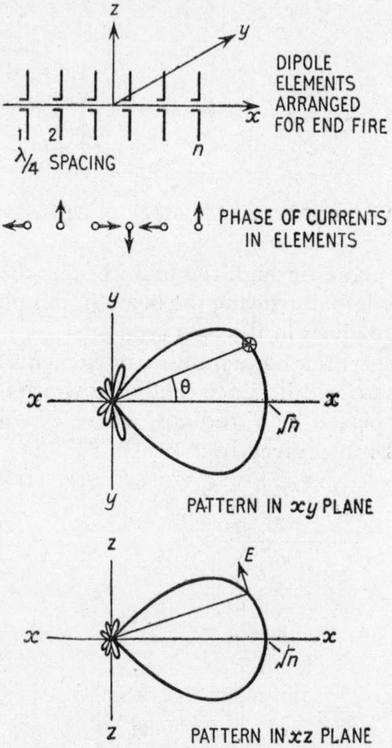

Fig. 10.21. A linear array of *n* half-wave dipole elements phased and spaced for end-fire operation.

spacing of one wavelength the array develops considerable end fire lobes [compare with Fig. 10.10 (c)]. The spacing usually adopted is therefore half a wavelength. With this spacing mutual impedance effects tend to cancel out. For consider a particular element near the middle of the array, the effect of the element on either side is to reduce its impedance. However the effect of the next but one element on either side (i.e., one wavelength away) is to increase the impedance. The cancellation is not complete, and the impedance of the element is reduced by 10 or 20 ohms. For the end elements the reduction is a little less, and for the last but one elements it is a little more.

The remaining linear array of importance is the end fire array. Consider n dipole elements driven with equal strength currents, as in Fig. 10.21, spaced a quarter wavelength between elements. The signal along the x axis to the right will be reinforced if the signal to the second element from the left lags the signal to the first element by $\pi/2$ radians or 90°, and the signal to the third element lags that to the second element by $\pi/2$ and so on. A suitably arranged transmission line carrying power from left to right would provide just this phasing if its velocity were assumed equal to the free-space velocity. Then in the *xy* plane at an angle θ to the *x* axis the phase lag between the signals arriving from consecutive elements is:

$$\phi = \frac{\pi}{2} - \frac{2\pi d}{\lambda} \cos \theta$$

where $d = \lambda/4$ or:

$$\phi = \frac{\pi}{2}(1 - \cos \theta)$$

The array factor or group pattern for *n* elements is therefore given by:

$$F = \sqrt{n}\left\{\frac{1}{n} \cdot \frac{\sin \{(n\pi/4)(1 - \cos \theta)\}}{\sin \{(\pi/4)(1 - \cos \theta)\}}\right\} \quad . \quad . \quad . \quad . \quad (10.23)$$

by analogy with equation (10.21). In the equatorial plane the dipole pattern is a circle so that the group pattern is also the resultant pattern for the array. In the *xz* plane the group pattern must be multiplied by the figure-of-eight dipole pattern suitably oriented. In the *yz* plane the pattern is the group pattern (a small circle) multiplied by the figure of eight. The two important patterns are shown in Fig. 10.21. The angle to the first null in the *xy* plane is of interest. This is given by the angle θ which makes $n\phi = 2\pi$

That is
$$n\frac{\pi}{2}(1 - \cos \theta) = 2\pi$$

or
$$\cos \theta = 1 - 4/n \quad . \quad . \quad . \quad . \quad . \quad (10.24)$$

For 8 elements, the value of θ is 60° and for 16 elements it is 41°. Thus the end fire array does not produce a particularly narrow beam in the direction of fire. It has the advantage of small back radiation.

▶ For an element near the middle of an end-fire array there is a very close cancellation of mutual impedance effect. The impedance correction due to an element on one side would be given by the mutual impedance multiplied by $+\mathrm{j}$ owing to the phasing of the current, while that due to an element on the other side would be the mutual impedance multiplied by $-\mathrm{j}$. Any departure from normal half-wave dipole impedance therefore occurs towards the ends of the array. ◀

Stacked Arrays

If a number of broadside-type linear arrays are placed one above the other we have stacked or rectangular arrays. Fig. 10.22 (a) shows such an array of hypothetical isotropic radiators. The dimension *W* is the horizontal aperture and *H* is the vertical aperture. If an *n* unit linear array is stacked *m* high the power gain over a single unit in the direction of maximum radiation, where all elements co-operate in phase, is *mn* by the same argument as the previous section. To obtain the polar diagram for the complete array, the group pattern of a linear array of *n* isotropic elements is deduced as in the previous section. The group pattern for a linear array of m isotropic elements is also obtained. These group patterns are solids of revolution. When they are multiplied together (one rotates about the y axis and one about the z axis) there results in general a forward beam and a backward beam as shown in Fig. 10.22 (b). For element spacings of a half wavelength the side radiation in the yz plane may be neglected. The beam width in the xy plane depends upon W and the beam width in the xz plane depends on H.

If now the individual isotropic elements are replaced by half-wave dipoles

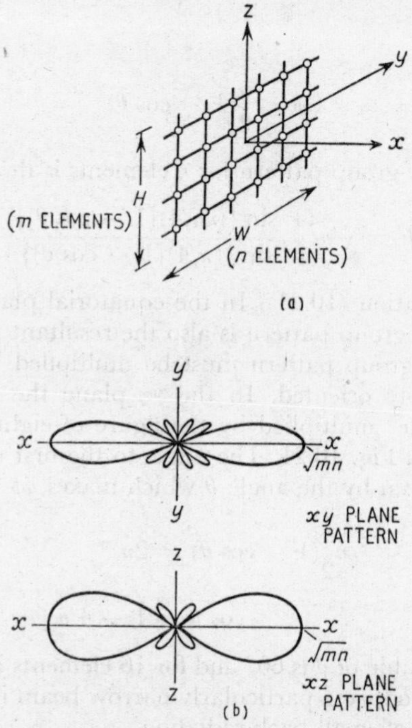

Fig. 10.22. Group patterns for $m \times n$ rectangular array.

arranged as in Fig. 10.23 (a) the polar diagram for the complete array is the product of the group pattern and the dipole pattern suitably oriented.

All the broadside arrangements considered so far radiate beams in two opposite directions. In practice one beam only is required. There are in general three methods of eliminating the backward beam. The first is to replace each element with a pair of elements excited for end-fire operation. The array then becomes two identical arrays spaced say a quarter wavelength apart and driven with signals phased either 90° or 270° depending upon the direction required. The second is to place a parasite of suitable length and at a suitable spacing behind each dipole. The third is to place a conducting sheet or screen at a quarter wavelength behind the array. Besides eliminating the backward beam the forward gain is also increased. The actual effect on the polar diagram is given by a product of the group pattern for the array and the pattern for the actual dipole element with its reflector, or other element. The use of two end fire dipoles, or a dipole with a parasite only, gives about 3 db extra gain, whereas a complete reflecting screen gives a theoretical extra gain of 6 db. For the latter case the group pattern for the array is multiplied by the pattern for a dipole with a reflecting screen at a quarter wavelength [see Fig. 10.13 (d)]. The actual order in which patterns are multiplied is immaterial but it is preferable to adopt the order given here. The total field strength gain for a $m \times n$ array of dipoles with a reflector is thus $2\sqrt{mn}$ or the power gain is $4mn$. The polar diagram for a 4×4 dipole array with reflecting screen is given in Fig. 10.23 (b).

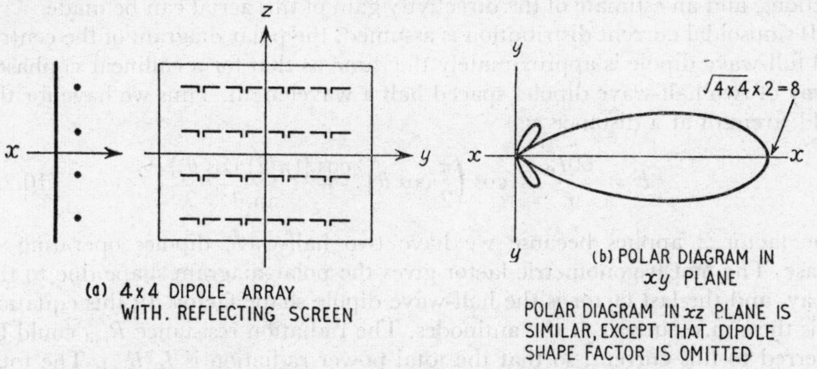

Fig. 10.23. Polar diagram for a 4×4 dipole array with reflecting screen one quarter wavelength behind the aerials.

The effect of the earth is taken into account by the method of images and the group pattern corresponding to an isotropic element at the mean height of the array above earth. The rigging, feeding and other practical details of such arrays are considered in more detail in Chapter 11.

Standing-Wave Radiators

The half-wave dipole is the simplest form of radiator having a standing wave. For conductors of greater length, higher modes of standing wave can be produced, and it is important to know the corresponding polar diagrams, because such standing-wave radiators are often employed as aerial elements.

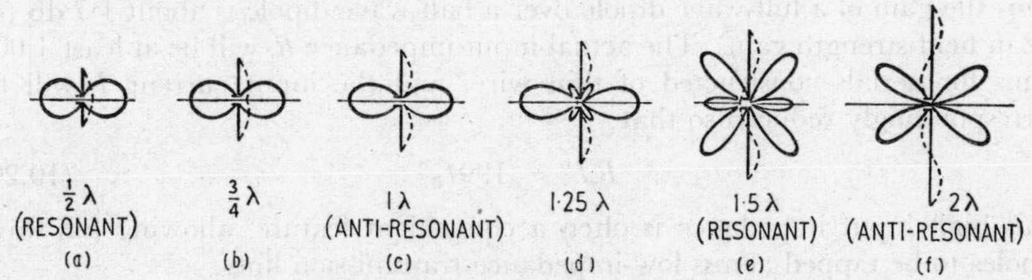

Fig. 10.24. Centre-fed aerials with standing waves (dotted lines show current distribution).

Next to the half-wave dipole, the centre-fed full-wave dipole shown in Fig. 10.24 (c) is of importance. By analogy with the half-wave transmission line the current distribution may be drawn in as shown by the dotted curves. Notice that this makes the current continuous at the feed point; i.e., it does not change sign across the feeding gap. This aerial is clearly an anti-resonant type of impedance. Owing to the radiation the current at the generator terminals will not be zero, but will have a small value dependent upon the aerial impedance. Reference to Fig. 9.12 shows that the ratio of aerial length to conductor radius (of cross-section) has to be taken into account in determining the impedance of a centre-fed full-wave dipole, whereas the value of 73 ohms is roughly applicable to all half-wave dipoles. The calculation of the input impedance of a full-wave dipole presents some difficulty and will not be given here. However, the polar diagram can be deduced by the methods of the previous sections, and an estimate of the directivity gain of this aerial can be made.

If sinusoidal current distribution is assumed, the polar diagram of the centre-fed full-wave dipole is approximately the same as that for a collinear cophased array of two half-wave dipoles spaced half a wavelength. Thus we have for the field strength at a distance r:

$$E = \frac{60I_0}{r}.2.\cos\left(\frac{\pi}{2}\cos\theta\right).\frac{\cos\{(\pi/2)\cos\theta)\}}{\sin\theta} \quad . \quad . \quad (10.25)$$

The factor 2 applies because we have two half-wave dipoles operating in phase. The first trigonometric factor gives the polar-diagram shape due to the array, and the last factor is the half-wave dipole shape factor. In this equation I_0 is the r.m.s. current at the antinodes. The radiation resistance R_{rad} could be referred to this current, so that the total power radiation is $I_0{}^2R_{rad}$. The total radiated power could also be calculated by integrating the power flow through a large sphere surrounding the aerial when the field strength is given by equation (10.25). When this is carried out a value of 199 ohms is obtained for R_{rad}. The question arises as to why this differs from $2 \times 73 = 146$ ohms. The explanation is the mutual impedance between the two halves of the aerial, which has a value of 26 ohms, thus accounting for the difference.

The maximum gain in a meridian plane, over a half-wave dipole radiating the same power, is therefore rather less than the 3 db which applies when mutual impedance is neglected. The extra power supplied to a full-wave dipole as compared with two half-wave dipoles is:

$$10 \log_{10} \frac{199}{146} = 1{\cdot}3 \text{ db}$$

Thus the gain of a full-wave dipole over a half-wave dipole is about 1·7 db (or 1·2 in field-strength gain). The actual input impedance R_i will be at least 1,000 ohms for aerials constructed of thin wire, and the input current I_i will be correspondingly reduced so that:

$$R_iI_i{}^2 = 199I_0{}^2 \quad . \quad . \quad . \quad . \quad . \quad . \quad (10.26)$$

This high input impedance is often a convenient feature, allowing full-wave dipoles to be tapped across low-impedance transmission lines.

The next case of interest is the centre fed $1\frac{1}{2}$ wavelength aerial shown in Fig. 10.24 (e). This aerial is resonant and its impedance will again be low, but not as low as for a half-wave dipole. The polar diagram can be deduced by an extension of the method of Appendix 9.3 or it may be obtained by the method of spaced isotropic elements suitably phased. The resulting diagram is shown in the figure and it will be observed that the single lobe of previous resonant cases has now broken into three lobes. The direction of the null is easily shown to be $\cos^{-1}(\frac{1}{3})$ or 71° to the wire.

As we proceed to centre driven aerials having higher modes of standing wave the two main lobes develop and they get progressively nearer to the axis of the wire. All these polar diagrams are, of course, sections of solids of revolution.

For lengths intermediate between integral numbers of half waves, the polar diagrams can generally be judged as intermediate between the two nearest multiple half-wave patterns. An important intermediate case is the $1\frac{1}{4}\lambda$ aerial shown in Fig. 10.24 (d). This can be shown to have the largest gain for the main lobe at right angles to the aerial and for this reason it is sometimes used in preference to the full-wave dipole. The unbalanced version of this aerial (i.e., the $\frac{5}{8}\lambda$ vertical aerial above a conducting plane) has one half of this polar diagram and is sometimes employed to obtain a strong surface wave. However, the small lobe which has started to appear is sometimes an objection. For these intermediate lengths the input impedance will be partly reactive.

If the above aerials are driven from a point other than the centre the polar diagrams are generally quite different. For example Fig. 10.25 (a) is a full-wave aerial driven a quarter wavelength from one end, and its polar diagram should be compared with the centre-driven case. Long standing-wave radiators can be

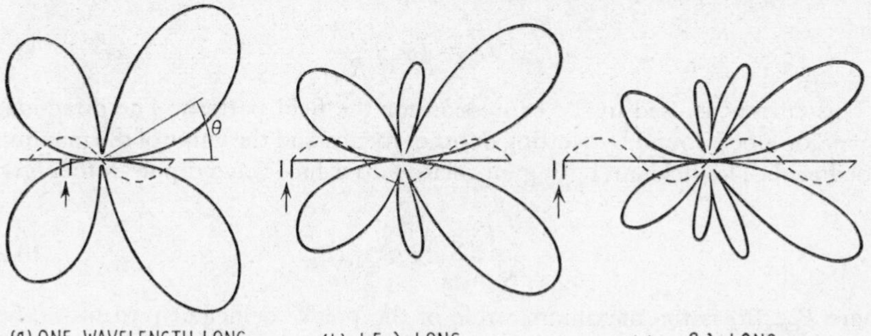

Fig. **10.25. Standing-wave radiators fed (a) at quarter-wave point, (b) and (c) at one end.**

driven from one end or at an anti-node of current. The polar diagrams for end or quarter-wave-from-one-end feeding are shown in Fig. 10.25 and it will be observed that for even numbers of half waves the diagrams differ from the corresponding centre-fed cases. Furthermore, owing to radiation loss, there is a travelling-wave component of current near the feed point in addition to the standing-wave current. This has the effect of causing the lobes to become unsymmetrical, and the lobes in the direction of the free end are somewhat strengthened as shown, due to the effect described in the next section. Strictly speaking, these aerials present an unbalanced load to a balanced feeder. In the end-fed cases the aerial presents a high impedance load and does not seriously unbalance the feeder.

The field strength from the end-fed standing-wave aerials of Fig. 10.25 can be calculated by the method of Appendix 9.3 if sinusoidal current distribution is assumed. The results, from which the shape of the polar diagrams may be deduced, are as follows:

$$E = \frac{60I_0}{r} \cdot \frac{\cos\{(m\pi/2)\cos\theta\}}{\sin\theta} \quad \text{(when } m \text{ is odd)}$$

$$= \frac{60I_0}{r} \cdot \frac{\sin\{(m\pi/2)\cos\theta\}}{\sin\theta} \quad \text{(when } m \text{ is even)} \quad . \quad . \quad (10.27)$$

where E is the r.m.s. field strength in volts per metre, I_0 is the r.m.s. value of the antinode current, and m is the total number of half waves in the standing-wave pattern. The trigonometric factor is the polar coefficient $P(\theta)$ and it has a maximum value greater than unity excepting for the case of $m = 1$ (the half-wave dipole). The gain of the major lobes cannot however be deduced from the maximum value of the polar coefficient because a knowledge of the radiation resistance is required if the aerial is to be compared with a half-wave dipole radiating the same power.

To determine the actual field-strength gain (over a half-wave dipole) in the direction of the large lobes the above field-strength equations are used to calculate the total power flow through a large sphere. The latter is equated to $I_0^2 R_{rad}$ where I_0 is the r.m.s. antinode current assumed, and R_{rad} is the radiation resistance corresponding to an antinode feed point. The antinode current is determined in terms of the half-wave dipole current, I_0', which gives the same total radiated power, thus:

$$I_0^2 R_{rad} = (I_0')^2 \times 73$$

or

$$I_0 = I_0' \sqrt{\frac{73}{R_{rad}}}$$

This current is used in the expression for the field pattern. The direction of the major lobe is found by plotting or other means and the value of the maximum is deduced. The field-strength gain relative to a half-wave dipole is then given by:

$$\sqrt{\frac{73}{R_{rad}}} \times P_{max}(\theta) \quad . \quad . \quad . \quad . \quad . \quad . \quad (10.28)$$

where $P_{max}(\theta)$ is the maximum value of the polar coefficient part of the field pattern.

Values of antinode radiation resistance, maximum field strength gain over half-wave dipole, and angle of major lobe are given in Fig. 10.26.

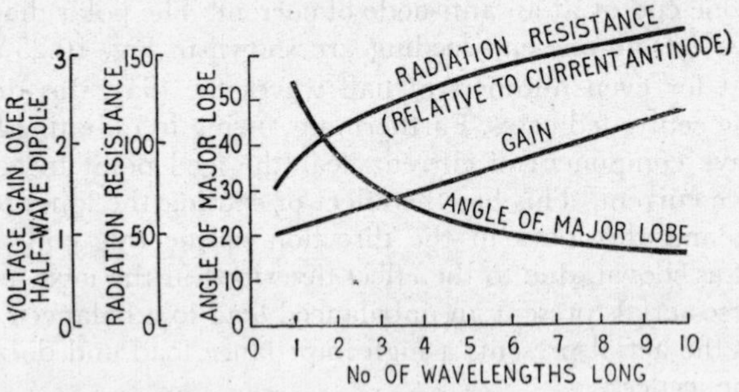

Fig. 10.26. Angle of major lobe, radiation resistance and voltage gain of end-fed resonant wire aerials.

Non-Resonant or Travelling-Wave Radiators

So far consideration has been given to resonant or standing-wave radiators and arrays of such elements. The bandwidth over which such elements will operate satisfactorily, even when made thick or caged is usually of the order of $\pm$ 10% of the resonant or anti-resonant frequency. Radio systems which employ reflections from the ionosphere are frequently required to operate on a number of widely spaced frequencies. It is often a requirement that the frequency must be changed rapidly from one value to another for day and night working. There is thus a need for an aerial element of much greater bandwidth. This need is met by the non-resonant or travelling-wave radiator. To prevent reflections and standing waves an absorbing resistance is required. This wastes some power (often as much as half the input power), but even so this type of aerial has the particular advantage of simplicity. In studying it the first problem is to determine the radiation from a single wire carrying a travelling wave.

Consider a long two-wire transmission line terminated so that no reflection occurs for travelling waves passing along the line. The spacing between wires is not important for the moment, because the radiation law applicable to current elements can be applied to one wire only. The effect of the second wire can then be allowed for by determining the group pattern for positive and negative elements with appropriate spacing. We then have to calculate the radiation from a long single wire having a current similar to the current in one leg of a transmission line carrying a travelling wave. For simplicity, the attenuation of the current wave is neglected, although for wire spacings which provide radiation, there will be a diminution of current amplitude along the line.

This single wire may be looked upon as a number of Hertzian dipoles arranged end to end fed by currents with phase lagging according to distance to the right. That is, it is similar to an end-fire array of collinear Hertzian

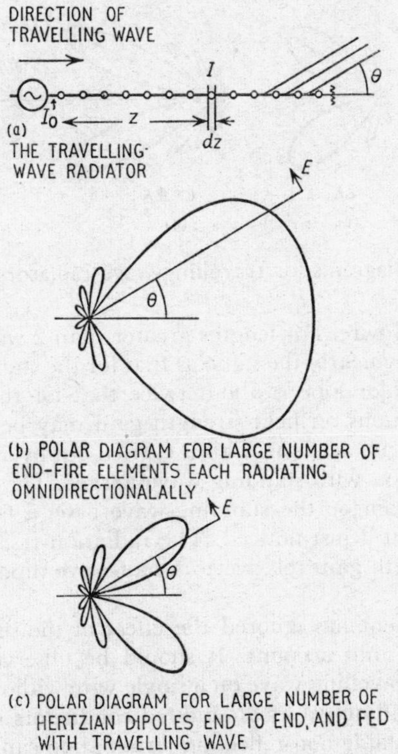

Fig. 10.27. Development of polar diagram for travelling-wave radiator.

dipoles, provided the velocity in the wire is assumed equal to that in free space. To find the polar diagram we could determine the group pattern for a large number of isotropic radiators excited in end-fire fashion and multiply by the pattern for a current element. The form of the polar diagram is therefore similar to that shown in Fig. 10.27 (c). The complete diagram is a solid of revolution about the wire. The travelling-wave radiator is therefore essentially an end-fire radiator with a sharp null in the forward direction which is a continuation of the wire. The actual calculation of the field pattern is more easily carried out using integration. This is done in Appendix 10.1 and only the results are given here in summarized form.

The field strength at a distance r on a bearing at an angle θ to the wire axis is given by:

$$E = \frac{60 I_0}{r} \cdot \frac{\sin\theta}{1-\cos\theta} \, . \sin\left\{\frac{\pi l}{\lambda}(1-\cos\theta)\right\}$$

$$= \frac{60 I_0}{r} P(\theta) \quad . \quad . \quad . \quad . \quad . \quad . \quad . \quad . \quad . \quad (10.29)$$

where l is the length of the wire and I_0 is the r.m.s. value of the travelling wave of current (assumed constant).

The polar coefficient is plotted in Fig. 10.28 for various lengths of wire. It will be observed that the major lobe gets narrower and nearer to the axis the

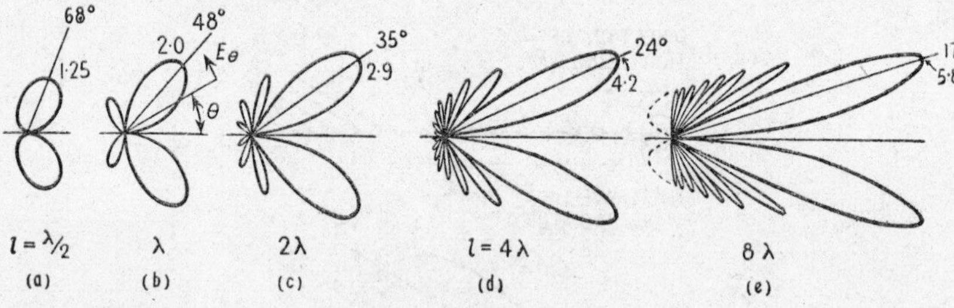

Fig. 10.28. Polar diagrams for travelling-wave radiators of various lengths.

greater the length of wire. For lengths greater than 2 wavelengths the angle of the major lobe is very nearly the same as that for the standing-wave aerial. The amplitude of the major lobe is about twice that for the standing-wave case. However, no deductions on field strength gain may be made without taking radiation resistance into account. This is carried out by a process similar to that outlined in connection with standing-wave aerials. The radiation resistance is somewhat higher than for the standing-wave case, a factor which offsets the voltage gain of about 2 just noticed. The radiation resistance, angle of major lobe and field strength gain relative to a half-wave dipole are all summarized in Fig. 10.29.

The above argument has ignored the effect of the second conductor. This must now be taken into account. It should be observed however that it is possible to excite a travelling wave on a single wire without a return conductor. The existence of standing waves on end-fed conductors was shown in the previous section. If a suitable non-reflecting termination can be applied to the end distant from the feed point then we have a single wire with a travelling wave.

This termination could be a suitable value of impedance having one end connected to the line, and the other connected to a large conducting sphere or a quarter-wave length of wire. Either of these devices serves to make one end of the terminating impedance at a low impedance to the surroundings. A similar device should strictly be connected to the free end of the feeder. It is not easy

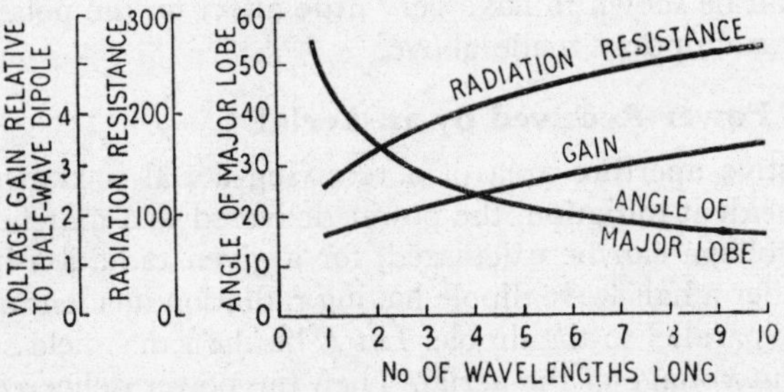

Fig. 10.29. Angle of major lobe, radiation resistance and voltage gain of travelling-wave radiator.

to excite a single wire in this way but there are alternative methods of approach which employ the return conductor or earth. If the return conductor is only a small fraction of a wavelength away from the radiating wire just considered, there will be little radiation because the return conductor will produce a field which just cancels that from the first conductor. When the return conductor is half a wavelength away a more favourable situation results. With the group-pattern method, the pattern for a single wire would be multiplied by a figure-of-eight pattern having its null in the direction of the single-wire null. Thus the side lobes would be augmented relative to the main lobes. A better method of employing the return conductor is to pull the two wires apart at one point so as to create a diamond shaped figure as in Fig. 10.30. If the wires are pulled

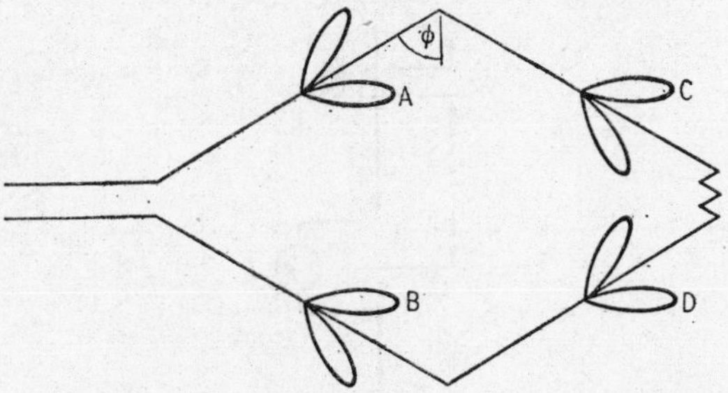

Fig. 10.30. Four travelling-wave radiators arranged to form an aerial.

apart far enough for the four lobes A, B, C and D to reinforce one another, extra gain is obtained. Furthermore, there is no difficulty in providing a suitable load resistance to prevent undue reflections from the termination. This is the basis of the rhombic aerial described in more detail in the next chapter. The angle ϕ is called the tilt angle and it should equal approximately 90° less the angle of the major lobe. The fact that the angle of the major lobe for a single-wire radiator changes only from about 24° to 17° when the length changes from 4 to 8 wavelengths explains why this type of aerial operates over a wide band of frequencies.

If the travelling-wave current falls to about 70% of its input value by the time it reaches the termination, the power lost in the termination will be one half of the input power. This loss must be taken into account when considering aerial gain, and has not been allowed for in Fig. 10.29. This amount of current attenuation can be shown to have very little affect on the polar diagram, thus justifying the assumptions made above.

Voltage and Power Received by an Aerial

If the effective aperture area of a receiving aerial is known for a certain direction of incident radiation, the power delivered to a matched load and the open-circuit voltage can be calculated, for a given radiation intensity. As an example consider a half-wave dipole having radiation incident upon it with the electric vector parallel to the dipole. Let E be the r.m.s. field strength and V_0 the open-circuit voltage of the aerial. Then the power delivered to a matched load of 73 ohms is:

$$P = \frac{(V_0/2)^2}{73} = A_e \cdot \frac{E^2}{120\pi} \quad . \quad . \quad . \quad . \quad . \quad (10.30)$$

Substituting for the absorption area A_e from Table 9.1 we get:

$$\frac{V_0{}^2}{4 \times 73} = \frac{30\lambda^2}{73\pi} \cdot \frac{E^2}{120\pi}$$

or

$$V_0 = \frac{E\lambda}{\pi}$$

$$= E\left(\frac{\lambda}{2} \cdot \frac{2}{\pi}\right) \quad . \quad . \quad . \quad . \quad . \quad (10.31)$$

The term in brackets may be considered to be the effective length of the aerial. It will be observed that the effective length for reception is equal to that for

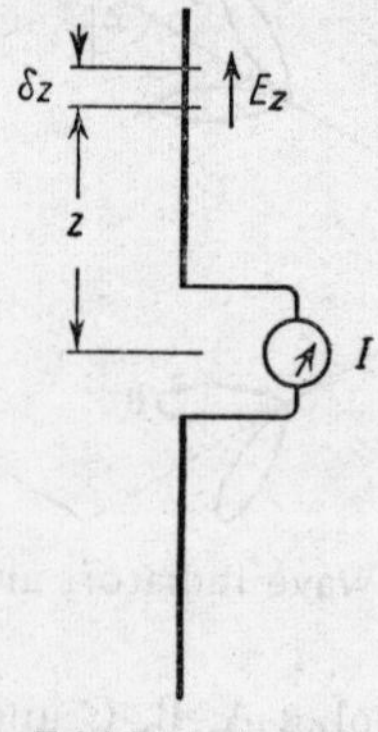

Fig. 10.31. E.M.F. induced in a dipole.

transmitting. This is a general result which follows from the Reciprocity Theorem.

▶ The general proof may be obtained by reference to Fig. 10.31. Let $I(z)$ be the current at the centre of the aerial when it is short-circuited, due to a series e.m.f. of 1 volt inserted at the point z. If E_z is the field strength at point z resolved in the direction of the aerial conductor, the voltage injected into the aerial by a short length δz is given by:

$$E_z \, \delta z$$

The total received current is therefore given by:

$$I = \sum (E_z \, \delta z) \, . \, I(z)$$

If the centre of the aerial is now broken and a zero-impedance generator is inserted which just cancels the current I, the voltage of this generator is the open circuit voltage:

$$V_0 = Z_D I$$
$$= Z_D \sum (E_z \, \delta z) \, . \, I(z)$$

where Z_D is the aerial impedance when transmitting.

Now the Reciprocity Theorem applies to a single aerial in the same way that it applies to two aerials. Thus $I(z)$ is also the current at a section z due to 1 volt drive at the centre.

Therefore $\sum I(z) \, \delta z =$ Area under current curve for 1 volt drive

$$= I_D l_e$$

where I_D is the current for 1 volt drive and l_e is the effective length of the aerial. If the field E_z is uniform and equal to E say, then:

$$V_0 = Z_D E I_D l_e$$

But $Z_D I_D = 1$ volt, hence

$$V_0 = E l_e \qquad \qquad (10.32)$$

Thus the open circuit voltage is equal to the field strength along the aerial multiplied by the effective length as deduced from transmitting considerations.

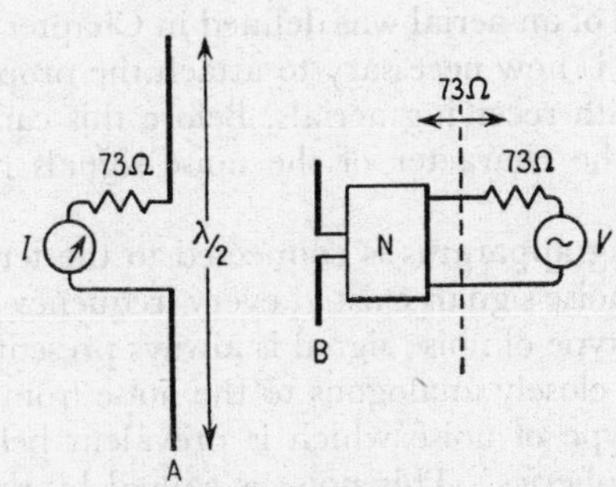

Fig. 10.32. Equivalence of aperture area of a half-wave dipole and a short dipole efficiently matched.

The open-circuit voltage is not necessarily an important criterion with receiving aerials. A short aerial with a small open-circuit voltage can deliver as much power to a load as a longer aerial if completely efficient matching can be achieved. For consider the half-wave dipole A and the short dipole B in Fig. 10.32. The short dipole is assumed to be made of perfectly conducting material. It will have a radiation resistance much smaller than 73 ohms and a capacitive reactance. The network N is assumed to be ideal and it transforms and matches the aerial impedance to 73 ohms. Then if we transmit from B to A, the power radiated by B is:

$$P_T = \left(\frac{V}{2}\right)^2 \times \frac{1}{73}$$

and the power received by A in the 73 ohm load is:

$$P_R = I^2 \times 73$$
$$= A_e P$$

where A_e is the effective aperture area of the half-wave dipole and P is the power density of the incident radiation.

From reciprocal considerations the generator V and the ammeter I may be interchanged, without affecting the received current. Thus the power radiated by A is also P_T and the power density at B is also P. The power received by B is also P_R and hence the absorption area of the short aerial is equal to that of the half-wave aerial. This result may seem surprising, but it has already been observed in connection with equations (9.19) and (9.20) that effective aperture is independent of length. The explanation is that the network N must contain positive reactance to cancel the aerial reactance, and the system is therefore highly resonant. It therefore has a strong re-radiated field which extends over the same area as for a large dipole. It interacts with the incident energy and abstracts power equivalent to that abstracted by a half-wave dipole.

In practice neither the aerial nor the network is loss free, and the short aerial inevitably delivers less power than a larger aerial. Nevertheless, it is important to appreciate the fact that but for conductor losses the short aerial is equivalent to the longer aerial.

Directivity Gain of Receiving Aerials

The directivity gain of an aerial was defined in Chapter 9 in relation to transmitting aerials, and it is now necessary to attach the proper significance to this term in connection with receiving aerials. Before this can be done, however, a brief explanation of the character of the noise signals received by an aerial must be given.

If suitable measuring apparatus is connected to the terminals of a receiving aerial it is found that noise signals exist at every frequency of the radio spectrum that is explored. One type of noise signal is always present, namely that known as thermal noise. It is closely analogous to the noise from resistors discussed in Volume 2. Another type of noise which is prevalent below about 20 Mc/s is that known as 'atmospherics'. This noise is caused by radiation from the impulsive electrical discharges associated with clouds and thunderstorms. This noise radiation can be guided by the ionosphere (see Chapter 14) and can travel over considerable distances, so that the resultant effect is rather similar to enhanced thermal noise. The third type of noise is known as man-made noise, and is caused by radiation from certain types of electrical apparatus.

Typical values for atmospheric noise levels are given in Chapter 11, but in general this type of noise falls to a low level above about 20 Mc/s. Noise from electrical apparatus can persist up to one or two hundred megacycles per second.

However, for a correctly sited receiving aerial, at frequencies above 20 Mc/s the noise is substantially all of the thermal type. The amount of this thermal noise can be deduced from a law of physics which states that the available noise power at the aerial terminals is given by:

$$P_{max} = kTB \quad \ldots \ldots \quad (10.33)$$

where k is Boltzmann's constant ($1{\cdot}38 \times 10^{-23}$ watts per degree Kelvin per cycle per second),

T is the absolute temperature of the bodies surrounding the aerial,

and B is the bandwidth in cycles per second.

If the aerial has a radiation resistance R_{rad} (assumed large compared with the copper loss resistance) and the r.m.s. open circuit noise voltage corresponding to the bandwidth is represented by V_n, then the maximum noise power is extracted by a matched load of resistance R_{rad}. Thus we have:

$$P_{max} = \frac{V_n^2}{4R_{rad}} = kTB$$

or

$$V_n^2 = 4kTBR_{rad} \quad \ldots \ldots \quad (10.34)$$

If this is compared with the noise voltage associated with a resistor it will be found to be the same, except that the radiation resistance of the aerial is substituted for the loss resistance of the resistor. However, a difficulty arises in determining the value of the temperature to be used in the above equations.

If the aerial were surrounded by a large enclosure at a uniform temperature T, then this value could be inserted in equation (10.33) to determine the available noise power due to the thermal radiation from the enclosure. If the aerial itself is at the same temperature it will emit an equal noise power, this being necessary to maintain thermal equilibrium. In practice the situation is more complex than this because the aerial is not surrounded by bodies at a uniform temperature. In addition to thermal radiation from the earth's surface there is thermal radiation from outer space which is received directly and also by reflection from the earth's surface. The contribution from outer space has a magnitude which depends upon the mid-frequency of the band under consideration. At frequencies of about 20 Mc/s the noise level per unit bandwidth, although less than the atmospheric noise at lower frequencies, is relatively high due to radiation from stars in the galaxy. This is known as cosmic or galactic noise, and it varies somewhat with time of day and direction in space. As the frequency is raised this noise falls very roughly according to a $1/f^{2 \cdot 4}$ law, until at frequencies of 200 Mc/s and above the noise level from outer space is negligible and the main contribution is from the surface of the earth. This situation may be described by assigning a temperature to the radiation at a certain frequency from a certain direction. In detailed work it would be necessary to determine a weighted value of T which makes allowance for the polar diagram of the receiving aerial. Generally however it is possible to employ a temperature corresponding to each frequency for aerials which do not have particularly sharp beams. Thus at 50 Mc/s the temperature for use in the above formula is about 5,000°K while at 150 Mc/s it is about 350°K. The latter temperature is comparable with the temperature of 300°K usually employed for the earth's surface. At microwave frequencies the radiation from outer space is to all intents and purposes zero, but for horizontally-directed microwave aerials, the effect of the earth's surface is to cause an effective temperature of 150°K. In practice, however, the noise caused by receiver input stages at frequencies in excess of 150 Mc/s is far greater than the noise power received by the aerial.

Bearing in mind therefore that a representative value of T can be found for each mid-band frequency, we see by equation (10.33) that if the aerial is matched to the load to extract the maximum noise power, the amount of that power is completely independent of the form of the aerial (provided the radiation resistance is much larger than the copper loss resistance). For example, two aerials connected in series or parallel would still have the same available noise power. Thus, if two dipoles are placed and connected in such a manner as to receive the maximum power from a plane wave travelling in a certain direction, the signal power received will be twice that for a single dipole, but the noise power will be the same. There is thus a 3-db gain in signal-to-noise ratio. If this is compared with say two transmitting dipoles in a broadside array it will be seen that the directivity power gain is equal to the signal-to-noise power ratio gain. This theorem is perfectly general for all directive aerials provided the noise power arrives with the same mean intensity from all directions.

If atmospheric or man made noise is considered, the same argument applies if it is arriving uniformly from all directions, but this does not occur in practice. If the interference arrives from all directions in a horizontal plane, then a large directivity gain in the horizontal plane will result in an improved signal-to-noise ratio. No improvement can be obtained for interference noise arriving from the same general direction as the desired signal, but noise arriving from some other direction can sometimes be reduced by placing a suitable null in that direction. Atmospheric noise is generally most intense from the directions of the tropics.

Where large aerial gains are employed the direction of maximum radiation is arranged to point at the receiving aerial and the direction of maximum

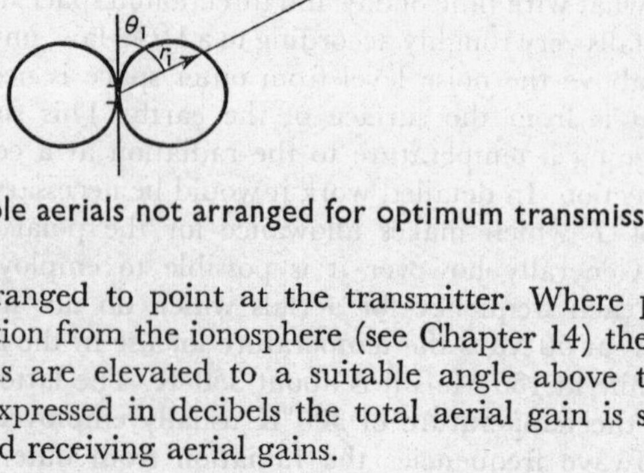

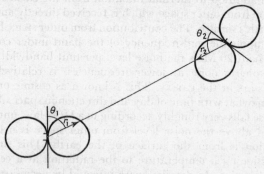

Fig. 10.33. **Dipole aerials not arranged for optimum transmission and reception.**

reception is arranged to point at the transmitter. Where propagation is by means of reflection from the ionosphere (see Chapter 14) the transmitting and receiving beams are elevated to a suitable angle above the horizontal. If the gains are expressed in decibels the total aerial gain is simply the sum of transmitting and receiving aerial gains.

If the directions of maximum radiation and maximum reception are not collinear then the total effective aerial gain is determined by multiplying together the appropriate radius vectors of the two polar diagrams. For example the two dipoles in Fig. 10.33 are not arranged for optimum transmission and reception. If the polar diagrams are normalized to unity in the direction of maximum radiation, the transmission relative to the optimum is given by the product $r_1 r_2$. For Hertzian dipole elements this is simply $\sin \theta_1 \sin \theta_2$.

APPENDIX 10.1

Field Strength due to a Travelling-Wave Radiator

Consider the travelling wave radiator in Fig. 10.27 (a) carrying a current I. For an element of length dz the contribution to the field at a large distance r at a bearing making an angle θ with the axis of the wire is obtained from equation (9.33) as follows:

$$dE_\theta = j\frac{60\pi[I]\,dz \sin\theta}{\lambda r}$$

If I_0 is the generator current then the current at a point z is given by:

$$I = I_0 \varepsilon^{-j\beta z}$$

where $\beta = 2\pi/\lambda$ is the phase constant. The attenuation of the current is neglected.

If the field from the current near the generator is taken as the reference phase the field from the element dz will be $\beta z \cos\theta$ radians in advance and it must have a phase factor $\varepsilon^{j\beta z \cos\theta}$ associated with it.

Thus the total field is:

$$E_\theta = \int_0^l \varepsilon^{j\beta z \cos\theta}\, dE_\theta.$$

$$= \int_0^l j\frac{60\pi}{\lambda r} \sin\theta\, I_0 \varepsilon^{-j\beta z(1-\cos\theta)} \varepsilon^{j\omega(t)}\, dz \quad . \quad . \quad . \quad (10.35)$$

If I_0 is an r.m.s. value then E_θ is also an r.m.s. value. The rotating phase term may be dropped for the present purpose. Carrying out the integration we find:

$$E_\theta = j\frac{60\pi I_0}{\lambda r}.\frac{\sin\theta}{-j\beta(1-\cos\theta)}\left[\varepsilon^{-j\beta z(1-\cos\theta)}\right]_0^l$$

$$= -\frac{60 I_0}{2r}.\frac{\sin\theta}{1-\cos\theta}\{\varepsilon^{-j(2\pi l/\lambda)(1-\cos\theta)} - 1\}$$

If the modulus of the factor inside the braces is taken we get:

$$|E_\theta| = \frac{60 I_0}{r}.\frac{\sin\theta}{1-\cos\theta}.\sin\left\{\frac{\pi l}{\lambda}(1-\cos\theta)\right\} \quad . \quad . \quad (10.36)$$

Since we are only interested in the field strength at the angle θ and not the phase, this expression may be used to determine the shape of the polar diagram for a single-wire travelling-wave radiator.

CHAPTER 11

L.F., M.F. and H.F. Aerials

PRESENT-DAY RADIO AERIALS are so diverse in type that, to make an orderly study of the subject, it is necessary to classify them in some manner. The first factor in the design of an aerial is the frequency or band of frequencies at which it must operate, so that classification by frequency of operation is perhaps the most convenient. The generally accepted classification of the frequencies with which we are concerned in this Chapter is given in Table 11.1, together with the main services for which they are used:

TABLE 11.1

Band	Frequency range	Wavelength range (metres)	Typical services
Very low frequency (V.L.F.)	3–30 kc/s	10^5–10^4	World-wide telegraphy
Low frequency (L.F.)	30–300 kc/s	10^4–10^3	Navigation, Broadcasting Long-distance communication
Medium frequency (M.F.)	0·3–3 Mc/s	1,000–100	Broadcasting
High frequency (H.F.)	3–30 Mc/s	100–10	Beamed communication services

There are no hard and fast rules for determining the choice of an aerial for a particular frequency, and many factors, electrical and structural, have to be taken into account. The most important of these factors are as follows:

(a) *Radiation efficiency;* i.e., the ratio of actual power radiated to total power delivered to the aerial terminals.

(b) *Maximum aerial gain and polar diagrams.* The principles for determining this information were established in Chapter 10.

(c) *The aerial impedance.* A knowledge of the aerial impedance is required to ensure efficient matching of the feeder or transmitter to the aerial.

(d) *Frequency characteristics.* The manner in which the above properties change with frequency is required for aerials which have to operate on more than one frequency, or for aerials having a wide bandwidth.

(e) *Structural considerations.* Besides being satisfactory from the electrical viewpoint, an aerial must be such that the supporting structure lends itself to economical design. With mobile aerials other factors have to be taken into account, such as streamlining for aircraft aerials.

The emphasis on these factors differs a little as between sending and receiving aerials and as between fixed and mobile aerials. However it is convenient to study aerial theory from the viewpoint of fixed transmitting aerials; the extension to receiving aerials is straightforward by virtue of the Reciprocity Theorem, and the extension to mobile aerials follows naturally.

Low-Frequency Aerials

In the case of transmitting aerials for land use, structures of considerable height, 250 metres or more, have often been employed. Even so they are only a small fraction of a wavelength high when operating in the v.l.f. band of frequencies. At the upper end of the l.f. band such structures would be of the order of a quarter wavelength. More generally however, heights of 100 metres or less are used and it is therefore true to say that most aerials operating at low frequencies are only a small fraction of a wavelength high.

It is difficult to achieve directivity at these frequencies, so that these bands are usually employed for services requiring omnidirectional coverage in the horizontal plane. For example transmitters working on very low frequencies are invariably employed for telegraph transmission to ships in all parts of the world. At the lower end of the low-frequency band one of the services provided is radio navigation for ships and aircraft, and all round coverage is required from each transmitting aerial. The polar diagram in a vertical plane is the upper half of Fig. 9.7 (a).

Owing to the comparatively small number of channels available in the very low-frequency band and the difficulty of designing efficient aerials, this band is reserved for comparatively few high power transmitting stations with massive aerial systems. The design of such aerials is very specialized both electrically and structurally. However the general principles involved are very similar for all low frequencies and the following remarks apply for v.l.f. and l.f. aerials.

Owing to the height problem, vertically polarized transmission is the only practicable form and this implies aerials consisting of vertical radiators. When a radiator such as a vertical wire or metallic mast is fed at the bottom between the aerial and ground plane, the current distribution up the mast is approximately as shown in Fig. 9.8 for heights up to an eighth of a wavelength. From equation (9.11) it may be deduced that the radiation resistance for such a radiator, one-tenth of a wavelength high, is only about 4 ohms. For v.l.f. aerials it is usually a small fraction of one ohm.

By itself this does not mean that aerials of low radiation resistance are bad radiators of power. If it were possible to match a source of radio frequency energy to a short aerial so that all the power were dissipated in the radiation resistance, then the short aerial would be as good a radiator as one with a much higher radiation resistance. However, inefficiency results because the radiation resistance is comparable with, or even less than, the total of the various loss resistances that occur in an aerial circuit. Furthermore the components required for matching introduce losses which increase as the aerial total resistance is reduced.

The current flowing at the base of the aerial is accompanied by an equal current in the earth connection and radial currents in the surface layers of the surrounding ground (see Chapter 5). The latter currents will cause losses. At large distances from the aerial these losses are unavoidable and are regarded as propagation losses. At short distances from the aerial, for example out to distances equal to the aerial height, these losses are regarded as part of the aerial efficiency problem. If no precautions are taken with the earthing system, the earth resistance might be as much as 10 ohms. For a radiation resistance of only 1 ohm most of the transmitter power would be wasted in heating the ground at the earth connection. With fixed transmitters it is usual to provide a large network of buried wires radiating from the earth terminal. Alternatively these wires may be supported on poles just above head height, when they are called a counterpoise earth. These earth wires should extend all round the aerial by a distance at least equal to the aerial height. This problem is not so serious with shipborne transmitters since the conductivity of sea water provides a reasonable earth for most situations.

A vertical or unipole aerial which is shorter than a quarter wavelength will, by analogy with short open-circuited lines, present a capacitive impedance between its base and earth. It may therefore be represented, at a particular frequency, by a resistance and capacitance connected in series. The resistance will be partly the radiation resistance and partly a resistance representing the various losses. The first step in matching the aerial is usually to load the aerial by a tuning inductance in series with the earth connection. This inductance will add further resistance losses. Of the total aerial resistance, only that part representing radiation resistance is responsible for power radiated. The remaining power is wasted in heating up the conductors, insulators, ground and nearby objects. The ratio of the radiation resistance to the total resistance is the aerial efficiency:

$$\eta = \frac{R_{\text{rad}}}{R_{\text{rad}} + R_{\text{loss}}} \quad . \quad . \quad . \quad (11.1)$$

The loss resistance multiplied by the square of the input current gives the total power wasted.

Thus for low-frequency aerials considerable attention must be paid to aerial conductor loss. Even though the frequency is low, skin effect is not entirely negligible and bare stranded copper or phosphor bronze wire is invariably employed. The gauge of wire used must be considered in relation to the radiation resistance and the structural features; the heavier the gauge of wire the more efficient the aerial. If conductors of small diameter are employed for aerials transmitting high power the voltage gradient near the conductor surface may be high enough to cause corona or brush discharge. This is a faint bluish glow due to ionization of the air near the conductor and this results in further loss of power. The loss in insulators is not usually serious, but nevertheless they must be kept clean. Ground loss can only be kept down to a tolerable figure by using extensive radial earth or counterpoise conductors. Other losses occur in non-radiating masts, guys etc., due to induced currents. For this reason guys are broken into short lengths by means of insulators. Masts which are not themselves the main radiator should preferably be supported at the base on an insulator.

From these considerations it is clear that the earthing and matching problem will be simplified if the radiation resistance can be increased in some way. From

Chapter 9 we may deduce that for short aerials the field strength at a distance is proportional to the sum, for all current elements, of the product of the current and the length of the current element. For the linear current distribution of Fig. 9.8 this product is $h \times I/2$ since the average current is only one-half of the base current I. Thus if an aerial of height $h/2$ could be made to have a uniform current of value I it would be just as effective a radiator. The height of this equivalent hypothetical radiator is called the effective height of the aerial. If the effective height of an aerial could be increased, then the field at a distance would be increased and so would the radiation resistance. The problem of increasing the radiation resistance may therefore be restated as the need to increase the effective height.

The main method of increasing effective height is the provision of top capacitance. That is, the upper end of the vertical radiator is connected to a system of horizontal conductors. These conductors have a certain capacitance to earth and they will require a charging current. The current at the top of the vertical radiator is no longer zero and the effective height will have been improved. The simplest aerials in this category are the inverted L and the T aerials shown in Fig. 11.1. If the length of the horizontal top from the aerial

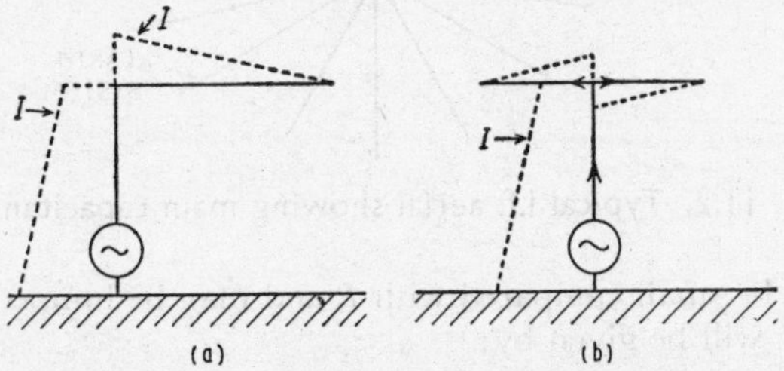

Fig. 11.1. The inverted L and T types of l.f. aerial, showing approximate current distribution.

connection to its extremity is of the same order as the aerial height, the effective height is increased from about $0{\cdot}5h$ to perhaps $0{\cdot}75h$. A more elaborate capacitance top will yield even better values of effective height. If the earth system consists of wires radiating out to a distance at least equal to the aerial height, the radiation from the conductors forming the top capacitance will be almost negligible, because the earth conductors will carry opposing currents. The short distance between these horizontal current elements effectively prevents radiation for it is small compared with a wavelength. However elaborate the top capacitance system, the actual radiator is the vertical conductor.

For very-low-frequency aerials the top capacitance may be a very extensive system of conductors requiring support from many masts. If the height is such that metallic masts must be used these should preferably be insulated at the base and top. Likewise all metallic stays must be insulated. Inevitably these masts and stays will waste some of the power from the radiator. If the masts are not insulated, for example as on ships, the power wasted will be greater and slight shadowing will occur in the direction of the masts.

A typical low-frequency aerial is illustrated in Fig. 11.2. Since all dimensions of the aerial are much smaller than a quarter wavelength, the behaviour of the aerial is largely determined by the capacitances shown.

Another reason for seeking to have a large top capacitance is to reduce the voltage on the aerial for a given radiated power. The aerial impedance, measured between the earth connection and the base of the radiating up-lead, will be a capacitive reactance many times the radiation resistance in magnitude, in series with a small resistance representing the sum of the radiation resistance, earth-loss resistance and other loss resistances. In matching to the aerial the first step is to tune out this capacitance C with an inductance L. The aerial

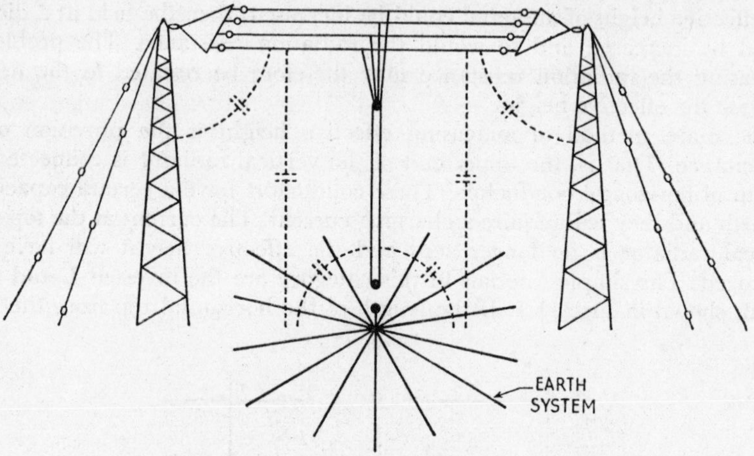

Fig. 11.2. Typical l.f. aerial showing main capacitances.

inductance will be small compared with L and may be lumped in with it. The voltage across L will be given by:

$$V_L = \omega LI = \frac{1}{\omega C} . I$$

$$= \sqrt{\frac{L}{C}} . I \quad . \quad . \quad . \quad . \quad . \quad . \quad (11.2)$$

where I is the aerial current at the base. This demonstrates that the larger the value of C the smaller the voltage at the aerial terminal. If the aerial voltage is too high, corona from the aerial conductors may occur and this will result in a loss of radiated power. A voltage gradient in air of about 30 kilovolts per centimetre will just cause corona or brush discharge. The voltage gradient depends on the conductor diameter, being greater for small conductors. For a single stranded 7/0·04 in. aerial wire, breakdown occurs for a peak aerial voltage of about 30 kilovolts.

This high ratio of reactance to resistance, or high Q, which is typical of most low-frequency aerials, causes the aerial current to decay relatively slowly when the transmitter is keyed off as in on-off telegraphy. Likewise the rate of growth of aerial current tends to be slow. This limits speed of working with on-off telegraphy. Since this is inherent with this type of aerial other systems of working have been evolved in which the frequency of the transmitter is changed slightly to transmit signals.

Another good example of a low frequency aerial is shown in Fig. 11.3. This is a radiator for a navigational system working on frequencies from about

70 kc/s to 130 kc/s. It consists of a self-supporting steel mast insulated at the base, having a curtain of copper wires and a conical top. The radiating wires are at an angle of about 80° to the ground, so that the capacitance per unit length near the top does not fall off quite so much as with a parallel radiator. The large conical top also has an appreciable capacitance to earth. The current does not fall to zero until the absolute tip of the aerial is reached. The earth system consists of 90 radial conductors equal in length to the total radiator height. Such a radiator will have a radiation efficiency of almost 45%, which is very good when it is considered that the total height is only of the order of 0·03λ.

The estimation of the actual capacitance of a horizontal 'top capacitance' system to earth presents considerable difficulty, because it depends upon so many factors. As an exceedingly rough rule the capacitance of one metre of wire

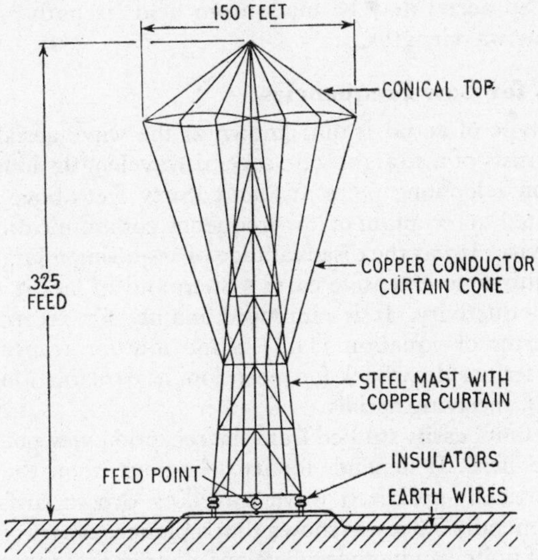

Fig. 11.3. Radiator for radio navigational system working on approximately 100 kc/s (3000 m).

may be taken to be 5 pF. Thus an aerial 30 metres high and similar to Fig. 11.2 would have a capacitance of about 0·0006 μF. The actual figure might vary widely from this, which must therefore only be taken as a measure of the order of the capacitance. For a high-power long-wave station the extensive aerial system usually employed may have a capacitance of as much as 0·03 μF. More usually for ship aerials and land structures of similar size the capacitance is about 0·001 μF.

Owing to the difficulty of predicting the performance of long-wave aerials it is important to be able to carry out measurements from which the aerial efficiency can be determined. One very approximate method of determining the total aerial resistance is the resistance variation method. In this method the aerial is tuned to resonance and the aerial current is noted on a thermo-couple type of current meter. A known non-inductive resistance of value comparable with the resistance being measured is then connected in the earth lead, and the aerial current is again measured. From the two current readings and the value of the known resistance, the total aerial resistance may easily be deduced. From an approximate knowledge of the effective height, the radiation resistance may be deduced using equation (9.9), and thence an estimate of the aerial efficiency may be made. Such a method is obviously very approximate.

A better method is to use a suitable impedance bridge and measure the aerial impedance over a considerable band of frequencies centred on the working frequency. Bearing in mind that radiation resistance varies as the square of the frequency, and conductor and most other significant losses vary as the square root of the frequency, an approximate separation of losses can be made. If insulator losses are an appreciable proportion of the total loss this method will be inaccurate, because dielectric and insulator leakage resistance, when converted to an equivalent series resistance in the aerial circuit, varies inversely as the frequency. Usually however, the insulator losses may be neglected. A further check on such an aerial may be made from field strength measurements at a distance of a few wavelengths.

Wave Aerials for Low Frequencies

An unusual type of aerial is that known as the wave aerial or the Beverage aerial. This consists of a straight wire several wavelengths long, usually carried by insulators on telephone poles at about thirty feet above the ground. It is particularly suited to reception of low-frequency communications and is capable of good directivity. It has the disadvantage of requiring a large area of ground, although it requires no extensive earth system and in fact it works better over soil of poor conductivity. It is employed mainly for reception, because the efficiency in terms of equation (11.1) is too low for transmitting. This low efficiency is no serious drawback for reception, as explained later in connection with l.f. and m.f. receiving aerials.

This aerial is more easily studied from the reception viewpoint and this course will be adopted here. It depends for its behaviour upon the horizontal component of a vertically-polarized wave travelling over a surface of finite conductivity. In Appendix 5.3 it was shown that a plane wave travelling tangentially over a surface of finite conductivity develops a horizontal component in order to supply the losses in the lower medium. At low frequencies the ratio of the horizontal to vertical components is about 2% for good soil and 8% for poor soil; i.e., the angle of forward tilt is from about 1 degree to 4 degrees. This tilt can be shown to extend upwards for about half a wavelength, so that there is a horizontal component which will produce an induced e.m.f. in the wire. This is a maximum when the wave is travelling in the direction of the wire.

In Fig. 11.4 (a) such a wave is travelling from left to right in the direction of the wire. In a small element of wire dx there will be an e.m.f. $E_H . \mathrm{d}x$, where E_H is the horizontal component of field strength of the wave. This e.m.f. will cause currents to flow in either direction from the element of wire. In the direction in which the wave is travelling a cumulative effect occurs, the current from the first element adding to that from each new element. This may be compared with the end-fire effect described in Chapter 10. In the opposite direction there is no such effect and by analogy with the end-fire aerials we may conclude that the signals interfere and produce a negligible resultant. At the end B the line is terminated to earth in an impedance equal to the characteristic impedance of the wire-to-earth circuit. A voltage will appear across this impedance which is approximately proportional to E_H and to the length of the line. At the end A the line is also terminated in its characteristic impedance to avoid reflection of interfering signals. The receiver is connected across the impedance at B for reception of signals from left to right. If it is inconvenient to have the receiver at this end, the scheme shown in Fig. 11.4 (b) may be used. In this case two wires are used arranged as a normal horizontal telephone pair. At the end B a reflection transformer is employed which receives the signal from the longitudinal circuit and transfers it to the transverse circuit, whence it is returned to the receiver connected to the transverse circuit at A. Such aerials should be at least one wavelength long, so that for the very low frequencies involved, several miles of line are required. They are therefore only suitable when a large area of poor conductivity land is available.

The polar diagram in a horizontal plane is similar in shape to the end-fire diagram of Fig. 10.21. In a vertical plane it is sensitive to downcoming signals

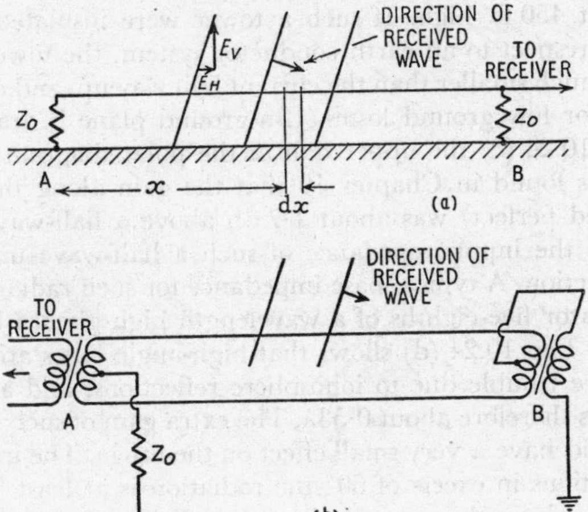

Fig. **11.4. The wave or Beverage aerial: (a) single-wire type; (b) two-wire type with reflection transformer.**

from the ionosphere. It is a broadband aerial and is satisfactory for reception over a wide band of frequencies in the v.l.f. and l.f. bands.

The Beverage aerial is not as effective as a very tall aerial designed to receive the vertical component, but nevertheless its simplicity and its directional properties make it attractive when a large area of poor conductivity soil is available. The use of two or more such aerials parallel to one another and spaced about half a wavelength will improve the directivity.

Medium-Frequency Aerials

The medium frequency band, 300 kc/s to 3 Mc/s (1,000 m to 100 m) is employed mainly for national broadcasting. The reasons for this choice are bound up with propagation, aerial and transmitter design and noise conditions for reception. Although aerial structures comparable with a quarter or half wavelength in height are possible in this waveband, it is still difficult to achieve any appreciable amount of directivity in a horizontal plane, and the band is therefore mainly suited to services requiring all round coverage. This type of coverage is that normally required for national broadcast transmitters. Vertical polarization is the only polarization for which efficient sending and receiving aerials are possible. To avoid interference between stations it is desirable that the field strength beyond a certain radius from the transmitter should fall off rapidly. This can be achieved so far as the surface wave (see Chapter 14) is concerned. It is desirable, therefore, with broadcast transmitting aerials, to have the maximum gain along the surface of the ground, and the minimum energy directed skywards. Even so, on the fringe area of such transmitting aerials, serious fading can be caused by interference between the ground wave and reflections from the ionosphere, particularly at night time.

Such transmitting aerials are designed for an allotted frequency, and there is usually no problem in achieving the bandwidth necessary for normal audio communications.

At the upper end of the frequency range, radiators one-half wavelength high are quite feasible. For example at 1 Mc/s (300 metres) a half-wavelength tower would be about 450 ft. high. If such a tower were insulated at its base and energized with respect to an earth conductor system, the tower current at the base would be much smaller than the current half way up, and conditions would be favourable for low ground losses. If a ground plane is drawn through the middle of Fig. 10.24 (c) the upper half of the polar diagram would apply to this case. It was found in Chapter 10 that the gain along the surface of the ground (assumed perfect) was about 1·7 db above a half-wave dipole in free space, and that the input impedance of such a half-wave unipole depended upon its cross-section. A typical base impedance for such radiators is 400 ohms. Actually a radiator five-eighths of a wavelength high gives a little more gain, but reference to Fig. 10.24 (d) shows that high-angle lobes are present. These are liable to give trouble due to ionosphere reflections, and a preferred compromise height is therefore about $0{\cdot}53\lambda$. The extra gain of such a radiator along the ground would have a very small effect on the range. The important feature is that for elevations in excess of 60° the radiation is at least 30 db below the maximum value along the ground. (For an efficient short radiator the field strength at an elevation of 60° is only 6 db below that along the ground.) Thus a $0{\cdot}53\lambda$ radiator provides improved fringe area reception.

Such a tower presents many design problems, both electrical and structural. An excessive taper towards the top, although desirable structurally is undesirable electrically, since it would cause a diminution of top current. A parallel mast is therefore favoured and this necessitates guys. The latter must be broken up into non-resonant sections by insulators. Such masts are usually constructed of steel and, if carefully welded for continuity, copper facing is unnecessary. Fig. 11.5 shows a typical radiator of this class together with current and voltage distributions and the polar diagram. Radial earth wires extending to a distance nearly equal to the mast height are invariably employed. Owing to the relatively high radiation resistance, in comparison with earth and other loss resistances, the efficiency of such a radiator would be of the order of 80% or 90%.

By using a small amount of top capacitance, as with l.f. aerials, small savings in height may be made. A suitable capacitance 'hat' would be a ring of diameter 4 or 5 times the mast diameter with radial spokes. Such a device may reduce the physical height by 5% to 10% without materially affecting the performance. A further method of reducing physical height for a negligible sacrifice in performance is to divide the mast at some point above the middle by means of an insulator. The upper section is then connected to the lower section through an inductance loading coil. This device may be used in conjunction with top capacitance, in which case the coil may be placed just below the capacitance hat and made to resonate with its capacitance. When the coil is placed near the middle the arrangement may be compared to a dipole shorter

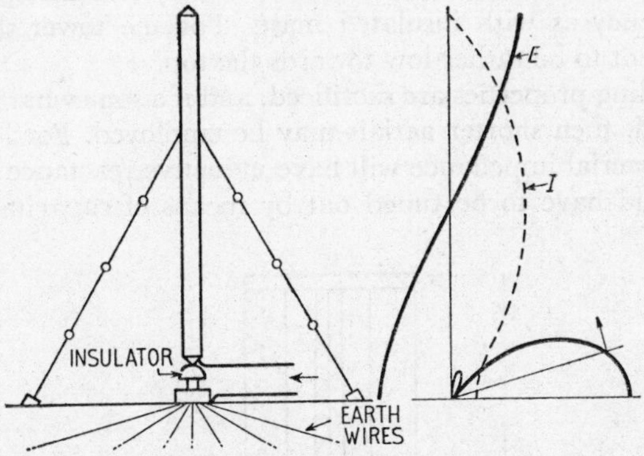

Fig. 11.5 Typical insulated mast radiator showing current and voltage distributions and polar diagram.

than a half-wavelength with a series coil to tune it. By the use of top capacitance and a coil, the overall height may be reduced to perhaps 0·4λ, and yet the current node may be placed about 0·03λ above ground so as to give good anti-fading performance. The sectionalizing of a mast does, of course, present

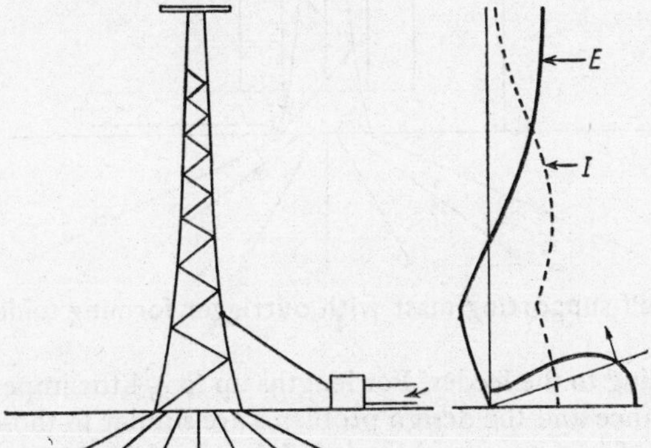

Fig. 11.6. Self-supporting mast radiator with shunt feed and capacitance top, showing approximate current and voltage distribution and polar diagram.

structural problems. The coil must have small losses and arrangements for de-icing it may be necessary.

The design of insulators for the base of such masts presents a considerable problem. These insulators may be eliminated by using the shunt feed method of Fig. 10.5 (c). This enables steel self-supporting towers to be used, the bottom of the tower being connected to the earth system. Fig. 11.6 shows such a radiator with a capacitance top. However, if the radiator is about a half-wavelength high, the impedance at a tapping point at a height of, say, $0{\cdot}12\lambda$ will be rather low and the feed current in the sloping wire will be somewhat high. This causes high-angle radiation which may upset the anti-fading properties, particularly on the feeder side of the tower. The current at the base is higher with this type of feed, as shown in Fig. 11.6, so that a better earth system is required to achieve the same efficiency as with insulated masts. For the tower shown the taper causes the current to be rather low towards the top.

If the anti-fading properties are sacrificed, and if a somewhat lower efficiency can be tolerated, then shorter aerials may be employed. For lengths between $\lambda/4$ and $\lambda/2$ the aerial impedance will have inductive reactance associated with it and this would have to be tuned out by means of capacitance during the

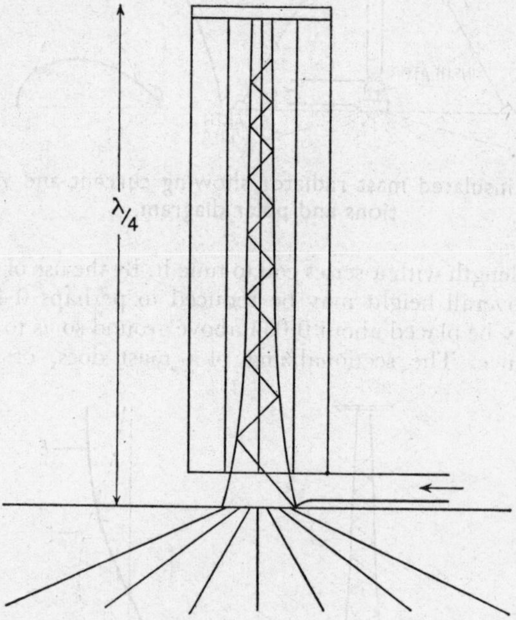

Fig. **11.7. Self-supporting mast with outrigger forming folded unipole.**

process of matching to the feeder. For lengths up to $\lambda/4$ the impedance will have capacitive reactance and the design problems are similar to those for l.f. aerials.

For radiators of quarter-wavelength height, the folded unipole principle of Fig. 10.4 may be used. Such a radiator is shown in Fig. 11.7 and is known as the outrigger type. A self-supporting tower without insulators may be employed, and wires are suspended from the top without insulators. The aerial is driven between a ring at the bottom to which the wires are attached, and the earth system radiating from the base of the tower. The earth system must be exceptionally good if high efficiency is required, because the bottom of the aerial is a current antinode.

Although all round coverage is the general rule with this type of radiator there are occasions where interference between neighbouring stations on similar frequency allocations renders it desirable to employ some directivity, or where the shape of the service area requires a departure from the circular polar diagram. In such cases two radiators may be used, excited from the same transmitter. Patterns similar to Figs. 10.10 and 10.11 are then available, together with other possibilities corresponding to other spacings and phasings.

Medium-frequency transmitting aerials are expensive structures. Although a arge part of the design can be carried out from theory and experience, it is usual to construct a model aerial and carry out field-strength measurements as a check on the calculations. If the scale of the model is say one hundredth then the frequency of excitation must be one hundred times the actual aerial frequency, in order to preserve the same current distribution. If the model is only a few feet high, it is feasible to make field strength measurements in a vertical plane at angles of elevation up to 90°.

High-Frequency Aerials

The high frequency band extends from 3 Mc/s to 30 Mc/s (100 m to 10 m). In this band half-wave dipoles may be constructed from wires rigged between masts, and horizontal or vertical radiating elements may be used. Vertical aerials may be erected for all-round coverage, but owing to the high frequency, ground-wave range is less than for lower frequencies. The range over sea water is rather greater because of the better conductivity, and vertical aerials may therefore be used for service to islands and ships.

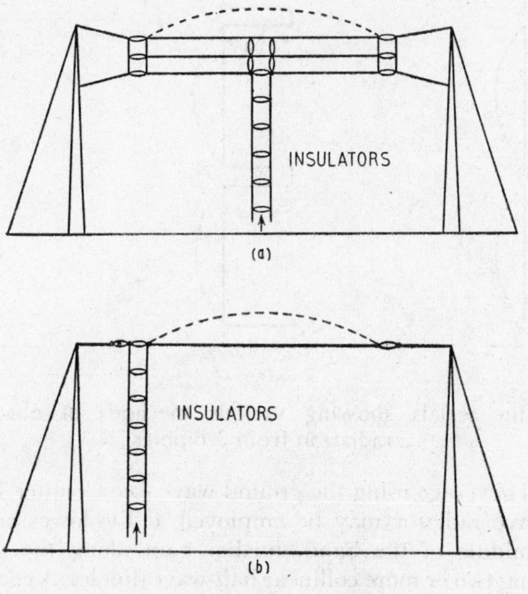

Fig. 11.8. (a) Horizontal half-wave folded dipole; (b) end-fed half-wave or Zeppelin aerial.

At the lower end of the h.f. band the simplest aerial is the horizontal half-wave dipole arranged to employ the earth as a reflecting plane. Such an aerial may be constructed by rigging wires between two masts of appropriate height. Generally speaking heights of between one-eighth and one-quarter of a wavelength would be used and the polar diagram in the vertical plane normal to the dipole would be similar to those in Fig. 10.13. The maximum gain is at high angles of elevation and would be 6 db for a perfectly conducting earth, but for normal soil it would be a little less, depending upon height and soil conductivity. There is no surface wave (see Chapter 14) from such an aerial if the vertical feeder is balanced and non-radiating. A typical aerial of this type is shown in Fig. 11.8 (a). The dipole is folded to raise the impedance to a value more suited to an open-wire line. The bandwidth would be about $\pm 5\%$. Such a transmitting aerial would be suitable for communication from a valley or over hills, by radiation directed on to the ionosphere (see Chapter 14) at nearly vertical incidence. The polarization is, of course, horizontal and all-round coverage is not provided.

An alternative method of feeding the aerial is to employ the delta match of Fig. 10.5 (a), the rigging in this case being quite obvious. A further alternative is the end-fed half-wave aerial shown in Fig. 11.8 (b). This is sometimes known as the Zeppelin aerial and is popular with radio amateurs. It is normally operated with the tuned feeder method of matching (see Chapter 4).

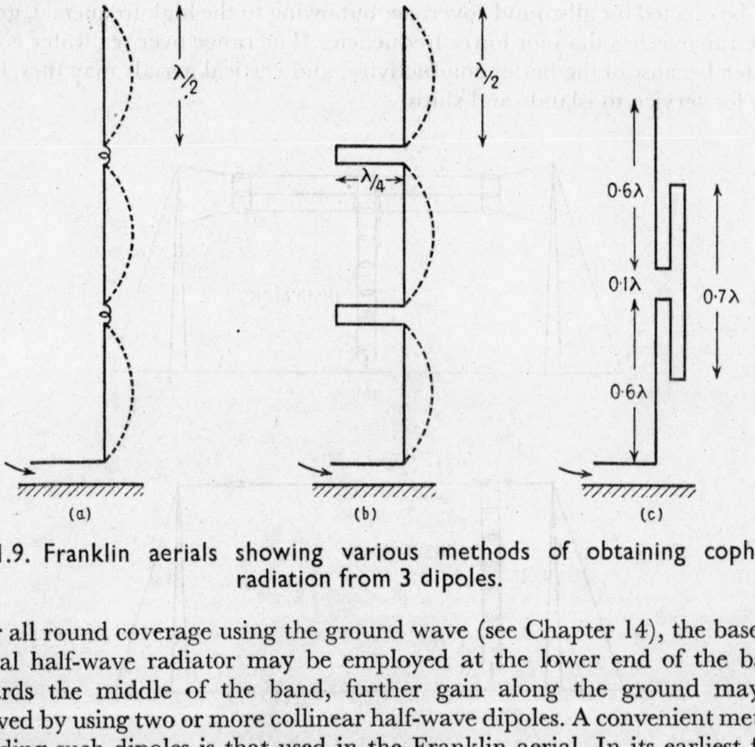

Fig. 11.9. Franklin aerials showing various methods of obtaining cophased radiation from 3 dipoles.

For all round coverage using the ground wave (see Chapter 14), the base-fed vertical half-wave radiator may be employed at the lower end of the band. Towards the middle of the band, further gain along the ground may be achieved by using two or more collinear half-wave dipoles. A convenient method of feeding such dipoles is that used in the Franklin aerial. In its earliest form shown in Fig. 11.9 (a) it consisted of a number of end-fed half-wave dipoles placed end to end. Alternate half waves have their radiation suppressed by means of suitable coils having distributed inductance and capacitance corresponding to a half wavelength. These coils were soon replaced by simpler and more efficient methods of suppression.

One of these methods of suppressing the radiation from alternate half waves is shown in Fig. 11.9 (b) where a half-wavelength of wire is folded back on itself; i.e., a quarter-wave short-circuited line is used. The short circuit will be a current antinode and the opposing currents in the two wires ensure that radiation from the suppressed half wave is a minimum.

Another form of this aerial shown in Fig. 11.9 (c) is known as the folded Franklin aerial. It may be considered as a number of half-wave dipoles slightly overlapping one another, with half-wave folded interconnectors for which the radiation is small. These methods of half-wave suppression only function efficiently when the aerial has a correctly placed system of standing waves.

The gain of such arrangements may be calculated approximately by considering them to be collinear dipoles. They provide all-round coverage and may be used effectively for service to a number of islands because propagation over sea is rather better than over land.

However, the present day tendency is for this band to be employed for communications employing beams reflected from the ionosphere (see Chapter 14). Frequencies up to about 20 Mc/s are reflected from the ionosphere, provided the correct angle of incidence is employed. The actual upper limit of frequency depends upon several factors which are considered in Chapter 14.

Owing to the more favourable size of the aerial elements compared with l.f. and m.f. aerials, it is possible to construct aerials of large aperture which produce a beam of radio energy. By designing the aerial in conjunction with the earth's surface as a reflector, such a beam may be directed at the ionosphere at an angle of elevation suited to the distance between transmitter and receiver and the frequency in use. As a general rule the nearer the frequency is to the upper limit of 20 Mc/s and the longer the circuit, the lower the angle of elevation of the beam. For example, transatlantic radio circuits on a frequency of say 15 Mc/s would have an aerial designed to give a beam at about 12° to 15°. For the lower frequencies the angle of elevation would be greater.

The aerials to provide such beams are in general of two types, the resonant type and the non-resonant or travelling-wave type. The former is used for fixed-frequency services. The latter is employed when the aerial has to operate on a number of frequencies to suit the changing ionospheric conditions.

Tuned or Resonant High-Frequency Arrays

The basic element for such arrays is the half-wave radiator, which may be centre fed or end fed. As a rule end feeding is employed since the higher impedance is more convenient for parallel connection to feeder lines of about 500 ohms characteristic impedance. The chief design problem is to feed the dipoles in such a way that the currents are in phase.

Horizontally- or vertically-polarized elements may be employed, but horizontal polarization has the advantage that the angle of elevation of the main beam can be controlled by the height of the array above the ground. Although there is little difference in the loss on reflection at the ionosphere and at the ground as between horizontal and vertical polarization, present day practice seems to favour horizontal polarization.

The simplest aerial in this category is the lazy-H shown in Fig. 11.10. It consists of two full-wave centre-fed dipoles, half a wavelength apart. The transmission line between the dipoles has constant-length spacers, and is twisted, so as to maintain the currents in phase in the four radiating elements. It functions as a unity-ratio transformer. The impedance of each full-wave dipole would be about 2,000 ohms, depending upon the wire diameter, so that the feeder would have an aerial load of about 1,000 ohms. This ignores the effect of the reflector curtain on the impedance. The reflector shown consists of untuned wires and would be spaced at a distance of a little less than a quarter wavelength behind the aerial. Smaller spacings down to one-eighth of a wavelength may be used, and this lowers the aerial impedance. The spacing between wires in the curtain should not be greater than one-tenth of a wavelength. The gain for a full-wave dipole over a half-wave dipole is 1·7 db and for two full-wave dipoles it is therefore about 4·7 db. The reflector increases this to about 10 db and the effect of the ground reflection is to raise it even more. At a mean height of one wavelength the beam is deflected upwards at an angle deducible from the appropriate group pattern in Fig. 10.13. The lower lobe of this group

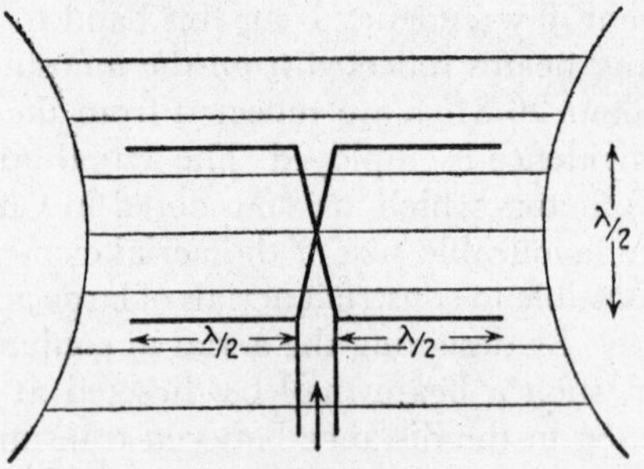

Fig. **11.10. The lazy-H aerial.**

pattern combines with the aerial polar diagram to give a beam at an elevation of about 15°.

The Sterba Array of Fig. 11.11 (a) achieves a rather similar object in a different manner. The arrows show the directions of current at a particular instant. The crossed wires would be rigged with uniform length spacers; i.e., they form a transmission line with a twist and do not radiate. The upper horizontal wire would have little radiation. The advantage claimed for this arrangement is that a current of power-supply frequency can be circulated for de-icing purposes. The aerial shown is for vertical polarization but it could also be rigged for horizontal polarization. A reflector curtain could be employed to form a unidirectional beam, or an identical aerial a quarter wavelength away could be used. This would be fed with a current at 90° or 270° to that in the first aerial, in order to achieve the desired direction of transmission. An alternative arrangement is two Franklin aerials each three half-wavelengths high as in Fig. 11.11 (b). This is also convenient for rigging and may be used vertically or horizontally.

For arrays requiring greater gain the Kooman or pine-tree array is one of the most used. A 4 × 4 array (4 horizontal radiators stacked 4 high) of this type is shown in Fig. 11.12 (a). If each full-wave dipole has an impedance of 2,000 ohms the feeder line will have a load of about 500 ohms, which is very close to the impedance of suitable feeder lines. Where the two feeder lines are paralleled the impedance is 250 ohms and a matching line or stub would be required. Alternatively, a preferable arrangement for the main feeder would be a four-wire balanced line with an impedance of 250 to 300 ohms. The gain of such an array is about 10 log (4 × 4) or 12 db, plus 6 db for a passive reflecting curtain, if used. It is more usual to employ parasitic reflectors behind each half-wave element because this reduces wind and ice loading on the masts. In this case the extra gain is about 3 db.

If the mean height of the array is h, the effect of the ground can be determined by multiplying the free-space polar diagram of the array by the group pattern corresponding to the height and the polarization. This will in general produce a main beam at an angle of elevation given by equation (10.12) for horizontal polarization. If the free-space beam is not too sharp, and the angle of elevation

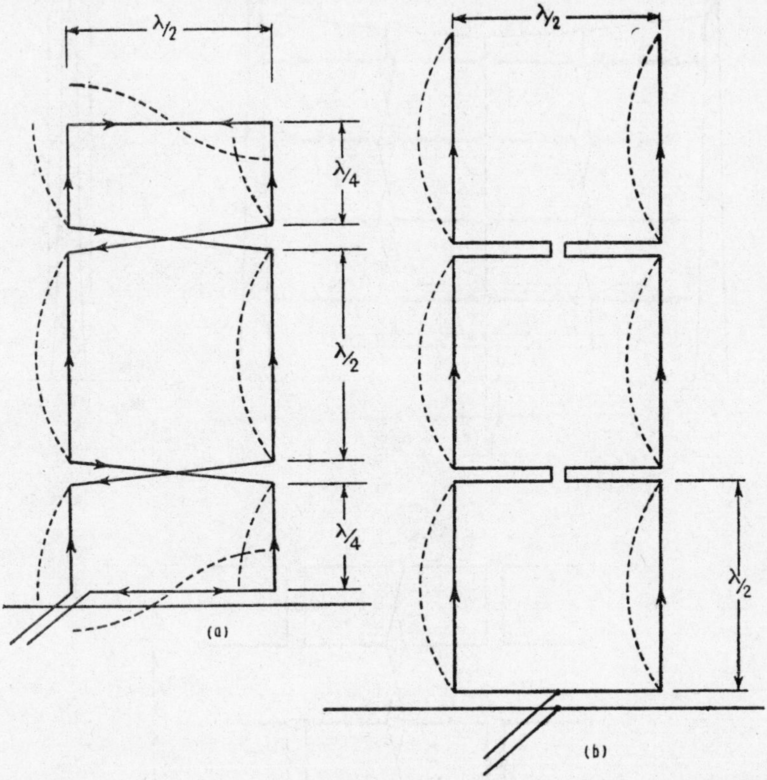

Fig. 11.11. H.F. arrays with vertical elements: (a) the Sterba array and (b) two Franklin aerials.

of the beam from the group pattern is not too large, the field strength will be increased by a factor of nearly 2 due to the effect of the ground reflection. However, if the free-space beam is sharp, it will have a diminished field strength in the direction of the group pattern maximum. Thus the field strength will be increased by a factor less than 2 depending upon the relative shapes of the free-space polar diagram and the group pattern due to the height above the ground. For horizontal polarization and a mean array height of 1 wavelength the angle of elevation of the main beam is 15°, and for $1\frac{1}{2}$ wavelengths it is 10°. A usual height is 1·1 to 1·2 wavelengths. Thus the total gain of a 4 × 4 pine-tree array with parasitic reflectors is 12 db, plus 3 db for the reflectors, plus nearly 6 db for the image, or a total figure of the order of 20 db.

The bearing of the main beam may be slewed up to about 10° on either side of the normal by suitably phasing the feed to one-half of the array. This may be carried out by introducing a suitable length of delay line at the points X or Y. For a slew of 10° the length of line inserted on one side would be $\lambda \sin 10°$ or about one-sixth of a wavelength. Any attempt at slewing by a greater angle results in a large secondary lobe on the other side of the normal.

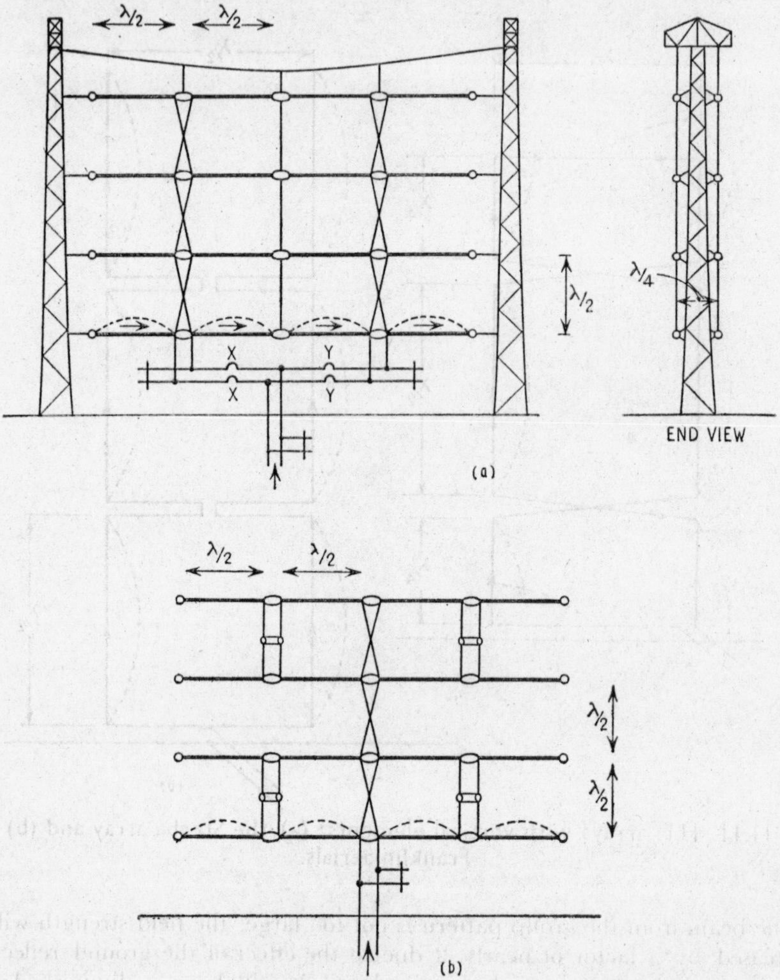

Fig. 11.12. (a) Pine tree or Kooman's aerial array; (b) a 4 × 4 dipole array using Franklin aerials.

Aerials of this type are often rigged between two masts. The aerial and reflector are spaced by suitable horizontal spreader beams attached to the mast. The aerial wires may be self-suspended between the masts, but at the lower frequencies it is usual to employ triatics from which the radiating wires are supported. A triatic is a non-radiating catenary wire suspended between the tops of the masts which supports vertical wires carrying the weight of the radiating elements. To avoid resonances the triatics and other supporting wires must be broken up by means of insulators, into lengths of a quarter wavelength or less.

When the radiating elements are single stranded conductors the bandwidth is only of the order of a few per cent. Double conductors or cages of 4 conductors may be used to increase the bandwidth to perhaps 5%.

An alternative method of rigging a 4 × 4 array is shown in Fig. 11.12 (b).

Tuned H.F. Aerials—The Resonant V

The resonant V aerial is probably one of the cheapest forms of transmitting or receiving aerial for providing a low-angle beam for fixed frequency working in the h.f. band. In its simplest form it consists of two wires in the form of a V

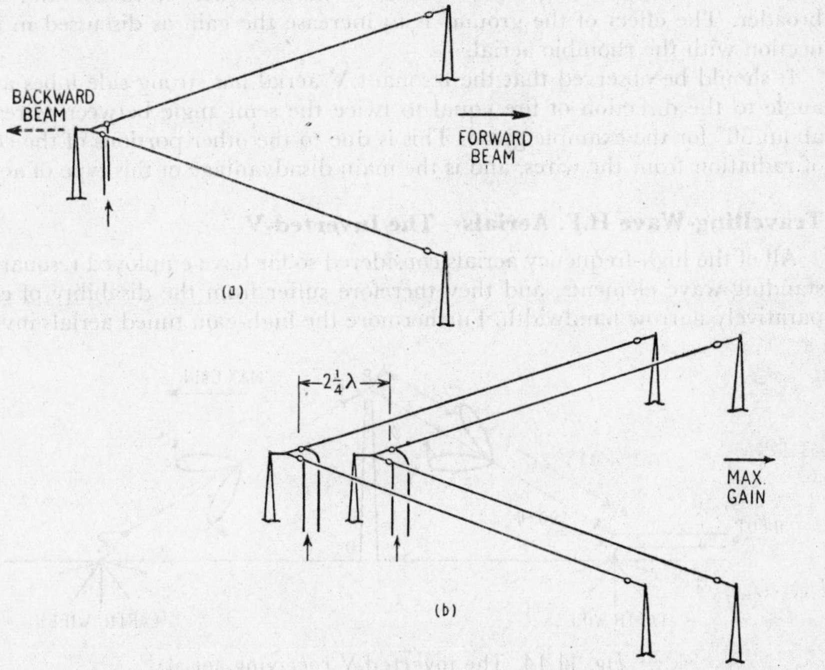

Fig. 11.13. The resonant-V aerial: (a) bidirectional form; (b) unidirectional form.

fed at the apex as in Fig. 11.13 (a). If the wires are made 8 wavelengths long the polar diagram for each will be similar to Fig. 10.25 (c), but with main lobes nearer to the axis of the wire. The semi-angle between the wires of the V should equal the angle of the major lobes. From Fig. 10.26 this angle is 18° for wires 8 wavelengths long. From Fig. 10.25 each wire will produce two main cones of radiation. These cones touch in the direction bisecting the angle between the wires; i.e., in the forward direction shown by the arrow the two wires produce fields which are in phase and the gain is increased by 6 db over that for one wire. (The effect of the ground is neglected for the moment.) However, a similar backward beam is also produced. This may be minimized and the forward gain increased by placing a similar V aerial in the plane of the first V, as shown in Fig. 11.13 (b), at an odd number of quarter wavelengths behind the first V.

The second V is fed with a suitably phased current so as to increase the forward gain. Usual figures are $2\frac{1}{4}$ wavelengths between the apices, for which the second aerial would have a current leading that in the first aerial by 90° and the forward gain would be increased by 3 db. The total gain is therefore roughly 9 db greater than that for a single wire. Adding 6 db gain (from Fig. 10.26) for the gain of this length of resonant wire over a half-wave dipole, we obtain a figure of about 15 db for the total gain.

Since the aerial has a negative image when erected horizontally above the earth the free-space polar diagram will be multiplied by a group pattern from Fig. 10.13 (d). The height above earth will usually be between a third of a wavelength and $1\frac{1}{4}$ wavelengths. The latter height is used for beams of about 15° elevation. At lower heights the beam is at a higher elevation and it is broader. The effect of the ground is to increase the gain as discussed in connection with the rhombic aerial.

It should be observed that the resonant V aerial has strong side lobes at an angle to the direction of fire equal to twice the semi-angle between wires, or about 36° for the example given. This is due to the other portions of the cones of radiation from the wires, and is the main disadvantage of this type of aerial.

Travelling-Wave H.F. Aerials—The Inverted-V

All of the high-frequency aerials considered so far have employed resonant or standing-wave elements, and they therefore suffer from the disability of comparatively narrow bandwidth. Furthermore the high-gain tuned aerials involve

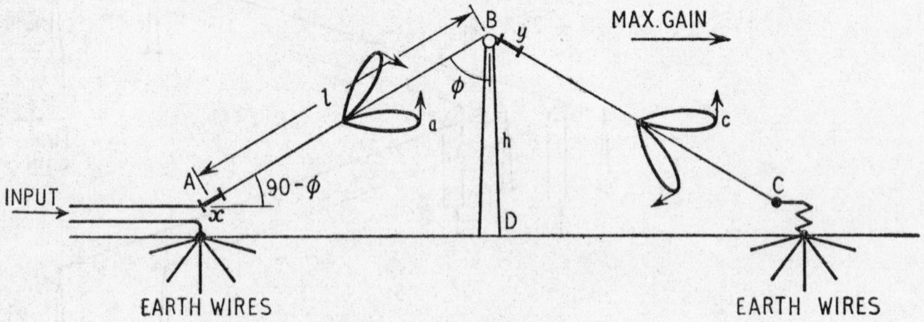

Fig. 11.14. The inverted-V receiving aerial.

considerable rigging and expense and they are only justified for fixed services operating on an allotted frequency. Where aerials are required to operate on a number of allotted frequencies it is necessary to employ travelling-wave radiators. The Beverage wave aerial for low-frequency reception has already been described and the inverted-V aerial for high frequency use is an extension of these principles.

The inverted-V aerial is very simple to construct and requires only one mast which should be non-conducting. It is illustrated in Fig. 11.14 and the direction of maximum gain is shown by the arrow. When used for transmitting, the energy is fed in by the unbalanced feeder to the input end A. At the end C a resistor is used to connect the aerial to a number of radial earth wires. This resistor is adjusted to give substantially travelling waves in the aerial wire ABC. The value is usually about 400 ohms. The length of the legs AB and BC could be 2 wavelengths at the lowest frequency, and 4 wavelengths at the highest frequency to be used, although aerials with legs down to one wavelength are employed. Reference to Fig. 10.29 shows that over this 2 to 1 band of frequency the angle of the major lobe changes by only a few degrees. This explains why such aerials remain reasonably efficient over a considerable bandwidth.

The best value of the angle ϕ for a given number of wavelengths l/λ in the leg AB is a compromise between two factors. The first factor is the angle of the major lobe corresponding to l/λ from Fig. 10.29. The second factor is the angle of tilt for which the fields of AB and BC combine to give the maximum gain. Since lobes 'a' and 'c' of Fig. 11.14 should combine in phase at a distance, and since these lobes are on opposite sides of the wire, a reversal of phase is required, either by reversal of current feed at B or by spacing towards the receiver. The second factor may be re-stated as the condition for which AB exceeds AD by half a wavelength. Thus if AB is one wavelength and AD is half a wavelength, current element 'y' is excited in phase with current element 'x', but it is half a wavelength nearer the receiver. Similarly if AB is 1·5 wavelengths and AD is one wavelength, current element 'y' is excited in antiphase with current element 'x', and because they are spaced one wavelength apart in the receiver direction, the lobes 'a' and 'c' combine in phase. Actually these two factors turn out to give values of ϕ very close to one another and the optimum is roughly the mean. The angles are summarized in Table 11.2. The optimum angles are derived from a more rigorous determination.

TABLE 11.2

l/λ =	1	2	4	6	8
Complement of major lobe angle	42°	55°	66°	70°	73°
Angle for which AB = AD + $\lambda/2$	30°	49°	61°	66°	70°
Optimum angle, ϕ	36°	52°	63°	68°	71°

If the inverted-V aerial were constructed above a perfectly-conducting ground plane, the image would carry currents oppositely directed to those in the aerial wire. The inverted-V and its image would therefore behave in a similar manner to the rhombic aerial of Fig. 10.30, and the maximum gain would be along the ground and the polarization would be vertical. However, when the aerial is constructed above normal or poor conductivity ground, the polar diagram in a vertical plane is difficult to determine. At low angles of elevation in the forward direction, the polar diagram is modified because vertical current elements have a negative image. The effect of this is that the gain along the ground is very much reduced. In practice the maximum gain takes place in a forward direction at about half the Brewster angle or a little lower. That is the aerial has a lobe in the vertical plane which lies between the Brewster angle and the horizontal. This uncertainty in the polar diagram renders the aerial somewhat unsuitable for transmitting and it is mainly employed for reception of frequencies up to 60 Mc/s. For ionospheric transmission it is more usual to employ horizontal polarization so that this aerial does not find application to this type of circuit. It is more suited to the upper end of the h.f. band for reception of ground or surface wave. The best reception occurs for signals coming from the right in the diagram. Because of their simplicity several such aerials may be erected side by side, half a wavelength apart, in order to increase the gain. Two poles may be used by suspending the points B from a triatic. The feeders must be of equal length.

It should be noted that the inverted-V aerial has considerable unwanted lobes of radiation due to the other portions of the radiation cones. This is the price that must be paid for simplicity. Since these lobes emit horizontal polarization in some directions the aerial will also receive horizontal polarization from these directions.

The principles of the design of travelling-wave aerials are treated in more detail in the next section.

Travelling-Wave H.F. Aerials—The Rhombic Aerial

A typical rhombic aerial is illustrated in Fig. 11.15 (a). It consists of 4 wires in the form of a diamond lying in a horizontal plane above the earth. In some

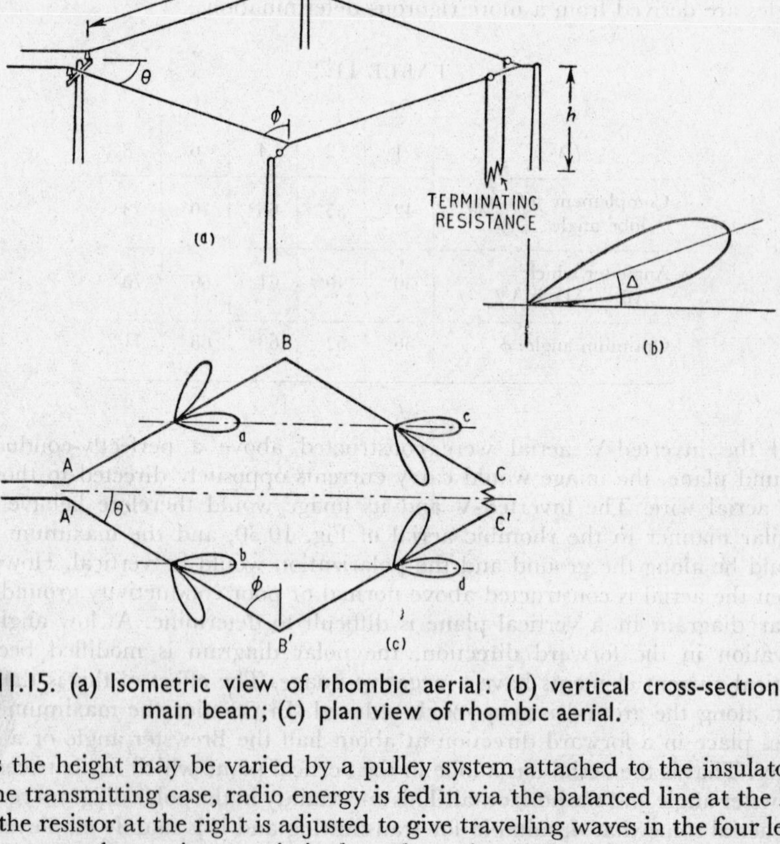

Fig. 11.15. (a) Isometric view of rhombic aerial: (b) vertical cross-section of main beam; (c) plan view of rhombic aerial.

cases the height may be varied by a pulley system attached to the insulators. In the transmitting case, radio energy is fed in via the balanced line at the left and the resistor at the right is adjusted to give travelling waves in the four legs. In free space the maximum gain is along the main axis from feed point to termination. In this direction the polarization is in the plane of the diamond; i.e., horizontal. The earth serves to deflect the main beam upwards at a small angle of elevation, but the polarization in the direction of the beam maximum remains horizontal. In free space the rhombic aerial is somewhat analogous to the inverted-V above a perfectly conducting plane.

The rhombic aerial can be used for transmitting or receiving. In the latter case the best direction of reception is, of course, for signals from the right. Owing to its relative simplicity it is widely used. It is therefore important to understand its performance and limitations.

The basic principles were described in Chapter 10 in connection with travelling waves on wires. Each wire produces a main hollow cone of radiation plus a number of side-lobe cones. In free space the ideal arrangement would be for the four main cones to provide signals which combine in phase along the main axis. The design of a rhombic aerial consists of the determination of just three factors, the leg length l, the tilt angle ϕ and the height h as shown in Fig. 11.15 (a). However the performance is a function of all three factors interconnected in a somewhat complicated manner. The height h mainly controls the angle of elevation, Δ in Fig. 11.15 (b), of the main beam, the direction of fire. However the best values of l and ϕ must be chosen in relation to h to achieve the maximum gain in the main beam. A fortunate feature of the rhombic aerial is that for fixed values of l, ϕ and h, a reduction of frequency below the optimum results in an increase of Δ, a condition which happens to suit ionospheric requirements. A better arrangement is, however, for h to be adjustable. If a fixed aerial is designed for a 2 to 1 frequency band, and is optimized for a frequency at the geometric mean, then the gain at the edges of the band may be between 3 and 6 db below the optimum frequency gain.

The portions of the radiation cones which do not combine to form the main beam, cause considerable side lobes having horizontal and vertical polarization. This is one of the most serious objections to the rhombic aerial. As with the inverted-V aerial, it is the penalty that must be paid for cheapness of construction.

In the treatment of the rhombic aerial, a considerable simplification results if the current is assumed to flow unattenuated to the termination. In practice about half the power is wasted in the termination, representing roughly the power that would be radiated backwards if the termination were fully reflecting. Since the input and termination impedances are usually about equal and of the order of 600–800 ohms resistive, the current at the termination end is attenuated to about 0·7 of the input value. The assumption of a uniform current travelling wave in the four legs of the aerial does not result in any serious errors in the prediction of performance.

For the rhombic aerial in free space, the field strength at points on the main axis can be calculated by a straight-forward vector summation of the field strengths due to the lobes 'a, b, c, d' of Fig. 11.15 (c). If $\theta = 90 - \phi$ is the semi-angle between the wires then equation (10.29) gives the field strength due to wire AB along the main axis. The field strength due to A′B′ is the same and it is in phase with that due to AB because the currents at corresponding elements in the two wires are in antiphase. Thus the field strength due to the wires AB and A′B′ is twice equation (10.29). If θ is not equal to the optimum angle of the major lobe it can be seen that in the horizontal plane the two lobes will combine to give a broader lobe. If θ is much larger than the optimum major lobe angle, the combined beam will have a dip along the main axis. This is one of the factors contributing to loss of performance at frequencies well removed from the optimum.

In order to find the field strength on the main axis due to AB and B′C′, it should be noted that the current at B lags $2\pi l/\lambda$ radians behind that at A. The current at B′ lags by a further π radians because it is in antiphase. Furthermore the leg B′C′ is $(2\pi l \cos\theta)/\lambda$ radians nearer to the receiver. The angle between the field vectors at a distance due to AB and B′C′ is therefore:

$$\frac{2\pi l}{\lambda} + \pi - \frac{2\pi l \cos\theta}{\lambda}$$

If E_{AB} is the field due to leg AB, the resultant is therefore:

$$2E_{AB} \cos \tfrac{1}{2}\left(\frac{2\pi l}{\lambda} + \pi - \frac{2\pi l \cos\theta}{\lambda}\right)$$

The factor by which the field from AB must be multiplied, to give the field from AB and B′C′, may therefore be simplified to:

$$2 \sin\left\{\frac{\pi l}{\lambda}(1 - \cos\theta)\right\}$$

A similar factor can be used to give the combined field strength of A′B′ and BC.

For optimum combination of the fields from the divergent and convergent parts of the aerial we get the same condition that was deduced for the inverted V, namely:

$$\frac{l}{\lambda}(1 - \cos\theta) = \tfrac{1}{2}$$

At the optimum frequency of the aerial this condition applies approximately. At the edges of the band this group factor will cause a further loss of gain.

The total field strength along the main axis is then given by:

$$E = 2 \times \{\text{equation (10.29)}\} \times 2\sin\left\{\frac{\pi l}{\lambda}(1 - \cos\theta)\right\}$$

$$= 4 \times \frac{60I}{r} \cdot \frac{\sin\theta}{1 - \cos\theta} \cdot \sin^2\left\{\frac{\pi l}{\lambda}(1 - \cos\theta)\right\}$$

$$= \frac{240I}{r} \cdot \frac{\cos\phi}{1 - \sin\phi} \cdot \sin^2\left\{\frac{\pi l}{\lambda}(1 - \sin\phi)\right\} \quad . \quad . \quad . \quad . \quad (11.3)$$

If this expression is plotted against ϕ for various values of l, the tilt angles for optimum gain can be found. It is these values which are quoted in Table 11.2.

The field at other points in the main beam in the horizontal plane is horizontally polarized. The field of the main beam in the vertical plane through the main axis is also horizontally polarized. At other points in the beam the polarization has horizontal and vertical components although the latter are small compared with the horizontal component.

The field strength in the vertical plane through the main axis is of interest for design purposes, because it is this pattern which is modified by the ground.

The calculation of this pattern involves vector addition of the fields from portions of the radiation cones not in a horizontal plane. The results only are quoted here because they are instructive and because they can be used for design purposes. They are shown in Fig. 11.16 for four tilt angles $\phi = 50°$,

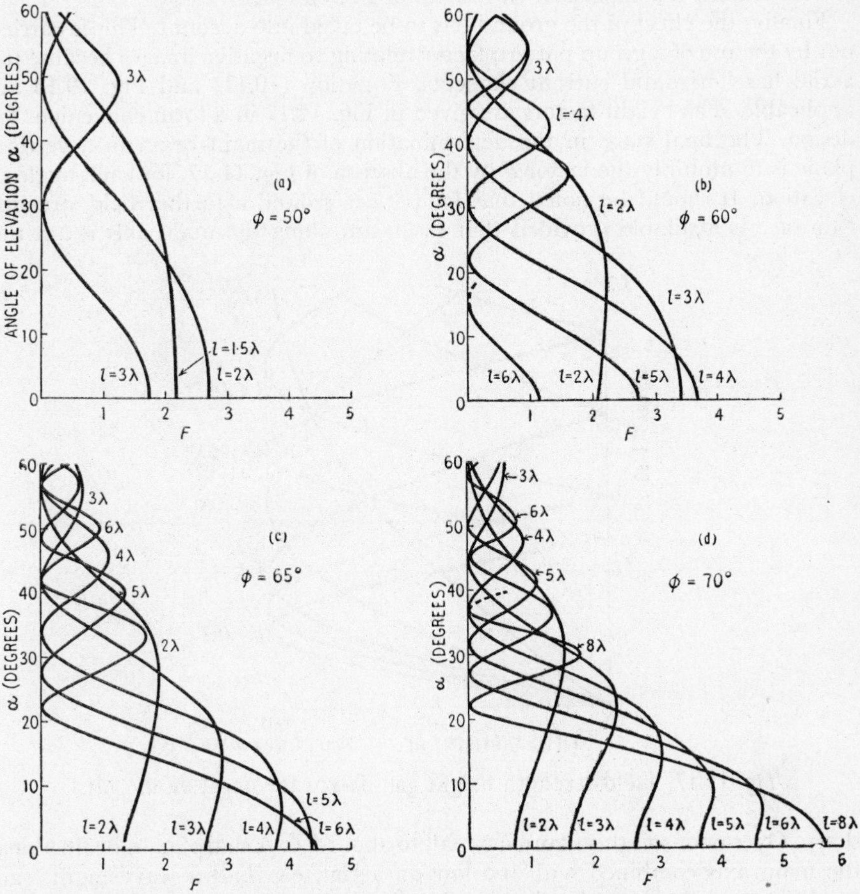

Fig. 11.16. **Field-strength gain factor F (Eq. 11.4) for rhombic aerials in free space.**

60°, 65° and 70° and various leg lengths l. They are plotted with field-strength gain factors F as abscissae, where:

$$E_\alpha = \frac{60I}{r}F \quad . \quad . \quad . \quad . \quad . \quad . \quad . \quad (11.4)$$

and the angles of elevation α as ordinates. I is the current in the four legs of the aerial, and E_α is the horizontal field strength in a vertical plane. The factor F includes the factor 4 of equation (11.3), which allows for the four wires. It is not the field-strength gain factor as compared with a half-wave dipole because of the impedance difference. If we take the figure of 600 ohms we have, equating the input power to the corresponding dipole power:

$$I^2 \times 600 = I_D{}^2 \times 73$$

or

$$I = I_D/2{\cdot}86$$

Substituting in equation (11.4) we obtain:

$$E_a = \frac{60 I_D}{r} \times \frac{F}{2{\cdot}86} \quad . \quad . \quad . \quad . \quad . \quad . \quad (11.5)$$

This enables a comparison with a dipole in free space.

Finally, the effect of the ground has to be taken into account. This is carried out by the use of a group pattern factor relating to negative images because the aerial has horizontal current elements. Equation (10.11) and Fig. 10.13 are applicable. The height factors are given in Fig. 11.17 in a form convenient for design. The final stage in the determination of the main beam in a vertical plane is to multiply the factor F by the abscissa of Fig. 11.17, for each angle of elevation. It should be noted that for perfect ground a further field strength gain of 2 is available provided that the beam along the main axis is not too

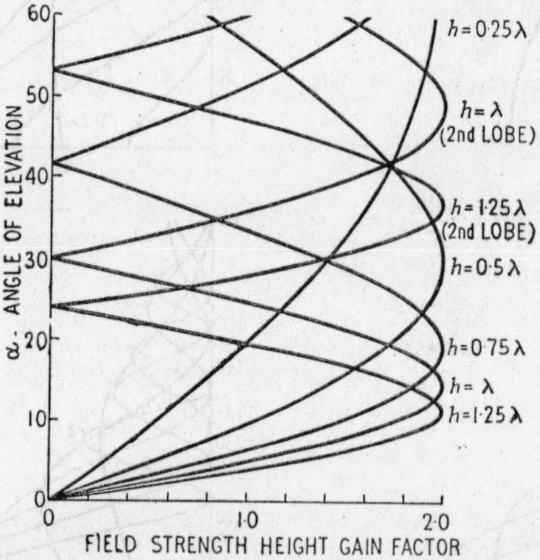

Fig. 11.17. Field-strength height gain factor for negative images.

sharp. Over poor soil this figure may fall to about 1·6. A sharp main beam along the main axis combined with too low an aerial, e.g. half a wavelength, can result in much loss of gain, a point that must always be borne in mind. Fortunately for a fixed aerial, reduction of frequency broadens the main lobe in free space so that combination with a height factor for lower electrical height results in no great loss of gain, but provides an increased angle of beam elevation. As already noted this condition matches ionospheric requirements and is an additional important feature which enables the rhombic aerial to operate over frequency bands of 2 to 1.

If the maximum gain is to be achieved from the ground reflection ahead of the aerial, then the reflecting zone should be flat and extensive. Any local roughness should not exceed about one-eighth of a wavelength in height. The zone should extend to at least two or three times the distance at which the mean reflected ray strikes the ground ($h/\tan \Delta$).

If the legs of a rhombic aerial are constructed from single wire the current at the points BB′ in Fig. 11.15 (c) will be smaller than that at the input owing to the impedance at BB′ being higher than the aerial input impedance. To counteract this drop of current it is common practice to construct each leg from three wires arranged as shown in Fig. 11.18. This reduces the impedance at BB′ and tends to keep the amplitude of the current wave more uniform throughout the aerial.

The terminating resistor presents a design problem when high transmitter powers are involved. The usual solution is to employ a transmission line made of iron wires at appropriate spacing to give the impedance required. Such a line

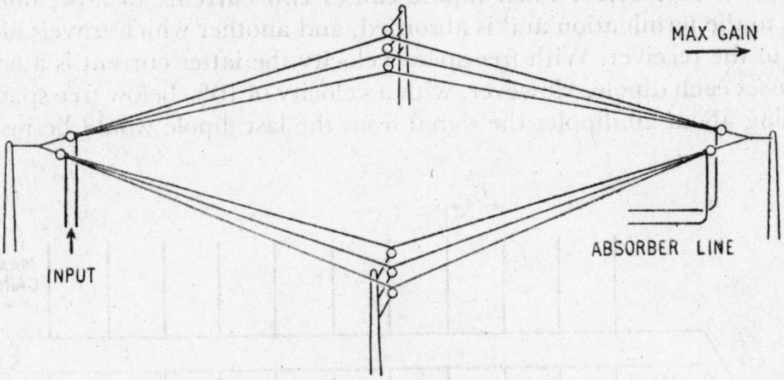

Fig. 11.18. Rhombic transmitting aerial.

has a high attenuation at radio frequencies, and the power is conveniently dissipated in the air.

Horizontal Array of Dipoles and The Fishbone Aerial

The horizontal array of dipoles is mainly employed as a receiving aerial for horizontal polarization. It consists of a number of approximately full-wave dipoles in a horizontal plane above the earth. These dipoles are arranged parallel to one another and spaced about a quarter wavelength apart at the mid-band frequency. They are connected to a feeder terminated to give as nearly as possible travelling waves. Fig. 11.19 shows a plan view of two such aerials, placed side by side in order to increase the directivity.

Consider first of all one of these dipole arrays in free space. It may be treated as a transmitting aerial for purposes of estimating gain and polar diagram. If the feeder is assumed loss free a signal applied to the feeder will excite the dipoles in the correct phase for end fire operation. The maximum gain will be in the direction of the arrow, and equation (10.23) shows that the maximum gain for 10 dipoles is about 10 db above a full-wave dipole or 11·7 db above a half-wave dipole. This equation also provides the polar diagram in a vertical plane. Continuing the assumption that the feeder is loss free, variation of the frequency about the mean for which the dipole spacing is a quarter wavelength still provides the correct phasing for end fire. At the frequency corresponding to quarter-wave spacing, mutual impedance effects are small, but they increase at lesser or greater spacings. This type of aerial generally has a bandwidth of $\pm$ 25% for a 2 db departure from optimum gain.

The effect of the ground is allowed for in the same way as for the rhombic aerial. The array is usually arranged at a height above ground, to give a beam of elevation appropriate to the optimum frequency. The ground provides 3 to 6 db extra gain but this is mainly offset by the loss in the termination.

The two aerials side by side increase the gain by nearly 3 db; i.e., the total gain is about 14 db. There is however a loss to be subtracted because the feeder is not loss free, and the velocity in the feeder does not provide optimum phasing. The usual gain obtained from the aerial shown is about 12 db.

The dipoles provide a loading on the transmission line of about 2,000 ohms each, and the velocity in the feeder is in fact 5 to 10% below that in free space. We now consider the aerial for reception in free space of a signal coming from the right in Fig. 11.19. Each dipole causes two currents to flow, one which travels to the termination and is absorbed, and another which travels along the feeder to the receiver. With free-space velocity the latter current is augmented as it passes each dipole. However, with a velocity of 10% below free space, after traversing about 20 dipoles the signal from the last dipole would be just about

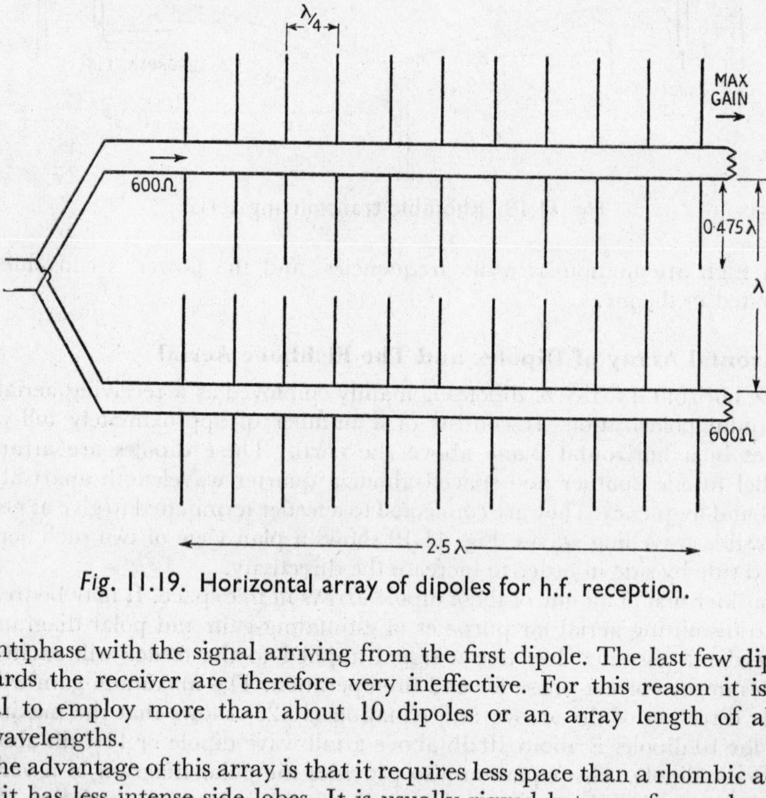

Fig. 11.19. Horizontal array of dipoles for h.f. reception.

in antiphase with the signal arriving from the first dipole. The last few dipoles towards the receiver are therefore very ineffective. For this reason it is not usual to employ more than about 10 dipoles or an array length of about 2½ wavelengths.

The advantage of this array is that it requires less space than a rhombic aerial and it has less intense side lobes. It is usually rigged between four poles with catenary wires as in Fig. 11.19. The sag should be kept to less than one-tenth of a wavelength. The aerial requires much wire, and a thin gauge (about 1½ mm dia.) is often used. It is not generally considered to have sufficient directivity gain or efficiency for transmitting.

The fishbone aerial is very similar, and is only suitable for receiving. A single unit is shown in Fig. 11.20. As compared with the horizontal array of dipoles, the dipoles are much closer together (about 0·1λ) and for this reason they are only loosely coupled to the travelling-wave feeder. This is carried out by small coupling capacitors, which are adjusted to give a velocity of not less than 0·9*c* in the feeder. It is sometimes employed with lengths up to 4 wavelengths, and a useful frequency range of 2 to 1.

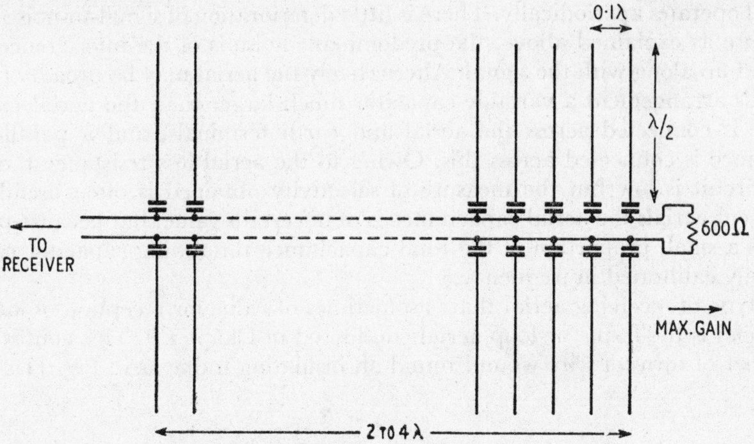

Fig. 11.20. The fishbone aerial for h.f. reception.

Receiving Aerials for the L.F. and M.F. Bands

The Reciprocity Theorem shows that a good transmitting aerial is also a good receiving aerial. However it is possible to make considerable economies when designing receiving aerials, because in the l.f. and m.f. bands aerial efficiency is relatively unimportant. The reason for this is that interference noise is nearly always many times greater than thermal noise in these bands. If all the noise from an aerial were thermal noise, a large loss resistance due to say a poor earth, would considerably reduce the available signal power without altering the available thermal noise power. Thus a poor signal-to-noise ratio would result. However if interference noise predominates then a large loss resistance attenuates both signal and noise with little effect upon signal-to-noise ratio. Thus the efficiency precautions necessary with transmitting aerials are not applicable to receiving aerials in this band.

For l.f. and m.f. reception, the inverted L or T aerial is generally employed with a simple earth pin or plate. The height of the aerial should be at least 5 metres and preferably higher. The vertical down lead is, of course, mainly responsible for picking-up signal and it should therefore be well away from metal structures. With metal masts the T aerial is preferable for this reason. If it is desired to reduce sky-wave interference the T aerial has a better performance than the inverted L. An elaborate top-capacitance system increases the effective height but the improvement in signal-to-noise ratio is small. If the field strength and effective height are known, the received open-circuit signal voltage is easily calculated. Noise field strengths can vary between wide limits depending upon the part of the world. Typical figures are between 10 and 1,000 microvolts per metre at 300 kc/s for an audio bandwidth, although larger figures are possible in tropical regions, and much lower figures in polar regions.

In Chapter 10 it was demonstrated that a short aerial could, in theory, be matched to a load so as to extract the same signal power as a half-wave dipole. A similar argument applies for a short unipole and a quarter-wave unipole. The ideal matching process consists of tuning the aerial with series inductance and then using an ideal step-up transformer. However, in practice the aerial is often coupled to the receiving amplifier directly without tuning, so that the aerial operates aperiodically. There is little deterioration of signal-to-noise ratio, because as explained above, the predominant noise is of the interference type picked up along with the signal. Alternatively the aerial may be broadly tuned. In this arrangement a variable capacitor much larger than the aerial capacitance is connected across the aerial and earth terminals, and a parallel inductance is connected across this. Owing to the aerial loss resistance the Q of the circuit is low but the measure of selectivity obtained is often useful. For different aerials the aerial capacitance is of uncertain value, but because it only forms a small proportion of the total capacitance the tuning capacitor can be roughly calibrated in frequency.

A type of receiving aerial that is sometimes of value for reception of low frequencies is the frame or loop aerial considered in Chapter 9. This consists of a number of turns of wire wound round an insulating frame as in Fig. 11.21 (a).

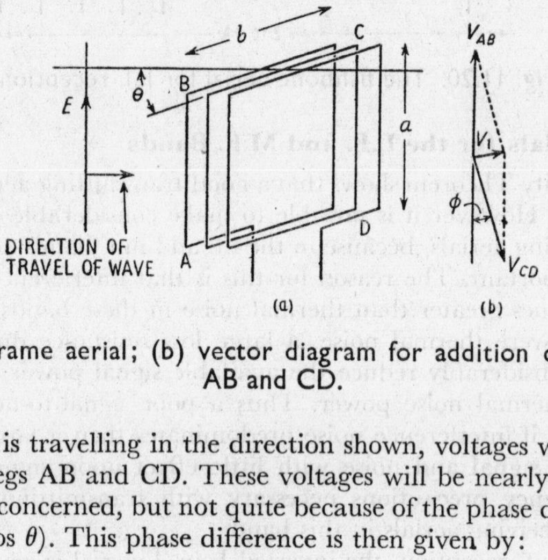

Fig. 11.21. (a) Frame aerial; (b) vector diagram for addition of e.m.fs in legs AB and CD.

If a plane wave is travelling in the direction shown, voltages will be produced in the vertical legs AB and CD. These voltages will be nearly in antiphase so far as the coil is concerned, but not quite because of the phase difference due to the spacing ($b \cos \theta$). This phase difference is then given by:

$$\phi = \frac{2\pi}{\lambda} b \cos \theta$$

If E is the field strength and a the height of the coil, the net voltage in one turn is obtained from the vector diagram of Fig. 11.21 (b). Since the angle ϕ is very small the resultant is given approximately by:

$$V_1 = Ea\frac{2\pi}{\lambda} b \cos \theta$$

For N turns the received aerial voltage is:

$$V_N = E\left(\frac{2\pi abN}{\lambda}\right) \cos \theta \quad . \quad . \quad . \quad . \quad . \quad . \quad . \quad (11.6)$$

If the area of the loop is A the term in brackets may be written as:

$$h = \frac{2\pi}{\lambda} NA \quad . \quad . \quad . \quad . \quad . \quad . \quad . \quad (11.7)$$

where h is often called the effective height of the frame aerial. The formula shows that for a large pick-up voltage a large area frame is desirable. It also shows that the received voltage is proportional to the number of turns. This is true up to a point, but a very flat optimum is reached at about 40 turns for low frequencies, beyond which the voltage decreases due to losses caused by proximity effect in the wires. At higher frequencies the optimum occurs at fewer turns and at very high frequencies only one turn can be used. The above equation also shows the directivity effect of the frame aerial. Maximum signal occurs when the frame lies in the plane of the electric vector. For a wave travelling at right angles to this, the signal received is zero. The polar diagram of the loop aerial is similar to that of a Hertzian dipole at right angles to the plane of the loop but the E and H vectors are interchanged.

The frame aerial has an impedance which is balanced to earth and it should therefore be connected to a balanced receiver. It has one disadvantage compared with a vertical aerial. This is the fact that it will also pick up steeply down-coming waves from the ionosphere of vertical or horizontal polarization, if the aerial orientation is suitable. This pick up occurs mainly in the horizontal portions of the aerial. It is thus liable to more noise pick up than a vertical aerial, which is insensitive to steeply downcoming waves and horizontal polarization. The loop aerial is sometimes called a magnetic dipole. The voltage pick-up equation can also be deduced by considering the flux linkages through the loop caused by the H vector of the received wave. If a suitable low-loss magnetic material is employed the frame may be reduced in size without loss of pick up. The magnetic material may be in the form of a cylinder with the coil wound round it in low capacitance solenoid form. The cylinder should be long compared with its diameter to minimize the de-magnetizing effect. The cylinder may also be in the form of a tube with little loss of pick up. For maximum pick-up the magnetic tube axis is placed at right angles to the direction of the wave being received.

The frame or loop aerial is widely employed for direction-finding purposes. It may be provided with an electrostatic screen; i.e., the turns may be placed inside a metallic tube bent into a circle or square. The tube must, of course, have an insulated joint so that it does not form a shorted turn. Such a screen reduces certain types of noise interference associated with charged particles of rain, snow or dust.

Receiving Aerials for the H.F. Band

Aerials for reception of h.f. signals can be divided into two main classes, those having no directivity gain (i.e., omnidirectional aerials) and those having directivity. The former are used for general communication purposes, while the latter are used on high-grade point-to-point long-distance circuits. Both types can be subdivided into aerials for vertical and horizontal polarization.

In receiving aerial design the requirement is always to achieve the best signal-to-noise ratio so that some knowledge of the nature of the noise is desirable. Up to about 20 Mc/s, noise is still predominantly of the general atmospheric and man-made interference type. For a well-selected receiving site the latter can usually be ignored and we are mainly concerned with atmospheric noise. Since this noise is well above the thermal noise corresponding to normal earth temperatures, it is not necessary to design receiving aerials with a high efficiency, for the reason given in the previous section. At frequencies above 20 Mc/s it is usually possible to achieve good aerial efficiency, and this course is generally adopted in practice.

It is not easy to quote typical values of atmospheric noise levels in the ionospheric band because they depend so much upon location, time of day, time of year, frequency and point in the sunspot cycle. However the level is in general lower than for the l.f. and m.f. band, and at 10 Mc/s typical figures are from 1 microvolt per metre to 10 microvolts per metre for an audio-bandwidth. In the tropics higher figures are experienced and local thunderstorms may cause a 10-db increase. Below 10 Mc/s the noise level depends to a very great extent upon the time of day. In general, as the frequency is reduced below 10 Mc/s, the noise falls during sunlight hours and rises steeply at night time. Below 2 or 3 Mc/s the noise rises to the figures previously quoted for the l.f. and m.f. band and they are less dependent upon time of day. The phenomenon of noise increase at night time in the band 3 to 10 Mc/s is due to the smaller absorption of radio waves in that part of the ionosphere above the part of the world in darkness. This causes noise to travel in from much greater distances and causes the

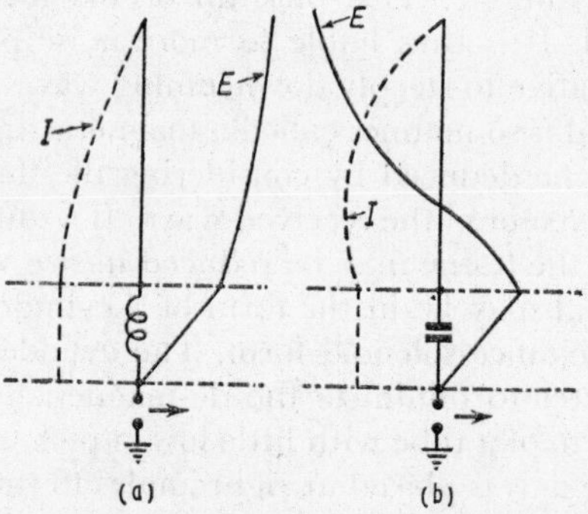

Fig. 11.22. Simple tuned receiving aerials: (a) height less than quarter wavelength; (b) height greater than quarter wavelength.

increased levels. Above 10 Mc/s the noise level falls gradually, until at the top end of the h.f. band the residual noise is largely of the thermal type. Its value can be deduced from the available noise power given by equation (10.33) provided the correct value of temperature T is known. This temperature is very high at a frequency of 30 Mc/s, but even so the noise field strength is only of the order of one-tenth of a microvolt per metre. Care must always be taken to avoid man-made interference.

For all-round reception of vertical polarization a simple vertical wire of about one-quarter wavelength is all that is required. Since high selectivity is desirable in this band, the aerial is often tuned. If the aerial is shorter than a quarter wave a series inductance is required. If a little longer than a quarter wave a series capacitance is used, sometimes called a shortening capacitor. The operation of tuning the aerial is then rather like bringing the aerial into quarter-wave resonance. The voltage and current distributions for these two cases are shown in Fig. 11.22. To reduce the tuning range of these components the aerial may be made broad-band by using a vertical cage of wires. A suitable spreader towards the top of the aerial provides the effect of an inverted cone, a desirable arrangement from the broadband point of view for reasons which are explained in the next Chapter.

For all-round reception of horizontal polarization, a good arrangement is two horizontal wires approximately a half-wavelength long and arranged as a V with a right angle between them. The feeder is balanced and connected at the apex. If we consider the polar diagram resulting from two dipole patterns one at right angles to the other, it can be seen that approximately all-round coverage is given. If such an aerial is placed at a height of about a quarter wavelength it is reasonably efficient for waves downcoming over a wide range of angles. The dipoles are usually made in wire-cage form so that with suitable tuning an octave frequency range is provided. Two such aerials covering two octaves can be rigged from 4 poles as shown in Fig. 11.23. The right-hand pole need only be half the height of the other three. Such an aerial is known as the quadrant or Wells aerial.

For point-to-point circuits a signal-to-noise ratio improvement can be obtained by using aerials of high directivity gain similar to those described for transmitting. This applies even though the noise may be still predominantly of the atmospheric or interference type. If the noise arrives in roughly equal

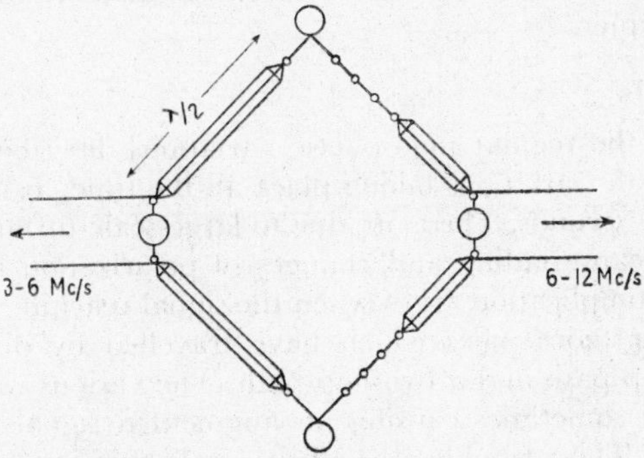

Fig. 11.23. The quadrant or Wells aerial for reception.

intensity from all directions, the available interference noise power is almost independent of aerial gain. However increased aerial gain means more power extracted from the signal wave as explained in Chapter 10. Thus the gain in signal-to-noise ratio roughly equals the aerial gain regardless of the relative intensity of interference and thermal noise. On important h.f. radio circuits it is therefore usual to employ high-gain receiving aerials such as the tuned arrays, the inverted-V, the rhombic and the horizontal arrays of dipoles. Some economies can usually be made as compared with transmitting aerials. For example, single-wire rhombic aerials are usually employed with simple resistor terminations, and the earthing arrangements with the inverted-V are less elaborate. Smaller diameter conductors than used for transmitting may also be employed. A high efficiency is not required because the noise is mainly incoming with the signal. At very low noise sites and at the higher frequencies it may be necessary to seek a higher aerial efficiency for reception. A high aerial efficiency is always required for transmitting because the power radiated directly affects signal-to-noise ratio.

Precautions must always be taken with the feeders from receiving aerials because of the low level of signal, particularly where transmitting and receiving aerials are in proximity. It is preferable to employ screened feeders for receiving aerials, whereas open-wire feeders are satisfactory for transmitting aerials. The coaxial type of feeder is often employed, because of its smaller size than screened twin, and lead covering is sometimes used in preference to copper braid since it is a more satisfactory screen. If the aerial is balanced, a suitable balanced-to-unbalanced transformer must be used to couple it to the feeder. This can usually be designed to cover the aerial bandwidth without adjustment; i.e., it is designed as a wideband transformer. The loss introduced by a well-designed transformer should not exceed 1 or 2 decibels.

If the feeder is well screened, the attenuation it introduces will not cause a serious degradation of signal-to-noise ratio, unless the attenuation is comparable with the power level difference between the interference noise and thermal noise. Where the noise is predominantly thermal noise, feeder attenuation causes a deterioration of signal-to-noise ratio, because it reduces the available signal power while the available noise power remains constant.

Suitable lightning arrestors consisting of spark gaps or gas-discharge tubes are desirable to protect matching transformers and feeder cables. These should be connected between each aerial conductor and earth on the aerial side of the matching transformer.

Diversity Aerials

In addition to the regular ionospheric variations described in Chapter 14, there are small-scale variations taking place all the time, at rates in the region of a cycle in a few seconds. These are due to large-scale turbulence in the ionosphere and they cause fading and changes of polarization in a downcoming wave. A further complication arises when the signal reaching a receiving aerial consists of two or more parts which have travelled by different paths, for example a one-hop path and a two-hop path. The various waves will interfere with one another sometimes causing an augmented signal and sometimes a diminished signal. These troublesome effects are known as multipath reception. If the frequency and the ionosphere were perfectly stable, the various waves would cause voltage vectors which would add up to give a stable resultant. However, the path lengths will differ by many wavelengths and quite small changes of frequency (as in modulation) and of mean height of reflection, will cause variations in the resultant. For example, if two paths have a time of transmission difference of one millisecond, and the frequency is 10 Mc/s then one path will have 10,000 more waves than the other. A change of frequency of one part in 10^4 (i.e., a change of 1,000 c/s) will cause a complete cycle of interference effects. A reflecting height change of a few wavelengths will have the same effect.

To provide a relief from these fading effects, diversity reception may be used. This may take several forms. In all cases two or more aerials are employed and usually each aerial is equipped with its own receiver and some form of electronic switching to enable rapid change-over from one aerial to another. This switching is usually carried out after the detection stage. Space diversity is the name given to the arrangement in which two aerials, usually of the rhombic type, are separated by a distance of 4 to 10 wavelengths. Both aerials are beamed on the transmitter and they may be spaced in line with the transmitter or broadside. The principle is that the two aerials do not experience fades at the same moment so that it is possible to switch to the one having the best signal-to-noise ratio. Sometimes, however, there will be fades affecting both aerials simultaneously.

The principle may be extended to three spaced aerials, although the improvement is not as large as the improvement on increasing from one to two aerials. Another form of diversity is known as polarization diversity. This is obtained by using two aerials one receiving horizontal polarization, for example the rhombic type, and another receiving vertical polarization, for example the inverted-V. The separation between aerials need not be very large, but the improvement given by polarization diversity is not as great as that with space diversity.

A more elaborate system of diversity is that known as the Multiple Unit Steerable Antenna system (M.U.S.A.). In this system several rhombic aerials are spaced in line towards the transmitter, as shown in Fig. 11.24. The cables to

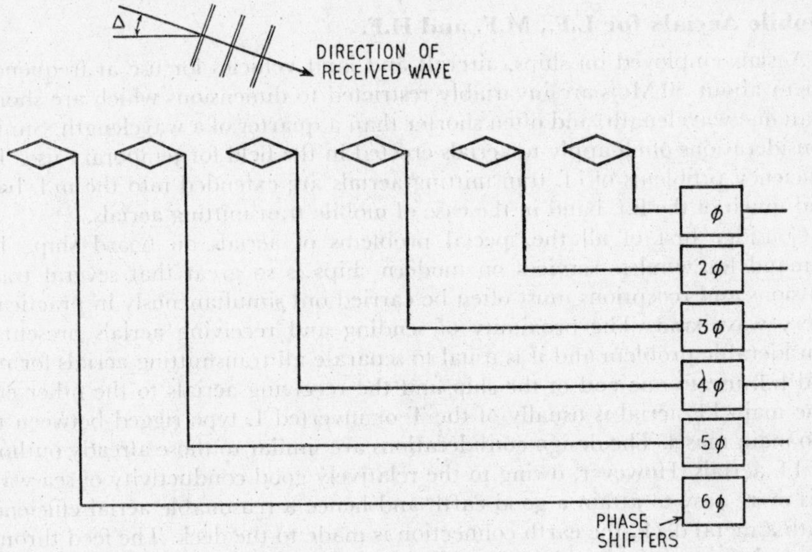

Fig. 11.24. The multiple-unit steerable aerial system for reception.

the receiving site are arranged as shown and variable phase shifters are inserted in each cable. These phase shifters are geared together and they cause progressively more phase shift for the more distant aerials. Consideration of end-fire theory shows that for a certain velocity in the cable and a certain phase shift, there will be an angle of elevation at which all aerials will augment one another. Variation of the phase shifters causes this angle to vary. This may be done automatically so as to pick up the best downcoming wave. Hence the term steerable antenna. The width of the beam is also less than that for a single rhombic aerial depending upon the number of units employed. Usually 6 aerials are employed and the beam width to the half power points is only 2·5 degrees. The average angle of elevation of downcoming wave on long circuits is given in Table 11.3.

This illustrates the point made in connection with single rhombic aerials, namely that as the frequency is reduced the angle of elevation increases. On short circuits it is necessary to take the actual geometric situation into account using the height of the reflecting layer. In the M.U.S.A. system the narrow angle of the beam enables the wave appropriate to the best path to be selected.

TABLE 11.3

Frequency (Mc/s)	Δ (degrees)
5	24·5
10	17
15	10·5
20	7

Mobile Aerials for L.F., M.F. and H.F.

Aerials employed on ships, aircraft and land vehicles for use at frequencies up to about 30 Mc/s are invariably restricted to dimensions which are shorter than one wavelength, and often shorter than a quarter of a wavelength. Similar considerations often apply to aerials erected in the field for temporary use. The efficiency problems of l.f. transmitting aerials are extended into the m.f. band and much of the h.f. band in the case of mobile transmitting aerials.

Consider first of all the special problems of aerials on board ship. The demand for wireless services on modern ships is so great that several transmissions and receptions must often be carried out simultaneously in practically every waveband. The proximity of sending and receiving aerials presents a considerable problem and it is usual to separate all transmitting aerials for m.f. and h.f. use to one end of the ship and the receiving aerials to the other end. The main l.f. aerial is usually of the T or inverted L type rigged between the two main masts. The design considerations are similar to those already outlined for l.f. aerials. However, owing to the relatively good conductivity of sea water it is more easy to attain a good earth and hence a reasonable aerial efficiency. With a metal deck, the earth connection is made to the deck. The feed through the deck from the transmitter must have a very low capacitance, otherwise the current flowing in the up lead to charge the top capacitance will be reduced.

For transmitting in the m.f. or lower h.f. band it is sometimes possible to employ the main mast as a radiator. A number of wires suspended from a short arm at the top of the mast enable it to be excited as a folded unipole in a similar manner to the outrigger type of aerial shown in Fig. 11.7. The aerial is driven between the metal deck and the lower ends of the wires, and a matching unit is fitted at this point. This enables the feeder to be of coaxial type.

For omnidirectional transmission in the middle part of the h.f. band a separate mast of 30–40 ft height is usually required. This may be excited as a folded unipole or it may be rigged with wires so as to form an inverted cone rather similar to Fig. 11.3. It will be shown in the next chapter that this imparts wideband properties to the aerial. However a matching circuit would still be required although its range would be less than for a thin aerial.

For h.f. transmission over greater distances using ionospheric transmission, it is often possible to rig a horizontal half-wave dipole between masts or funnels. In this case the arrangement of the aerial and feeder is similar to that already described for use on land.

For reception on board ship, a number of whip aerials are usually employed, although for the lower frequencies it is usually possible to employ the T or inverted-L aerial. It is often necessary to employ band-stop filters in the receiving aerial feeder to reject high-level signals from the transmitting aerials. Several receivers are often required to share one aerial and suitable coupling networks are used to prevent mutual disturbances.

In the case of aircraft flying long distances, it is usually necessary to employ ionospheric communication and h.f. aircraft aerials are therefore required. These used to consist of a trailing wire of about 50 metres length, let out and drawn in by means of a small winch. This aerial would be driven between the wire and the metallic structure of the aircraft. At frequencies below 1 Mc/s the radiation resistance would be a few ohms down to small fractions of an ohm. Even so impedance measurements indicate that the series resistance is 10 ohms or more, so that low efficiencies are inevitable. The losses occur in the metal work of the aircraft, and the main aerial insulator.

However, with present-day aircraft speeds, this type of aerial is no longer practicable. One alternative is a simple wire aerial such as the T or inverted L arranged between the top of the tail fin and a small mast at the forward end of the fuselage. Such an aerial is also rather inefficient because the separation between aerial wire and fuselage is only of the order of a metre or so. It is not easy to predict which part of the aerial contributes most to radiation, and the structure itself may radiate. The solid polar diagram is usually extremely ragged and cannot be predicted. The performance of such aerials is checked by impedance measurements over a range of frequencies, and by polar diagram measurements using models.

When used for transmitting, these wire aerials are prone to corona troubles due to the high voltage gradients combined with the low air pressure at high altitudes. When used for receiving they are liable to have a high noise level due to a phenomenon known as precipitation static. This arises because the aircraft acquires an electric charge from dust particles, rain or snow. This charge leaks away from points or parts of small radius such as wires. If this occurs from the aerial or near the aerial it causes additional noise at the receiver input. This difficulty may be alleviated by brush dischargers at the wing tips, but a more satisfactory method is to use aerials having a lower impedance and to keep the aerials away from parts having a high charge density.

Higher aircraft speeds and the need to reduce precipitation static have necessitated the design of aerials known as 'suppressed aerials'. Such aerials are built into the structure of the aircraft in such a way that streamlining is preserved. One form of such an aerial is the loop excited aerial shown in Fig. 11.25 (a). It consists of a small loop having perhaps 2 or 3 turns which is placed as shown so that it couples via the magnetic field to the whole wing and fuselage of the aircraft. For transmitting, it induces currents in the aircraft structure which radiate. The transmitter must of course be matched to the relatively low impedance presented by the loop. Such an aerial proves to be more efficient than the wire aerials and less prone to precipitation static. Another method of exciting the wing is the end fed method of Fig. 11.25 (b). A short section at one wing tip is insulated and the drive is applied across the gap. The wing is thus excited like an end-fed aerial. Yet another method which is efficient and almost immune from precipitation static is the notch aerial in Fig. 11.25 (c). This may be considered to be part of a slot aerial. It may be driven at a point towards the end of the notch so that relatively low impedance cable may be used. For the h.f. band this slot tends to be rather large but it is practicable for large aircraft. All of these aerials have irregular polar diagrams, and the efficiencies are low compared with conventional aerials, but the results achieved are the best in the circumstances. Where the structure forms one terminal of the aerial it is important to ensure that the screen of the coaxial feeder is connected to the structure by a low-impedance connection.

The problem of designing vehicle aerials for this band is also formidable. The only feasible type of aerial is that known as the whip aerial, which consists of a copper rod, made from sections of gradually reducing diameter. The thick bottom end is supported by an insulator which is flexibly mounted so that the aerial can bend over almost to the horizontal. The top of the vehicle should be metallic. Such a rod aerial will have a linearly-tapered current distribution over most of the lower and ionospheric bands of frequencies. Equation (9.11) gives the radiation resistance. If a height of rod of 5 metres is assumed the radiation

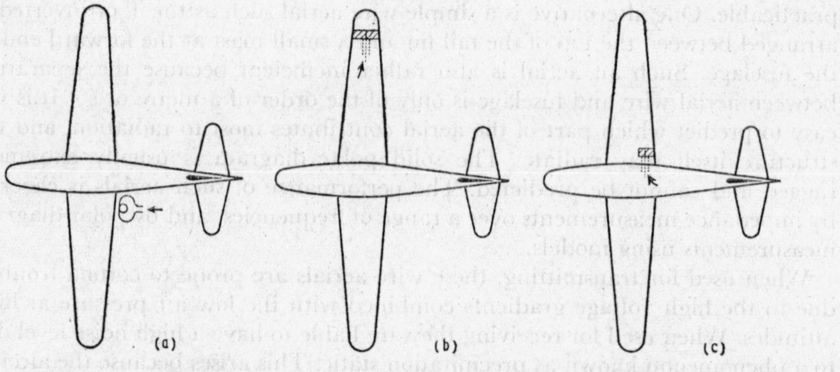

Fig. 11.25. H.F. suppressed aerials for aircraft: (a) the loop excited aerial; (b) the end-fed wing; (c) the notch aerial.

resistance at 3 Mc/s is about 1 ohm. Measurements of the impedance of such an aerial give a series resistance of about 5 ohms showing that at this frequency the aerial efficiency is about 20%. Earthing of the vehicle with simple earth spikes makes little difference to these figures owing to the large capacitance of the vehicle to earth. At lower frequencies the aerial efficiency falls off rapidly. For example at 1 Mc/s it is only about one-eighth of one per cent. The efficiency of such an aerial does not improve much above the figure of 20% up to 20 Mc/s. In military practice two 5 metre rods are used arranged as a V with a few feet separation between the tips of the rods. This serves to provide a higher capacitance and lower aerial insulator voltage as explained in connection with l.f. aerials. The rods are usually hauled over to an angle of about 40°. The aerial may then be resolved into a vertical component giving vertically-polarized ground-wave coverage, and a horizontal component giving horizontally-polarized sky-wave coverage. For such low heights it is very difficult to make proper allowance for the effect of the earth, because the assumption of perfect conductivity becomes very inaccurate at low heights. Performance and range can only be deduced by experience.

For temporary aerials erected in the field it is often not possible to employ masts exceeding 5 or 10 metres height; i.e., a small fraction of a wavelength in the lower h.f. and m.f. bands. For the latter frequencies the inverted L or T aerial must be used and the low efficiency must be tolerated. For the middle range of the h.f. band better efficiency may be achieved by using horizontal dipoles, because the height is now of the order one-eighth to one-quarter of a wavelength. Reflection from the ground will give some gain in the upward directions thus improving communication by means of the ionospheric wave. Best reception occurs with a similar dipole aerial when the tops are parallel or in line.

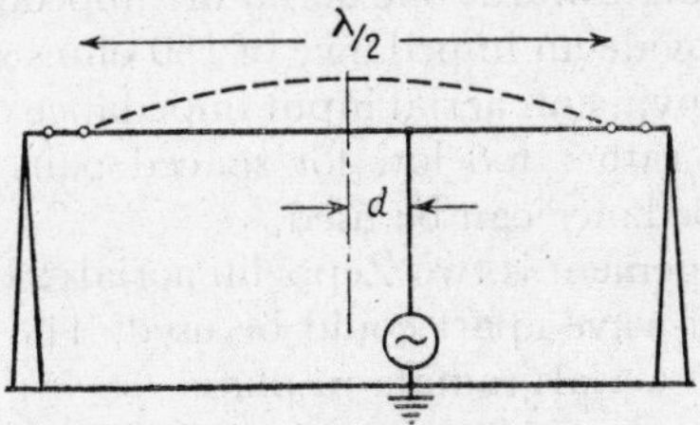

Fig. 11.26. The Wyndom aerial.

There are several methods of feeding the dipole which should preferably be a half-wave long. If centre fed a low-impedance feeder is required. Other methods of feeding which have already been described are those used in the folded dipole and the Zeppelin aerials of Fig. 11.8. Another simple method is to use a wire arranged as an inverted L in which the horizontal top is either a quarter or half a wave long. The up-lead current is high in the former case and it will provide all-round coverage by means of vertically-polarized ground or surface wave. If a wide-range matching unit is not available the length of top plus the up-lead can be made half a wavelength giving a high resistive input

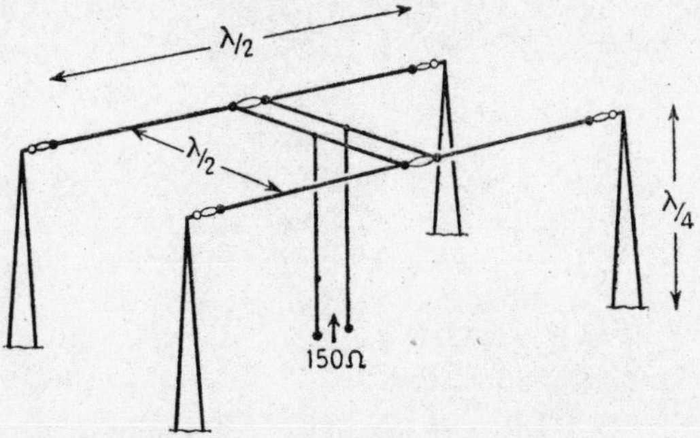

Fig. 11.27. Two half-wave dipoles arranged to produce gain in an upward direction.

impedance. Another method of feeding is that used in the Wyndom aerial shown in Fig. 11.26. The top radiating element is a few per cent less than half a wave long. In a manner analogous to the tapped resonant line of Fig. 4.8, this wire may be fed at a point offset from the centre where the impedance is essentially resistive and of magnitude dependent upon the offset distance *d*. The up-lead has an impedance to surroundings of 500 to 600 ohms, and the correct value of *d* for reasonable matching is about one-twelfth of a wavelength. The aerial is driven between the up-lead and an earth pin, and good earth conductivity is desirable.

For short-distance communication, using reflection from the ionosphere, it is sometimes desirable to use more upward gain. This can be achieved with two half-wave dipoles spaced one half-wave apart in a horizontal plane. These may be rigged from 4 masts as in Fig. 11.27 at a preferred height of about a quarter wavelength. A convenient characteristic impedance for the feeder joining the two dipoles is 150 ohms. At the middle, where the two aerials are joined in parallel, each aerial has its impedance transformed by a quarter-wave line. Thus at this point looking towards one aerial the impedance is about 300 ohms. The two in parallel provide an impedance of 150 ohms so that the rising feeder can also be 150 ohms, giving an aerial input impedance of the same value. Such a feeder impedance is rather too low for spaced pair, but low-loss balanced cable of about this impedance can be used.

An alternative arrangement is two Zeppelin aerials a half-wave apart, or two full-wave dipoles a half-wave apart could be used. The feeders must of course be arranged so that the aerials radiate in phase.

CHAPTER 12

V.H.F. and U.H.F. Aerials

IT MUST BE UNDERSTOOD that there is no clear dividing line between the aerials for one frequency band and those for another band. Several of the aerials described in Chapter 11, such as the dipole arrays and the travelling-wave aerials, may be employed in the bands to be considered in this chapter. At the upper end of the band to be considered here the microwave aerials described in the next chapter may also be used. However, as the frequency increases, new problems arise, and new methods become practicable. In this chapter the general problems and methods of the 30 to 3,000 Mc/s range of frequencies are considered. The generally accepted classification of the bands in this range is given in Table 12.1 together with a few of the services for which they are employed.

TABLE 12.1

Band	Frequency range (Mc/s)	Wavelength range (metres)	Typical services
Very high frequencies (V.H.F.)	30–300	10–1	Communications between vehicles, aircraft and ships. Radio relay telephony. Television
Ultra high frequencies (U.H.F.)	300–3,000	1–0·1	Aircraft navigation, landing, etc. Radar

Excepting for the lower part of the v.h.f. band, dipole aerials are of such a size that they can be constructed from rigid aluminium or copper tubing. At the higher frequencies the diameters can be increased in relation to the length, in order to improve the bandwidth. Unipole aerials at the higher frequencies are so short that they are often called stub aerials. The basic theory of unipole and dipole aerials applies well at these frequencies, but greater consideration must be given to the geometry of the region where the feeder is connected to the aerial. At these frequencies the curves of Fig. 9.11 and 9.12 may be used for design purposes but a check by means of impedance measurement is usually desirable. Up to about 300 Mc/s radio-frequency bridges may be used. Above this frequency, slotted-line standing-wave detectors can be employed.

Greater consideration must also be given to the run of the feeder cable in relation to dipole aerials. For example, consider a horizontal dipole at the top of a metal mast having the feeder cable (which should be balanced) running up the mast. This makes a symmetrical arrangement with the mast lying in a negligible electric field. Such a case would be expected to agree closely with the theory of a dipole at the appropriate height above the ground. If we had considered a vertical dipole mounted on a metal mast, the actual method of mounting would have to be taken into account to determine the performance in terms of polar diagram and radiation resistance. Only if the dipole were offset on a horizontal arm at a distance of a wavelength or more could the simple theory be expected to apply with any accuracy. The feeder cable should of course run along this arm so that it does not unduly disturb the dipole field.

In this band feeder attenuation is often a serious factor, and because for a given outside diameter balanced twin cable has a higher attenuation than coaxial cable, the latter is usually preferred. This presents a problem when feeding balanced aerials such as a half-wave dipole, because coaxial cable is unbalanced. This problem is considered in the next section.

In the band considered here propagation is almost entirely by means of the space wave (see Chapter 14), and range is dependent upon the height of transmitting and receiving aerials. For fixed ground-to-ground communications, it is therefore usually a requirement that the aerial should be suitable for mounting on a tall mast. This is a feasible proposition for the aerial dimensions appropriate to this band. For ground-to-ground service there is little to choose between the propagation properties of horizontally- and vertically-polarized radiation. However, from the point of view of interference between stations, and residual noise in the area concerned, it is sometimes convenient to use horizontal and sometimes convenient to use vertical polarization.

The reduced dimensions of aerials in the v.h.f. and u.h.f. bands is one reason for the choice of such frequencies for mobile communications. Reasonably efficient aerials can be designed for vehicle, aircraft and ship use. The special problems of mobile aerials are considered briefly at the end of the chapter.

The Connection of Balanced Aerials to Unbalanced Feeders

Before considering the devices that may be employed for connecting a balanced aerial, such as a centre-fed dipole, to an unbalanced feeder, e.g., a coaxial cable, it is desirable to study the consequences that may arise if direct connection is adopted. The situation is shown in Fig. 12.1 (a) and (b). The dipole is assumed to be half-wave resonant with an impedance of 73 ohms. In addition each section of the aerial will have an impedance to earth mainly capacitive, represented by Z_e' and Z_e''. The latter impedances will be mainly impedances to the mast or feed cable in most practical cases. Ideally they should be equal, for example in the symmetrical case of a horizontal dipole attached to a vertical mast. Generally they will be reasonably well balanced and for the present purposes they will be considered to be equal to one another. Looking into the end of the cable there are also three impedances to consider. The characteristic impedance (assuming the distant end to be correctly terminated) of the circuit between the centre conductor and the inside of the screen which is here taken to be 73 ohms, the impedance of the screen to earth and that of the centre conductor to earth. The impedance Z_{se} of the screen to earth is the impedance to currents flowing on the outside of the screen. This circuit has distributed inductance and capacitance, and the impedance at any frequency will generally be of uncertain value. The impedance Z_{ce} of the centre conductor to earth may be taken to be infinite due to the screening effect of the outer conductor.

Consider now the transmitting case shown in Fig. 12.1 (b) where the source of voltage is in between the cable terminals. If $Z_{se} = Z_{ce}$ it can be seen from the general symmetry that there will be no current in the hypothetical earth connection, and that the transmitting current will flow in the aerial as desired. However Z_{se} will usually be a relatively low impedance and because Z_{ce} is very high, a current will flow through Z_{se}, in addition to the current which will flow in the aerial. Thus there will be radiation from the outer conductor of the cable due to these currents. The current in the screen will destroy the nulls and generally upset the pattern of the required polar diagram. It can be seen that one method of restoring balance is to raise the impedance of Z_{se} to a high value

In the receiving case shown in Fig. 12.1 (c), the most serious consequence is that noise voltages E_n picked up on the cable screen can cause currents to flow through the hypothetical earth, dividing between the two impedances Z_e and thence into the input of the cable. Again a high impedance in series with Z_{se} will prevent or reduce the circulation of these noise currents.

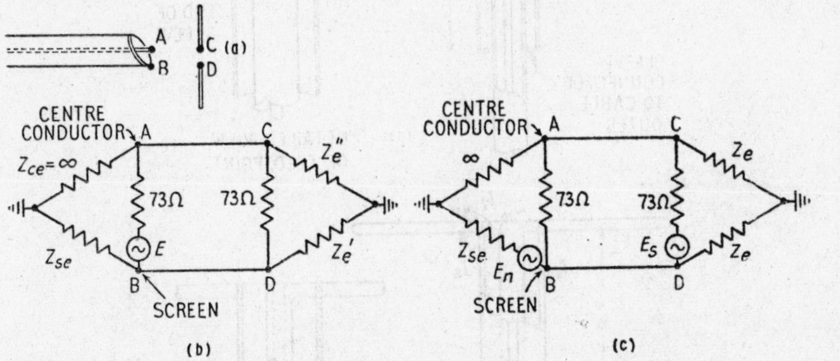

Fig. 12.1. The connection of an unbalanced cable to a balanced load: (a) coaxial cable and a dipole aerial; (b) circuit conditions for transmitting; (c) receiving conditions.

Whether a balancing device is required or not depends entirely upon the magnitude of these effects and the circumstances of the problem. When the noise is mainly thermal, and no great polar-diagram accuracy is required, the unbalanced cable is often connected directly to a balanced aerial. Where great polar diagram accuracy is required a balancing device known as a balun is required.

The simplest form of balun is the type shown in cross section in Fig. 12.2 (a). This consists of a quarter-wave choke placed in series with the screen outer. It is therefore only effective over a narrow band of frequencies on either side of that for which the sleeve is a quarter wavelength. This choke reduces currents on the outside of the cable to a negligible value, and the dipole operates in a well-balanced condition.

Another form of balun is the slotted feed shown in Fig. 12.2 (b). The outer screen has two slots a quarter wavelength long diametrically opposite to one another. The balanced impedance is connected to the outside of the screen, one terminal to each of the two sections. The inner conductor is connected at the extremity to one section of the screen and one terminal of the balanced load. It can be seen that the impedance looking back into the cable is well balanced from the viewpoint of symmetry. Also, since the slots behave as high quarter-wave impedances the currents flowing on the edges of the slots will be small. In the transmitting direction the current I_1 flowing in the line formed by the inner and the leg of the outer to which it is connected will be small because from the section AA it appears as a high impedance. The main cable current flows between the inner and the other leg of the outer and thence into the balanced load. The inner conductor is sometimes increased in diameter over the last quarter wavelength to preserve a smooth impedance because the current distribution on the inner is not uniform around a circumference.

The baluns described so far are only suitable for a narrow band on either side of the frequency for which the choke or slot corresponds to a quarter wave in

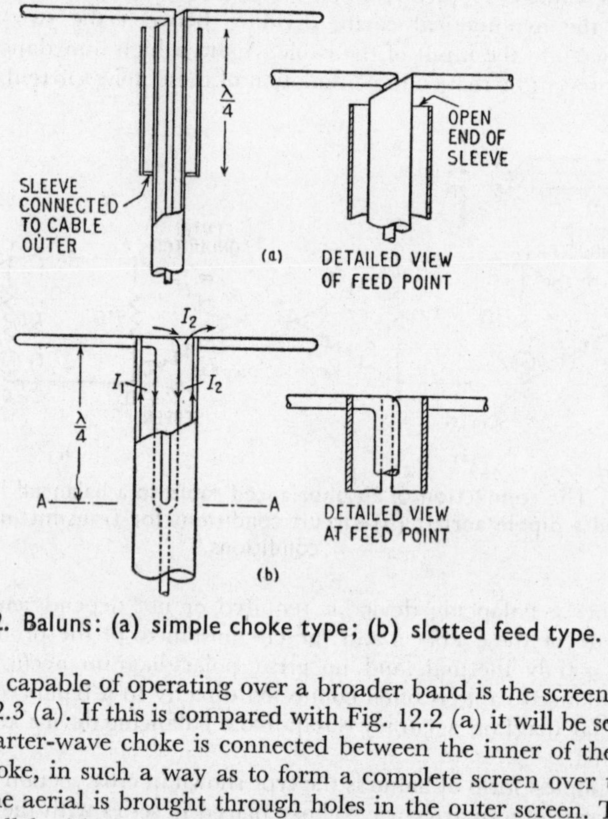

Fig. 12.2. Baluns: (a) simple choke type; (b) slotted feed type.

length. A balun capable of operating over a broader band is the screened type shown in Fig. 12.3 (a). If this is compared with Fig. 12.2 (a) it will be seen that an identical quarter-wave choke is connected between the inner of the feeder and the first choke, in such a way as to form a complete screen over the end of the cable. The aerial is brought through holes in the outer screen. The impedance in parallel with the aerial is twice that of a single choke. At the frequency for which the balun is a half wavelength overall, this impedance is very high. At other frequencies this shunting impedance is twice the single-choke sleeve impedance or from equation (3.22)

$$2jZ_0 \tan \frac{2\pi l}{\lambda}$$

where Z_0 is the characteristic impedance between the choke sleeve and the outer of the feeder and l is the length of a single choke. If the length l is a quarter wave at the frequency for which the aerial is a half-wave dipole, then this shunting impedance provides the correct type of susceptance for annulling the aerial susceptance on either side of resonance. By suitable choice of Z_0 and the aerial thickness, this balun can be designed to give good matching and balancing over nearly an octave band.

Another type of balun is shown in Fig. 12.3 (b). This is similar in principle to

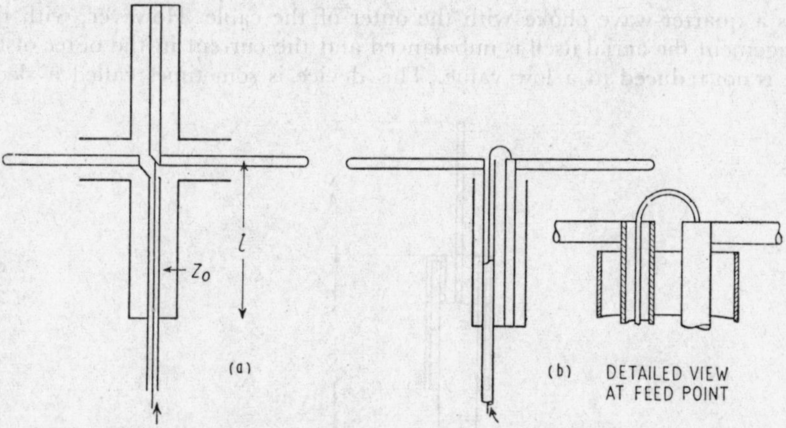

Fig. 12.3. Broadband baluns: (a) fully-screened type: (b) quarter-wave type.

Fig. 12.3 (a) except that the second choke shares the same outer screen as the first choke. It has all the advantages of the balun just described besides being only half its size. The inner of the cable which is bent over as shown in the figure must be kept as short as possible, since this wire has an inductance which causes a small unbalance.

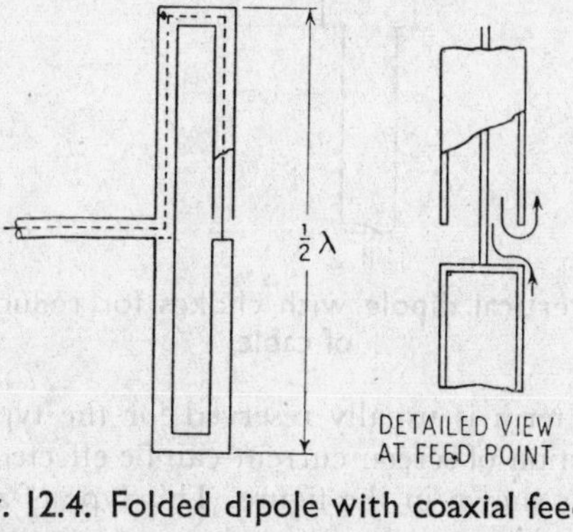

Fig. 12.4. Folded dipole with coaxial feed.

The degree of balance can be checked easily by a piece of thick wire or tubing bent to form a short-circuited line a quarter-wave long. This is connected to the aerial terminals in a symmetrical manner. A suitable r.f. voltmeter between the short-circuited end of this line and the outer of the cable should show a negligible voltage in comparison with the aerial voltage, if the balance is effective.

A very simple and effective conversion from unbalanced feeder to balanced aerial occurs with the folded dipole in which the coaxial-cable feed is through the tubular aerial conductor as shown in Fig. 12.4. The current on the inside of the outer conductor of the coaxial feed flows over the edge and back on the outside of the aerial conductor as shown in the diagram.

Sleeve Aerials

A type of aerial for vertical polarization which enables a coaxial feeder to be employed is shown in Fig. 12.5. In this device the lower half of the aerial dipole forms a quarter-wave choke with the outer of the cable. However, with this arrangement the aerial itself is unbalanced and the current in the outer of the cable is not reduced to a low value. This device is sometimes called a sleeve

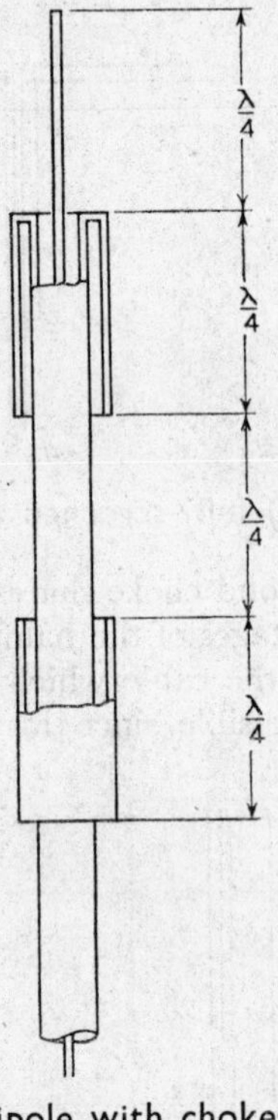

Fig. 12.5. Half-wave vertical dipole with chokes for reducing current in outer of cable.

dipole, although this term is usually reserved for the type of aerial described below. Further reduction of screen current can be effected by another quarter-wave choke spaced as shown in the figure. This type of aerial is only suitable for fixed frequency working.

The development of the sleeve unipole from a conventional quarter-wave unipole is shown in Fig. 12.6. It may be considered to be a quarter-wave unipole with the feed point displaced to a point of higher impedance. Fig. 12.6 (a) shows the normal unipole with an input impedance of about 37 ohms. Fig. 12.6 (b) shows a unipole fed at about the mid-point. The impedance at this feed point would be about 100 ohms and the cable would have to be of this impedance. By feeding at a point about 35% of the height, an impedance of 70 to 75 ohms is obtained, suitable for normal cable of this impedance. In a manner analogous to Fig. 4.8 the reactance at these alternative feed points is very small.

In the case of Fig. 12.6 (c) the unipole is voltage fed. The impedance would be a few hundred ohms depending upon the diameter. The feed through the stub is a quarter-wave long and its characteristic impedance may be chosen to

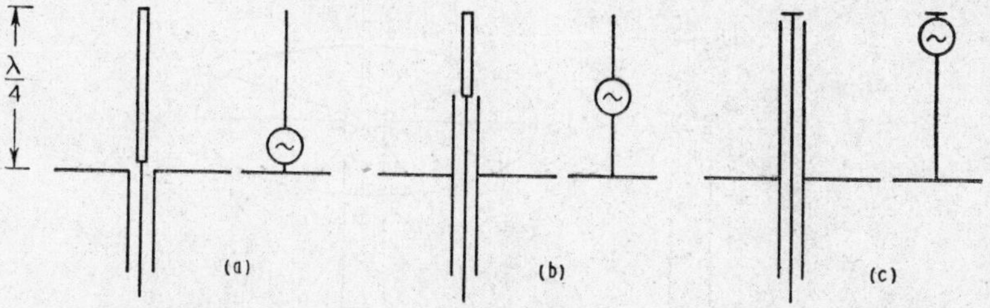

Fig. 12.6. Development of sleeve aerials (b) and (c) from quarter-wave unipole (a).

transform the aerial impedance to the feeder impedance. Sleeve unipole lengths up to half a wavelength may be used if arrangements are made for matching.

These aerials usually have diameters of the order of one eighth of the length, in order to achieve a good bandwidth. They are often called sleeve stub aerials. The main advantage of this type of aerial is that it may be made much more robust than the base-fed unipole, particularly when large diameter cylinders are required for wide bandwidth.

The dipole equivalent of Fig. 12.6 (b) is shown in Fig. 12.7. The feeder is

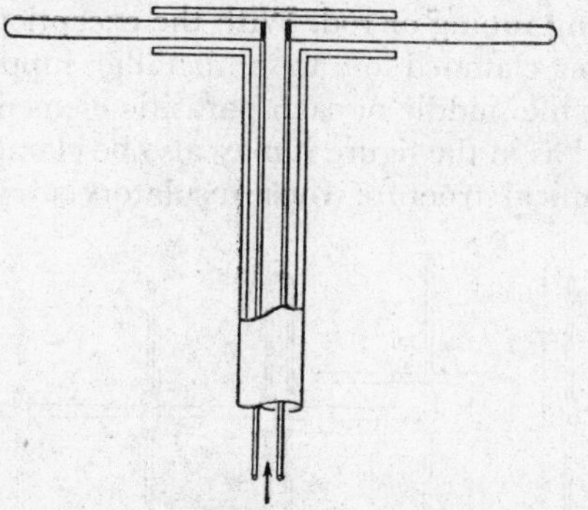

Fig. 12.7. Sleeve dipole with balanced feeder.

balanced and the input impedance is roughly twice that of the quarter-wave unipole fed at its mid point. This type of sleeve dipole can be made with balun and susceptance compensation as in Fig. 12.3 (a).

Ground-Plane Aerials

Where it is not important to have accurate polar diagrams, and it is merely desired to reduce the current in the cable outer to reasonably low values, the ground plane aerials shown in Fig. 12.8 may be used. The rods should preferably extend to a radius of a quarter wavelength from the axis, but where this is not convenient a radius of one-eighth of a wavelength is usually satisfactory. The aerial impedance is not easily predicted, and measurement is usually necessary if reasonable matching is to be achieved. Ground planes of one or two wavelengths diameter cause considerable upward tilting of the polar diagram in the vertical plane.

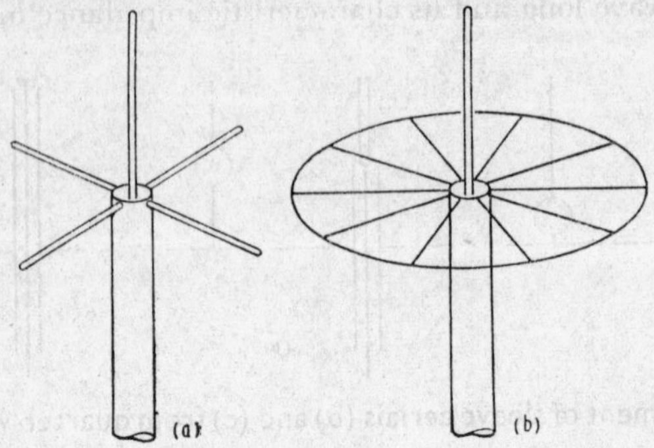

Fig. 12.8. Ground-plane aerials: (a) crossed-rod type; (b) cartwheel type.

The Yagi Aerial

The basic principles of parasitic reflectors and directors were discussed in Chapter 10. It was explained that a reflector behind a dipole and a director in front of the same dipole could both be employed to achieve extra gain. The resulting arrangement is known as a three-element Yagi aerial after its originator. Such an aerial is a very convenient and economical means of achieving about 5·5 db gain in the v.h.f. and u.h.f. bands because the elements may be made of self-supporting tubing or rod. With the exception of the driven dipole, the elements may be clamped on to a metallic support rod as shown in Fig. 12.9 (a) because the middle of each parasitic element is a voltage node. If the dipole is shunt fed as in the figure it may also be clamped to the support rod making a rigid mechanical structure whose insulators carry no appreciable stress.

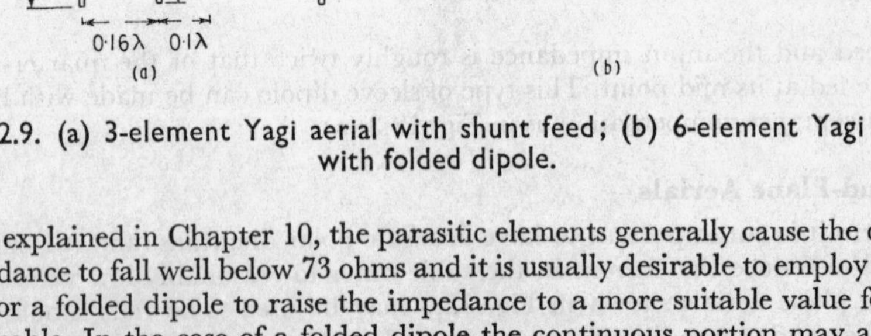

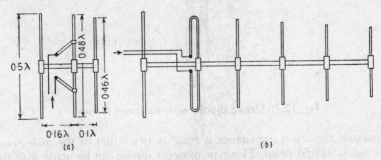

Fig. 12.9. (a) 3-element Yagi aerial with shunt feed; (b) 6-element Yagi aerial with folded dipole.

As explained in Chapter 10, the parasitic elements generally cause the dipole impedance to fall well below 73 ohms and it is usually desirable to employ shunt feed or a folded dipole to raise the impedance to a more suitable value for the feed cable. In the case of a folded dipole the continuous portion may also be clamped to the support rod.

The H aerial, consisting of a dipole and a reflector, and the 3-element Yagi aerial with a shunt feed or a folded dipole, are very popular for television reception. In this application it is usual to connect coaxial cable direct to the balanced aerial because the use of a balun is not justified.

Additional gain may be obtained by using more directors in the line of fire as shown in Fig. 12.9 (b). The spacing between rods is usually between 0·15 and 0·25 wavelengths. For each additional director the lengths of the rods must be adjusted or determined from a model to achieve maximum gain. The more distant the director from the dipole, the more is the capacitive reactance required to provide correct phasing of parasitic current. The lengths of the rods therefore taper off as in Fig. 12.9 (b). The maximum practicable gain is about 10 db which is obtained with an array length of about $1\frac{1}{2}$ wavelengths; i.e., an aerial with a reflector and 4 or 5 directors.

The Yagi aerial is essentially a fixed-frequency device, but it is usually possible to achieve a bandwidth of $\pm 3\%$ which is sufficient for television reception in the v.h.f. band. It is also satisfactory for low-power transmitting purposes.

The Corner Reflector

A half-wave dipole placed parallel to the intersection of two conducting planes can provide considerable directivity, if the angle between the planes and the position of the dipole are correctly chosen. The dipole should lie on the semi-angle plane. There are then two main parameters, the angle between the planes and the distance of the dipole from the apex. If the planes are considered to be perfect reflectors, and semi-infinite in extent, the operation of the aerial may be explained by image theory.

The simplest case occurs when the angle between the planes is a right angle and the dipole is half a wavelength from the apex. The cross-section is shown in Fig. 12.10 (a).

There will be negative images at A and B corresponding to the single reflections represented by the rays 'a' and 'b'. In addition there is a positive image at C corresponding to the double reflection represented by the ray 'c'. If four dipoles are spaced and phased as shown, without the conducting planes present, the tangential electric field in the plane represented by PY and PX is zero. This condition must always be satisfied by the dipole and image system. Since there can be no tangential electric field at the surface of a conducting plane the planes may be re-inserted without changing the field of the four dipoles. Thus the field in the sector due to the dipole and the two conducting planes is the same as the field in that sector due to the four suitably phased dipoles with no conducting planes present.

Along the main axis of PO extended, the field strength due to the dipole O and its images is four times the field strength of a dipole in free space carrying the same current. This follows because images A and B are spaced half a wavelength behind O and they carry a current phased by this amount, and image C is one wavelength behind O with the same phase. Thus all images reinforce the direct signal from the dipole. For a given dipole current the gain along the main axis is therefore 12 db.

However, there will be currents in the conducting planes and the dipole impedance will be considerably modified by the presence of the planes. The resistive part of the dipole impedance will be given by:

$$R_D = 73 + R_{OC} - 2R_{OA}$$

where R_{OC} is the resistive part of the mutual impedance between the dipole O and its image C spaced by one wavelength, and R_{OA} is the resistive part of the mutual impedance between O and A, which are spaced by 0·707 wavelengths. The figures can be read off from Fig. 10.15. In this manner the dipole impedance is found to be about 123 ohms together with a reactance. The dipole power radiated, is therefore about 123/73 = 1·7 times the power radiated from a dipole in free space carrying the same current. For a fair comparison with a dipole in free space the figure of 12 db must therefore be reduced by 2·6 db, giving an aerial gain along the main axis of about 9·4 db.

If the dipole spacing from the apex is reduced to a quarter wavelength, then

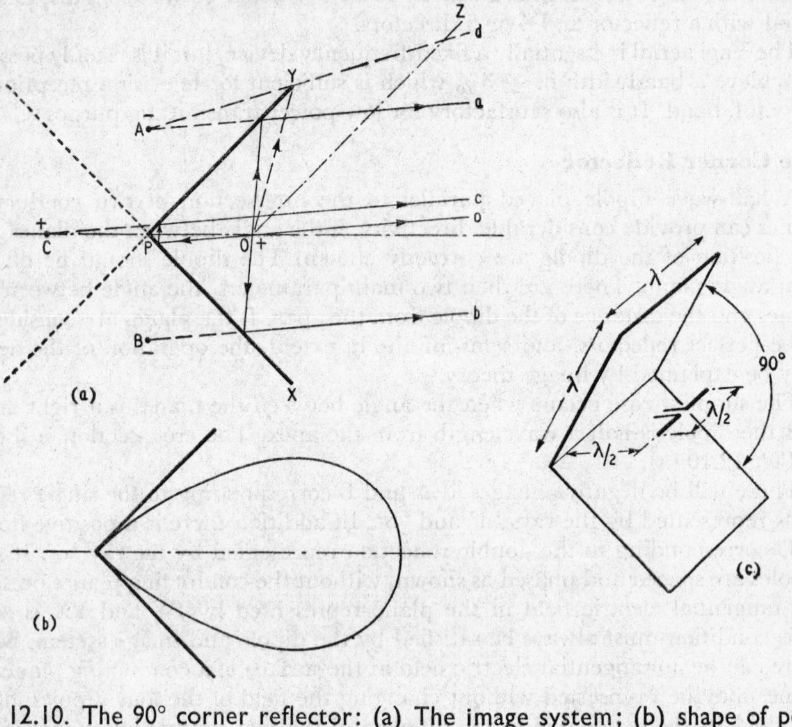

Fig. 12.10. The 90° corner reflector: (a) The image system; (b) shape of polar diagram for infinite reflectors; (c) practical form of corner reflector.

image C and the object dipole O cancel out along the main axis, leaving images A and B to produce a gain of 6 db for a given dipole current. If the mutual impedances due to the images are worked out for this case, the dipole resistance component is found to be about 27 ohms. The power radiated for a given current is only 27/73 = 0·37 times that for a dipole in free space. A gain of 4·3 db must therefore be added to the 6 db gain giving a gain of 10·3 db, or slightly greater than before.

From quite small spacings out to half a wavelength the forward gain is roughly constant at 9 or 10 db, and the equatorial plane polar diagram is of the shape shown in Fig. 12.10 (b). The meridian plane polar diagram in the plane of the main axis is much broader. The dipole resistance component changes from 123 ohms to 27 ohms over an octave band so that the corner reflector cannot be classed as a broadband aerial. At small spacings the dipole resistance is so low that conductor losses become significant and the aerial efficiency falls to a low figure.

If the spacing of the dipole from the apex is increased to one wavelength it can easily be seen that the fields along the main axis cancel out. At this spacing the beam has split into two and there is a null along the main axis. At a spacing of 1·5 wavelengths the gain rises to a value of about 13 db, but the size of the reflectors has to be so large that the aerial tends to become impracticable. The usual spacing employed is a little less than a half wavelength. At a spacing of 0·35 wavelength the dipole resistive component is about 72 ohms although there is a large reactive component. Below this spacing the resistive component falls rapidly with a resultant poor efficiency. Thus a spacing of 0·4 to 0·5 wavelength is usually most convenient although facilities must be provided for proper matching. At such a spacing, reflectors consisting of a square sheet about one wavelength by one wavelength in size provide results nearly in accordance with the above theory which assumed semi-infinite reflectors. The reason for this can be seen from Fig. 12.10 (a). For a reflector of length one wavelength all rays within the angle between OY and OZ (where OZ is parallel to PY) will be lost as compared with the semi-infinite reflector. This represents

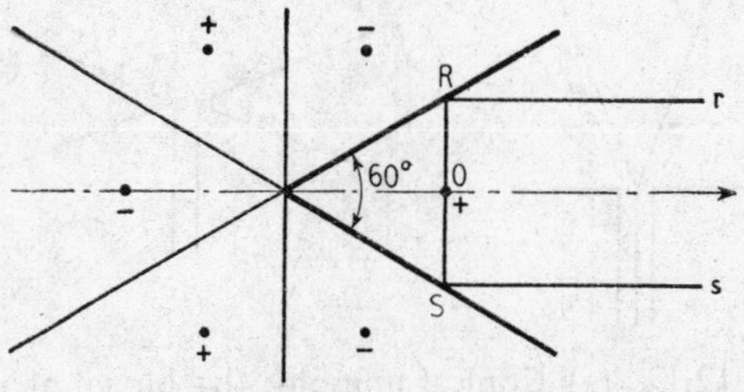

Fig. 12.11. Image system for reflectors inclined at 60° to one another.

a comparatively small proportion of the total energy. Furthermore the limiting ray 'd' is at an angle well removed from the main axis. Thus reflectors of this size provide an aerial of gain very nearly equal to that calculated for semi-infinite reflectors. The main beam of the aerial in the dipole equatorial plane is a little broader than for semi-infinite planes, and there is some radiation at angles exceeding $\pm 45°$ due to direct radiation in the direction OY, and to diffraction round the edge of the reflector.

The practical form of the aerial is shown in Fig. 12.10 (c). The reflectors may be constructed from wire mesh or a number of wires parallel to the dipole. In the latter case the wire spacing should be of the order of 0·1 wavelength or less. It is not essential that the reflector should be of high conductivity because the current density is low relative to that in the aerial dipole. The use of steel wire mesh or netting is usually quite satisfactory.

The image system for reflecting planes at 60° is given in Fig. 12.11. It can be checked that, with the planes absent, the tangential field of this object and image system is zero at the location of the planes. For a spacing between dipole O and the apex of one wavelength, it is clear that the field along the main axis is zero. For spacings less than about 0·75 wavelength the forward gain allowing for dipole impedance is fairly constant at about 11 db. At a spacing of a half wavelength the dipole resistive component is about 70 ohms. At smaller spacings the resistive component falls rapidly and resistance or heat loss in the dipole itself may become significant, and cause low aerial efficiency.

The important regions of the reflectors are shown by the areas near R and S in Fig. 12.11, where the rays 'r' and 's' parallel to the main axis are formed. This suggests that a better shape of reflector exists in which the whole area is employed in producing parallel rays. Such a reflector is one having a parabolic cross-section. Consideration of such aerials is left until Chapter 13 although they are sometimes used at v.h.f. and u.h.f. As compared with parabolic reflectors, the corner reflector has the merit of simplicity.

Broad-Band Aerials

For some applications in the v.h.f. and higher frequency bands it is necessary to be able to design aerials with much greater bandwidths than those of conventional thick dipoles. These applications occur mostly in connection with military radio problems but they may occur in the future in connection with television. Frequency bandwidths of the order of 4 to 1 and greater can be obtained by using one of the many forms of metallic conical aerials, the simplest of which are shown in Fig. 12.12. Such aerials are operable over a

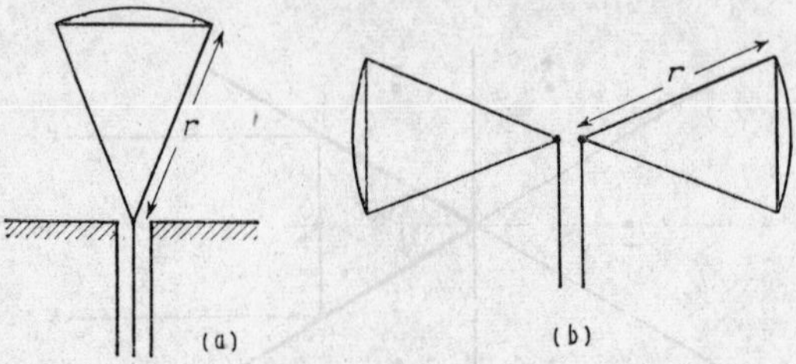

Fig. 12.12. (a) Conical unipole; (b) biconical aerial.

band in which the slant distance r varies from a quarter wavelength up to one wavelength or even more. Over such a band the polar diagram is roughly of usual unipole or dipole form, and the input impedance is such that with a suitably chosen feeder the standing-wave ratio is always less than 2.

To gain a complete understanding of why such an aerial has a large bandwidth necessitates the solution of Maxwell's equations with appropriate boundary conditions corresponding to the cone. However a qualitative understanding is possible without too much difficulty. As a first step we consider the infinite cone of semi-angle θ_1 and ground plane, shown in Fig. 12.13 (a). If it is postulated that lines of electric force are portions of circles with centre at the apex, then it can be deduced that the capacitance per unit length of cone measured along the slant surface is constant. For if we take the elementary capacitor formed by a thin strip of width dr, on the surface of the cone and the corresponding ring on the metallic ground plane, then as the radius r increases, the area and spacing increase in proportion to r. Thus the capacitance per unit length remains constant. Similarly, for the inductance per unit length, we see that the surface current density on the cone and on the ground plane, falls off as the inverse of the radius r. The tangential magnetic field thus falls off in the same way. The magnetic field is strongest near the cone due to its higher current density, and it falls off towards the ground plane. Without working out the field distribution we can see that the flux linkages for a length dr are independent of r, because the area of the annular segment is proportional to r and the magnetic field at a given angle θ to the vertical is inversely proportional to r. Thus the inductance per unit length is constant irrespective of the radius r. Thus we find that such a configuration has a constant characteristic impedance in just the same manner as a parallel-wire or coaxial line. The above argument should be compared with the parallel-strip transmission line of Chapter 5.

Our basic assumptions lead to the conclusion that the infinite cone and ground plane will support a TEM wave similar to that in a coaxial line. The *total* alternating current at any radius from the apex, in the cone and in the ground plane is constant, assuming the system to be loss free. A similar argument applies to double cones of the forms shown in Fig. 12.13 (b) and (c). In fact we may look

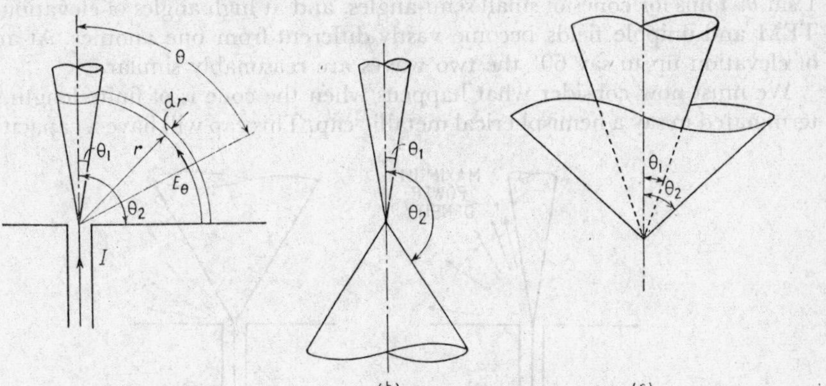

Fig. 12.13. Various forms of double conducting cones of infinite length, capable of supporting TEM waves.

upon the coaxial line as the limiting case of Fig. 12.13 (c) where the two cone angles have become zero.

We now have to observe that the energy density of the wave is greatest near the surface of the cone in Fig. 12.13 (a). This follows because the electric-field strength and magnetic-field strength are greatest at the surface of the cone. It follows from equations (5.5) to (5.8) that the electric-field strength at the point r, θ in the figure is given by:

$$E_\theta = \sqrt{\frac{\mu}{\kappa}} \cdot \frac{I}{2\pi r} \cdot \frac{1}{\sin\theta} \qquad (12.1)$$

and the magnetic field strength by:

$$H = \frac{I}{2\pi r} \cdot \frac{1}{\sin\theta} \qquad (12.2)$$

where I is the total feed current.

Thus for small semi-angles of cone, the energy density is very great near the surface of the cone as depicted by the arrows in Fig. 12.14 (a). For larger angles the field and energy density are more uniform over a wavefront, as in Fig. 12.14 (b).

We now turn to examine the radiated field from a short unipole and a conducting plane. From Chapter 9 this has some points of similarity to the TEM wave we have been considering. For example, the lines of electric force follow meridians near the ground plane. In fact near the ground plane, the TEM wave and the wave from a unipole are almost identical and both approach a plane wave at large distances. However at high angles of elevation the TEM wave and the wave from a unipole become very different from one another. From equation (9.33) the field strength of the unipole can be written as:

$$E_\theta = \frac{60\pi}{r} \cdot \frac{Il}{\lambda} \sin\theta \quad . \quad . \quad . \quad . \quad . \quad . \quad . \qquad (12.3)$$

Thus as the angle of elevation increases and the angle θ falls, the field strength falls off as $\sin\theta$. However for the TEM wave the field strength increases as $1/\sin\theta$. Thus for cones of small semi-angles, and at high angles of elevation, the TEM and unipole fields become vastly different from one another. At angles of elevation up to say 60° the two waves are reasonably similar.

We must now consider what happens when the cone is of finite length, and terminated in say a hemispherical metallic cap. This cap will have a capacitance

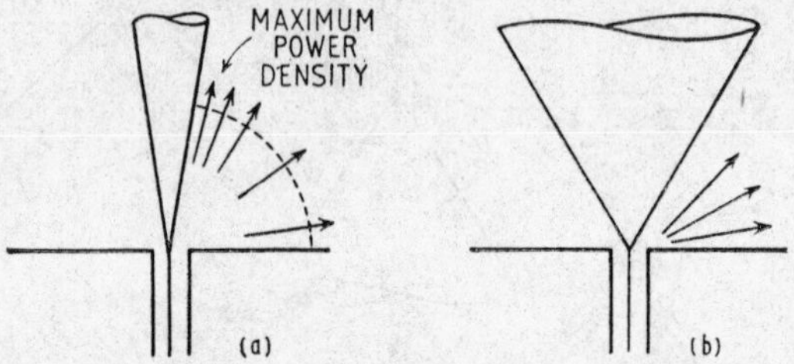

Fig. 12.14. Infinite cones above a conducting plane: (a) showing maximum power density near surface of thin cone; (b) showing more uniform power density near surface of thick cone.

to the ground plane and the current will not fall to zero until the top of the cap is reached. However the junction of the cone and cap is a discontinuity and a reflection would occur if we are considering TEM waves. A reflection will also occur from the current zero at the top of the cap. For very small cone angles these two reflections are practically coincident and the reflection factor will be approximately unity as with conventional unipoles and dipoles. Because the TEM and unipole fields are so widely different at high angles of elevation, strong reflected waves are necessary so that the difference between the incident and reflected fields forms the correct type of near field for unipole radiation. This explains why normal unipoles and dipoles, which are comparatively thin, operate with strong standing waves, and have therefore a relatively narrow bandwidth in the neighbourhood of resonance.

Consider now the case of a conical unipole of semi-angle 30°. If the length of the cone is of the order of quarter or half a wavelength, it can be deduced that the distant field is roughly of the usual unipole form. If we imagine a TEM wave starting out from the feed point, there will be a small reflection from the end of the cone, but some current will flow over the cap to the current node at the centre of the cap. This latter current is radial so that it will cause negligible radiation in the axial direction, a condition which fits the distant field. We have already seen that thick cones support a TEM wave which is roughly compatible with the distant field. Thus the reflected fields due to the reflections from the end of the cone and the centre of the cap are not particularly strong, because the modification necessary to the TEM field is not great. In other words the incident wave on the cone has a strong travelling-wave component, indicating that it must weaken considerably by radiation before the top of the cone is reached. In a very qualitative manner we can now see that a medium-angle cone supports waves which are more suited to launching the type of radiation that must come from a unipole. The magnitude of the reflection factor corresponding to this case is much smaller than for a thin aerial of similar length. Thus the input impedance fluctuations with change of frequency are much less, and the aerial has broadband characteristics.

This is about as far as one can go with a qualitative discussion. The full theory has been worked out but it is very complicated. The more usual approach is by impedance and polar diagram measurement. The most commonly used semi-angle is 30° for which the characteristic impedance of an infinite cone and ground plane is about 78 ohms. The measured input resistance of a conical unipole fluctuates about this value as shown in Fig. 12.15. The input reactance

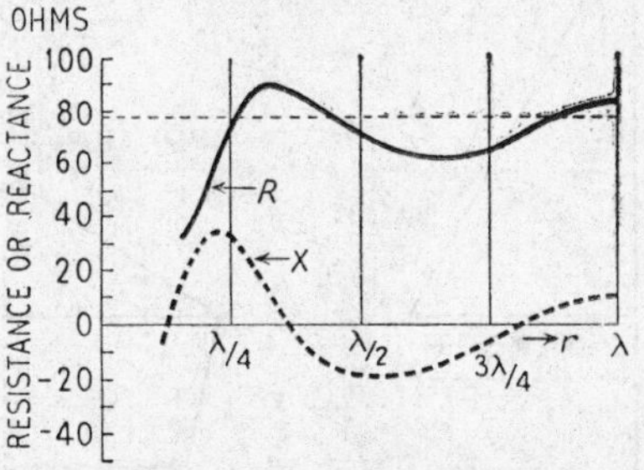

Fig. 12.15. Resistance and series reactance for a conical unipole of 30° semi-angle above a ground plane (with hemispherical cap similar to Fig. 12.12 (a)).

in series with this resistance is also shown. The polar diagram is roughly of short unipole form for a cone length r of between a quarter and a half wavelength. From a half wavelength to one wavelength certain preferred directions of radiation appear, mainly along the ground plane and at angles of elevation of about 60°. However there are no null directions as with thin aerials. The difference of field strength between a preferred direction and a weaker direction is not great and for most practical purposes the polar diagram can be considered to be of unipole shape.

The actual form of end cap is not critical. Another cone, of semi-angle about 60°, may be used instead of the hemispherical cap. If the end cap is omitted the current will flow over on to the inside of the cone. Even this does not seriously alter the broadband performance.

Biconical Aerial

The biconical aerial is the name given to the double cone aerial oı Fig. 12.12 (b). It requires a balanced feeder and the impedance is about 150 ohms for cones of 30° semi-angle. Its performance is easily deduced from the previous section. Standing-wave ratios of less than 2 can usually be obtained without difficulty over the band for which the cone slant length is between a quarter and one wavelength.

To reduce weight the cones are often constructed in cage form as with cage dipoles. They are usually constructed on an axial insulating rod or tube.

Discone Aerial

The discone aerial is another form of conical aerial which is simple to construct and has a performance rather similar to a biconical aerial. It is shown in Fig. 12.16 (a). It consists of a disc D and a cone C, fed as shown. The cone semi-angle is usually about 30° or a little less. The disc diameter is usually about three-quarters of the diameter of the cone base, so that over most of the band it is small compared with a wavelength. The aerial may thus be considered as

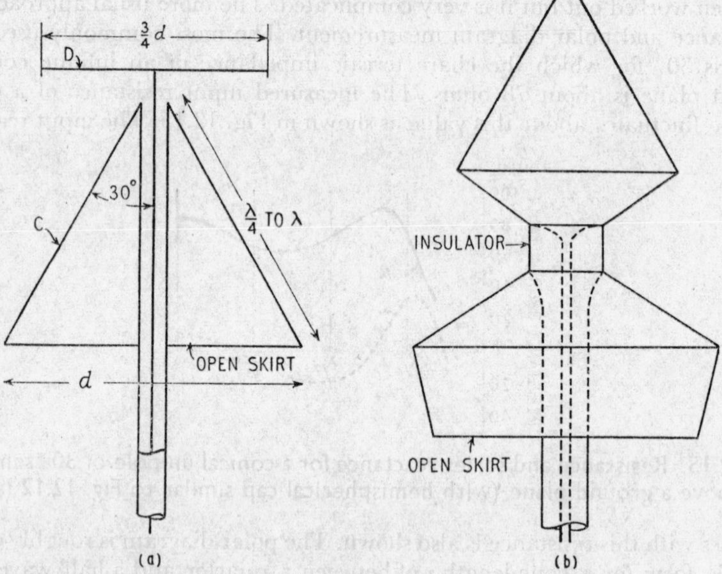

Fig. **12.16. (a) The discone aerial and (b) vertical biconical aerial.**

a cone fed against the capacitance of the disc. Its performance follows from results on a cone and ground plane. Thus it gives a small s.w.r. for cone slant heights of between a quarter wavelength and one wavelength. The bottom end of the cone is usually left open as this helps to reduce the current in the feeder or mast. The best value of coaxial feeder impedance is usually about 50 ohms.

Vertical Biconical Aerial

An aerial of similar performance to the discone aerial is shown in Fig. 12.16 (b). The aerial shown has a cone in the neighbourhood of the feed point which has a large semi-angle (about 60°) so that the resultant impedance is a good deal less than the biconical aerial of Fig. 12.12 (b). The best value of coaxial feeder impedance is about 60 ohms and the s.w.r. is less than 2 over a 2 to 1 frequency band. The total surface length of the aerial should be one wavelength at the middle of the band. The underside of the skirt is open in order to reduce current on the outside of the feeder as with the aerial in Fig. 12.5.

Aerials for Vertical Polarization Giving All-Round Coverage

The requirements of broadcasting in the v.h.f. and u.h.f. bands necessitate aerials which provide radiation of uniform intensity in all directions in a horizontal plane. The plane of polarization used may be vertical or horizontal, but in this section we are concerned with vertically-polarized radiation. Since range is usually limited to line of sight or a little greater, the aerial is installed at the top of a tall mast. Because the wavelength is small compared with the mast

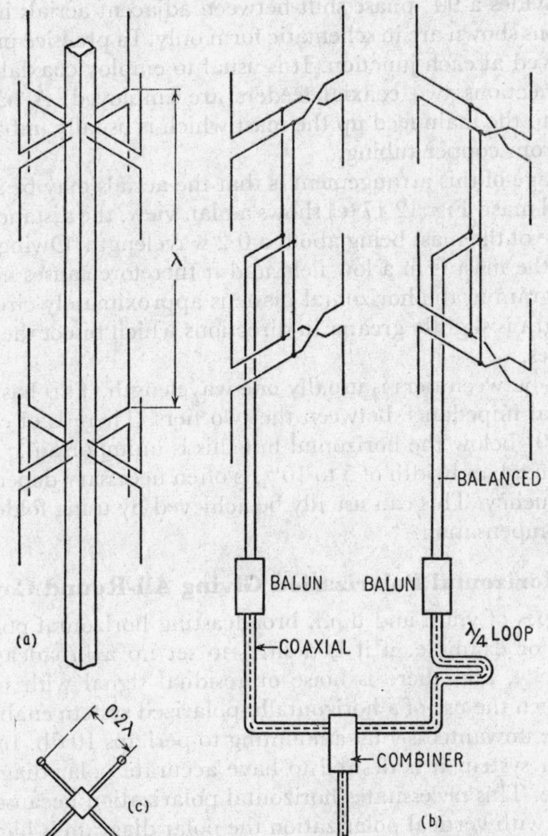

Fig. 12.17. Broadcast v.h.f. aerial for vertical polarization: (a) isometric view showing two tiers; (b) arrangement of feeders and (c) plan view of aerial.

height it is possible to use an array of aerials which gives all-round gain in the horizontal plane. The type of pattern that is required is that shown in Fig. 10.18 for vertical collinear dipoles. However, the construction of an aerial consisting of a number of collinear dipoles presents considerable mechanical difficulty.

The main problem is to provide the feeds to the dipoles. The feeds could not be run outside the dipoles, unless the dipoles were offset from the mast by at least a quarter wavelength. With a metal mast this would cause shadowing in certain directions. Because of these difficulties the true collinear dipole array is not often used. The usual solution is to employ four dipoles in a ring as shown in Fig. 12.17 (a). This figure shows two tiers of four dipoles giving a gain in the horizontal direction of a vertical plane of about 3 db. In each ring the dipoles are fed with equal-amplitude currents, but the relative phases of the four feeds are 0°, 90°, 180° and 270°. Each dipole in the lower ring and the one above it in the upper ring is fed in the same phase. Fig. 12.17 (b) shows the feeder arrangement to achieve this phasing. Dipoles opposite to one another in the ring have their connections crossed to give a 180° phase change. The quarter-wave loop provides a 90° phase shift between adjacent aerials in the ring. The interconnections shown are in schematic form only. In practice proper matching must be achieved at each junction. It is usual to employ coaxial feeders. In the balanced connections two coaxial feeders are employed. A balun is used to connect these to the main feed up the mast which is usually unbalanced coaxial feeder made from copper tubing.

The advantage of this arrangement is that the aerials may be supported from a central metal mast. Fig. 12.17 (c) shows a plan view, the distance of the dipoles from the centre of the mast being about a 0·2 wavelength. Owing to the phasing of the dipoles the mast is in a low field and it therefore causes negligible losses. The polar diagram in the horizontal plane is approximately circular, although the field strength is slightly greater in directions which bisect the angle between adjacent dipoles.

The spacing between tiers is usually one wavelength. This has the advantage of a low mutual impedance between the two tiers. There is of course a null in directions at 30° below the horizontal but this is unimportant.

For television a bandwidth of 5 to 10% is often necessary depending upon the mid-band frequency. This can usually be achieved by using folded dipoles, and susceptance compensation.

Aerials for Horizontal Polarization Giving All-Round Coverage

For some types of v.h.f. and u.h.f. broadcasting horizontal polarization may be desirable. For example, if it is desired to set up a broadcast system on a certain frequency, and there is noise or residual signal with mainly vertical polarization, then the use of a horizontally-polarized system enables discrimination against the unwanted signal amounting to perhaps 10 db. In some types of aircraft beacon system it is desired to have accurate polar diagrams with all-round coverage. This necessitates horizontal polarization because, as explained in Chapter 10, with vertical polarization the polar diagram is highly dependent upon ground constants. There is thus a need for aerials providing horizontal polarization and all-round coverage.

Perhaps the simplest aerial of this type is the magnetic dipole considered in Chapter 10. At the frequencies under consideration here, only one turn can be employed. If the perimeter of the loop is less than about a quarter of a wavelength the current round the loop will be reasonably uniform, and the polar diagram for a horizontal loop will be as in Fig. 10.7 (b); i.e., similar to that for a vertical dipole but with E and H interchanged. The polar diagram in a vertical plane may be made sharper (i.e., the gain in a horizontal direction may be increased) by stacking such loop aerials one above the other at, say, half wavelength spacing. However, consideration must be given to the supporting mast and feeder, and these must not unduly reduce gain or waste power. The problem is rather similar to that with the vertically-polarized omnidirectional aerial. One solution is the clover-leaf aerial shown in Fig. 12.18. It consists of four equally spaced magnetic dipoles. The mast has a central conductor which together with the mast functions as a coaxial feeder. The loops are all fed in phase, one end of each being connected to the mast and the other end to the inner conductor. In this case the radiating loops do not need to have uniform current and they may have a perimeter up to about half a wavelength. This type of aerial is usually designed by modelling.

We now return to a consideration of loop aerials of larger diameter. If a loop has a perimeter of about half a wavelength, the current will be a minimum at the feed point and a maximum opposite to it. The polar diagram in a horizontal plane will not be circular and the aerial will be unsuitable for broadcasting. To obtain omnidirectional features with loop aerials of this perimeter and larger,

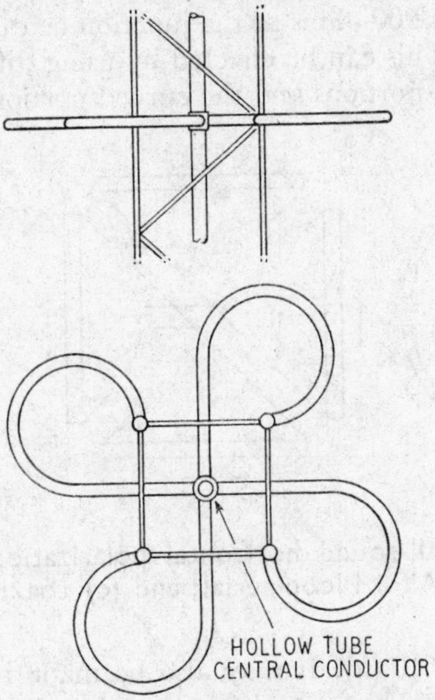

Fig. 12.18. The clover-leaf aerial for all-round horizontal polarization.

arrangements must be made to feed the loop in phase at several uniformly distributed points. Even if the current round a loop is reasonably uniform there is an upper limit to the diameter of loop that may be used. Up to a loop diameter of $0{\cdot}58\lambda$, the currents at the two ends of a diameter co-operate to provide the maximum field strength in the plane of the loop. For greater diameters the field strength in the plane of the loop falls and the maximum gain occurs in directions making a large angle with the plane of the loop. For diameters exceeding $1{\cdot}2\lambda$ the polar diagram in a vertical plane breaks up into a gradually increasing number of lobes. Thus loop aerials with uniform current are not suitable for broadcasting unless the diameter is less than about $0{\cdot}58\lambda$.

Three aerials in this class are shown in Fig. 12.19 in plan view. The first simply consists of four dipoles end to end, and bent to form a circle. The current would not be uniform and the diameter works out to be $0{\cdot}64\lambda$ which is a little above the limit given above. However for many purposes it provides sufficiently uniform all-round coverage. The dipoles are usually of the folded type in order to provide more bandwidth and a higher impedance for feeding. The second aerial may be considered to be made from four end-fed dipoles with the ends bent as shown so as to produce a more uniform current in the loop. The sections of the aerial consisting of two conductors carrying opposing current have little radiation. The mean diameter of this arrangement can be made of the order of $0{\cdot}3\lambda$ which is well within the limit given above. The polar diagram is similar to that of a magnetic dipole. The fact that the loop is square does not seriously affect the horizontal-plane polar diagram, except for problems requiring very precise polar diagrams. The third arrangement shown in Fig. 12.19 (c) is known as the coaxial loop aerial. The four cuts in the loop are fed in phase. Each section is about a half wavelength long, and the radial cable feed therefore enters the radiator at a voltage node. The sections are therefore voltage fed and the impedance at the cut is high, of the order 1,500–2,000 ohms. It is desirable to transform this to about 200 ohms at the junction centre so that the impedance suits a 50-ohm cable. This can be effected by using different characteristic impedances for the radial portions and the curved portions. This aerial is really a

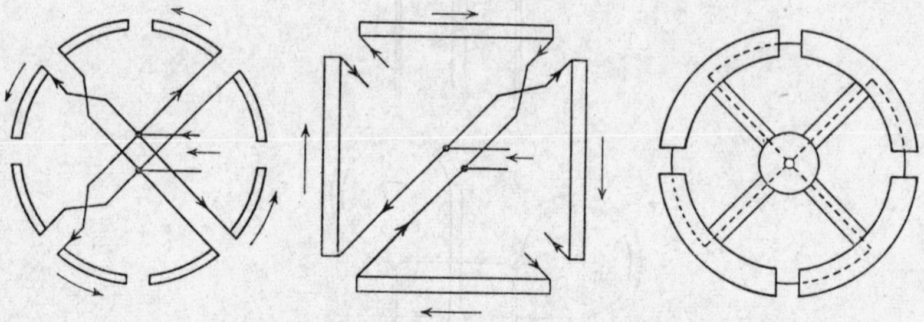

Fig. 12.19. Aerials for all-round horizontal polarization (plan view): (a) four dipoles; (b) Alford loop aerial; and (c) coaxial loop aerial.

coaxial form of Fig. 12.19 (a). It may also be made in square form with the cuts at the corners, the horizontal plane polar diagram being sufficiently accurate for most purposes.

A very convenient form of aerial for all-round horizontal polarization is the slot aerial. In its simplest form it consists of a metal sheet having a vertical slot, bent round to form a cylinder as shown in Fig. 12.20. The method of operation is similar to that of the slot in an infinite sheet considered in Chapter 10 except that the currents flow right round the outer surface of the cylinder, in paths that are mainly horizontal loops. By analogy with loop aerials, if the circumference of the cylinder exceeds about a quarter wavelength the loop currents will not be uniform. However, it is usual to make the single slotted cylindrical aerial about one-eighth of a wavelength in diameter, the resulting polar diagram in a horizontal plane being roughly circular. The inside of the cylinder suppresses radiation from the slot in an inward direction. This type of slot has its first resonance at a slot length well in excess of a half wavelength depending upon the cylinder diameter. This may be explained by considering the slot to be a transmission line having a heavy shunt inductance loading due to the cylinder. This causes the phase velocity of currents along the edges of the slot to be higher than free-space velocity. Such slot aerials may be arranged in vertical stacks to provide directivity or gain in a horizontal direction. However the limit to diameter causes it to be rather slender structurally.

This may be overcome by increasing the diameter of the cylinder to about the limit of $0{\cdot}6\lambda$ and using four slots equally disposed, in a rather similar manner to the loop aerial with four co-phased feed points.

One very well-known form of this aerial consists of 32 vertical slots in a vertical metallic cylinder placed at the top of a tall mast. The slots are arranged in 8 tiers, there being four slots facing say north, south, east and west in each tier. Fig. 12.21 shows the general arrangement. The four slots in a tier have a performance much the same as a single vertical dipole but with E and H interchanged, and having about the same gain. The 8 tiers thus behave similarly

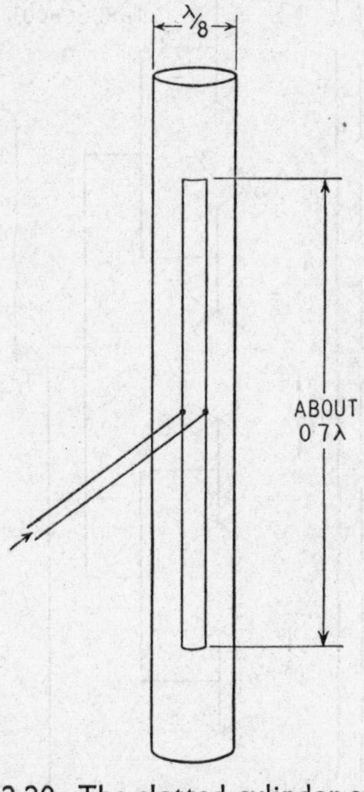

Fig. 12.20. The slotted cylinder aerial.

to a vertical collinear, co-phased array of dipoles, and the power gain over a half wave dipole, in any horizontal direction is therefore 8 or in decibels, 9 db. The diameter of the cylinder must be chosen with due regard for the wavelength. For the example given here the diameter is $0{\cdot}6\lambda$. The spacing between tiers is one wavelength. With aerials of this type the object is to obtain currents flowing round the surface of the cylinder in circumferential directions. In the plan view cross-section of Fig. 12.21 (b) the currents at a particular instant would be flowing in a circle as shown. The current density would be greatest at the sections such as A. The slots have horizontal bars behind them to prevent radiation flowing inwards. These bars are about $0{\cdot}1\lambda$ behind each slot forming a square in plan view as in Fig. 12.21 (b). Due to the shunt inductance loading on the slot the length of slot for the first resonance is about $0{\cdot}75\lambda$. Fig. 12.21 (c) shows in single line form the arrangement of the internal feeders.

The slot, if fed at the middle, presents a balanced load of rather high impedance, and rather narrow bandwidth (only 1 or 2%). For most purposes it is desirable to have an unbalanced feed suitable for coaxial feeder, a lower impedance and a greater bandwidth. These requirements are met by a feed of the type shown in Fig. 12.21 (d). For frequencies just below resonance a slot presents inductive reactance (as compared with a dipole which presents capacitive reactance) so that a series capacitive reactance provides the correct type of bandwidth compensation. The type of feed shown is developed from the

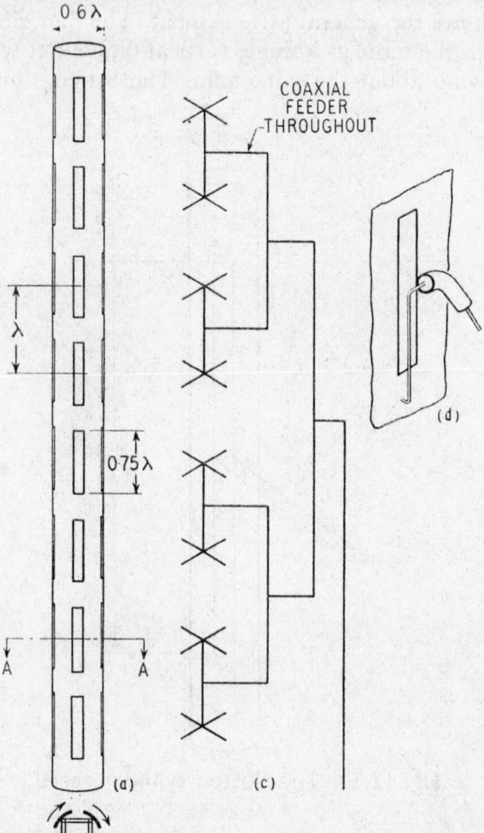

Fig. 12.21. A high-gain slot aerial for v.h.f. broadcasting: (a) arrangement of slots; (b) plan cross-section at A; (c) feeder layout; and (d) feed to slot.

folded slot, and it provides the correct type of compensating reactance and is suitable for coaxial feeder. The resulting aerial has a bandwidth of ± 4%.

Turnstile Aerial

A further type of aerial which provides all-round horizontal polarization is the turnstile aerial. This consists of two crossed dipoles in a horizontal plane, one dipole being fed 90° out of phase with the other. This could be effected by having an extra quarter-wave of feeder in the connection to one aerial, known as a quarter-wave loop. Fig. 12.22 (a) shows a plan view of two short crossed dipoles. In a direction θ to dipole A, at a distant point P, the field magnitude due to dipole A is proportional to $\sin\theta$ and that due to dipole B is proportional to $\cos\theta$. The vectors representing these two fields are however at 90° time phase to one another. Thus the resultant field at P is the vector sum of two vectors at right angles to one another, and proportional to $\sin\theta$ and $\cos\theta$ as in Fig. 12.22 (b). The resultant is therefore a constant independent of θ; i.e., all-round horizontal polarization is produced. If half-wave dipoles are substituted for short dipoles, the change in the pattern in a horizontal plane is not very great and this forms the basis of the turnstile aerial.

Returning to Fig. 12.22 (a) if the field on a vertical axis above the aerial is examined it will be found that the electric vector rotates in a horizontal plane. The instantaneous field strength in a horizontal plane due to dipole A is, say, proportional to $\sin\omega t$ (where $\omega = 2\pi\times$ frequency of signal applied to dipoles) and in the direction OX of Fig. 12.22 (a). The instantaneous field due to dipole B is proportional to $\cos\omega t$ and in the direction OY. The resultant field is a vector of fixed amplitude rotating in a horizontal plane about a fixed axis. Reversal of the connections to one dipole reverses the direction of rotation.

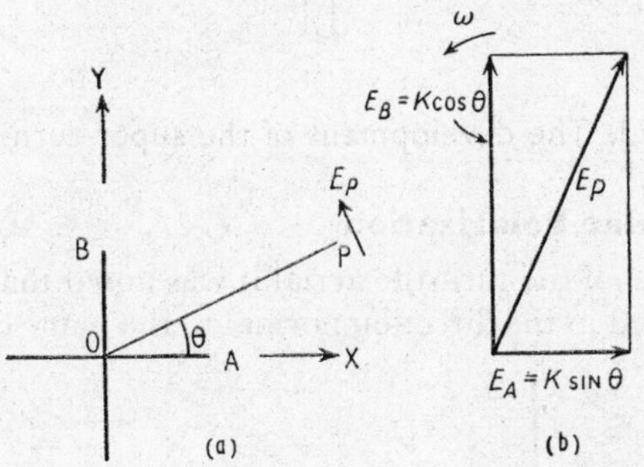

Fig. 12.22. (a) The turnstile aerial (plan view); (b) vector diagram of field at a point P.

This upward and downward radiation with the simple turnstile aerial represents considerable loss of power. The power density of the horizontal polarization in the plane of the aerials is the same as the maximum power density due to one aerial alone. Since one aerial radiates 3 db less power than the complete turnstile aerial, the power density of the horizontally-polarized radiation is 3 db below the maximum radiation of a half-wave dipole radiating the same power. This is the main disadvantage of the simple turnstile aerial for producing horizontally-polarized radiation.

This shortcoming is rectified in the super-turnstile aerial. In this aerial the dipoles are replaced by four flat sheets arranged as shown in Fig. 12.23 (a). Two of these sheets in a vertical plane are shown in Fig. 12.23 (b). The sheets are attached to the metallic mast by the bars A leaving a slot which is driven at the points XX. The currents flow mainly radially out from the mast, and the shape of the sheets is such that upward and downward radiation is largely cancelled out. The other pair of sheets would be driven with current at 90° time phase from the first pair, as with the simple turnstile aerial. The slot length is generally greater than a half wavelength for resonance. This method of driving avoids the need for insulators. To reduce windage the sheets may be replaced with grids of the form shown in Fig. 12.23 (c). The final aerial is usually designed by modelling and the power density in a horizontal plane is similar to the equatorial power density of a normal dipole radiating the same total power. Such aerials may be stacked to produce greater gain in the horizontal direction.

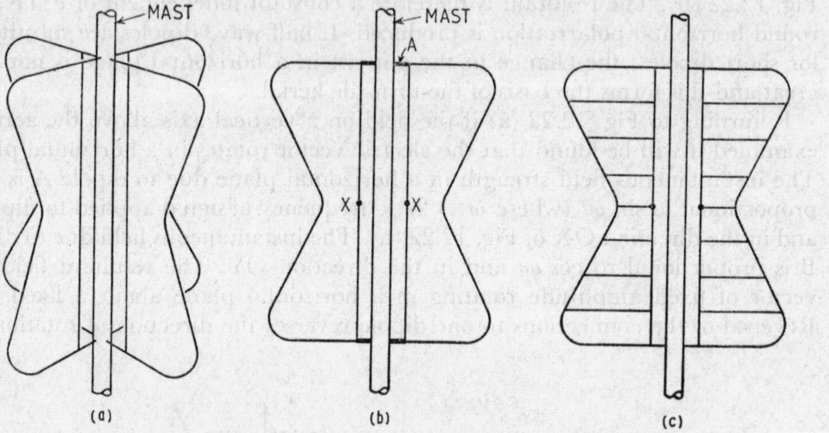

Fig. 12.23. The development of the super-turnstile aerial.

Aerials for Circular Polarization

In the description of the turnstile aerial it was noted that circularly-polarized radiation is produced in the direction normal to the plane containing the aerials.

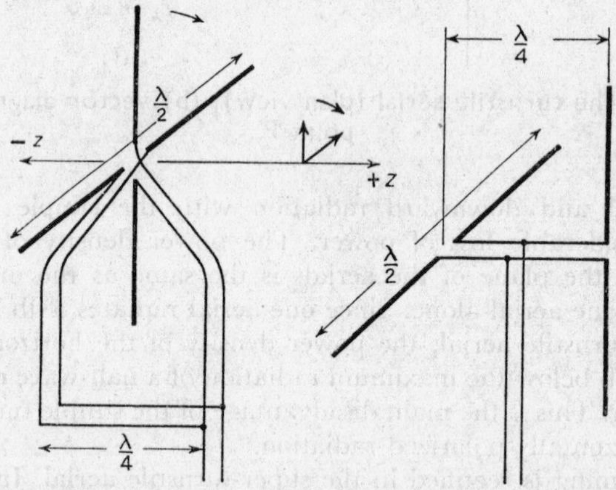

Fig. 12.24. Aerials for circular polarization; (a) crossed dipoles with feeds in quadrature; (b) cross dipoles displaced a quarter wavelength.

This will now be considered in greater detail. Two crossed dipoles are shown in Fig. 12.24 (a). The horizontal dipole is fed with a current lagging the vertical-dipole current by 90°. For the connections shown it is clear that for radiation flowing to the right, looking in the direction of propagation, the electric vector at a point on the z axis rotates in an anti-clockwise direction. At a particular instant, proceeding in the direction of increasing *z*, the electric vector has its tip lying on a right-handed spiral, because as it moves away from the source the vector must lag progressively. This is known as right-handed circular polarization. In the other direction to the left of the aerials, the vector at a point rotates clockwise and the polarization is left-handed.

If we consider a conducting sheet parallel to the plane of the aerials, the image will have the same direction of phase rotation as the aerial although its instantaneous phase is 180° away from the aerial phase. If the sheet is placed to the left of the aerial it is clear that the radiation from the image has right-handed circular polarization. Thus circular polarization undergoes a change of direction on reflection from a conducting sheet. This property is of value in some radio systems and meets a need in circularly-polarized aerials. In other systems one of the aerials, either sending or receiving, may be plane polarized (i.e., a single dipole) but its direction in the plane normal to the line of propagation may be uncertain. In such cases by making the other aerial circularly polarized, transmission between aerials can be effected whatever the direction of the dipole. In problems of this nature, circularly-polarized aerials

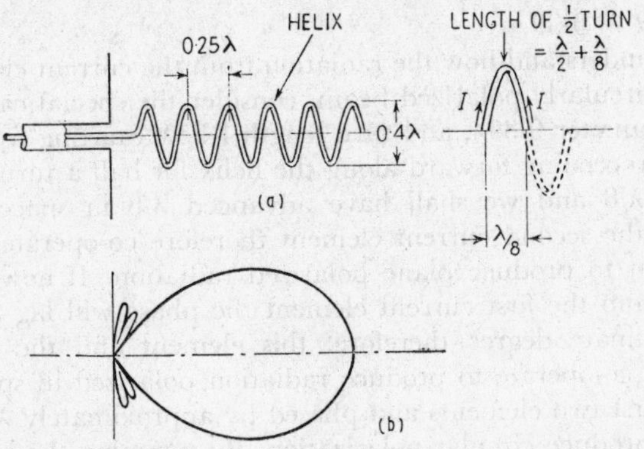

Fig. 12.25. (a) the helical aerial and (b) polar diagram.

are of importance. Generally a beam of circularly-polarized radiation is required.

The turnstile aerial placed a quarter wavelength in front of a conducting screen provides the simplest directional circularly-polarized aerial. To avoid the complication of feeding two dipoles lying in the same plane, they may be separated by a quarter wavelength as in Fig. 12.24 (b). In this case, they must be fed in phase as shown. Such an aerial emits, say, right-handed circular polarization along one axial direction and the same rotation along the other axial direction. It cannot therefore be used with a reflecting sheet. However two Yagi aerials may be used with the same common axis, but lying in two planes at right angles to one another. To avoid feed complications they may be staggered by a quarter wavelength and fed in phase as for Fig. 12.24 (b).

Perhaps the simplest aerial to provide a circularly-polarized beam is the helical aerial. This consists of a helix made from thick copper wire or tubing fed between one end and a ground plane as in Fig. 12.25 (a). In order to excite the mode in which a beam of radiation is formed in the direction of the axis, the diameter of the helix and the spacing between turns must be correctly chosen. In order to obtain an approximate idea of the magnitude of these parameters we assume that a forward-travelling wave of current exists on the helix and that the phase velocity along the helical conductor is equal to the free-space velocity. With these rather broad assumptions the beam mode occurs when the current in a short element of one turn, and the current in the corresponding short element of the next turn, are phased so that the end-fire effect occurs. Thus, if the spacing between turns is $a\lambda$ where a is of the order of a quarter, the phase of the second element should lag by an angle corresponding to $a\lambda$ or $(\lambda + a\lambda)$. If the length of a turn is $(1 + a)\lambda$ this condition of phasing will occur. A pitch of $\lambda/4$ and a turn length of $1\frac{1}{4}\lambda$ should therefore provide the desired effect. From the geometry of the helix the diameter in wavelengths is therefore:

$$d = \frac{\sqrt{\{(1 + a)^2 - a^2\}}}{\pi}$$

$$= \frac{\sqrt{(1 + 2a)}}{\pi} \quad . \quad . \quad . \quad . \quad . \quad . \quad (12.4)$$

If $a = \frac{1}{4}$ then $d = 0{\cdot}39$.

In order to understand how the radiation from the current elements adds up to produce a circularly polarized beam, consider the special case of a helix of pitch $0{\cdot}25\lambda$, diameter $0{\cdot}39\lambda$, and turn length $1{\cdot}25\lambda$. Starting from one current element and proceeding forward along the helix for half a turn the phase will lag by $\lambda/2 + \lambda/8$ and we shall have advanced $\lambda/8$ in space. Referring to Fig. 12.25 (a) the second current element therefore co-operates with the first current element to produce plane polarized radiation. If now we proceed a quarter turn from the first current element the phase will lag by $\lambda/4 + \lambda/16$. To an approximate degree therefore, this element and the one $\lambda/2 + \lambda/8$ further on will co-operate to produce radiation polarized in space in a plane at 90° to the first two elements and phased by approximately $\lambda/4$. That is the four elements produce circular polarization. By summing the radiation in the axial direction, from all elements of one turn, it can be shown that approximately circular polarization is produced. If there are n turns and the above conditions exist for the production of the end-fire effect, then the power gain in the axial direction is increased n times.

If a helix is designed to the above dimensions at a particular frequency, then if the frequency is decreased, the pitch in wavelengths is decreased, and the phase shift round one turn is decreased. Thus the aerial tends to be self-compensating so far as the end-fire effect is concerned. In practice the helical aerial performs well over a band of frequencies where the upper to lower frequency ratio is about 1·5 or a little more.

The complete analysis of an aerial of such complicated geometric form would be very difficult. There is no justification for the assumption of free-space phase velocity of the wave on the helix, and for uniform current distribution. However, measurements indicate that the phase velocity for the dimensions quoted above is about $0{\cdot}95c$, and that over the middle range of the helix the current distribution is roughly uniform; i.e., the current is a forward-travelling wave. Thus for a pitch of $0{\cdot}25\lambda$, the length of a turn should be shortened to $0{\cdot}95 \times 1{\cdot}25\lambda$ or about $1{\cdot}18\lambda$ and the diameter reduced to $0{\cdot}375\lambda$. Such an aerial of 8 turns (i.e., 2 wavelengths long) would have a gain of about 13 db and a beam width between half-power points of about 32°. The impedance would be about 150 ohms. It would operate satisfactorily down to a frequency corresponding to a pitch of $3\lambda/16$ and up to a frequency corresponding to nearly $5\lambda/16$. The form of the polar diagram is shown in Fig. 12.25 (b) for the frequency corresponding to a pitch of a quarter wavelength. The ground plane should be of the order of a wavelength in diameter.

If a helical aerial is used at one end of a link and a single dipole aerial at the other end of the link there is of course a 3 db loss of received power as compared with crossed dipoles. The dipoles must lie in a plane at right angles to the axis of the helix for optimum transmission. If helical aerials are used at both ends of a link, they must both be right handed (or left handed). If a right-handed helix is at one end of a link and a left-handed helix at the other, then transmission is theoretically negligible.

V.H.F. and U.H.F. Aerials for Reception

Receiving aerials for the v.h.f. and u.h.f. bands are generally designed on the same basis as transmitting aerials. Apart from man-made noise, particularly ignition interference in the lower v.h.f. band, the noise is mainly thermal. Thus directivity gain in the receiving aerial results in an improved signal-to-noise ratio.

The feeders from v.h.f. and u.h.f. receiving aerials are usually made from flexible coaxial cable. Typical attenuations are given in Table 4.1. Attenuations at other frequencies may be obtained by interpolation, remembering that attenuation is proportional to the square root of frequency. The loss in the feeder cable represents a deterioration in signal-to-noise ratio, because it reduces signal power, and leaves the available noise power practically unchanged (unless the noise radiation picked up by the aerial is very high). Feeder lengths must therefore be kept very short particularly at the higher frequencies. Good matching of the receiving aerial to the feeder and of the feeder to the receiver is particularly desirable at frequencies above about 100 Mc/s, where it is difficult to achieve amplification with a low noise factor.

Aerials for Reception of Scattered Signals

The use of the scattering mode of propagation for ranges well beyond the horizon is becoming increasingly common. There are two main types of scatter propagation (see Chapter 14). One employs scattering from the E layer due to irregularities of electron density in that layer, and is known as ionospheric scatter. The other employs scattering from the troposphere and is due to irregularities of refractive index in the troposphere.

Ionospheric scatter usually employs frequencies of 30 to 50 Mc/s, while tropospheric scatter may employ almost any frequency in the u.h.f. band. The transmitting aerials for these modes of propagation call for no special comment. For ionospheric scatter they may be of the rhombic or dipole-array type. Corner reflector and Yagi types have also been used with wire-rigging methods of construction. For tropospheric scatter, transmitting aerials of almost any of the types dealt with in this chapter can be used, but the need for very high gain usually results in the use of the parabolic-reflector type of aerial described in Chapter 13.

However, the receiving aerials used for these modes of propagation do call for special comment. It should be noted that the directivity–gain theory for receiving aerials given in Chapter 10 assumes implicitly that the received wave is a plane wave and the gains deduced by this theory are sometimes called plane-wave gains. When the received signal is of the scatter type it is no longer a single plane wave, and may be considered to consist of a number of weak plane waves of differing amplitudes and phases, and arriving from different directions falling mainly within a certain solid angle. The amplitudes, phases and directions of these wavelets are continually changing. The actual observed aerial gain with such a received signal may well be less than the plane-wave gain. As a rough rule, if the solid angle over which the received wavelets arrive is greater than the solid angle of the receiving-aerial beam (assuming plane-wave reception) then gain degradation will occur. The amount by which the observed gain falls short of the plane-wave gain is called the gain degradation, assuming these gains are specified in decibels. Aerials must therefore be designed to keep this gain degradation as small as possible.

The gain of aerials for ionospheric scatter is often no more than one-half of the plane-wave gain in decibels. This is because the directions of arrival (particularly in azimuth) are spread over a large angle. With tropospheric scatter the spread of direction of arrival is much smaller and for aerial gains up to 30 or 40 db there is often very little gain degradation.

The nature of the received signal with the scatter modes of propagation is such that the envelope of the received signal, for a steady transmitted continuous wave, follows statistical laws of distribution. The number of fades per unit time varies over wide limits. A rough figure is from one fade in 10 seconds up to 10 fades per second or more. The tendency is for the higher fading rates to be associated with the higher frequencies. The effects of the fades may be reduced considerably by employing two or more aerials in space diversity. Spacings of 10 or 20 wavelengths in the ionospheric case are usually sufficient to reduce the correlation between the fades on two adjacent aerials to small proportions. Spacings of the order of 100 wavelengths are employed in the tropospheric case but since the aerial aperture may be as much as 30 wavelengths wide, the actual distance of separation between aerials is not very great.

V.H.F. and U.H.F. Aerials for Mobile Use

Aerials for vehicle, aircraft and ship use for operating in the v.h.f. and u.h.f. bands are generally speaking easier to design than aerials for lower frequencies, owing to the fact that quarter-wave and half-wave aerials are feasible from the structural viewpoint. For vehicles with a metal top, a whip aerial between a quarter and a half wave in length is efficient for all round transmission and reception. For aircraft, at frequencies of 100 Mc/s (3 metres) and upwards, the aerial may take the form of a stiff streamlined sword blade projecting from the fuselage. Again, the length should lie between a quarter and half a wavelength. Such an aerial is unacceptable for speeds in excess of about 500 m.p.h. and the modern tendency is to employ the tail fin as an aerial. With this technique applied to a metal aircraft, the upper portion of the fin is made of wood or plastics, and a metal coating or foil is placed round the leading edge as shown in Fig. 12.26. The aerial is driven between the metal base and the lower edge of the foil. Such aerials are designed by a trial and error method involving impedance measurements at each stage. Generally speaking this type of aerial has a good bandwidth, often better than one octave, and it may be used for two or more transmissions or receptions by using separating filters of the transmission-line type.

For ship use, the ground-plane aerial may be employed if a large bandwidth is not required. However, the demand for aerials on a ship is often in excess of the number of suitable positions, and it is therefore more economical to employ a few wideband aerials and use separating filters of the transmission-line type to separate the various transmissions and receptions. Suitable broadband aerials are therefore of the discone or conical types shown in Fig. 12.16. The transmitting aerial may be mounted at one end of a yard arm and the receiving aerial at the other end. The shadow of the mast then provides a useful amount of attenuation in the path between the aerials. These aerials should be mounted as high as possible and at least a wavelength away from other metal work.

The problem of aerial matching is often severe with mobile installations, particularly if the wireless equipment is required to match to any frequency within a wide band. With whip or rod aerials it is sometimes possible to tune

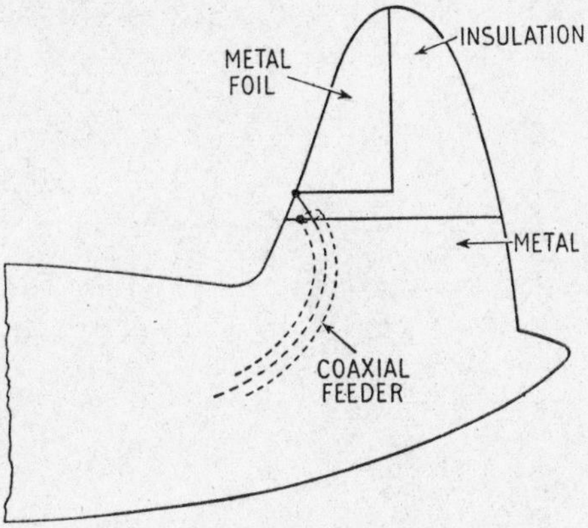

Fig. 12.26. V.H.F. fin aerial for aircraft.

them to quarter-wave resonance by making them telescopic, thereby providing a great simplification. If this is not possible and the feeder is a small fraction of a wavelength long, the tuned feeder method of matching may be adopted, and a manually-operated matching unit at the input to the feeder may be used. Where the feeder is longer it is imperative to carry out matching at the base of the aerial. This may be located at an inaccessible point and remotely operated controls may be necessary. Where the bandwidth is not too great (say $\pm$ 10%) suitable compensating networks or stubs may be employed at the base of the aerial, thereby eliminating the matching operation on the part of the operator, and providing the equivalent of a broadband aerial.

For the higher frequencies in the bands under consideration, aerials of the sleeve stub or dipole type may be employed. In the aircraft case such an aerial may be streamlined. These aerials may be designed to have inherently greater bandwidth than whip aerials, and susceptance-compensating shunts may be used to give even more bandwidth. With metal aircraft it is sometimes possible to use the slot aerial provided the resultant polar diagram is acceptable.

Generally speaking, all of these mobile aerials produce polar diagrams that are very ragged due to the irregular metallic structure around the aerial. The nulls and peaks are sometimes only separated by a few degrees. The envelope of the polar diagram conforms roughly to the normal polar diagram of the aerial.

At the upper end of the v.h.f. band and in the u.h.f. band, directional aerials may be designed for mobile use. The Yagi aerial is often convenient and has been used on low-speed aircraft for homing systems.

CHAPTER 13

S.H.F. Aerials

WHEN WE APPROACH the centimetre-wave range the possibilities in aerial design change quite rapidly. In the previous chapters it has been seen that the larger the extent of the array relative to the wavelength the narrower is the beam width, but in the frequency ranges treated there it is not readily possible to construct an array of dimensions much greater than one or two wavelengths. At centimetre wavelengths, on the other hand, an array of quite moderate size can have dimensions which are a large number of wavelengths.

This means that at centimetre wavelengths it is readily possible to construct and handle aerials designed to radiate power in narrow beams, and it is this which makes possible the two principal uses of centimetre waves—radar and point-to-point radio links. Table 13.1 is the completion of Tables 11.1 and 12.1.

TABLE 13.1

Band	Frequency range (Mc/s)	Wavelength range (cm)	Typical services
Super high frequencies (S.H.F.)	3,000–30,000 > 30,000 Mc/s	10–1 < 1	Radio and television relay links Radar

The requirements of an aerial for a point-to-point link are generally simple—high gain with a beam-width which is narrow in both horizontal and vertical planes. For radar the requirements are more diverse and more stringent. According to the purpose of the radar a beam may be required which is narrow in both planes, or narrow in one plane and broad in the other, or shaped to follow some particular law, and in all cases the side lobes should be as small as possible. In addition it may be necessary to swing the beam rapidly in one or both planes, or make it perform some other continuous motion.

As has been seen in Chapter 10 such properties could be produced by two-dimensional arrays of suitably phased dipoles. However at centimetre wavelengths it is not easy to feed such elements in the correct phase or to avoid the disturbing effects of mountings and feeder lines, which are relatively large. More convenient methods are available, using techniques similar to those of optics, and the electrical equivalents of mirrors and lenses. In fact the region is a transition one between the longer radio wavelengths, in which the wavelength is generally of the same order as the dimensions of the aerial, and the optical region in which wavelengths are exceedingly small compared with the dimensions of the optical components. In the centimetre wave region both longer wave and optical techniques are applicable, and are used together.

Diffraction theory shows (see Appendix 13.1) that if an aperture has a maximum dimension D in any given plane, then the minimum angle θ (radians) in which radiation can be concentrated in that plane is given to an order of magnitude by:

$$\theta \approx \frac{\lambda}{D} \quad . \quad . \quad . \quad . \quad . \quad . \quad . \qquad (13.1)$$

In this context 'aperture' means the plane area through which the radiation of an aerial system is finally emitted. One can thus produce highly directive beams such as have no counterpart in long-wave practice.

Reflectors

In centimetre-wave aerials considerable use is made of metal sheets, acting as reflectors, as means of directing the radiation. The corner reflector described in the previous chapter is an example of this technique. For the larger apertures,

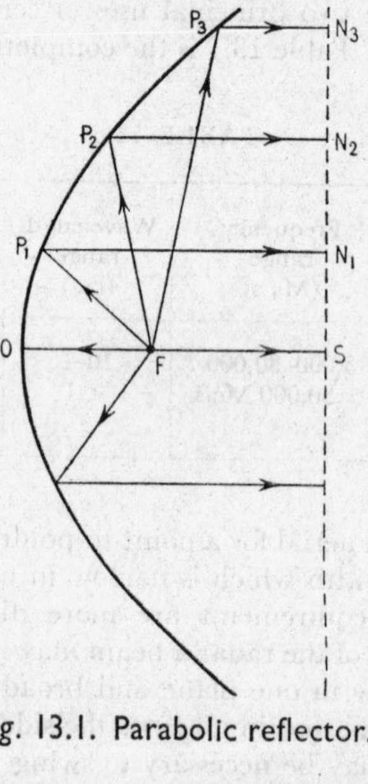

Fig. 13.1. Parabolic reflector.

however (greater than about two wavelengths), a smaller beam angle for a given aperture is obtained with a reflector shaped as a parabola.

The parabola, shown as a two-dimensional curve in Fig. 13.1, is a geometrical curve whose properties can most easily be appreciated by imagining it as a perfectly reflecting mirror. The point F is a particular point fixed in relation to the parabola and is called the *focus*. The distance OF is the *focal length*. The important property of the parabolic mirror is that all rays of light emanating from a point source at F are reflected from the mirror as a beam parallel to OF, the axis of the parabola.

An additional property of the parabola is that the path length of all rays is constant. For example, in Fig. 13.1, $FP_1 + P_1N_1 = FP_2 + P_2N_2$.

Thus the action of the parabola is to convert a spherical wave front coming from the focus into a plane wave front at the mouth of the parabola, as shown in Fig. 13.2 (a). The part of the radiation from the focus which does not strike the mirror continues as a spherical wave, diverging from the main beam. It is

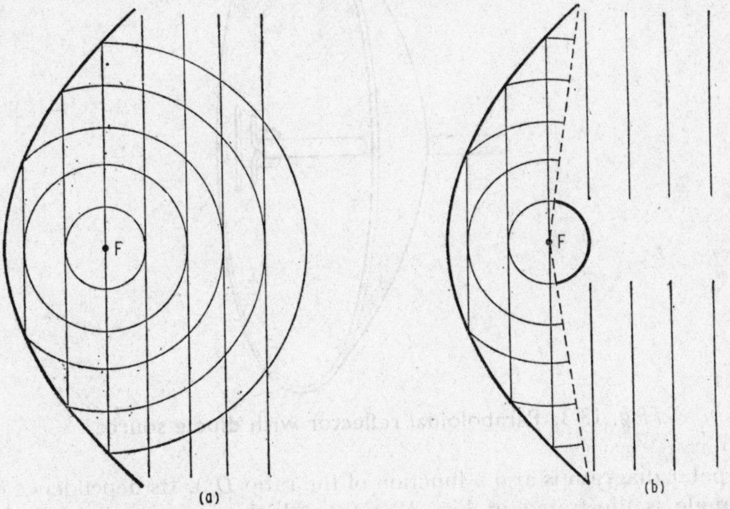

Fig. 13.2. Reflection of wavefronts by parabolic mirror: (a) with omnidirectional source at focus; (b) with partially shielded source at focus.

clear that this is a waste of power. It could be removed by partially shielding the source as in Fig. 13.2 (b), at the expense of losing the central part of the main beam.

Paraboloidal Reflector

Rotation of the parabola of Fig. 13.1 about the axis OS generates the surface known as a paraboloid, illustrated in Fig. 13.3, and would produce a parallel beam of circular cross-section. This is the beam-forming property used in the motor-car headlight or in the searchlight.

However, at radio frequencies the wavelength is not negligible compared with the aperture dimensions, and a point source is not practically realizable. Under these conditions the paraboloid gives rise to a beam which is slightly divergent, and cannot be calculated by geometrical optics. Thus the polar diagram of the source and reflector shows a narrow main lobe in the direction of the axis of the paraboloid. In addition the polar diagram contains small side lobes.

On the assumption that the aperture is uniformly illuminated, that is, the field amplitude and phase are constant over the area of the aperture, it can be shown (see Appendix 13.1) that the power gain of a paraboloid of aperture diameter D, relative to a half-wave dipole, is given by:

$$G = 6\left(\frac{D}{\lambda}\right)^2 \qquad (13.2)$$

This assumes that D is fairly large compared with the wavelength. For example, a paraboloid 10 wavelengths in diameter has a gain of 600, or nearly 28 db, over a half-wave dipole.

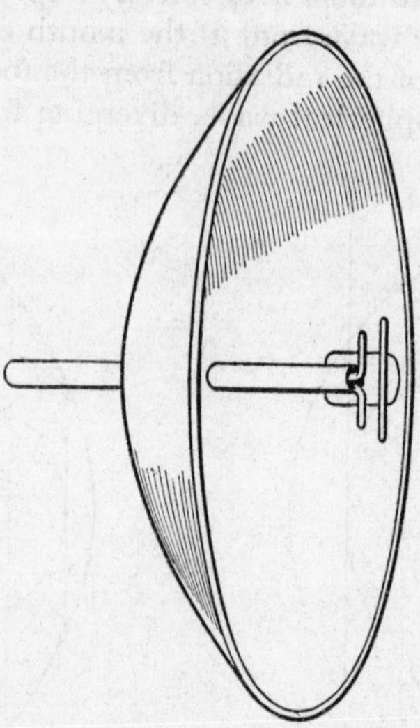

Fig. 13.3. Paraboloidal reflector with dipole source.

The polar diagram is also a function of the ratio D/λ. Its dependence on the polar angle is illustrated in Fig. 13.4 (a), which gives the theoretical polar diagram of a paraboloid of aperture diameter equal to 10λ. As it is difficult to

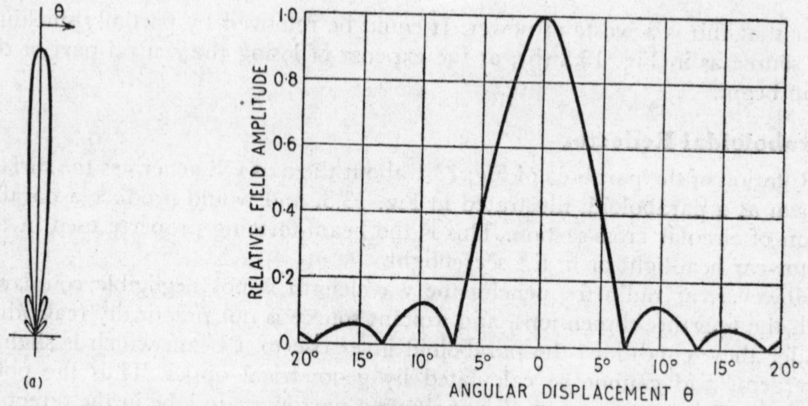

Fig. 13.4. Radiation pattern of paraboloid of diameter $D = 10\lambda$: (a) in polar co-ordinates; (b) in Cartesian co-ordinates.

interpret such a narrow polar diagram it is more useful to draw it on a Cartesian plot as in Fig. 13.4 (b). (The general form of this curve is given in Fig. 13.36.) It will be seen that the main beam is accompanied by small side lobes of which the first and largest has a theoretical amplitude of 13% of the main beam, that is, the side lobe level is at least 17.6 db below the maximum level.

In practice the illumination is never uniform, but usually tapers off towards the outside edge, the distribution being dependent on the method of feeding the paraboloid. The method shown in Fig. 13.3, consisting of a dipole with a reflector in front to suppress forward radiation from it, is a typical one. This type of feed gives a beam width which is about 25% wider than the theoretical value shown in Fig. 13.4, and, measured between half-power points, is approximately $74\lambda/D$ degrees in the plane of the dipole, $66\lambda/D$ degrees in a plane perpendicular to the dipole.

It is found in practice that, for most types of feed, beam-widths lie within the range $(1{\cdot}2 \pm 0{\cdot}2)\lambda/D$ radians. Other forms of feed are dealt with in a later section.

With the increase of beam-width there comes a consequent decrease of gain, usually to around 65% of that given by equation (13.2). However, tapering illumination has an important advantage, that it serves to decrease the amplitude of the side lobes, and in practice these can be reduced to at least 20 db below the main beam.

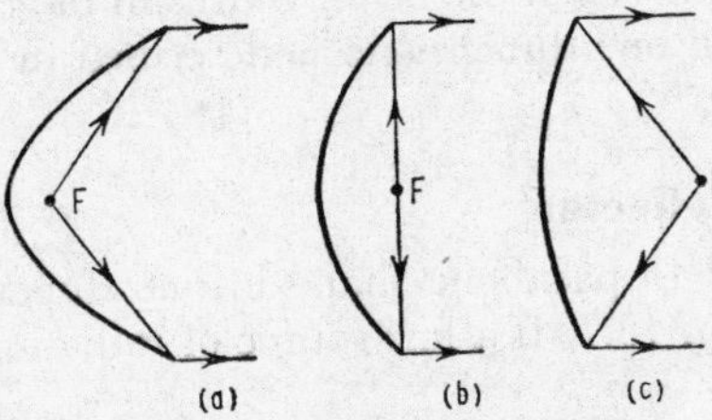

Fig. 13.5. Parabolic reflector with (a) focus inside aperture plane; (b) focus in aperture plane; (c) focus outside aperture plane.

A paraboloid with given aperture may be designed with a large or small focal length as in Fig. 13.5. If the focal length is small so that the focus is well inside the aperture, as in Fig. 13.5 (a), it is difficult to get a source giving adequately uniform illumination over such a wide angle; on the other hand a large focal

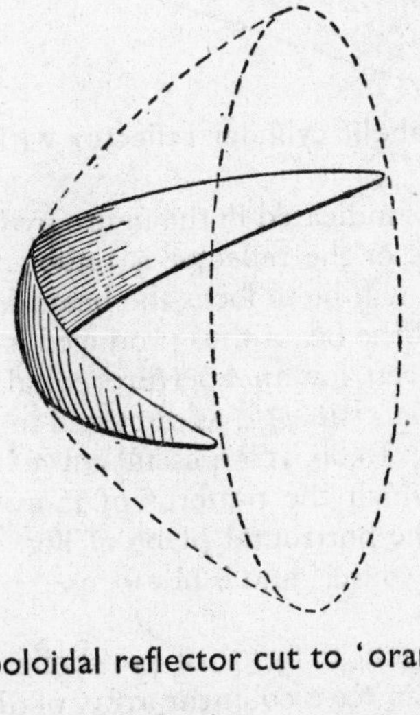

Fig. 13.6. Paraboloidal reflector cut to 'orange peel' shape.

length, as in Fig. 13.5 (c), may make it difficult to focus all the radiation from the source on to the mirror. Usually the arrangement which gives the maximum gain is that in which the focus lies in the plane of the aperture, as in Fig. 13.5 (b), and this is the most commonly used form. The geometry of the parabola shows that, when the focus lies in the plane of the aperture, the focal length is one-quarter of the aperture diameter.

The beam formed by a paraboloid, being roughly equal in width both in and perpendicular to the plane of the dipole, is usually spoken of as pencil-shaped. A certain amount of control of the beam shape can be obtained by cutting off parts of the paraboloid. A typical cut paraboloid is the 'orange-peel' shape shown in Fig. 13.6, which, having a large horizontal aperture and a small vertical aperture, will give a beam narrow in the horizontal plane and wider in the vertical plane.

Only a limited amount of beam shaping can be produced by this means; where a large difference between the beam widths in the two planes is required reflectors shaped only in one dimension, as described in the next section, are used.

Parabolic Cylinder Reflector

A plane sheet curved to parabolic shape in one dimension only forms the parabolic cylinder of Fig. 13.7. If a line source of radiation is placed along the

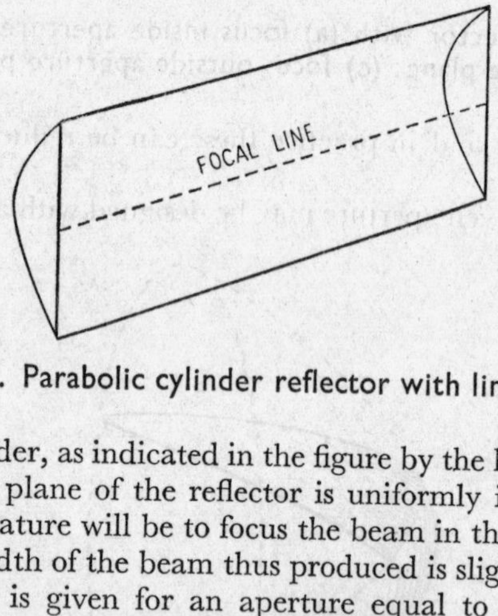

Fig. 13.7. Parabolic cylinder reflector with line source.

focal line of the cylinder, as indicated in the figure by the horizontal dotted line, so that the aperture plane of the reflector is uniformly illuminated, the effect of the parabolic curvature will be to focus the beam in the vertical plane.

The theoretical width of the beam thus produced is slightly less than that for the paraboloid, and is given for an aperture equal to 10λ by the curve of Fig. 13.8. This is the function $(\sin \phi)/\phi$ as discussed in Appendix 13.1, where its general form is given in Fig. 13.36. It is a useful curve in aerial theory, providing a simple standard with which the patterns of more complex aerials can be compared. The beam in the horizontal plane of Fig. 13.8 is dependent on the form and extent of the line source, and is not focused by the reflector, which has no curvature in that plane.

Fig. 13.9 shows two practical forms of parabolic cylinder aerial. That of Fig. 13.9 (a) uses as a line source a collinear array of dipoles, which produces in the horizontal plane a polar diagram as discussed in Chapter 10 and illustrated in Fig. 10.18.

To a first approximation the gain of this aerial may be taken as that of a uniformly illuminated aperture equal in dimensions to the aperture of the reflector. For dimensions a and b the gain relative to a half-wave dipole is shown in Appendix 13.1 to be:

$$G = 7{\cdot}7 \frac{ab}{\lambda^2} \quad . \quad . \quad . \quad . \quad . \quad . \quad (13.3)$$

The form shown in Fig. 13.9 (b), a short parabolic cylinder enclosed by parallel plates, is a commonly-used type known, from its shape, as a 'cheese'

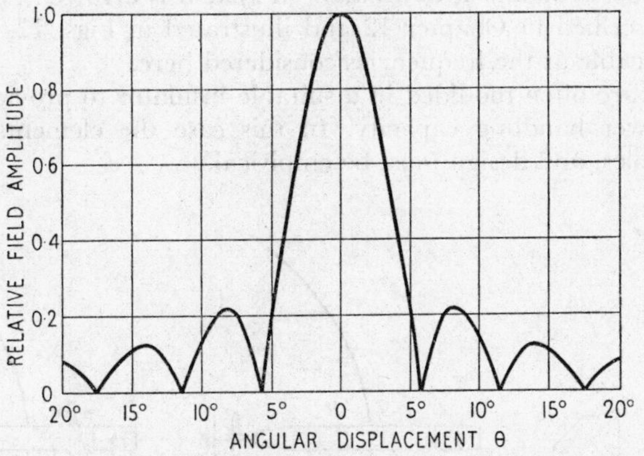

Fig. 13.8. Radiation pattern of parabolic cylinder of aperture equal to 10λ.

aerial. In the illustration the cheese is fed from a probe excited by a coaxial line. Placed as shown it will produce a sharp beam in the horizontal plane, and a wide beam in the vertical plane. Its beam is therefore 'fan-shaped'. This type of aerial is much used in ship-borne radar, where the narrow horizontal beam

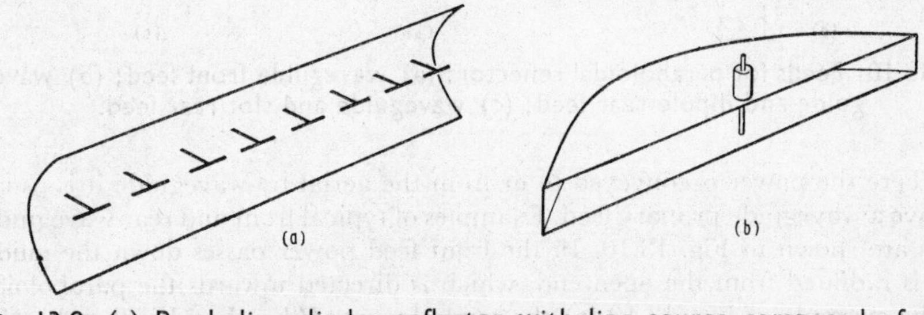

Fig. 13.9. (a) Parabolic cylinder reflector with line source composed of eight dipoles; (b) parabolic cheese aerial with probe source fed by coaxial line.

is necessary for discrimination of surface targets, and the broad vertical beam makes it insensitive to rolling or pitching of the vessel.

Primary Feeds for Paraboloid

In the two previous sections the aerial system has two clearly defined parts—the reflector and the source which feeds it. It is convenient to call the source the primary radiator and the reflector the secondary radiator. Some of the principles of design of the secondary radiator have been discussed; now we shall deal in more detail with the design of the primary radiator or primary feed.

The secondary radiator which best combines compactness and simplicity is the paraboloid, and for this there is a wide choice of primary feeds. The simplest is a dipole fed from a coaxial line, with a parasitic dipole or small plane reflector in front to prevent direct forward radiation, as illustrated in Fig. 13.3. If a parasitic dipole is used it is placed at a distance of about $\lambda/8$ in front of the driven dipole. For a plane reflector the spacing is less critical and may be up to about $0{\cdot}4\lambda$.

Feeding of a dipole from a coaxial line is complicated by the fact that a change from an unbalanced to a balanced system is involved. The methods of balancing described in Chapter 12 and illustrated in Figs. 12.2 and 12.3 are equally applicable at the frequencies considered here.

Such feeds are often moulded in a suitable insulator to provide rigidity and adequate power handling capacity. In this case the elements are far from idealized dipoles, and design must be empirical.

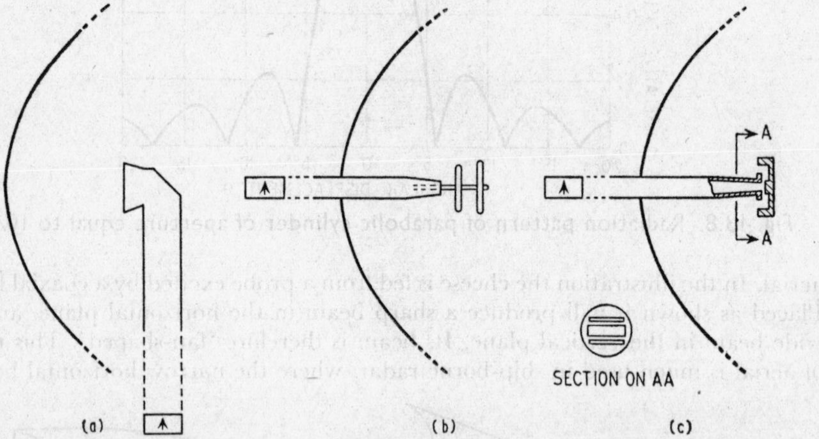

Fig. 13.10. Feeds for paraboloidal reflector: (a) waveguide front feed; (b) waveguide and dipole rear feed; (c) waveguide and slot rear feed.

Where the power is conveyed to or from the aerial by waveguide it is usual to have a waveguide primary feed. Examples of typical front and rear waveguide feeds are shown in Fig. 13.10. In the front feed power passes down the guide and is radiated from the open end, which is directed towards the paraboloid. In the example of Fig. 13.10 (a) the guide has an *H*-bend and is flared at its end into a small horn. The radiating properties of open-ended guides and horns will be discussed later in more detail; here it will suffice to say that flaring to dimensions of about one wavelength will give a radiation pattern which satisfactorily illuminates the paraboloid. Flanges may be used on the horn mouth to adjust the pattern, and irises to aid in matching the waveguide to the horn.

In the rear feed illustrated in Fig. 13.10 (b) the power from the open-ended guide is re-radiated on to the paraboloid by the first of two dipoles, a second dipole being used to suppress direct forward radiation. The dipoles are supported as shown on a conducting plate, which, being perpendicular to the electric-field vector, has little effect on the radiation. The guide is slightly tapered to improve matching.

A simpler and fairly satisfactory feed is formed by replacing the dipole assembly by a small flat reflecting sheet. In another form of this, illustrated in Fig. 13.10 (c) a cap placed over the end of the guide directs the energy back towards the paraboloid through two apertures. The orientation of the feed is of course chosen to give the polarization required. As shown the arrangement of Fig. 13.10 (a) gives horizontal polarization, while those of Figs. 13.10 (b) and (c) give vertical polarization.

Primary Feeds for Parabolic Cylinder

The cheese aerial of Fig. 13.9 (b) finds considerable use in applications where a beam is required to be narrow in one plane, but broad in the other. A common waveguide feed for the cheese is the 'hoghorn', in which the waveguide is flared in its broad dimension and connected to a portion of a small cheese, so that, as shown in Fig. 13.11 (a), radiation from the guide is reflected at the parabolic

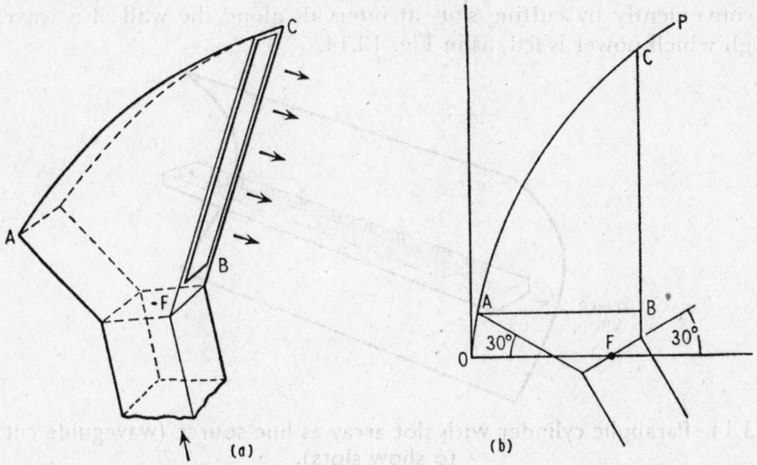

Fig. 13.11. (a) Hoghorn feed; (b) geometrical construction of hoghorn.

face AC, whose focus is at F, and emitted through the aperture BC. Fig. 13.11 (b) indicates one possible geometrical construction. The hoghorn combined with a cheese forms a rigid and compact aerial system.

A hoghorn may equally well be used as a feed for a cut paraboloid.

For a cheese with hoghorn feed the polarization is parallel to the flat sides, whereas with the probe feed of Fig. 13.10 (b) the polarization is perpendicular to the flat sides. Which polarization is used will depend upon the requirements of the system. With polarization parallel to the flat sides the same restriction of dimensions exists as for the H_{10} wave in a rectangular waveguide; i.e., the spacing between the sides of the cheese must be greater than half a wavelength. For polarization perpendicular to the flat sides there is no restriction on the spacing between these sides, as in the 'thin cheese' of Fig. 13.9 (b). A form of waveguide feed for vertical polarization is shown in Fig. 13.12.

As a uniform line source for a parabolic cylinder a thin cheese may be used. This combination illustrated in Fig. 13.13 is particularly applicable where the required aperture is of the order of 10λ in length.

For larger sizes of parabolic cylinder, however, a slot array feed is of more convenient size than the thin cheese. Arrays of slots have been discussed in

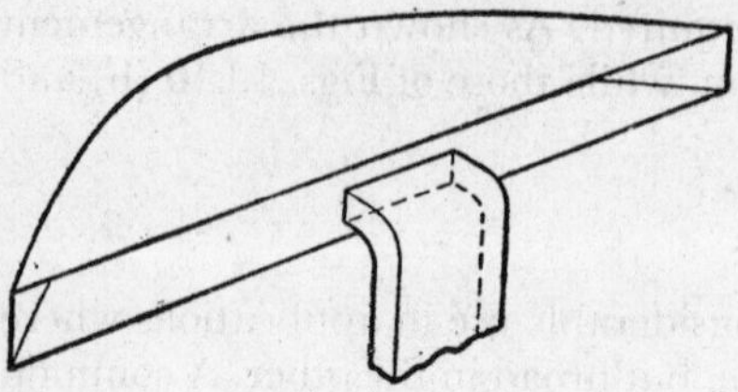

Fig. 13.12. Cheese aerial with wave-guide feed.

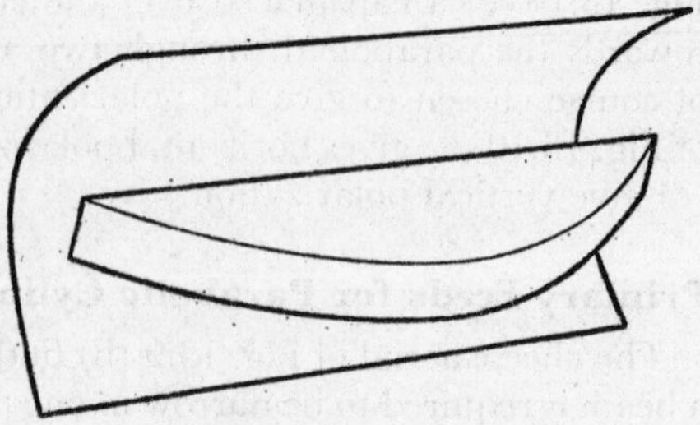

Fig. 13.13. Parabolic cylinder with cheese aerial as line source.

Chapter 12; in this instance a linear array is required. This can be constructed very conveniently by cutting slots at intervals along the wall of a waveguide through which power is fed, as in Fig. 13.14.

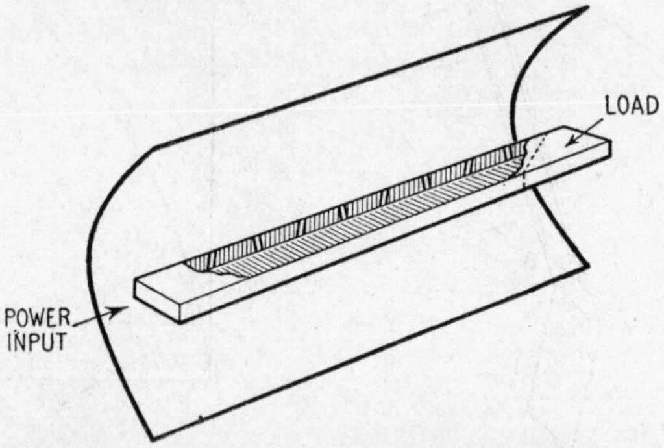

Fig. 13.14. Parabolic cylinder with slot array as line source (waveguide cut away to show slots).

It was shown in Chapter 6 that slots in a waveguide could be placed either to interrupt or not to interrupt current flow in the wall. Slots which interrupt current flow act as magnetic dipoles [Fig. 10.6 (a)] and radiate power. The

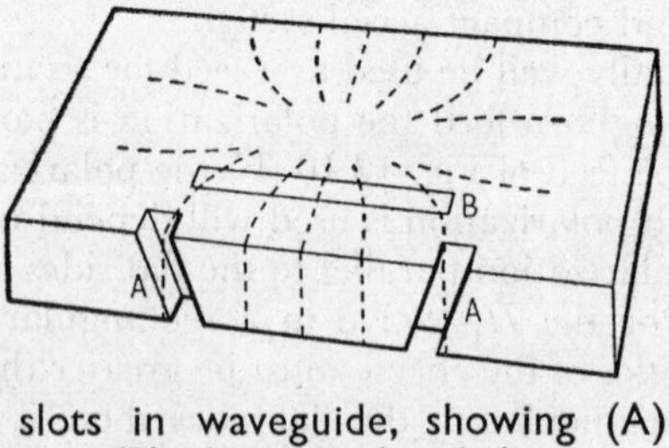

Fig. 13.15. Radiating slots in waveguide, showing (A) shunt inclined slot, (B) shunt displaced slot.

two forms of radiating slot chiefly used in linear arrays are shown in Fig. 13.15 (compare Fig. 6.18). Both interrupt the lateral current in the wall and therefore act as shunt resistances across the guide, and are called 'shunt inclined' and 'shunt displaced'. Their effect may be varied by choice of the amount of inclination or displacement. The type used in practice will depend on the operational requirement, since clearly one will produce a horizontally-polarized wave and the other a vertically-polarized wave.

Primary and Secondary Radiators

A successful design of aerial system requires careful experimental work in measuring amplitude and phase distributions in both the primary and secondary radiators. Where a primary source is used to feed a paraboloid the equi-phase surfaces in the region where the secondary radiator is to be placed should be spherical. Otherwise a uniform phase distribution across the aperture will not be obtained, and this will result in broadening of the polar diagram and increase of side-lobe amplitude. The polar diagram of the feed should also have the requisite amplitude to illuminate the reflector correctly. The following principles relating to the amplitude distribution as measured at the final aperture are of general application:

(i) A uniform amplitude distribution gives maximum gain

(ii) An amplitude distribution tapering from a maximum at the centre towards the sides results in reduced gain but reduces side lobes

(iii) An amplitude distribution tapering from a maximum at the edges towards the centre (inverse taper) gives a sharper main lobe but increased side lobes and reduced gain.

Inaccurate mirrors and badly placed feed supports result in large and irregular side lobes. For simple aerials the permissible departure of the reflector from its theoretical shape is usually taken as that which results in changes in path length not exceeding $\lambda/8$. A small displacement of a portion of a reflector will cause an error in the wave front of approximately twice the displacement. Thus a reflector should not diverge from its theoretical shape at any point by more than $\pm \lambda/16$. For special shapes or for very low side lobes the tolerance may be much less.

A front feed waveguide must cross the aperture parallel to the *H* vector of the radiation. In any other direction it would produce appreciable scattering of power. The same is true of any metal supporting bars. If supports parallel to the *E* vector are necessary they must be of dielectric.

The reflector need not be of solid metal. A considerable reduction of weight and windage without appreciable effect on the polar diagram may be obtained by the use of mesh, perforated metal or rod construction. Perforated surfaces are insensitive to polarization. The perforations can be regarded as short waveguides for which the frequency is well beyond cut-off; for example, in a wire-mesh reflector with square holes the side of the square must be smaller than $\lambda/\sqrt{2}$. Constructions of strips or rods are sensitive to polarization. In order to act as reflectors the strips must be parallel to the electric field at the surface. The space between strips must act as a waveguide beyond cut-off, and the spacing must therefore be less than $\lambda/2$.

Beam-Shaping Aerials

In special applications, mainly in radar, particular shapes of polar diagram are required. An example is the *cosecant pattern*, required in airborne radar to produce a ground-reflected signal whose amplitude is independent of range for a given height. The vertical-plane pattern required for this purpose is $E = E_0 \operatorname{cosec} \theta$, θ being measured from the horizon, and is illustrated within typical limits of θ in Fig. 13.16.

Any such pattern can be produced by a line source feeding a cylindrical reflector whose section is not parabolic but of a shape calculated by optical principles. The method is beyond our scope here, but an example of the results obtained by it is shown in Fig. 13.16. A practical difficulty is that of manufacturing reflectors of such shapes within the necessary tolerances.

A second method of obtaining special beam shapes depends on the use of the Fourier Transform Method developed by J. F. Ramsay. Briefly this method enables one to calculate the aperture distribution required to give a particular polar diagram. It is dealt with in Appendix 13.2. The method is of great theoretical importance, but is of limited application because the required aperture distributions are often difficult to produce. Aerials designed by the

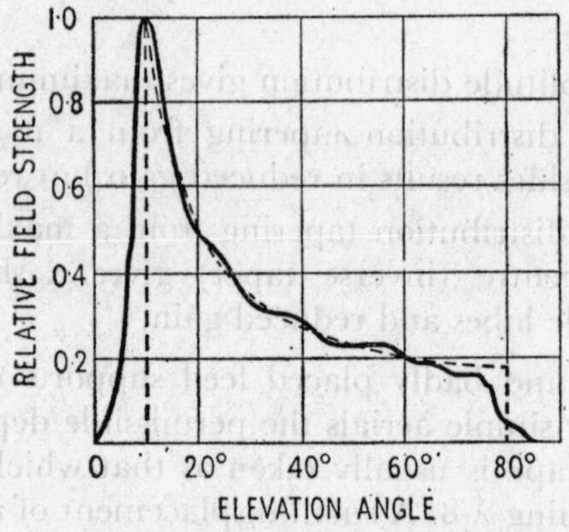

Fig. 13.16. Typical radiation pattern of cosecant aerial for operation between 10° and 80°. Dashed line, theoretical; full line, experimental.

optical method are always wasteful of aperture compared with those designed by the Fourier method, but the aperture distributions involved are usually more practical.

Scanning Methods

In radar application it is important to be able to move or *scan* the beam so as either to search a prescribed region in space or to follow a particular target. The system of scanning used will depend on the use for which the radar is intended. Large movements require rotation of the whole aerial system, which, for the smaller centimetre-wave aerials at least, is a relatively simple mechanical problem. Where rotation of the aerial system relative to a fixed transmission line is required a rotating joint must be incorporated at an appropriate position. Small movements of the beam can be obtained by either mechanical or electrical means.

Fig. 13.17 (a) illustrates *helical scanning*, where the aerial is moved continuously, rotating rapidly in azimuth and oscillating slowly in elevation, so that its pencil beam traces out a helix.

A second type is *spiral scanning*, which is illustrated in Fig. 13.17 (b). Spiral scanning can be accomplished by rotating eccentrically the feed to a paraboloid and slowly increasing the eccentricity, or by a similar movement of the paraboloid with the feed fixed. Sideways movement of the feed in the plane of the focus will swing the beam, as in Fig. 13.18, but only a limited movement is possible before serious defocusing of the beam occurs. A tilt θ of the feed relative

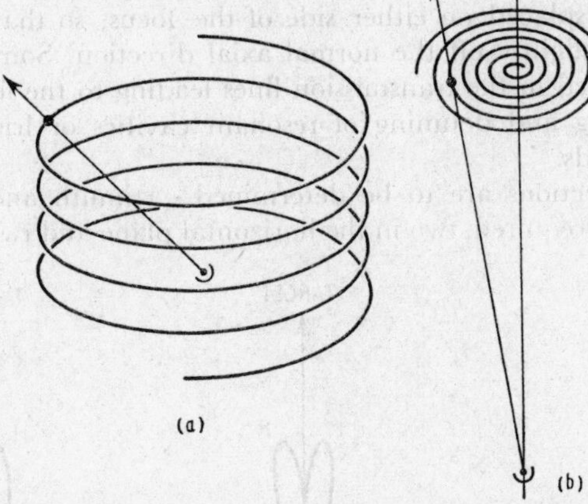

Fig. 13.17. Radar aerial scanning systems: (a) helical scanning; (b) spiral scanning.

to the paraboloid produces a beam displacement of about $0{\cdot}8\theta$, whereas a tilt of the paraboloid relative to the feed displaces the beam by about $1{\cdot}8\theta$. Thus scanning by movement of the paraboloid is more effective than movement of the feed, although it may be mechanically less convenient.

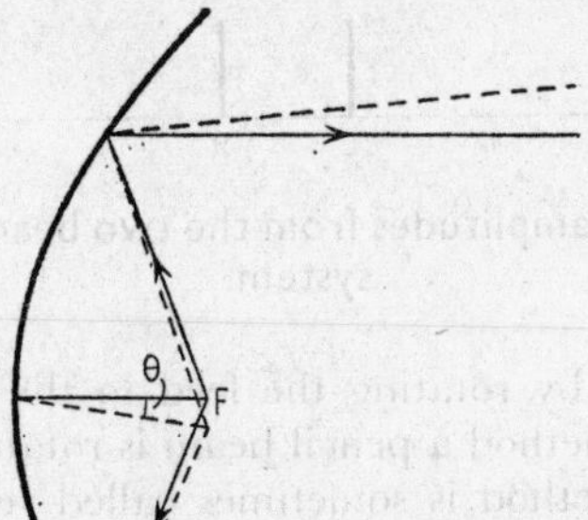

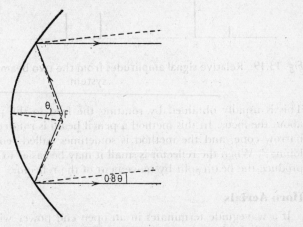

Fig. 13.18. Angular movement of beam produced by movement of feed relative to paraboloid.

In radar systems where it is desired to fix on a particular target, and especially in an automatic following system, an abbreviated form of scanning, 'beam splitting', is used. In the U.S.A. the technique is known as 'lobing'. If information is required concerning one angle only, azimuth for example, the beam is switched rapidly between two positions which differ only slightly in azimuth.

Signals received in these two positions are compared, visually or electrically, and Fig. 13.19 indicates how these signals vary when the aerial is directed near to the target. The difference between the two signals, which vanishes when the aerial is pointing exactly to the target, may be used to direct the aerial so that it follows any movement of the target.

This beam split can be produced by having two primary feeds placed side by side, slightly displaced on either side of the focus, so that each produces a beam which is slightly off the normal axial direction. Some form of rapid switching is required in the transmission lines leading to the feeds, which may be done by tuning and detuning of resonant cavities or irises, or by other mechanical methods.

Where two directions are to be determined—azimuth and altitude—four beam positions are required, two in the horizontal plane and two in the vertical.

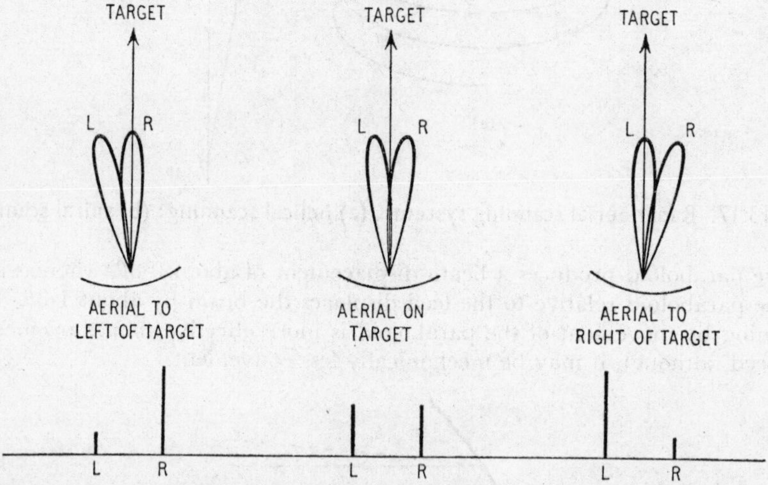

Fig. **13.19. Relative signal amplitudes from the two beams of beam-splitting aerial system.**

This is usually obtained by rotating the feed to the paraboloid eccentrically about the focus. In this method a pencil beam is rotated so that it sweeps out a narrow cone, and the method is sometimes called 'conical scanning (conical lobing)'. When the reflector is small it may be easier to leave the feed fixed and produce the beam split by movement of the reflector.

Horn Aerials

If a waveguide terminates in an open end power will be radiated from the open end. As the aperture dimensions are normally comparable with the wavelength the aperture is small and thus, as in any aerial system with a small aperture, the radiation pattern is very broad. The aperture may be increased by flaring out the waveguide to a horn shape. Several such types of horn aerial are illustrated in Fig. 13.20. A horn flared in only one dimension is called a 'sectoral horn', one flared in both dimensions is a 'pyramidal horn'. The sectoral horn shown in Fig. 13.20 (a) is flared in the H-plane of the H_{10} mode in the feeding guide, and is therefore an H-plane sectoral horn.

The radiation pattern of a horn can be calculated if the aperture dimensions and aperture field distribution are known. An exact calculation is difficult, but if as a rough approximation the aperture distribution is taken as uniform, then the radiation pattern is given by the expressions in Appendix 13.1 and by Fig. 13.36. For the horns of Fig. 13.20 (a) and (b) the field over the aperture is approximately the same as it would be for an H_{10} wave in a waveguide of the same dimensions as the aperture. Thus the field tapers in the horizontal plane but is uniform in the vertical, and therefore, as discussed in the section on Primary and Secondary Radiators, the pattern in the horizontal plane will be relatively free from side lobes.

Since the wave has to travel farther to reach the outside edges of the aperture than to reach its centre the phase will vary across the horn aperture. A large phase variation gives rise to unduly large side lobes, and so in order to have as uniform a phase front as possible a very long horn with small flare angle would

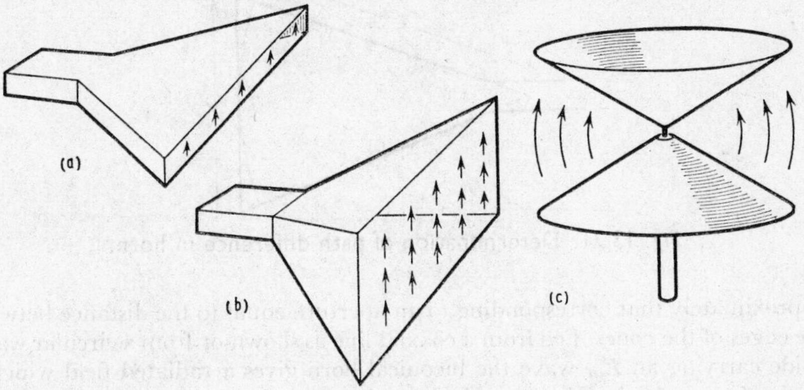

Fig. 13.20. Types of horn aerials: (a) sectoral; (b) pyramidal; (c) biconical.

be required. This is inconvenient from a practical standpoint, and a compromise length must be adopted.

▶ The criterion usually taken is that the phase variation should not exceed 90°. For a phase variation of 90° the value of δ as indicated in Fig. 13.21 is λ/4, and hence from the geometry of the figure:

$$L = \frac{D^2}{2\lambda} \quad . \quad . \quad . \quad . \quad . \quad . \quad (13.4)$$

This value of L therefore represents the optimum length for a horn whose largest aperture dimension is D.

The exact expression for the gain of a sectoral or a pyramidal horn cannot be given in simple terms, but for a horn of optimum length of aperture dimensions a, b an approximate expression for the gain, relative to a λ/2 dipole, is:

$$G \approx 4{\cdot}5\,\frac{ab}{\lambda^2} \quad . \quad . \quad . \quad . \quad . \quad (13.5)$$

Gain and beam width are further dealt with in Appendix 13.3. ◀

Horns of this compromise length are still inconveniently long—the flare angle being in the region of 20°—and have not been much used. However, a much wider flare is permissible, with a consequent reduction in length, if the phase is corrected by means of a lens placed in the aperture. Although the first microwave lenses were designed for this specific purpose it soon became clear that lenses were themselves important components having focusing properties analogous to those of optical lenses. A lens-connected horn can then be regarded as serving merely as a guide for the radiation from the waveguide to the lens, and it is best to consider the design as a lens problem. This is treated in the following section.

The 'biconical' horn of Fig. 13.20 (c) can be regarded as a horn with a 360° flare in one dimension. This is the biconical aerial already treated in Chapter 12 from a different point of view. Being circularly symmetrical, it has a circular polar diagram in the horizontal plane. In the vertical plane its beam width is

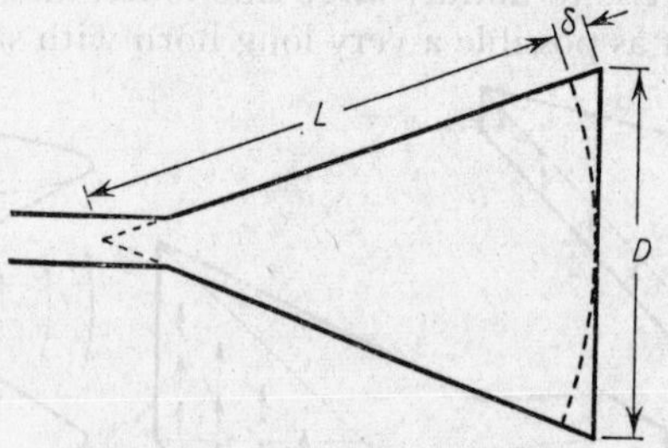

Fig. 13.21. Determination of path difference in horn.

approximately that corresponding to an aperture equal to the distance between the edges of the cones. Fed from a coaxial line as shown or from a circular waveguide carrying an E_{01} wave the biconical horn gives a radiated field which is vertically polarized; fed by an H_{01} wave in a circular guide it gives a radiated field which is horizontally polarized.

The aperture of the biconical horn may also be lens-corrected.

Lens Aerials

The parabolic reflector is one example of an optical device which can be applied at centimetre wavelengths to focus waves and thus to act as an aerial; the lens is another such device which has similar properties.

An optical lens operates by virtue of having an index of refraction greater than unity, and is shaped so as to refract suitably the light rays incident upon it; a lens made of dielectric material will operate similarly for radio frequencies. At radio frequencies, however, it is also possible to construct a medium having an index of refraction less than unity, and this also can be made to have the focusing properties of a lens. The metal plate lens to be considered shortly is an important example of the latter type.

Thus there are two distinct types of lens aerial—the dielectric lens and the metal-plate lens. The essential difference is seen in the fact that in a dielectric lens the travelling wave front is slowed down by the lens medium; in the metal-plate lens the wave front is speeded up by the lens medium. Fig. 13.22 illustrates that as a result of these properties a convergent dielectric lens with a real focus must be thinner at the edge than at the centre (as in optics); a convergent metal-plate lens must be thicker at the edge than at the centre.

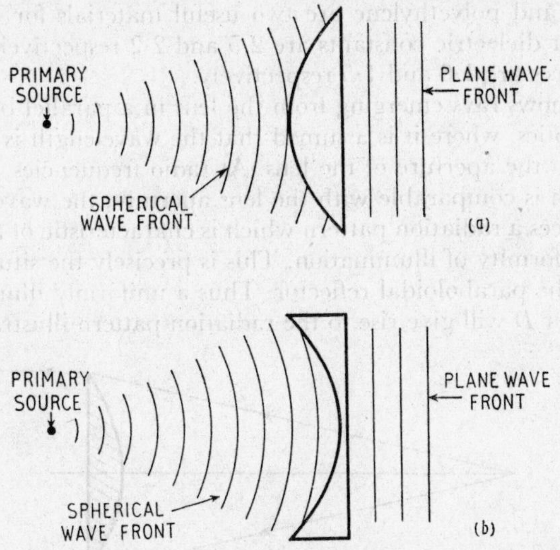

Fig. 13.22. Comparison of action of (a) dielectric lens; (b) metal-plate lens.

Simple Dielectric Lens

If the lens in Fig. 13.23 is to transform a spherical wave from a source situated at F into a plane wave front, then the requirement is that all ray paths from F to the plane surface of the lens should have equal electrical length. It is shown in Appendix 13.4 that this requirement is met by a plano-convex lens whose curved face has a hyperbolic shape. The distance l of the point F from the curved face is the focal length of the lens. It can be shown that the hyperbolic

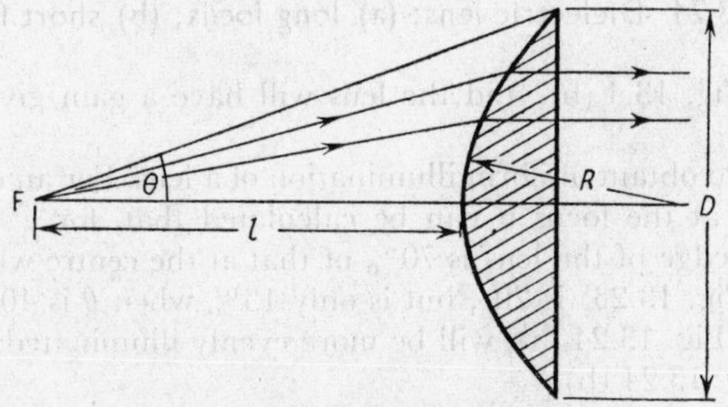

Fig. 13.23. Ray paths in dielectric lens.

shape of the lens can be represented approximately by a segment of a sphere of radius R such that:

$$R = (n - 1)l \qquad (13.6)$$

In this equation n is the index of refraction of the lens material. As in optics the index of refraction is the ratio of the velocity of the wave in air to the velocity in the dielectric, and this ratio, by equation (5.11), is related to the relative dielectric constant κ_r (assuming permeability unity) by the relation:

$$n = \frac{c}{v} = \kappa_r^{1/2} \qquad (13.7)$$

Polystyrene and polyethylene are two useful materials for the construction of lenses. Their dielectric constants are 2·5 and 2·2 respectively and thus their refractive indices are 1·6 and 1·5 respectively.

Fig. 13.23 shows rays emerging from the lens in a parallel beam as given by geometrical optics, where it is assumed that the wavelength is negligibly small compared with the aperture of the lens. At radio frequencies, however, where the wavelength is comparable with the lens aperture, the wave emerging from the lens produces a radiation pattern which is characteristic of the lens aperture and of the uniformity of illumination. This is precisely the situation previously discussed for the paraboloidal reflector. Thus a uniformly illuminated circular lens of diameter D will give rise to the radiation pattern illustrated for the case

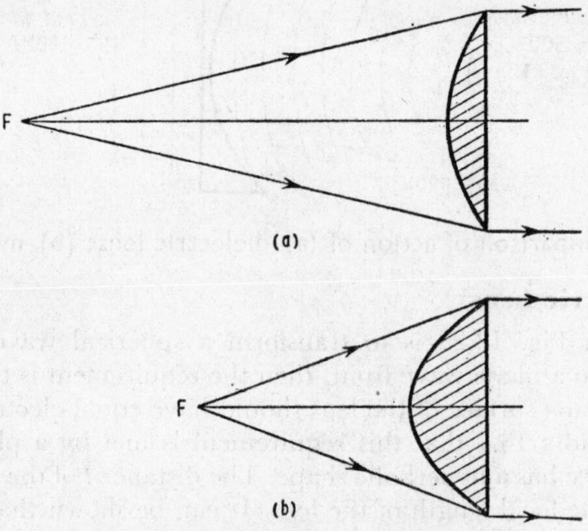

Fig. 13.24. Dielectric lens: (a) long focus; (b) short focus.

of $D = 10\lambda$ in Fig. 13.4 (b), and the lens will have a gain given by equation (13.2).

It is not easy to obtain uniform illumination of a lens. For an omnidirectional radiator placed at the focus it can be calculated that, for $n = 1{\cdot}5$, the field intensity at the edge of the lens is 70% of that at the centre when the angle of the cone (θ in Fig. 13.23) is 20°, but is only 13% when θ is 40°. Thus a long-focus lens, as in Fig. 13.24 (a), will be more evenly illuminated than the short-focus lens of Fig. 13.24 (b).

A tapered illumination is often desirable, as discussed for the paraboloid, in order to reduce side lobes, and this may be controlled by choice of the focal length of the lens and by adjustment of the beam incident on the lens from the primary source.

Stepped Dielectric Lens

The thickness of a dielectric lens is discussed in Appendix 13.5, where it is shown that the thickness increases rapidly as the focal length is reduced. A simple lens of the type just described may be many wavelengths thick and consequently heavy and bulky.

When this is so, the condition that the time should be the same for all paths is unnecessarily restrictive; it is permissible for path lengths to differ by integral multiples of a wavelength without affecting the uniformity of phase of the emergent wave. Thus sections of the lens may be removed, giving the stepped effect shown in Fig. 13.25 (a) where the steps are cut in the plane face. It is shown in Appendix 13.5 that the thickness w of such a step is given by:

$$w = \frac{\lambda}{n - 1} \qquad (13.8)$$

For a dielectric with $n = 1{\cdot}5$, each step will therefore be equal to twice the free-space wavelength.

In Fig. 13.25 (b) the steps are shown cut in the curved face, and the form of the face in this case is also dealt with in Appendix 13.5. This latter form is preferable, being stronger mechanically than the form of Fig. 13.25 (a). It is

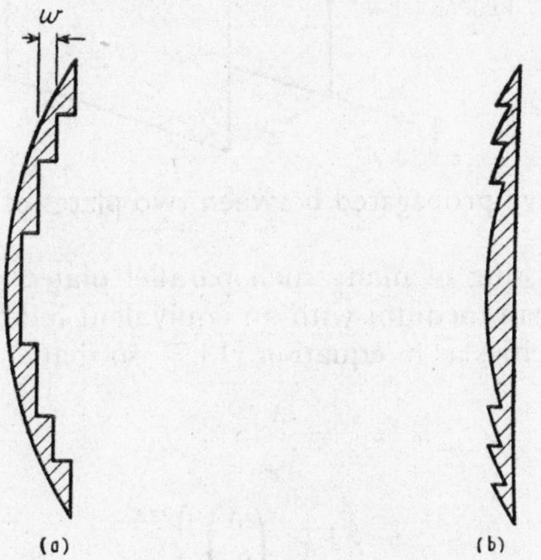

Fig. 13.25. Stepped dielectric lenses.

clear that the maximum thickness of the lens will be of the order of $\lambda/(n - 1)$, since at no point need the phase be corrected by more than 2π.

This stepped or zoned lens has the great advantage of a considerably reduced weight. It has the possible disadvantage that, since w is dependent on λ, the lens must be designed for the frequency at which it is to be used. It will be usable however over a small frequency range on either side of the design frequency. This is dealt with in a later section.

Metal-plate Lenses

Consider a wave propagated between two infinite parallel planes spaced a distance a apart, as in Fig. 13.26, and having its electric vector parallel to the plates as shown. This can be regarded as a part of a rectangular waveguide carrying an H_{10} wave as in Fig. 6.3, but having its dimension b infinitely large. Equation (6.4) gives the equation for the wavelength in the guide λ_g, which is dependent only on the dimension a, as:

$$\frac{1}{\lambda_g} = \left\{\frac{1}{\lambda^2} - \frac{1}{(2a)^2}\right\}^{1/2}$$

By equation (6.7) the phase velocity of the wave in the guide is given by:

$$v = c\frac{\lambda_g}{\lambda}$$

and this velocity is always greater than c.

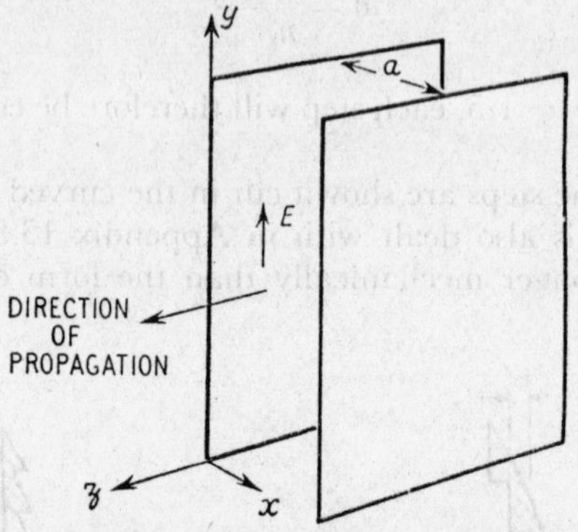

Fig. 13.26. Wave propagated between two plates of metal-plate lens.

A structure consisting of many such parallel plates with spacing a can be regarded as a uniform medium with an equivalent index of refraction n given by the ratio of velocities as in equation (13.7), so that

$$n = \frac{c}{v} = \frac{\lambda}{\lambda_g}$$

$$= \left\{1 - \left(\frac{\lambda}{2a}\right)^2\right\}^{1/2} \quad . \quad . \quad . \quad . \quad . \quad . \quad (13.9)$$

From the form of equation (13.9) the index of refraction is always *less* than

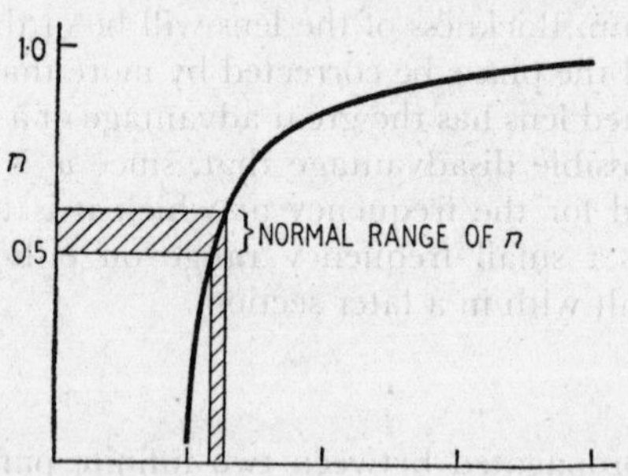

Fig. 13.27. Index of refraction n in metal-plate lens as function of plate spacing a.

unity; its variation with spacing is shown in Fig. 13.27. Clearly a must not be less than the critical value $\lambda/2$.

Thus a lens may be constructed from parallel metal plates. It differs fundamentally from the dielectric lens previously considered in that, whereas the dielectric lens corrects phases by slowing down a wave front, the metal-plate lens operates by speeding up the wave front. A convergent metal-plate lens must therefore have plates which are concave in shape, and the arrangement of such a lens is shown in Fig. 13.28.

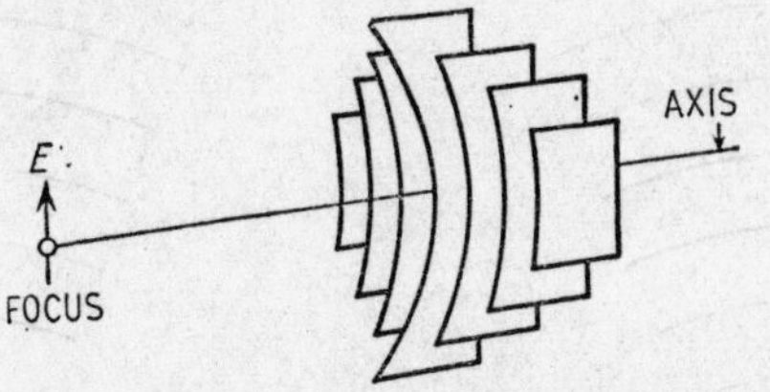

Fig. 13.28. Arrangement of metal-plate lens.

It is shown in Appendix 13.6 that the hyperbolic face of the dielectric lens is replaced by an elliptical face in the metal-plate lens. Except in the smallest lenses, a metal-plate lens is always stepped, the path length being reduced by one wavelength at each step in the form of Fig. 13.29. The appropriate equations are given in Appendix 13.6. Fig. 13.30 shows clearly how stepping considerably reduces the size and mass of a lens.

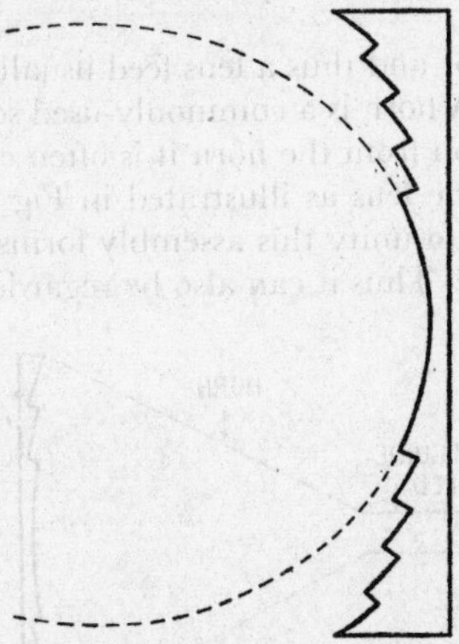

Fig. 13.29. Plate shape in stepped metal-plate lens, elliptical contour with five zones, $n = 0{\cdot}5$, focal length 40λ.

To reduce the thickness of the lens n should be as small as possible; therefore the value of the spacing a should be as nearly equal to $\lambda/2$ as possible. On the other hand a spacing near to $\lambda/2$ imposes severe restrictions on the accuracy of the spacing since n then varies rapidly with a. In practice a compromise value between $n = 0{\cdot}5$ ($a = 0{\cdot}577\lambda$) and $n = 0{\cdot}6$ ($a = 0{\cdot}625\lambda$) is generally used.

Primary Sources for Lenses

Primary sources used as feeds for lenses—either dielectric or metal plate—should fulfil similar requirements to those for reflectors. In a lens of given aperture the focal length can be chosen at will, but it is usual to choose a focal length approximately equal to the aperture dimension. This is greater than is

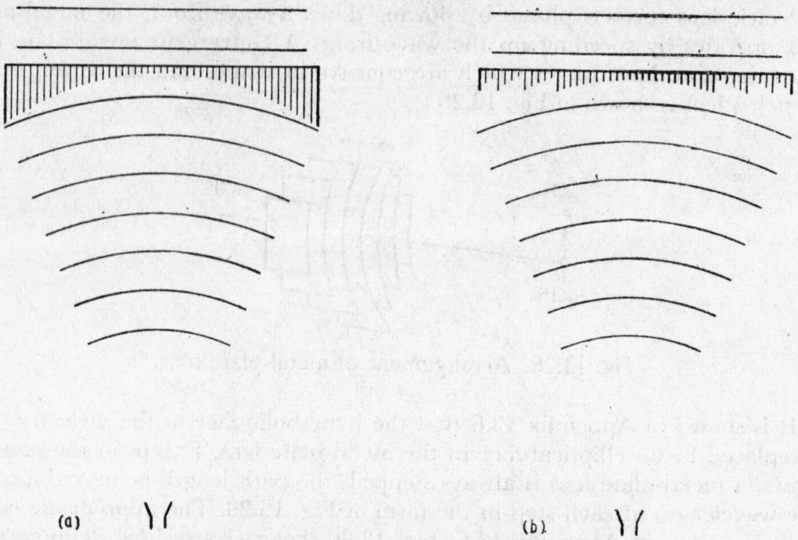

Fig. 13.30. Section of stepped and unstepped metal-plate lenses perpendicular to plates.

usually used for a reflector and thus a lens feed usually has to be more directive than one for a reflector. A horn is a commonly-used source.

To avoid stray radiation from the horn it is often convenient to continue the sides of the horn up to the lens as illustrated in Fig. 13.31. For ratios of focal length to aperture equal to unity this assembly forms a horn of flare angle 53° with a lens in its aperture. Thus it can also be regarded as a horn of flare wider

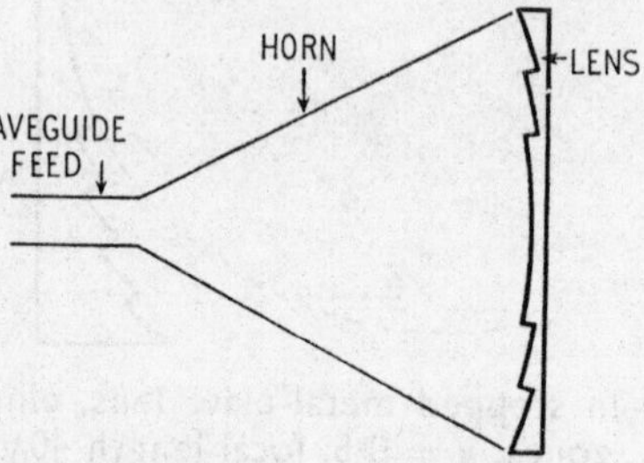

Fig. 13.31. Pyramidal horn with lens-corrected aperture.

than the optimum in which a suitable phase correction is applied at the aperture by means of the lens.

▶ Tolerances and Bandwidth in Lenses

In Appendix 13.7 expressions for acceptable tolerances in the various types of lenses are derived, and these are collected in Table 13.2.

These give the following figures for typical lenses. In a stepped polystyrene lens with three steps, used at a wavelength of 3 cm, tolerances of $\pm 0{\cdot}04$ in dielectric constant or $\pm$ 3 mm in thickness are permissible. This dimensional tolerance is about 70% greater than the corresponding tolerance for a parabolic reflector. For a 3-stepped metal-plate lens ($n = 0{\cdot}6$), also at 3-cm wavelength, a tolerance of $\pm\ 0{\cdot}4$ mm in spacing must be met.

TABLE 13.2

Type of aerial	Tolerance		Bandwidth, per cent
Parabolic reflector	Surface contour	$\pm \frac{\lambda}{16}$	wide
Unstepped dielectric lens	Thickness	$\pm \frac{\lambda}{16(n-1)}$	wide
	Refractive index	$\pm \frac{\lambda}{16t}$	
Stepped dielectric lens	Thickness	$\pm \frac{t}{16}$	$\frac{25}{p-1}$
	Refractive index	$\pm \frac{n-1}{16}$	
Unstepped metal-plate lens	Thickness	$\pm \frac{\lambda}{16(1-n)}$	$\frac{25n\lambda}{(1-n^2)t}$
	Plate spacing	$\pm \frac{n\lambda a}{16(1-n^2)t}$	
Stepped metal-plate lens	Thickness	$\pm \frac{t}{16}$	$\frac{25n}{1+pn}$
	Plate spacing	$\pm \frac{na}{16(1+n)}$	

$n =$ refractive index
$t =$ lens thickness
$a =$ plate spacing
$p =$ number of zones

It is interesting to compare these requirements with the tolerance for a parabolic reflector. In the parabolic reflector the contour has to be maintained within $\pm\ \lambda/16$, which places a severe limitation on the allowable warping or twisting. In a lens on the other hand, where the rays enter and emerge from opposite sides, it is clear that a relatively large amount of warping and twisting can be tolerated, since they will not appreciably affect the path length. This is an important advantage for the lens, particularly for large apertures and short wavelengths.

In an unstepped dielectric lens the lens shape is not dependent on wavelength and thus it can be used over a wide wavelength range. In the metal-plate lens the refractive index is a function of wavelength, and a lens designed for a particular wavelength can therefore operate only over a limited range of wavelength. From their construction all stepped lenses are clearly dependent on wavelength. Figures for the useful bandwidth of lenses are given also in Table 13.2, and derived in Appendix 13.8. The useful bandwidths of the two typical lenses discussed above, expressed as a percentage of the design wavelength, are respectively 12% and 5%.

Path-Length Lenses

The metal-plate lenses discussed in the preceding section are composed of plates set parallel to the electric vector of the wave and operate by virtue of the velocity change produced by the plates. If, however, a stack of plates is arranged perpendicular to the electric vector, as in Fig. 13.32 (a) they will act as a set

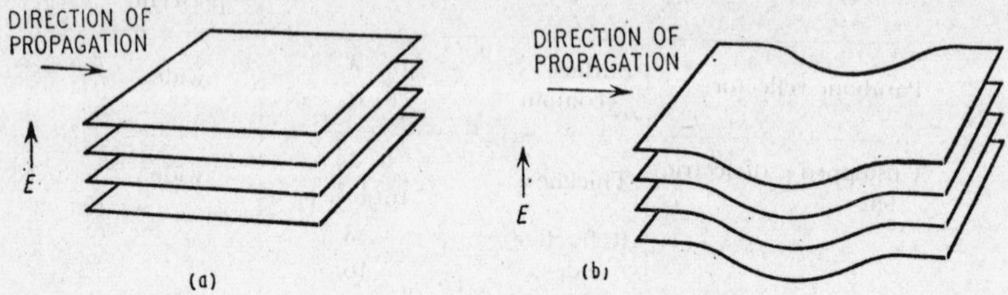

Fig. 13.32. (a) *H*-plane stack of metal plates; (b) *H*-plane stack with increased path length.

of strip transmission lines, and in Chapter 5 it was shown that the velocity of a wave in a strip transmission line is the same as its velocity in free space. Thus a wave entering the stack of plates is unaffected in velocity, but the actual length of path can be increased by deformation of the plates, as for example, in Fig. 13.32 (b).

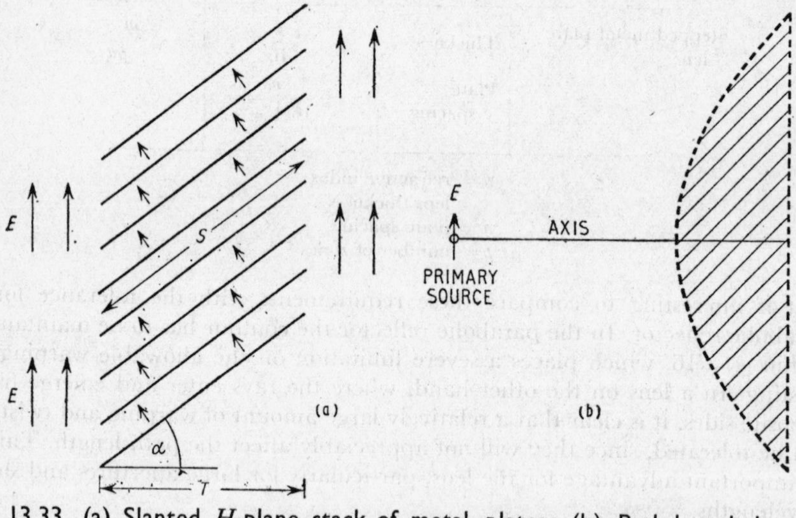

Fig. 13.33. (a) Slanted *H*-plane stack of metal plates; (b) Path-length lens of slanted plate construction.

The slanted stack of plates of Fig. 13.33 (a) will produce an increase in path length of $S - T$. The increase of path length may be regarded as equivalent to a decrease in velocity, so that the stack has an effective refractive index n given by:

$$n = \frac{S}{T} = \sec \alpha \qquad (13.10)$$

α being the angle between the stack and the wave direction. In this case n is clearly greater than unity. The stack of plates is thus equivalent to a solid dielectric, and so when shaped in hyperbolic form, as in Fig. 13.33 (b), will act in the same way as a dielectric lens (see Appendix 13.9). Lenses of this type are known as 'path-length' lenses.

The path-length lens has the inherent disadvantage that the inclined plates distort the uniformity of amplitude distribution across the aperture, resulting in an increase of side-lobe level.

Artificial Dielectrics

In the construction of dielectric lenses it is possible to use artificial dielectrics in place of the ordinary dielectric materials. The properties of ordinary dielectrics are dependent on the regular arrangement of the molecules in a lattice structure; artificial dielectrics simulate this lattice structure on a large scale by means of discrete metallic elements.

A simple form of artificial dielectric is composed of a volume distribution of metal spheres, equally spaced. The effective refractive index of such a material can be calculated to be approximately:

$$n = \{(1 + 4\pi Na^3)(1 - 2\pi Na^3)\}^{1/2} \quad . \quad . \quad . \quad . \quad (13.11)$$

where N is the number of spheres per unit volume and a the radius of the sphere. The spheres should be small compared with the design wavelength (in practice $a < \lambda/8$ is satisfactory) and the spacing between spheres should be less than a wavelength.

Although spheres are simplest to calculate other forms such as discs, strips, or rods are lighter, have higher refractive indices, and are more easily assembled. Approximate values of refractive index are given in Table 13.3.

TABLE 13.3

Artificial Dielectrics

Type of particle	Refractive index n
Sphere	$\{(1 + 4\pi Na^3)(1 - 2\pi Na^3)\}^{1/2}$
Disc	$(1 + 5{\cdot}3Na^3)^{1/2}$
Strip	$(1 + 7{\cdot}8Nw^3)^{1/2}$

$N =$ number of elements per cubic metre
$a =$ radius in metres
$w =$ width in metres

APPENDIX 13.1

Radiation from Uniformly Illuminated Aperture

It has been shown that ideally the field over the aperture plane of a paraboloid is uniform and in phase, and the radiation will therefore be the same as that of the system illustrated in Fig. 13.34, where a plane wave is incident on an aperture, of the same shape as the aperture of the paraboloid, pierced in an infinite conducting sheet. The radiated field of such a system (i.e., the field produced on the right-hand side of the infinite sheet by the penetration of the plane wave through it) can be readily calculated, and the result is fundamental in the theory of microwave aerials.

To calculate the radiation we use the theorem known as Huygens' Principle. According to this, each point on a wave front can be considered as a source of a secondary spherical wave. The secondary waves diverging from these sources combine to form a new wave front, which is the envelope of the secondary waves.

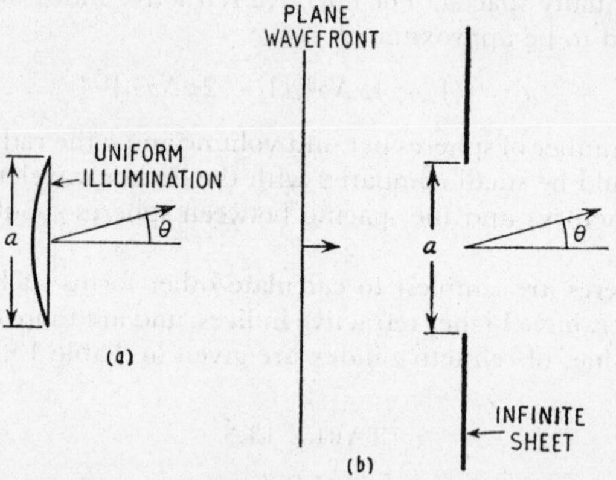

Fig. 13.34. (a) Paraboloid with uniformly illuminated aperture; (b) equivalent uniformly illuminated aperture in infinite plane sheet.

Fig. 13.35 illustrates the propagation of an infinite plane wave front as visualized by Huygens' Principle, and shows how it continues as a plane wave.

Consider first of all a slot of width a as in Fig. 13.34, having infinite length in the direction normal to the paper. By Huygens' Principle the field in the slot is represented by a line of points each of which radiates a spherical wave. If there are n points with spacing d then the far field can be calculated as in Chapter 10 for a linear array. Taking θ as the angle shown in Fig. 13.35 in place of that in Fig. 10.17 (a) we see that equation (10.20) for the electric field becomes:

$$E = E_1 \frac{\sin \{(n\pi d/\lambda) \sin \theta\}}{\sin \{(\pi d/\lambda) \sin \theta\}} \quad . \quad . \quad . \quad . \quad (13.12)$$

where E_1 is the field of one of the individual point sources. This pattern is of the form illustrated in Fig. 10.17 (c), and the angle out to the first nulls is given by equation (10.22) as:

$$\theta \approx \pm \frac{\lambda}{nd} \text{ radians}$$

If we pass to a continuous field distribution across the aperture by letting $n \to \infty$ and $d \to 0$ in such a way that $nd = a$ then this becomes:

$$\theta \approx \pm \frac{\lambda}{a} \text{ radians} \quad . \quad . \quad . \quad . \quad . \quad . \quad (13.13)$$

The angle to half-power points is roughly half this value. These values are in accordance with equation (13.1).

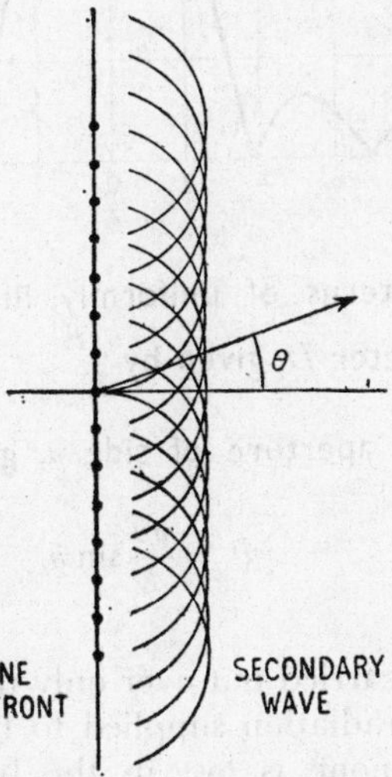

Fig. 13.35. Plane wavefront with secondary Huygens waves.

In the direction of the maximum radiation, $\theta = 0$ and equation (13.12) becomes:

$$E_{max} = nE_1$$

and thus the field relative to the maximum is given by:

$$E = E_{max} \frac{\sin\{(n\pi d/\lambda) \sin \theta\}}{n \sin \{(\pi d/\lambda) \sin \theta\}}$$

As $d \to 0$ this becomes:

$$E = E_{max} \frac{\sin \{(\pi a/\lambda) \sin \theta\}}{(\pi a/\lambda) \sin \theta} \quad . \quad . \quad . \quad . \quad . \quad (13.14)$$

The curve of this function is illustrated in Fig. 13.36.

For a rectangular distribution of sources representing an aperture of dimensions a, b as in Fig. 13.37 it follows that the corresponding expression for the field, in terms of the angles θ and ϕ shown in the figure, is:

$$E = E_{max} \frac{\sin \{(\pi a/\lambda) \sin \theta\}}{(\pi a/\lambda) \sin \theta} \frac{\sin \{(\pi b/\lambda) \sin \phi\}}{(\pi b/\lambda) \sin \phi} \quad . \quad . \quad (13.15)$$

The gain relative to an isotropic radiator is therefore given through equation (9.5) by:

$$G_0 = \frac{4\pi {E_{max}}^2}{\int_{-\pi/2}^{\pi/2} \int_{-\pi/2}^{\pi/2} E^2 \cos \theta \, d\theta d\phi} \quad . \quad . \quad . \quad . \quad . \quad (13.16)$$

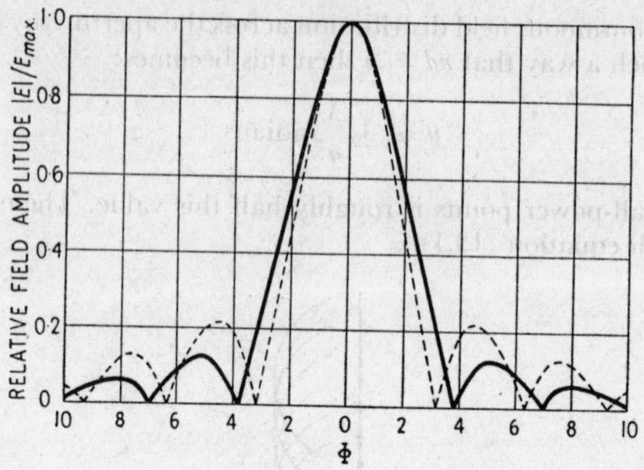

Fig. 13.36. Radiation patterns of uniformly illuminated apertures; full line: circular aperture of diameter D, given by $\dfrac{|E|}{E_{max}} = 2\left|\dfrac{J_1(\Phi)}{\Phi}\right|$, where $\Phi = \dfrac{\pi D}{\lambda}\sin\theta$. dashed line: rectangular aperture of side a, given by $\dfrac{|E|}{E_{max}} = \left|\dfrac{\sin\Phi}{\Phi}\right|$, where

$$\Phi = \frac{\pi a}{\lambda}\sin\theta.$$

where the integration is carried out over only the forward hemisphere, on the assumption that all the radiation supplied to the aperture is radiated in the forward direction, and none is lost in the backward direction. For large

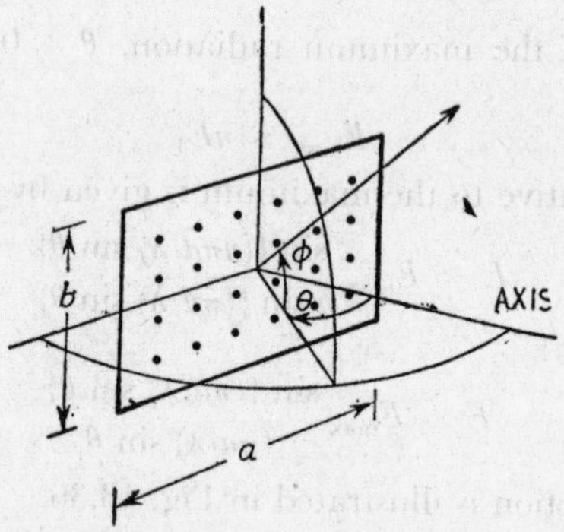

Fig. 13.37. Distribution of sources representing rectangular aperture.

apertures and relatively narrow beams $\sin\theta$ and $\sin\phi$ in the integral can be replaced by θ and ϕ respectively, and $\cos\theta$ by 1. The integral in the denominator then becomes:

$$E_{\max}{}^2 \int_{-\pi/2}^{\pi/2} \int_{-\pi/2}^{\pi/2} \frac{\sin^2(\pi a\theta/\lambda)}{(\pi a\theta/\lambda)^2} \frac{\sin^2(\pi b\phi/\lambda)}{(\pi b\phi/\lambda)^2} \, d\theta d\phi$$

Since only small values of θ and ϕ contribute significantly to the value of the integral it is permissible to replace the limits of integration by ∞ and − ∞, and we can then use the standard form:

$$\int_{-\infty}^{\infty} \frac{\sin^2 x}{x^2}\, dx = \pi$$

Thus the required integral is evaluated as $E_{max}{}^2\lambda^2/ab$, and the gain of a rectangular aperture relative to an isotropic radiator is therefore given by equation (13.16) as:

$$G_0 = \frac{4\pi ab}{\lambda^2} \quad . \quad . \quad . \quad . \quad . \quad . \quad . \quad (13.17)$$

Hence, by equation (9.12) the gain relative to a half-wave dipole is:

$$G = 7{\cdot}7\,\frac{ab}{\lambda^2} \quad . \quad . \quad . \quad . \quad . \quad . \quad . \quad (13.18)$$

The expression (13.17) does in fact hold more generally in the form:

$$G_0 = 4\pi\,\frac{\text{area of aperture}}{\lambda^2} \quad . \quad . \quad . \quad . \quad (13.19)$$

from which we can deduce the expression for the gain of a uniformly-illuminated circular aperture of diameter D:

$$G_0 = \left(\frac{\pi D}{\lambda}\right)^2 \quad . \quad . \quad . \quad . \quad . \quad . \quad . \quad (13.20)$$

Hence the gain relative to a half-wave dipole is:

$$G = 6\left(\frac{D}{\lambda}\right)^2 \quad . \quad . \quad . \quad . \quad . \quad . \quad . \quad (13.21)$$

Comparison of equations (13.19) and (9.22) shows that the effective aperture of the aerial is equal to its geometrical aperture.

The expression corresponding to equation (13.15) for a circular aperture can be shown to be:

$$E = 2E_{max}\frac{J_1\{(\pi D/\lambda)\sin\theta\}}{(\pi D/\lambda)\sin\theta} \quad . \quad . \quad . \quad . \quad (13.16)$$

where J_1 is the Bessel function of the first order, as used in Chapter 6. This expression is shown in graphical form in Fig. 13.36.

APPENDIX 13.2

Relationship between Aperture Distribution and Polar Diagram

In Appendix 13.1 the field produced by radiation from an aperture is treated as a limiting case of a finite array. We can start instead with an infinitesimal element of an array, as in Fig. 13.38. The field dE produced by the element is, by equation (9.31):

$$\mathrm{d}E = \frac{A'}{s}\varepsilon^{\mathrm{j}\omega(t-s/c)}\,\mathrm{d}z$$

where A' is an amplitude constant. Putting $s = r$ in the denominator and

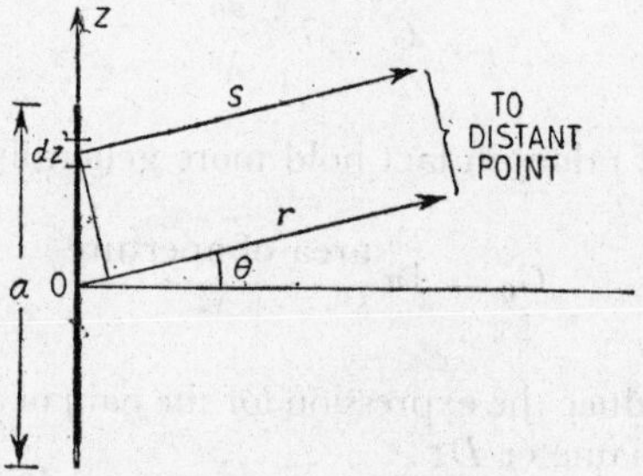

Fig. 13.38. Continuous linear array of elementary sources.

$s = r - z \sin\theta$ in the exponential (as was done in Appendix 9.3) the total field can be evaluated as:

$$\begin{aligned} E &= \int_{-a/2}^{a/2} \frac{A'}{r}\varepsilon^{\mathrm{j}\omega(t-r/c)}\varepsilon^{\mathrm{j}\omega z \sin\theta/c}\,\mathrm{d}z \\ &= \int_{-a/2}^{a/2} A\varepsilon^{\mathrm{j}\omega z \sin\theta/c}\,\mathrm{d}z \\ &= \int_{-a/2}^{a/2} A\varepsilon^{\mathrm{j}2\pi z \sin\theta/\lambda}\,\mathrm{d}z \end{aligned}$$

If the amplitude distribution is not constant over the aperture, A will be a function of z (if the phase varies also A will be complex). Then the expression becomes:

$$E = \int_{-a/2}^{a/2} A(z)\,\varepsilon^{\mathrm{j}2\pi z \sin\theta/\lambda}\,\mathrm{d}z \quad . \quad . \quad . \quad . \quad (13.17)$$

Thus E is determined in terms of A and we have the solution to the problem: *to calculate the polar diagram produced by a given aperture distribution.*

If equation (13.17) is written with infinite limits (which will not affect the value of the integral since $A(z)$ is zero for $|z| > a/2$) it has the form known in mathematics as the Fourier integral:

$$E(\sin\theta) = \int_{-\infty}^{\infty} A(z)\,\varepsilon^{\mathrm{j}2\pi z \sin\theta/\lambda}\,\mathrm{d}z \quad . \quad . \quad . \quad . \quad (13.18)$$

where $E(\sin\theta)$ is written in place of E to indicate that it is a function of $\sin\theta$

only. The important mathematical property of a Fourier integral is that it may be 'transformed', which in this case means that we can write:

$$A(z) = \frac{1}{\lambda}\int_{-\infty}^{\infty} E(\sin\theta)\,\varepsilon^{-j2\pi z\sin\theta/\lambda}\,d(\sin\theta) \quad . \quad . \quad . \quad (13.19)$$

This remarkable result gives the answer to the converse problem: *to calculate the aperture distribution required to give a specified polar diagram.* Equations (13.18) and (13.19) are known as the Fourier Transforms of each other.

In general the required aperture will extend from $-\infty$ to $+\infty$ but, if a finite aperture is chosen such that it includes most of the energy in the infinite aperture, it will give a good approximation to the specified polar diagram.

APPENDIX 13.3

Gain of Pyramidal Horns

The derivation of expressions for the gain of horns is beyond our scope, but values of the gain can be obtained from the curves of Figs. 13.39 and 13.40.

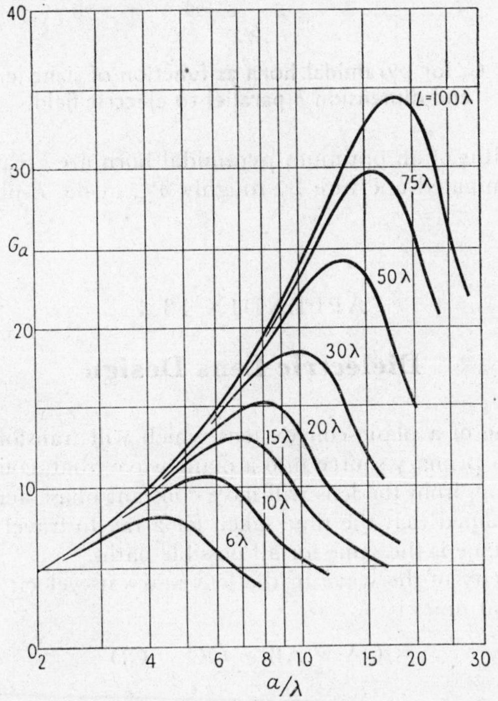

Fig. 13.39. Factor G_a for pyramidal horn as function of slant length from apex L and dimension *a* perpendicular to electric field.

In these are given values of two factors G_a and G_b which are dependent respectively on the dimensions *a* and *b* of the aperture, *a* being perpendicular to the electric field, b parallel to the electric field, and also on the slant length L of the horn measured from apex to aperture. The gain G of the pyramidal horn relative to a dipole is obtained as the product $G = G_a G_b$.

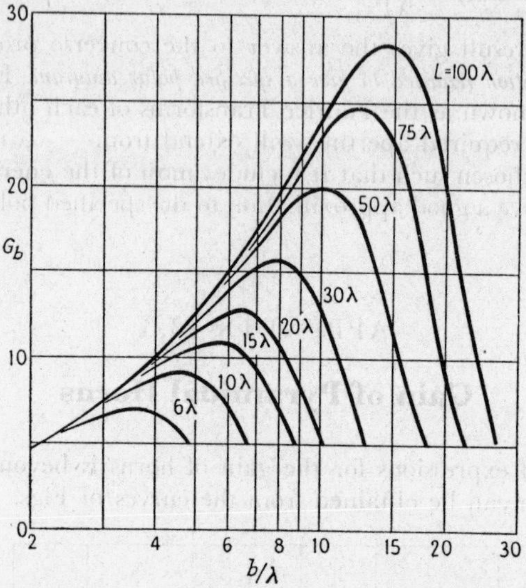

Fig. 13.40. Factor G_b for pyramidal horn as function of slant length from apex L and dimension b parallel to electric field.

The beam widths of an optimum pyramidal horn are greater than those of a uniformly illuminated aperture by roughly 5% in the E-plane and 50% in the H-plane.

APPENDIX 13.4

Dielectric Lens Design

To find the shape of a plano-convex lens which will transform the spherical wave front from a primary source into a plane wave front, consider Fig. 13.41. The wave emerging from the lens will have constant phase across the aperture if the lens is so shaped that the time taken for a ray to travel from the source to the aperture plane is the same for all possible paths.

If v is the velocity of the wave in the lens and c its velocity in air then the condition for equal times is:

$$\frac{\mathrm{OA}}{c} + \frac{\mathrm{AB}}{v} = \frac{\mathrm{OC}}{c} + \frac{\mathrm{CD}}{v}$$

that is,

$$\frac{r}{c} = \frac{l}{c} + \frac{x}{v} \qquad (13.20)$$

Equation (5.11) gives the expression for the wave velocity in a dielectric. If the relative dielectric constant of the lens material is κ (the relative permeability being taken as unity) then the ratio n of the velocities in air and in the dielectric is:

$$n = \frac{c}{v} = \kappa_r^{1/2}$$

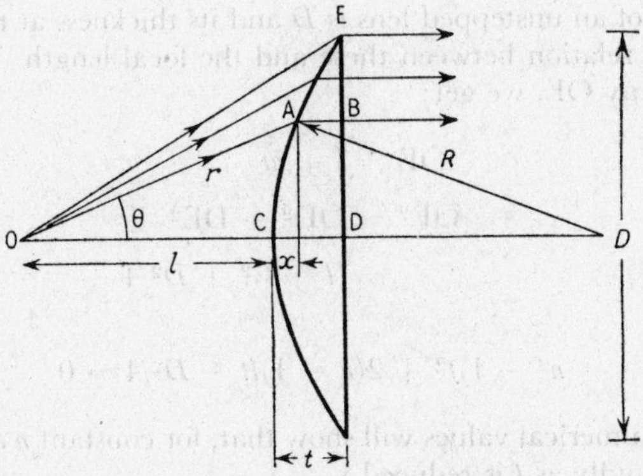

Fig. 13.41. Ray paths in plano-convex dielectric lens.

The constant n is called the *index of refraction* of the dielectric, as in optics. Hence equation (13.20) can be written:

$$r = l + nx \quad . \quad . \quad . \quad . \quad . \quad . \quad . \quad . \quad . \quad . \quad (13.21)$$

$$= l + n(r \cos \theta - l)$$

This simplifies to:

$$r = \frac{(n-1)l}{n \cos \theta - 1} \quad . \quad . \quad . \quad . \quad . \quad . \quad . \quad (13.22)$$

which represents the required contour of the lens in polar co-ordinates. For a dielectric lens n always exceeds unity, and in this case equation (13.22) is the polar form of the equation of the curve known as the hyperbola. The distance l is the focal length of the lens.

It can be shown that, if θ is small, the radius of curvature R of this hyperbola is approximately:

$$R = (n - 1)l \quad . \quad . \quad . \quad . \quad . \quad . \quad . \quad (13.23)$$

This means that so long as θ is small the hyperbolic lens could be replaced by a plano-convex spherical lens of radius equal to $(n - 1)l$. This is the normal optical formula.

It may be noted that in the derivation of equation (13.22) the law of refraction is not used, but it is easy to show that the law is satisfied at the boundary of a lens of this form.

APPENDIX 13.5

Stepped Dielectric Lens

If the diameter of an unstepped lens is D and its thickness at the centre is t it is easy to find the relation between these and the focal length. Writing equation (13.21) for the ray OE, we get:

$$\mathrm{OE} = l + nt$$

and

$$\mathrm{OE}^2 = \mathrm{OD}^2 + \mathrm{DE}^2$$
$$= (l + t)^2 + D^2/4$$

Hence

$$(n^2 - 1)t^2 + 2(n - 1)lt - D^2/4 = 0 \quad . \quad . \quad . \quad (13.24)$$

Substitution of numerical values will show that, for constant n and D, the thickness increases rapidly as l is reduced.

When the thickness of the lens of Fig. 13.25 (a) is to be reduced in steps of width w such that the electrical length of the path at the step is reduced by one wavelength, we have:

$$\frac{w}{v} - \frac{w}{c} = \text{time of one oscillation}$$

$$= \frac{1}{f} = \frac{\lambda}{c}$$

λ being the free-space wavelength. Hence:

$$w = \frac{\lambda}{n - 1} \quad . \quad . \quad . \quad . \quad . \quad . \quad . \quad . \quad (13.25)$$

Since no part of the lens needs to correct the phase by more than one wavelength it follows that the maximum thickness of the lens is of the order of $\lambda/(n - 1)$.

For the lens of Fig. 13.25 (b) stepped on its convex face, each zone will be hyperbolic but its focal length must be greater than the previous one by the amount $\lambda/(n - 1)$ of equation (13.25). Thus if the zone on the lens axis is called the first, then the equation of the pth zone (corresponding to equation (13.22) for the unstepped lens) is given by:

$$r_p = \frac{(n - 1)l_p}{n \cos \theta - 1} \quad . \quad . \quad . \quad . \quad . \quad (13.26)$$

where

$$l_p = l_1 + \frac{(p - 1)\lambda}{n - 1} \quad . \quad . \quad . \quad . \quad . \quad . \quad (13.27)$$

APPENDIX 13.6

E-Plane Metal-Plate Lens

The metal-plate lens of Fig. 13.42 can be dealt with in the same way as the dielectric lens in Appendix 13.4, and the same expression is found for the contour of the lens, viz.:

$$r = \frac{(1 - n)l}{1 - n \cos \theta} \quad . \quad . \quad . \quad . \quad . \quad . \quad (13.28)$$

In this case however, with $n < 1$, the curve represents the polar form of an ellipse.

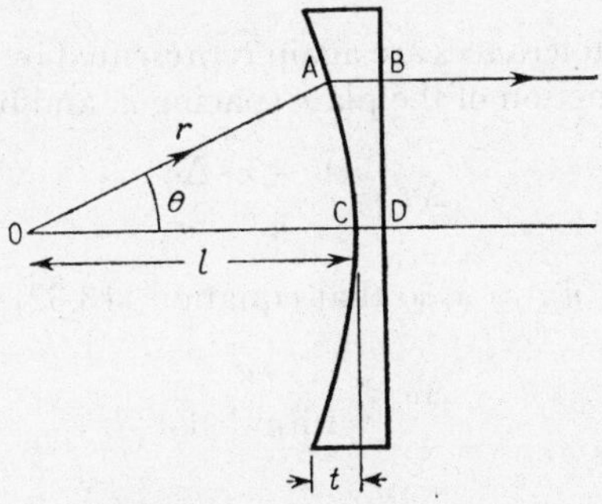

Fig. 13.42. Ray paths in plano-concave metal-plate lens.

Step calculations for the plate lens are the same as for the dielectric lens carried out in Appendix 13.5, so that, for the lens of Fig. 13.31, the equation of the pth zone of the surface is:

$$r_p = \frac{(1 - n)l_p}{1 - n \cos \theta} \quad . \quad . \quad . \quad . \quad . \quad . \quad (13.29)$$

where

$$l_p = l_1 + \frac{(p - 1)\lambda}{1 - n} \quad . \quad . \quad . \quad . \quad . \quad . \quad (13.30)$$

APPENDIX 13.7

Tolerances in Lenses

In a dielectric lens there may be errors in both n and the thickness t. Let the maximum acceptable path error be $\lambda/8$, and assume that errors due to variations of n and t each contribute a maximum of $\lambda/16$.

A small change of thickness Δt in the lens of Fig. 13.41 will vary the path OCD by $(n - 1)\,\Delta t$, and if this is not to exceed $\lambda/16$, then

$$\Delta t \leqslant \frac{\lambda}{16(n - 1)} \quad . \quad . \quad . \quad . \quad . \quad . \quad (13.31)$$

A change of Δn in refractive index will vary the path OCD by $t\Delta n$, and therefore:

$$\Delta n \leqslant \frac{\lambda}{16t} \quad . \quad . \quad . \quad . \quad . \quad . \quad . \quad (13.32)$$

These expressions hold also for a stepped dielectric lens, but in this case $(n-1)t$ is approximately one wavelength (see Appendix 13.5) and equations (13.31) and (13.32) reduce to:

$$\Delta t \leqslant \frac{t}{16} \quad . \quad . \quad . \quad . \quad . \quad . \quad . \quad . \quad . \quad (13.33)$$

and

$$\Delta n \leqslant \frac{n-1}{16} \quad . \quad . \quad . \quad . \quad . \quad . \quad . \quad (13.34)$$

For a metal-plate lens tolerances are again represented by equations (13.31) and (13.32). But Δn is a function of the plate spacing a, and from equation (13.9):

$$\Delta n = \frac{1-n^2}{n}\frac{\Delta a}{a}$$

In a stepped lens $(1-n)t \approx \lambda$, so that equation (13.32) becomes:

$$\Delta a \leqslant \frac{na}{16(n+1)} \quad . \quad . \quad . \quad . \quad . \quad . \quad . \quad (13.35)$$

APPENDIX 13.8

Bandwidth of Lenses

The dielectric constant of the solid dielectrics used in lenses is substantially independent of frequency, and the bandwidth of an unstepped dielectric lens is therefore very large.

For a stepped dielectric lens with p steps the path length L_p through the final zone is related to the path length L_1 through the first zone by:

$$L_p = L_1 + (p-1)\lambda$$

where λ is the design wavelength. When the lens is used at a wavelength $\lambda + \Delta\lambda$ close to the design wavelength, L_p will increase relative to L_1 by an amount $(p-1)\Delta\lambda$. If this difference is limited as before to $\lambda/8$, then we have:

$$\Delta\lambda \leqslant \frac{\lambda}{8(p-1)}$$

and thus the percentage bandwidth B of the stepped dielectric lens is:

$$B = \frac{2\Delta\lambda}{\lambda} \times 100 = \frac{25}{p-1} \text{ per cent} \quad . \quad . \quad . \quad (13.36)$$

In an unstepped metal-plate lens the effective dielectric constant is a function of frequency, and the lens will therefore have a relatively narrow bandwidth.

A departure of $\Delta\lambda$ from the design wavelength causes a change Δn in the refractive index, where, by equation (13.9):

$$\Delta n = \frac{\partial n}{\partial \lambda} \Delta\lambda$$

$$= -\frac{1 - n^2}{n} \frac{\Delta\lambda}{\lambda}$$

If t (Fig. 13.42) is the difference between the maximum and minimum thickness of the lens, then the path difference between the central and the outside rays caused by the change $\Delta\lambda$ is $t\,\Delta n$. If this is limited to $\lambda/8$ then we have:

$$t \frac{1 - n^2}{n} \frac{\Delta\lambda}{\lambda} \leqslant \frac{\lambda}{8}$$

Hence $$\Delta\lambda \leqslant \frac{\lambda^2}{8t} \frac{n}{1 - n^2}$$

and the percentage bandwidth is:

$$B = \frac{2\Delta\lambda}{\lambda} \times 100$$

$$= \frac{25n}{1 - n^2} \frac{\lambda}{t} \text{ per cent} \quad . \quad . \quad . \quad . \quad . \quad (13.37)$$

For a stepped metal-plate lens with p steps it can be shown that the bandwidth is given by:

$$B = \frac{25n}{1 + pn} \text{ per cent} \quad . \quad . \quad . \quad . \quad . \quad (13.38)$$

APPENDIX 13.9

Path-Length Lens

The shape of a path-length lens made of tilted plates as in Fig. 13.43 can be calculated in the same way as for the dielectric lens in Appendix 13.4. For

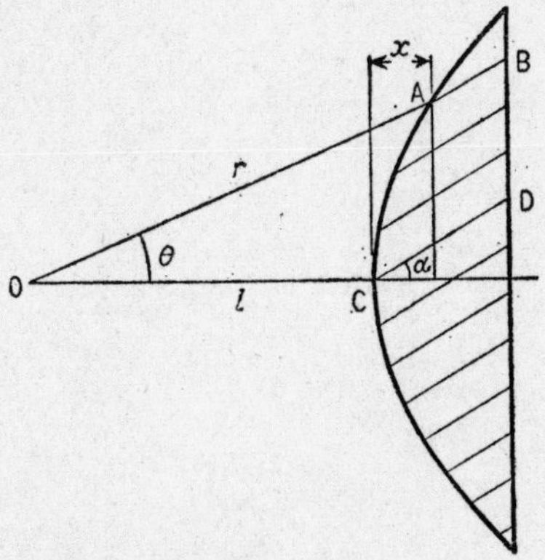

Fig. 13.43. Slanted plate path-length lens.

equality of the paths OAB and OCD we have:

$$r = l + x \sec \alpha$$

$$= l + (r \cos \theta - l) \sec \alpha$$

Hence

$$r = \frac{(\sec \alpha - 1)l}{\sec \alpha \cos \theta - 1} \quad . \quad . \quad . \quad . \quad . \quad . \quad . \quad (13.39)$$

By equation (13.10) the equivalent refractive index n of the stack is equal to $\sec \alpha$, and therefore equation (13.39) has the same form as equation (13.22)—a hyperbolic shape as for the dielectric lens.

CHAPTER 14

Wave Propagation

IN THIS CHAPTER we deal with the effect of the earth and its surrounding atmosphere on the propagation of electromagnetic waves.

The factors affecting propagation are so multifarious and depend so much on meteorological and extra-terrestrial phenomena of which we cannot have complete knowledge that no theories can give a precise answer to the problem of calculating the distribution of radiated field from a given transmitter. Here, much more than in any other branch of radio, we have to supplement theory with observations, observations which are being recorded daily at stations throughout the world. Although the effects are complicated a good approximation to the radiated field can usually be found by the application of theories appropriate to the conditions of a particular problem, or by the use of charts and routine procedures based on accumulated practical experience.

Propagation in Free Space

The simplest case of wave propagation is that of propagation from a transmitter into an infinite surrounding free space. Of course these conditions are not met with in practice since the transmitter can never be very far from the earth's surface, and the space surrounding it is never exactly free space. The free-space field calculated under these conditions is, however, a useful reference with which actual fields can be compared, and in most cases gives an upper limit which will not be greatly exceeded.

Consider a transmitter in free space radiating a mean power P watts, and let the power be radiated uniformly in all directions. Such an omnidirectional radiator may be used as the standard, results obtained being readily transformable to any other radiating system. At a distance d sufficiently far from the source for the radiated field to be considered as plane the electric field strength E has been shown in equation (9.3) to be given by the relation:

$$E = \frac{(30P)^{1/2}}{d} \text{ volts per metre} \quad . \quad . \quad . \quad . \quad (14.1)$$

It is convenient in plotting field strengths to choose a definite value of P so that equation (14.1) becomes a function of the single variable d. The value of P normally used is 1 kW, and equation (14.1) then becomes:

$$E = \frac{173}{d} \text{ volts per metre} \quad . \quad . \quad . \quad . \quad . \quad (14.2)$$

Electric field being thus inversely proportional to distance, equations (14.1) and (14.2) represent what is known as the Inverse Distance Law. The variation with distance of the standard field given by equation (14.2) is shown in Fig. 14.1.

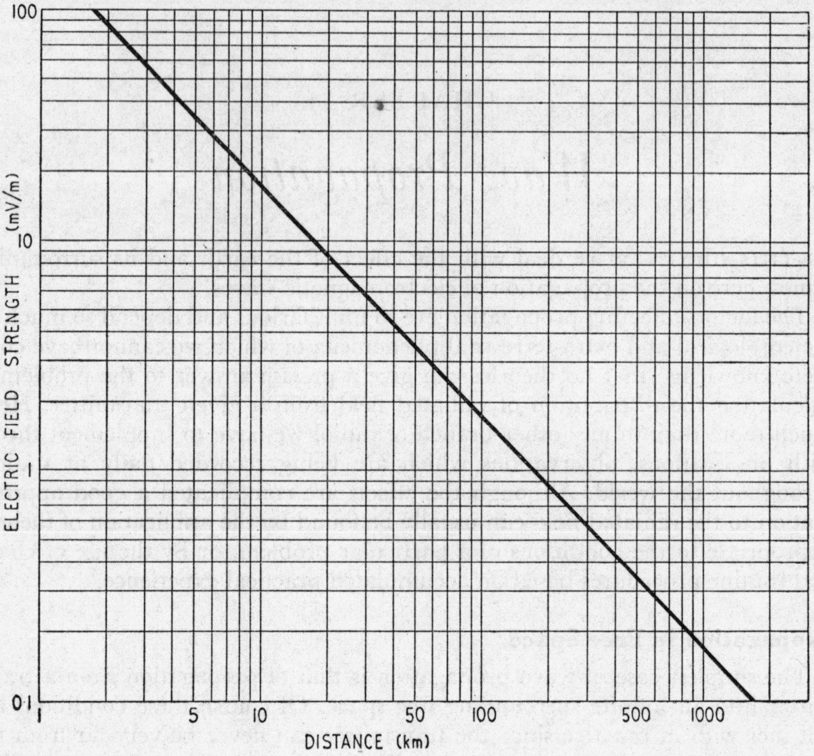

Fig. 14.1. Field strength from an omnidirectional aerial radiating 1 kW into free space.

Propagation around the Earth

Since the waves emitted from a transmitter travel outwards in space so that the wave front at any point forms part of the surface of a continually expanding sphere, the wave at that point can be regarded as having travelled in a straight line from the centre of the sphere, and hence the complete wave radiated can be regarded as made up of an infinite number of rays all diverging in straight lines from the centre.

It is then evident that when a transmitter and a receiver are situated at a distance above the earth's surface a signal will be received at the transmitter if a straight line can be drawn joining the two, as in Fig. 14.2 (a). In addition to this direct wave the figure illustrates that there can be a reflected wave arriving at the receiver after reflection at the earth's surface. These two make up the space wave. If, however, the separation is such that the curvature of the earth hides the transmitting and receiving aerials from each other, as in Fig. 14.2 (b), there will be no direct or reflected wave reaching the receiver from the transmitter.

If the paths of the direct and reflected waves were the only paths it would be impossible to receive signals from a transmitter situated beyond the horizon.

In fact there are two other important means by which signals may be received beyond the horizon; these are respectively by surface wave and by ionospheric wave (or sky wave), and are illustrated in Fig. 14.3.

The surface wave is produced by energy travelling close to the ground and

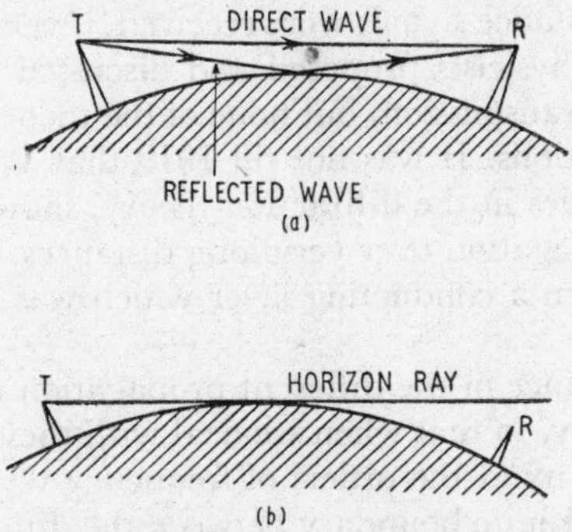

Fig. 14.2. Ray paths over a curved earth.

guided by it to follow the curvature of the earth. This is the phenomenon of diffraction, the same phenomenon as that which enables sound waves to bend round a corner. The direct wave, the reflected wave, and the surface wave may be present together, and it is not always necessary to separate them. The combination is normally referred to as the ground wave.

The relations between the various wave paths may be summarized as follows:

Space wave = direct wave + ground reflected wave

Ground wave = diffracted surface wave + direct wave + ground reflected wave.

The ionospheric wave, on the other hand, is dependent on waves leaving the transmitting aerial in an upward direction. These pass to the upper atmosphere

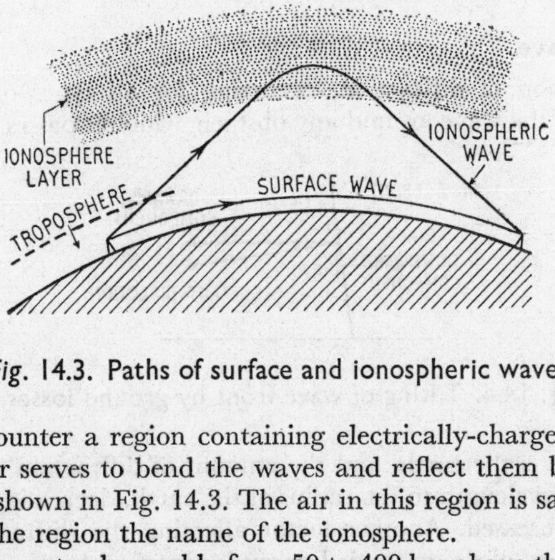

Fig. 14.3. Paths of surface and ionospheric waves.

where they encounter a region containing electrically-charged particles. This conducting layer serves to bend the waves and reflect them back towards the earth again, as shown in Fig. 14.3. The air in this region is said to be ionized, which gives to the region the name of the ionosphere.

The ionosphere extends roughly from 50 to 400 km above the earth's surface.

Waves confined to lower reaches of the atmosphere travel in the troposphere, which occupies the first 10 km above the earth's surface.

These phenomena were not understood in the early days of radio, and the historical development shows the theoretical difficulties involved. In 1901 Marconi demonstrated that signals could be transmitted across the Atlantic, and soon other long-distance signals were received. Over the next eighteen years mathematicians and physicists proposed and discussed several mechanisms to explain long-distance transmission, but none of the theories agreed satisfactorily with practical observations. It was not till 1919 that Watson in Great Britain cleared up the difficulties in the diffraction theory, showing that it failed completely to explain propagation over very long distances, and derived a formula based on reflection from a conducting layer which was in full agreement with the facts.

The relative importance of the different propagation mechanisms is strongly dependent on frequency, so that when we deal with these different mechanisms it is helpful to bear in mind the orders of frequency which they chiefly affect. Of course there is no definite boundary between the different frequency ranges, but for the moment Table 14.1 will illustrate very roughly the important changes with frequency.

TABLE 14.1

Frequency	Main mechanism of propagation
< 500 kc/s	Surface wave
500 kc/s–1·5 Mc/s	Surface wave for short distance Ionospheric wave for longer distances
1·5 Mc/s–30 Mc/s	Ionospheric wave
> 30 Mc/s	Space wave within line of sight

In our subsequent discussion it will be convenient to discuss the various propagation mechanisms as they affect frequencies in ascending order; the first to be treated is the surface-wave component of the ground wave.

The Surface Wave

The phenomenon of diffraction, occurring for all types of wave motion, causes bending of the wave around any obstacle which it passes. For the surface

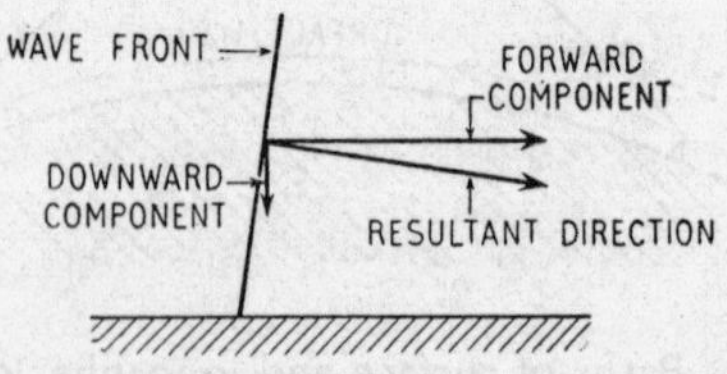

Fig. 14.4. Tilting of wave front by ground losses.

wave the obstacle is the earth, and the amount of diffraction is dependent on the ratio of the wavelength to the radius of the earth, decreasing steadily as the wavelength is decreased. Another factor affecting the diffraction is the imperfect conductivity of the ground. Energy is absorbed by currents induced in the earth, to supply which a continuous flow of energy takes place from the wave downwards into the earth. Thus the wave front is tilted slightly forward, as shown in Fig. 14.4, and hence the bending of the wave is assisted.

Because of the energy dissipated in the earth the wave suffers attenuation as it proceeds, and this attenuation is dependent on the conductivity and permittivity of the ground. The ground constants have values which differ considerably for different types of ground; typical values are given in Table 14.2.

TABLE 14.2

Ground Constants

Type of ground	Relative permittivity	Conductivity (mho/m)
Sea water	80	5
Fresh water	80	0·005
Moist soil	15–30	0·005–0·01
Rocky ground	7	0·001
Dry soil	4	0·001–0·01

The depth of penetration of the current into the ground is a function of the ground constants and of the frequency. Penetrations of the order of 15 m occur at broadcast frequencies, decreasing to one or two metres at the frequencies of short-wave communication. A theoretical treatment shows that at low frequencies the surface wave is dependent mainly on the conductivity and is strongest for high conductivity. At the higher frequencies a high permittivity is the important factor in giving a strong surface wave. Thus for all frequencies surface-wave propagation is best over sea, worst over dry ground.

Where the frequency is so low (and hence the wavelength so long) that the height of a normal ground-based aerial in terms of wavelength is small the surface wave is the important factor in the ground wave. Under these conditions the two components of the space wave have equal magnitude and opposite phase and so give zero resultant. There is no simple relationship for the variation of field strength with distance in this case, but the curves of Figs. 14.5 and 14.6 illustrate the way in which the field varies for different frequencies. They are calculated for a short vertical dipole aerial radiating a power of 1 kW, and show propagation over average soil and sea water respectively. A general deduction from these curves is that the difference between propagation over land and over sea is negligible for very low frequencies, but increases rapidly as the frequency is increased. It is also clear that for a given power the range obtainable decreases as the frequency is increased.

That the attenuation is dependent much more on ground constants than on the earth's curvature is illustrated in Fig. 14.7, where for a given frequency actual propagation is compared with propagation over a flat earth for typical values of permittivity and conductivity.

▶ For surface-wave propagation it is usual to take as a reference level not the free-space field [equation (14.1)] of an omnidirectional aerial, but the field which would exist for a short vertical unipole aerial placed on a hypothetical flat perfectly-conducting earth. Using equation (9.3) for the field strength of an isotropic radiator and the value of 3 deduced in Chapter 9, p. 263, for the power gain of a short unipole, we can deduce that the r.m.s. field in the ground plane at a distance d is given by:

$$E = \frac{(90P)^{1/2}}{d} \text{ volts per metre} \quad . \quad . \quad . \quad . \quad (14.3)$$

If the standard value of 1 kW is taken for P as before, then equation (14.3) becomes:

$$E = \frac{300}{d} \text{ volts per metre} \quad . \quad . \quad . \quad . \quad . \quad . \quad (14.4)$$

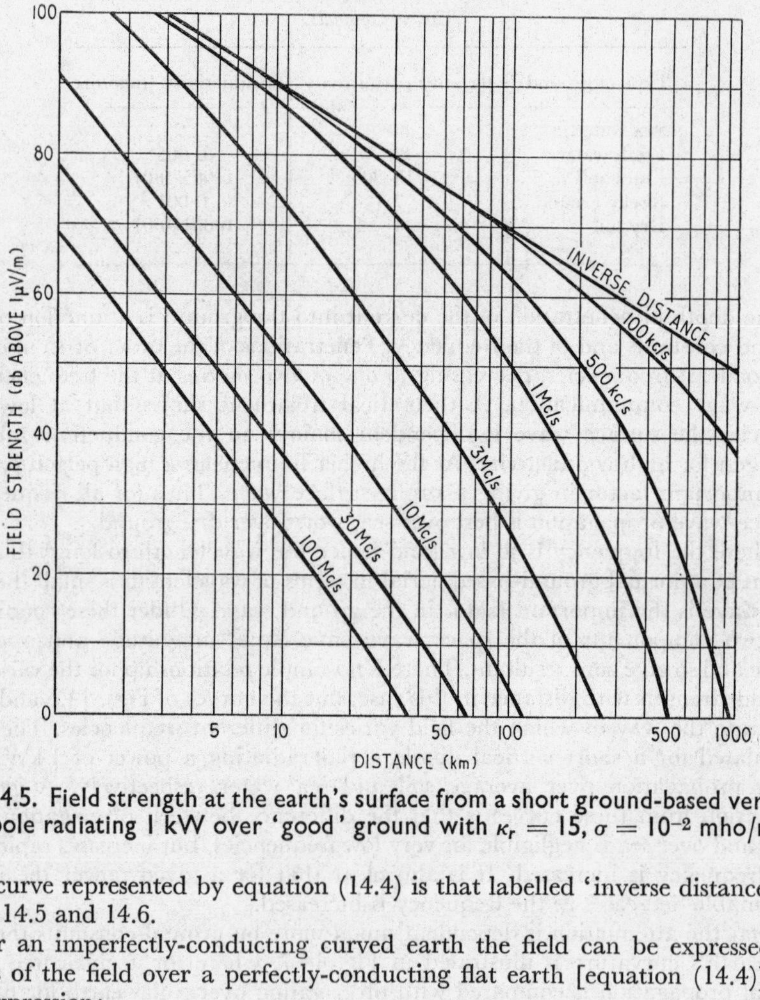

Fig. **14.5. Field strength at the earth's surface from a short ground-based vertical dipole radiating 1 kW over 'good' ground with $\kappa_r = 15$, $\sigma = 10^{-2}$ mho/m.**

The curve represented by equation (14.4) is that labelled 'inverse distance' in Figs. 14.5 and 14.6.

For an imperfectly-conducting curved earth the field can be expressed in terms of the field over a perfectly-conducting flat earth [equation (14.4)] by the expression:

$$E = \frac{300}{d} A \text{ volts per metre} \quad . \quad . \quad . \quad . \quad (14.5)$$

where A is an attenuation factor expressing the effect of the curvature and the earth constants. The formulae by which A is determined are complicated, but an outline of the treatment is given in Appendix 14.1.

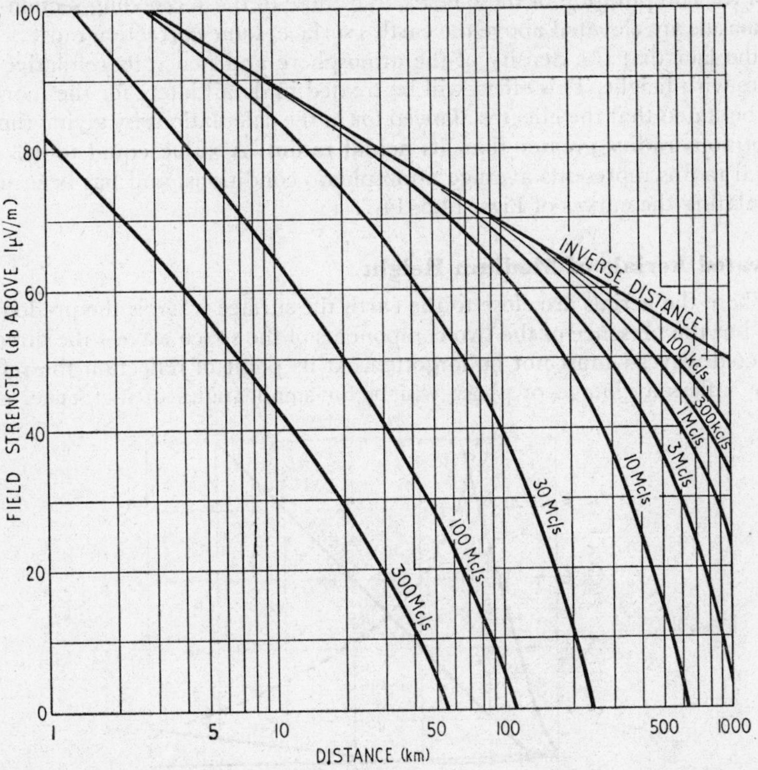

Fig. 14.6. Field strength at the earth's surface from a short ground-based vertical dipole radiating 1 kW over sea water with $\kappa_r = 80$, $\sigma = 5$ mho/m.

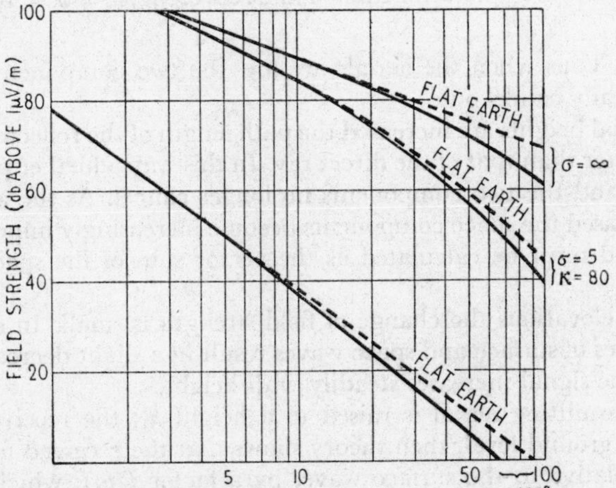

Fig. 14.7. Comparison of the influence of ground constants and earth's curvature on field strength (1 kW at 30 Mc/s).

In the computation of these fields, and those of the succeeding section where the aerials are elevated above the earth's surface, some correction must be made for the fact that the density of the atmosphere and hence its refractive index varies with height. This effect will be treated in detail later; for the moment it can be stated that the effect is allowed for in the calculations by giving the earth a fictitious radius greater than its actual radius. A value equal to 4/3 of the actual radius represents average atmospheric conditions, and has been used in calculating the curves of Figs. 14.5–14.7. ◀

Elevated Aerials of Medium Height

Where the aerials are close to the earth the surface wave is the predominant one, but the presence of the two components of the space wave—the direct and reflected waves—must not be forgotten. At its point of reflection the reflected wave suffers a change of phase which, for small angles of incidence, is very

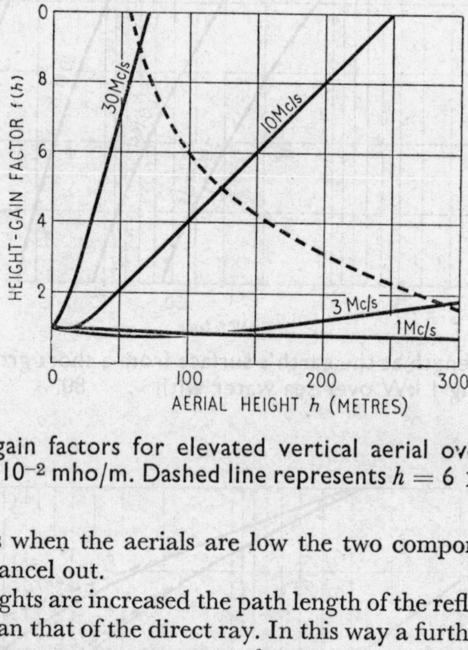

Fig. 14.8. Height-gain factors for elevated vertical aerial over 'good' ground with $\kappa_r = 15$, $\sigma = 10^{-2}$ mho/m. Dashed line represents $h = 6 \times 10^6 f^{-2/3}$ metres.

nearly 180°. Thus when the aerials are low the two components of the space wave practically cancel out.

As the aerial heights are increased the path length of the reflected ray becomes sensibly greater than that of the direct ray. In this way a further phase change is introduced, and the two components no longer cancel. As the aerial height is further increased the space components become increasingly important, and the resultant field must be calculated as the vector sum of the space and surface waves.

For small elevations the change of field strength is small. In some cases the relative phases of surface and space waves result in a slight decrease at first, but eventually the signal increases steadily with height.

If the transmitting aerial is raised to a height h_1, the received field being measured at ground level, then theory shows that the received field strength is increased, relative to the surface wave, by a factor $f(h_1)$, which is called the Height-Gain Factor. It is a function of frequency and of the earth constants.

The form of variation of $f(h)$ is shown in Figs. 14.8 and 14.9 for a number of different frequencies. The advantage to be gained by raising the aerial is seen to be much greater over land than over sea, much greater for high frequencies than for low frequencies.

If now the receiving aerial is set at a height h_2 the signal strength is further increased by the multiplying factor $f(h_2)$, whose value is again obtained from Fig. 14.8 or Fig. 14.9.

These curves are subject to a number of limitations, the principal one being that for a given frequency neither aerial should exceed the height given by the dashed line in Figs. 14.8 and 14.9. The calculation of height-gain factors is dealt with in Appendix 14.2.

All the curves given above are for vertical polarization. For horizontally-polarized waves the ground losses are much greater, and so for low aerials the signal strength decreases with distance much more rapidly than with vertical polarization. Increase of the height of the aerials reduces the ground losses, and

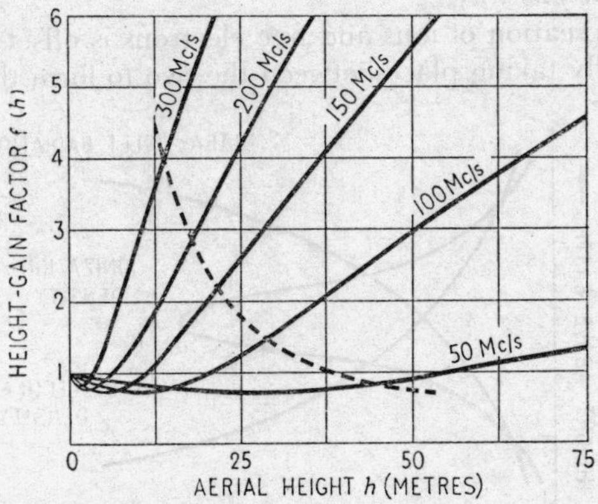

Fig. 14.9. Height-gain factors for elevated vertical aerial over sea water with $\kappa_r = 80$, $\sigma = 5$ mho/m. Dashed line represents $h = 6 \times 10^6 f^{-2/3}$ metres.

hence the difference between the two polarizations is steadily reduced as the aerial height is increased.

The propagation curves given here assume a smooth earth, and take no account of local variations such as hills and buildings. Such obstructions will be considered later in some detail, but here it may be said that they produce shadow effects resulting in a decreased signal strength behind the obstruction. The effect is small if the dimensions of the obstacle are small in comparison with the wavelength. Thus a small hill will have a negligible effect on the ground wave at 1,000 m wavelength but a large effect at 10 m wavelength.

When the frequency is so high that aerials can conveniently be elevated to heights of the order of one wavelength or more then the surface wave becomes of small importance compared with the space wave, and can be neglected. This is the case for the v.h.f. region and beyond. We shall return to this important case, but turn now to a consideration of the ionospheric wave, which, as will be seen from Table 14.1, assumes importance when the frequency exceeds about 500 kc/s. Between this frequency and about 30 Mc/s the ionospheric wave plays a major part in providing long-distance communication. Before considering this wave in detail we must examine the nature of the ionosphere in which reflection of the wave occurs.

The Ionosphere

Of the energy which reaches this planet from the sun only a small part is detected by our senses in the form of light and heat. A large part is in the form of ultra-violet light—electromagnetic waves of wavelengths shorter than those of visible light. At these wavelengths interaction can take place between the wave and molecules of the gases of the earth's atmosphere, which can result in electrons being separated from their parent molecules and becoming 'free' electrons, existing as separate negatively-charged particles. The molecule losing the electron, left with a resultant positive charge, is known as an ion. The amount of such ionization produced is dependent on the strength of the ultra-violet radiation and on its wavelength—different wavelengths being necessary to ionize the different gases. Energy is absorbed from the ultra-violet wave in producing ionization, and as the wave proceeds its energy is eventually completely absorbed in this way.

The process of creation of ions and free electrons is offset by recombination which is continually taking place between the two to form the original neutral

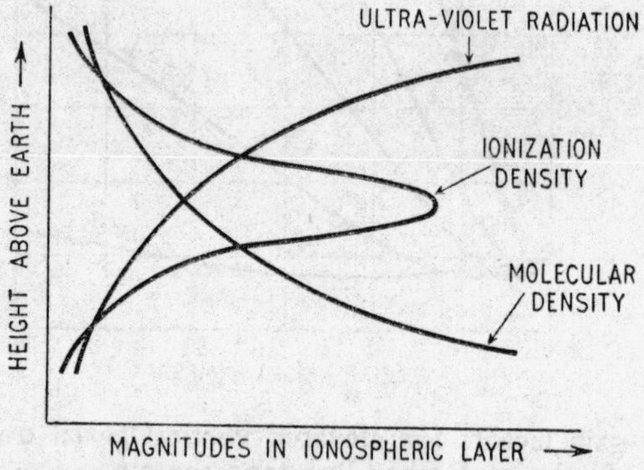

Fig. 14.10. Formation of a single ionized layer.

atom. In the lower atmosphere the number of molecules is so great that recombination takes place almost immediately after ionization, but in the upper atmosphere where the number of molecules is very much smaller the chance of a meeting between ion and electron is very much less, and hence recombination takes place at a much slower rate.

As a result of these two opposing mechanisms there exist regions in the upper atmosphere where a large amount of ionization is present, the amount being determined by an equilibrium between the rate at which ions are produced and the rate at which recombination takes place. If we consider ultra-violet radiation from the sun entering the earth's atmosphere the gases it meets first of all are very rarefied and hence little ionization can be set up. As the radiation penetrates further the number of molecules increases and hence the ionization increases. But more and more energy is now being used up and soon the amount of ionization which the radiation can produce begins to decrease. There is thus a certain height at which ionization is a maximum, and the region around this height is known as an ionization layer. The distribution of the several factors is shown in Fig. 14.10.

The part of the atmosphere in which ionization can take place in appreciable quantity is called the ionosphere. Its lower limit is about 50 km above the earth's surface and it extends upwards to at least 400 km. It is well established that in this region several different ionization layers occur. The mechanism of their formation is explained above although, in the absence of precise information regarding the temperature and composition of the ionosphere, any particular theoretical treatment is largely conjectural and would be inappropriate here. Meteors and cosmic radiation are other possible agencies in the production of ionization.

Below the ionosphere lie two other regions—the troposphere which extends from the earth's surface up to a height of about 10 km, and the stratosphere which lies between the troposphere and the ionosphere. In the troposphere the temperature varies appreciably with altitude; in the stratosphere it is almost constant. The space and surface waves travel in the troposphere.

For a preliminary understanding of the importance of the regions of ionization

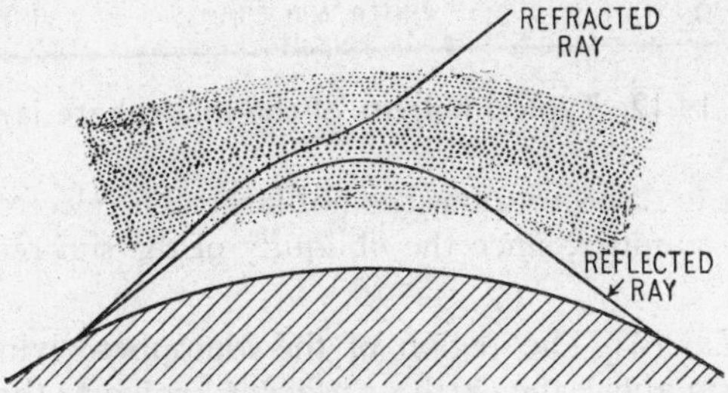

Fig. 14.11. Typical ray paths in ionosphere.

it is sufficient to state that the index of refraction depends on the degree of ionization and hence any wave travelling through the region will be bent from its straight path. At frequencies below a certain critical value it may be bent so much as to be returned back to the earth. The two possibilities are depicted in Fig. 14.11.

The Structure of the Ionosphere

Experimental measurements have shown that there are three main ionization layers, which are designated by the symbols D, E and F, in order of height. At times the F layer splits into two separate layers called F_1 and F_2. They vary in intensity and in height with diurnal and seasonal variations in the ionosphere. It might be thought that layers would cease to exist during the night when radiation from the sun is absent, but because of the limited rate of recombination, particularly in the higher regions, a certain amount of ionization does persist throughout the night.

The ionospheric structure also varies widely over the earth's surface, for the strength of the sun's radiation will obviously vary with geographical latitude. An illustration of the variations in height over Britain is given in Fig. 14.12.

The layers will now be considered separately.

D *Layer*. This is a region of low ionization density which does not have the well-defined maximum associated with other layers. It occurs only during daylight hours and extends rather diffusely from about 50 km to about 100 km above the earth's surface.

In this region the density of electrons is not sufficient to cause appreciable bending, but radio waves may suffer considerable attenuation in passing through it.

E *Layer.* This layer occurs during daylight hours and has its maximum density at heights between 100 and 150 km. It remains very weakly ionized throughout the night. During daylight hours its height remains practically

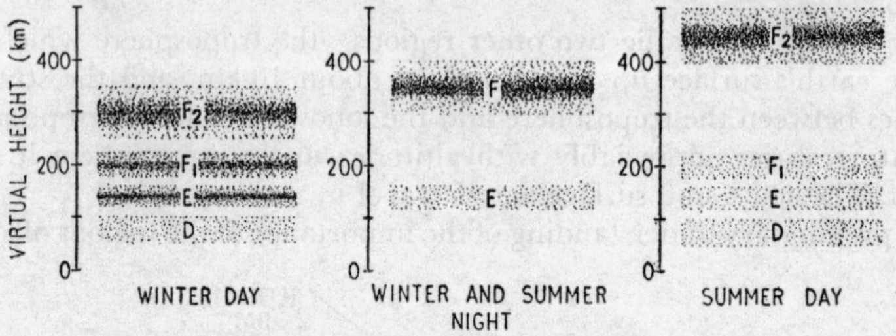

Fig. 14.12. Typical heights of the ionosphere layers.

constant, and day to day variations are not large. The electron density is lower in winter than in summer, since the obliquity of the sun reduces the ionizing effect.

F, F_1 *and* F_2 *Layers.* The region of the ionosphere lying between about 150 km and 500 km above the earth's surface is known as the F region.

A single F layer occupies this region during the night, but in the daytime it divides into two layers, the lower known as F_1 and the upper as F_2.

The F_1 layer at around 200 km shows no great variations in height, and again

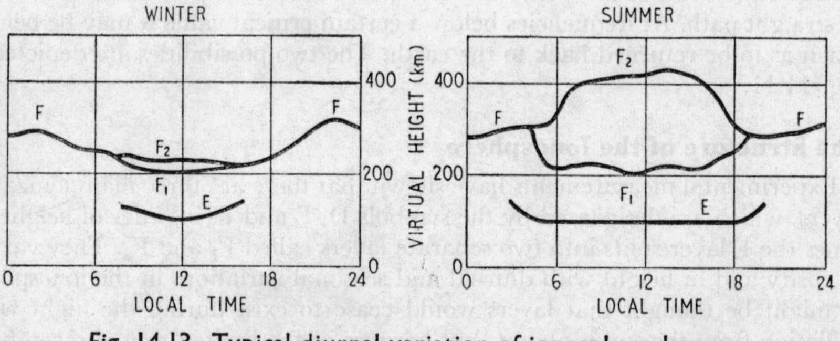

Fig. 14.13. Typical diurnal variation of ionosphere layers.

its density is lower in winter than in summer. As would be expected, the F_2 layer, the uppermost and most highly ionized of all the layers, shows considerably greater variations than the others. Its daytime height is very dependent on solar heating of the upper atmosphere, and varies between about 150 and 300 km during the winter, and between 300 and 500 km during the summer. The night-time layer is likewise dependent on atmospheric temperature, and very variable in height and density.

Fig. 14.13 gives an average picture of the variation in height of the layers. The foregoing description can be summarized by noting that the daytime ionosphere consists of one absorbing region (the D), followed in ascending order by the E, F_1 and F_2 layers. The night-time ionosphere consists almost solely of the F layer.

The allocation of letters to these layers was made by Sir Edward Appleton, who did much of the early investigation work. The F layer, discovered by him, is also known as the 'Appleton Layer'. The E layer was originally known as the 'Kennelly-Heaviside Layer'.

Wave Propagation in the Ionosphere

The effect of the ionosphere on wave propagation is very dependent on frequency. At low frequencies, up to about 100 kc/s, the change in electron density from zero to maximum occurs within a distance small compared with the wavelength. In these circumstances the layer may be considered as an abrupt discontinuity acting as an almost perfect reflecting surface. At great distances the wave propagates as though it travelled between two concentric conducting spheres, one being the earth and the other the lower edge of the ionosphere. The wave is attenuated by loss of energy due to imperfect conductivity at these two surfaces. It is this mechanism which accounts for very long distance propagation at low frequencies.

At much higher frequencies, where the wavelength is sufficiently short that in the distance of a wavelength the ionization density changes only slightly, the

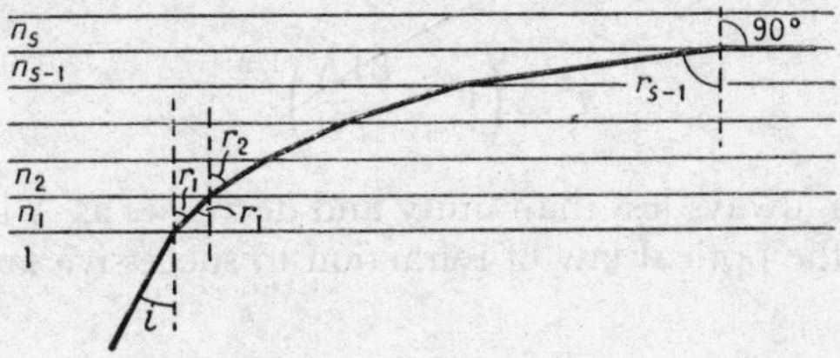

Fig. 14.14. Refraction of ray by layers of successively increasing electron density.

ionosphere must be treated as a dielectric with a continuously variable refractive index and a low conductivity. A wave incident on the ionosphere sets in motion the free electrons and it can be shown that the presence of these electrons gives the ionosphere an effective refractive index less than unity. As the refractive index is unity in a region without ions, a wave ascending into the ionosphere encounters a region where the refractive index gradually falls as the electron concentration increases with height. If we regard the wave as a single ray possessing characteristics similar to those of a ray of light it is evident that the ray will be refracted in the ionized layer according to the laws of optics. If for simplicity the layer is considered to be divided into a number of thin strips of constant electron density, each strip having a greater electron density than the one beneath it then successive refraction at the boundaries between the strips will cause bending of the ray in the manner shown in Fig. 14.14. If the layer is sufficiently thick refraction will continue until the angle of refraction reaches 90°, when the ray will have reached its highest point and will then start its downward journey back to earth. In practice, of course, the variation of electron density is continuous and the path of the ray will likewise be a continuous curve.

As the angle of incidence at the starting point of the ray is reduced the wave penetrates more deeply into the layer before being reflected, and a critical angle of incidence may be reached beyond which the electron density is not sufficient for the ray to be totally reflected. Such a ray is called an escape ray. The effect of alteration of the angle of incidence is shown in Fig. 14.15. The critical angle is a function of frequency, and for any given ionization distribution the frequency at which the critical angle reaches zero is known as the *critical frequency*. This is the maximum frequency which can be reflected at vertical incidence.

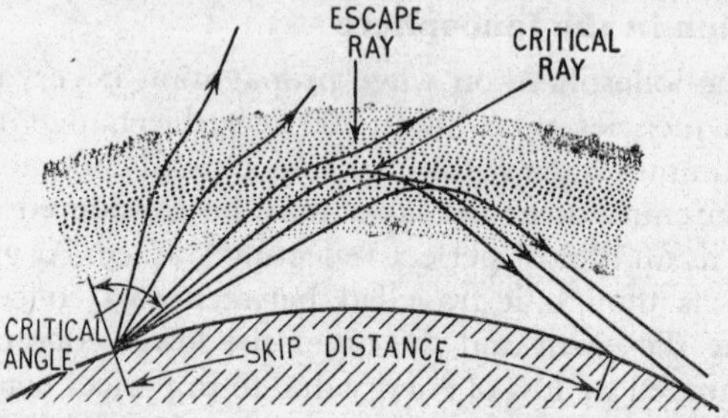

Fig. 14.15. Dependence of ionospheric rays on angle of incidence.

▶ In Appendix 14.3 it is shown that for an ionosphere with a density of N electrons per cubic metre, the refractive index n for a wave of frequency f is given by:

$$n = \left(1 - \frac{81N}{f^2}\right)^{1/2} \quad . \quad . \quad . \quad . \quad . \quad . \quad (14.6)$$

It is clear that n is always less than unity and decreases as N increases.

Application of the optical law of refraction to successive layers of Fig. 14.14 gives:

$$\frac{\sin i}{\sin r_1} = \frac{n_1}{1}, \quad \frac{\sin r_1}{\sin r_2} = \frac{n_2}{n_1}, \ldots \frac{\sin r_{s-1}}{\sin 90°} = \frac{n_s}{n_{s-1}}$$

whence $\sin i = n_s$. With a continuous distribution of ionization, then, a ray entering at an angle of incidence i will be reflected at a height where the ionization is such that n has the value:

$$n = \sin i \quad . \quad . \quad . \quad . \quad . \quad . \quad . \quad (14.7)$$

If the ray is nearly horizontal, $\sin i$ is nearly unity and quite a small value of ionization is needed to give the requisite value of n. As the angle of incidence decreases the ray must penetrate farther into the ionized layer in order to reach a sufficiently small value of n.

In the limit, for vertical incidence, $\sin i$ approaches zero, and hence the wave will be reflected back on its path at the height at which n is zero. This condition is attained when:

$$\frac{81N}{f^2} = 1$$

From it we can determine an upper limit of frequency for the wave, given by $f_N = 9\sqrt{N}$. A wave of frequency f will reach a refractive index of zero at a height where the electron density N is such that $f = f_N$ and will be reflected at this height. If N_{max} is the maximum electron density in an ionized layer all waves of frequency less than $f_{N_{max}}$ entering the ionosphere at vertical incidence will be reflected back to earth. This frequency, called the *critical frequency* and denoted by f_o, is therefore given by the relation:

$$f_o = 9\sqrt{N_{max}} \text{ c/s} \quad . \quad . \quad . \quad . \quad . \quad . \qquad (14.8)$$

To aid in the understanding of the reflection process at vertical incidence we can consider the velocity of the wave in the medium. In any medium where the velocity is a function of frequency there exists both a phase and a group velocity, as discussed in Chapter 6. The wave energy is propagated at group velocity, and this is shown in Appendix 14.3 to be given by:

$$v_g = c\left(1 - \frac{81N}{f^2}\right)^{1/2} \quad . \quad . \quad . \quad . \quad . \quad . \qquad (14.9)$$

Thus the group velocity decreases with increasing N until, at the height where the refractive index is zero, the velocity is also zero. At this height the wave comes to a stop, and then retraces its path with ever increasing velocity.

Determination of Critical Frequencies

The ionosphere characteristics are determined from measurements of the critical frequencies of the various layers. The commonest method is that in which a transmitter radiates vertically upwards in short pulses. A nearby

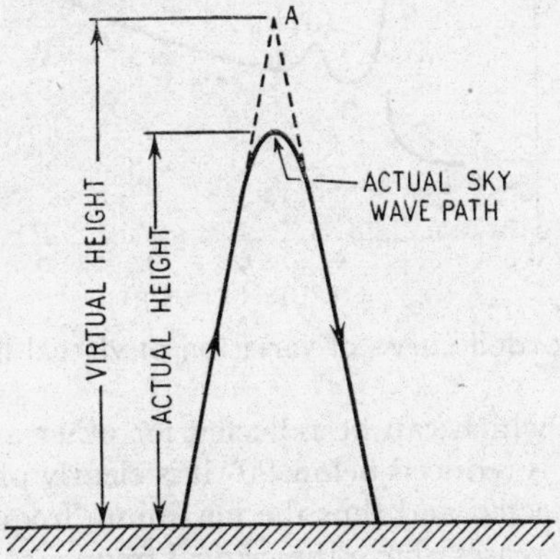

Fig. 14.16. Difference between actual and virtual heights (base line exaggerated for clarity).

receiver picks up both the direct signal and that reflected from the ionosphere, and measures the time difference between them. From this measurement the height at which reflection is taking place is calculated. The height actually determined is the *virtual height*, indicated in Fig. 14.16, and is the height from which the wave would appear to be reflected, if it be assumed that the ionosphere is replaced by a mirror-like reflecting surface at the level of A and that the wave velocity is equal to the velocity of light. As the velocity in the ionosphere is always less than the velocity of light the virtual height is always greater than the actual height.

A typical record showing the dependence of virtual height on frequency is given in Fig. 14.17. In this it will be seen that for frequencies at the lower end of the range the reflecting level increases slowly with frequency until a critical frequency is reached where the virtual height suddenly increases rapidly. The discontinuity in the curve at this point occurs at the critical frequency for the E layer, represented by f_oE. As this critical point is passed the measured virtual height drops back to a fairly steady value, greater than the previous one. The wave is now passing through the E layer, and being reflected from a higher layer, which in this case is the F_1 layer. Then comes $f_o F_1$, and at a still higher frequency the critical value $f_o F_2$ for the F_2 layer is found. The further critical frequency involving f_x will be discussed later. The apparent increase in the measured height in the vicinity of a critical frequency is caused by the large time delay in the ionized layer, occurring as a result of the much reduced velocity near this frequency.

It is from curves such as these, regularly recorded at many stations throughout the world, that ionospheric information is obtained.

The critical frequency for any layer represents the maximum frequency at which reflection from the layer at vertical incidence can take place, but it is not

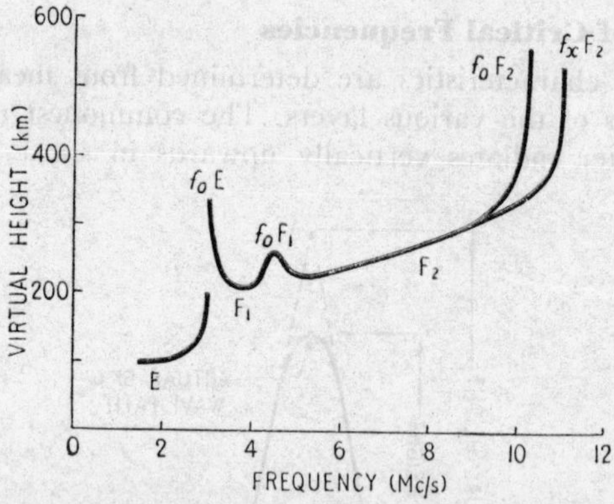

Fig. 14.17. Typical recorded curve of variation of virtual height with frequency

the highest frequency which can be reflected for other angles of incidence. As the angle of incidence is reduced below 90° it is clearly progressively more easy for the wave to be reflected and thus the maximum frequency at which reflection can take place increases above the critical frequency. For a given angle of incidence the maximum frequency at which reflection can take place is called the maximum usable frequency (m.u.f.).

Maximum Usable Frequency

It will be shown presently that the maximum usable frequency for any given transmission distance is calculable from the critical frequency by multiplying by an m.u.f. factor, which is a function of the transmission distance. With this distance is associated a certain angle of elevation of the transmitted wave. Both elevation angle and m.u.f. factors are given in Figs. 14.19–14.21. At the m.u.f. the ray path is that of the critical ray shown in Fig. 14.15, and the transmission distance is thus the minimum distance at which the ionospheric wave reaches the earth again. This minimum distance is called the skip distance. A smaller distance would require an angle of incidence greater than the critical angle. No ionospheric wave is received at distances less than the skip distance.

For a given angle of incidence i (with the vertical) the wave is reflected, according to equation (14.7), at a height where $n = \sin i$. For reflection at the height of maximum ionization the substitution of equations (14.6) and 14.8) gives:

$$\sin i = \left\{1 - \left(\frac{f_o}{f}\right)^2\right\}^{1/2}$$

and hence:

$$f = f_o \sec i \quad . \quad . \quad . \quad . \quad . \quad . \quad . \quad (14.10)$$

The frequency calculated from this last equation—the secant law—for a given angle of incidence is the maximum frequency at which a wave incident at this angle will be returned from the layer. For two points at a given distance apart on a flat earth and a given ionospheric height it is easy to find the angle of incidence and hence the highest frequency which, when transmitted from one of the points, would be returned from the layer to the other point. This frequency is the maximum usable frequency for communication between those two points, and is given by equation (14.10). The factor sec i forms the m.u.f. factor. This relation holds for distances up to about 1,000 km; for greater distances the curvature of both earth and ionosphere make necessary a modification which can be effected by introducing a correcting factor k so that equation (14.10) becomes:

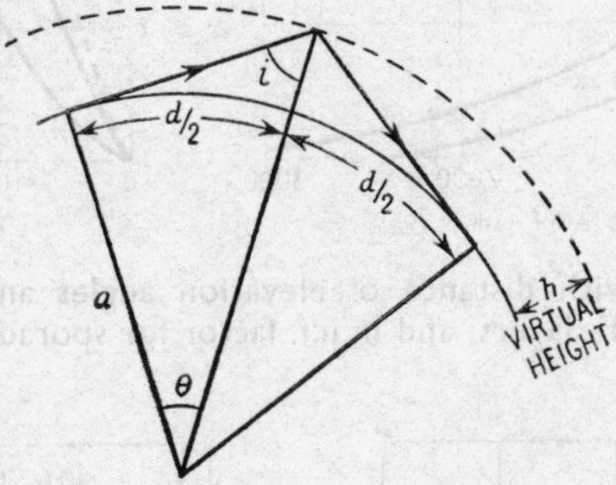

Fig. 14.18. Determination of maximum angle of incidence of ray on ionosphere.

$$f_{\text{m.u.f.}} = kf_o \sec i \quad . \quad . \quad . \quad . \quad . \quad . \quad (14.11)$$

It is convenient to include the factor k in the m.u.f. factor.

If the operating frequency, the critical frequency, and the ionospheric height are given there will be a minimum angle of incidence for reflection and hence a minimum distance, which is the skip distance. Each layer of the ionosphere has its particular value of skip distance for a given frequency, these values being functions of the critical frequency and the height of the layer. The higher the frequency the greater is the skip distance.

Because of the curvature of the earth and the ionosphere, there is a maximum value of the angle of incidence of a ray on the ionosphere, the maximum varying with the ionospheric height. This occurs for a ray which leaves the earth at grazing incidence as shown in Fig. 14.18, in which case i is obviously given by:

$$i = \sin^{-1} \{a/(a + h)\} \quad . \quad . \quad . \quad . \quad . \quad (14.12)$$

Then the maximum distance which can be covered is, from the geometry of the figure:

$$d = 2a \cos^{-1} \{a/(a + h)\} \quad . \quad . \quad . \quad . \quad . \quad . \quad (14.13)$$

For distances less than this maximum the ray must leave the earth at a greater elevation angle, calculable from the geometry of the path.

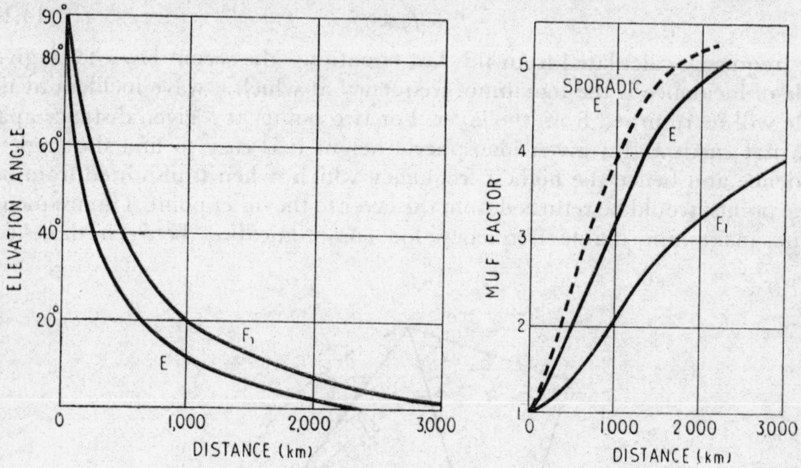

Fig. 14.19. Variation with distance of elevation angles and m.u.f. factors for E and F_1 layers, and m.u.f. factor for sporadic E.

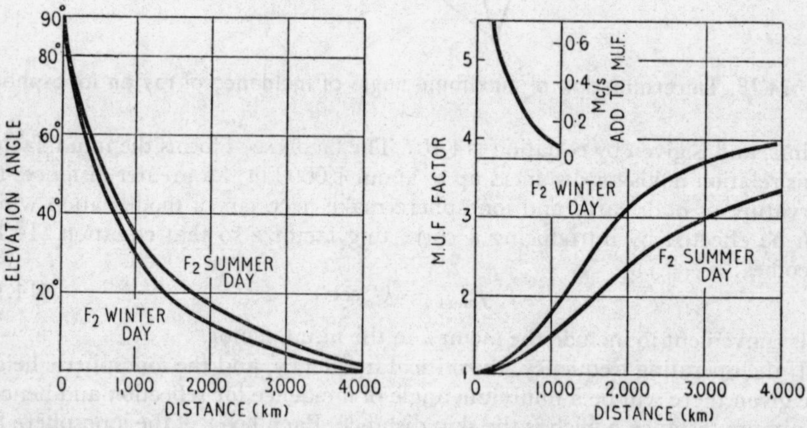

Fig. 14.20. Variation with distance of elevation angles and m.u.f. factors for day-time F_2 layer.

This elevation angle as a function of transmission distance is given in Figs. 14.19–14.21 for the standard heights of the different layers. These figures show also the m.u.f. factors as a function of distance. A wave emitted at an elevation angle near zero would suffer considerable ground attenuation, so it is usual to consider an elevation of about 4° as the practicable minimum. ◀

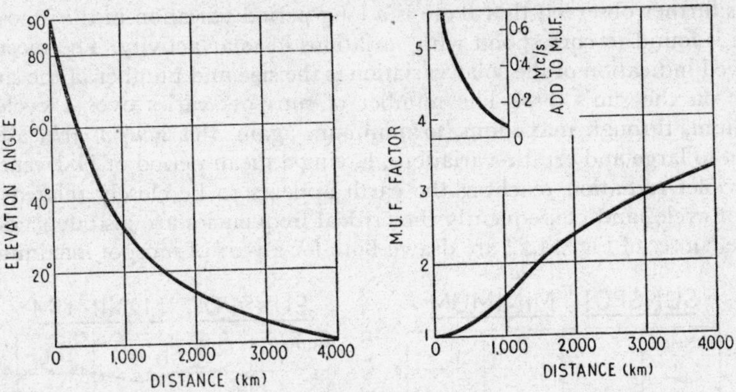

Fig. 14.21. Variation with distance of elevation angle and m.u.f. factor for night-time F layer.

Effect of Earth's Magnetic Field

A wave travelling in an atmosphere which is not ionized is unaffected by the earth's magnetic field. In the ionosphere, however, the electrons are set in motion by the wave, and the earth's magnetic field then exerts a force on the electrons, producing a twisting effect on their paths. This reacts on the wave, with the result that it is split up into two components, the *ordinary* and the *extraordinary* waves. The properties of the ordinary wave are practically the same as those of a wave without a superimposed magnetic field, which we have so far been considering. The critical frequency of the extraordinary wave is indicated by f_x, and it will be seen from Fig. 14.17 that it is only in the upper regions of the F_2 layer (and also the F layer) that the extraordinary wave becomes distinguishable from the ordinary.

In the calculation of m.u.f. we may allow for the effect of the extraordinary ray at short ranges by making a standard addition to the m.u.f. as calculated from f_oF and $f_o F_2$. This is shown in Figs. 14.20 and 14.21. When the distance exceeds about 1,000 km the correction is negligibly small.

The extraordinary wave is treated more fully in Appendix 14.4.

Regular Ionospheric Variations

Because of the continual changes in the earth's position relative to the sun, the amount of ultra-violet radiation received at any point in the ionosphere is continually varying. This gives rise to diurnal and seasonal variations of the ionization density and hence of the critical frequencies and, to a lesser extent, of the heights of the layers. Typical diurnal variations are illustrated in Fig. 14.22. It will be seen that variations of the critical frequencies for the E and F_1 layers, represented by f_oE and $f_o F_1$, are quite regular, rising to a maximum at mid-day and falling off to a low value during hours of darkness.

For the F and F_2 layers the effect is complicated by a considerable heating effect which takes place in these higher reaches of the atmosphere, resulting in an expansion of the layer. A time lag associated with this thermal effect is the cause of the peak occurring around sunset during the summer months. It will be seen from Fig. 14.22 that the diurnal variation in critical frequency is much greater in winter than in summer.

It is further observed that there is a long-period variation in the ionosphere, which is found to correspond with variations in solar activity. The most easily observed indication of the solar variation is the size and number of the sunspots visible on the sun's disc. The number of sunspots varies over a cycle from minimum, through maximum, to minimum again, this *sunspot cycle*, although subject to large and erratic variations, having a mean period of 11·1 years. The ultra-violet radiation reaching the earth appears to be closely related to the sunspot cycle, and consequently the critical frequencies are also dependent on it. The curves of Fig. 14.22 are drawn both for a year of sunspot maximum and

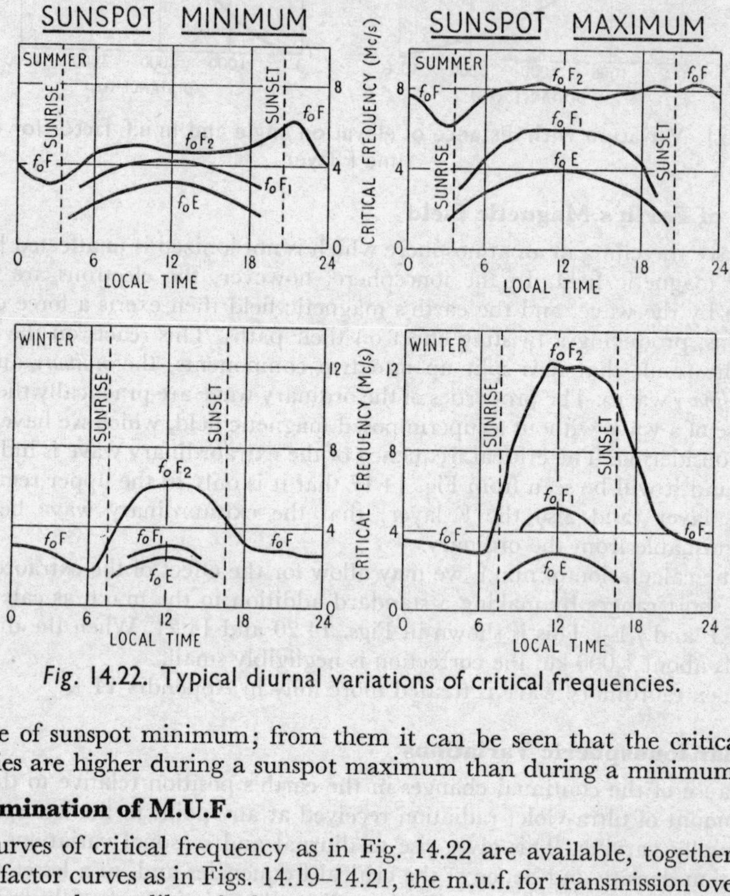

Fig. 14.22. Typical diurnal variations of critical frequencies.

for one of sunspot minimum; from them it can be seen that the critical frequencies are higher during a sunspot maximum than during a minimum.

Determination of M.U.F.

If curves of critical frequency as in Fig. 14.22 are available, together with m.u.f. factor curves as in Figs. 14.19–14.21, the m.u.f. for transmission over any distance can be readily calculated. The critical frequency for the appropriate time half-way along the transmission path (i.e. at the reflection point) is read off and multiplied by the appropriate m.u.f. factor. The curves of Fig. 14.23 are derived in this way from Figs. 14.19–14.21 and Fig. 14.22, and are representative of summer and winter conditions at sunspot minimum and maximum.

For distances up to about 2,000 km, which is the maximum reached in a single reflection from the E layer, the m.u.f. of Fig. 14.23 may be that determined by E, F_1 or F_2, whichever is the greatest. Up to 3,000 km F_1 or F_2 may control the m.u.f.; beyond this and up to the limit of distance, 4,000 km, transmission can only be by the F_2 layer.

From the curves of Fig. 14.23, taking as an extreme example the winter sunspot-maximum curves, a frequency of 30 Mc/s is usable to cover a distance of 2,000 km when it is mid-day at the centre of the path. The frequency would have to be reduced to about 8 Mc/s to reach the same distance during the night.

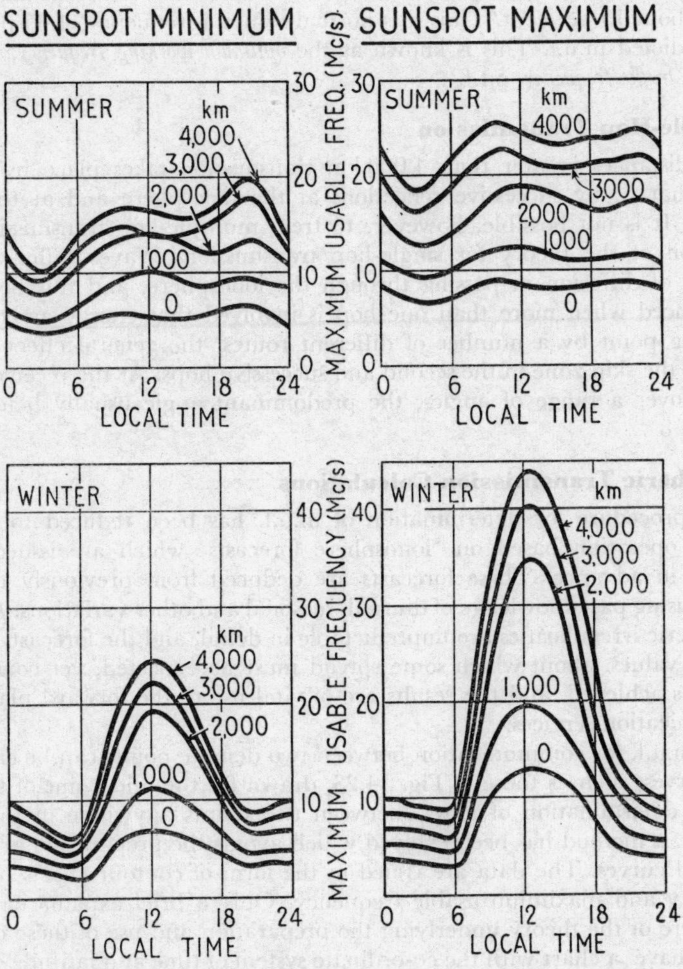

Fig. 14.23. Typical diurnal variations of m.u.f. for various distances, obtained from Fig. 14.22 by means of the m.u.f. factors of Figs. 14.19–14.21.

It might be thought, then, that it would be preferable to use the lower frequency at all times. That this is not so is shown in the following section.

Optimum Working Frequency

Another effect of the presence of free electrons is to give rise to a certain conductivity in the ionosphere, and hence to a partial absorption of the waves passing through. It is shown in Appendix 14.3 that this effect is important only at the lower edge of the ionosphere, and [by equation (14.36)] that the conductivity and hence the absorption are dependent on the inverse square of the frequency. Thus ordinarily the highest possible frequency gives the strongest sky-wave signal at the receiver, and so it is desirable to work as closely as possible to the maximum usable frequency.

Operating frequencies are chosen from predictions of m.u.f. based on a monthly average, and in practice there are daily variations from this mean of up to about 15 per cent. Thus it is normal to use a frequency of 85 per cent of the predicted m.u.f. This is known as the *optimum working frequency*, o.w.f. (or *optimum traffic frequency*, o.t.f.).

Multiple-Hop Transmission

For distances greater than 4,000 km transmission takes place by multiple hops; that is, by successive reflections at the ionosphere and at the earth's surface. It is not possible, however, to treat multiple-hop transmission as an extension of the theory for single-hop transmission. Waves suffer a certain amount of diffusion in passing through the ionosphere, and this becomes so pronounced when more than one hop is involved that energy arrives at the receiving point by a number of different routes, the general effect being to obscure the skip zone in the second and successive hops. At the receiver energy arrives over a range of angles, the predominant angle usually being of the order of 8°.

Ionospheric Transmission Calculations

The procedure for determination of m.u.f. has been reduced to a simple routine operation based on 'ionosphere forecasts' which are issued several months in advance. These forecasts are deduced from previously measured values, using past knowledge of diurnal, seasonal and other variations. Although ionospheric irregularities are unpredictable in detail, and the forecasts relate to average values, about which some spread must be expected, yet considerable success is achieved, and the results are of vital use to the forward planning of communication services.

The m.u.f. for communication between two definite points can be calculated from curves, such as those of Fig. 14.23, drawn for the mid-point of the path. For the determination of m.u.f. between two points anywhere in the world, however, a method has been evolved which avoids the preparation of a multiplicity of curves. The data are issued in the form of contour charts of critical frequency and maximum usable frequency. Only a brief explanation can be given here of the theory underlying the preparation and use of these charts.

▶ If we have a chart with the co-ordinate system of time and latitude shown in Fig. 14.24, we can enter on it, along the parallel of latitude appropriate to each observing station, the monthly mean of the critical frequencies observed at that station for each hour of the day. With sufficient data from stations all over the world it is possible to join up points of equal critical frequency and form a contour map showing world distribution of critical frequency. If this map is placed under a transparent cylindrical projection of the world of the same size, Fig. 14.25 (in this projection longitude and latitude are represented on linear scales), then we can transpose longitude for time by sliding one on the other horizontally, and can hence determine the mean critical frequency at any place and at any local time.

This procedure would be satisfactory if the critical frequency were the same along any parallel of latitude at equal values of local time. The ionization of the

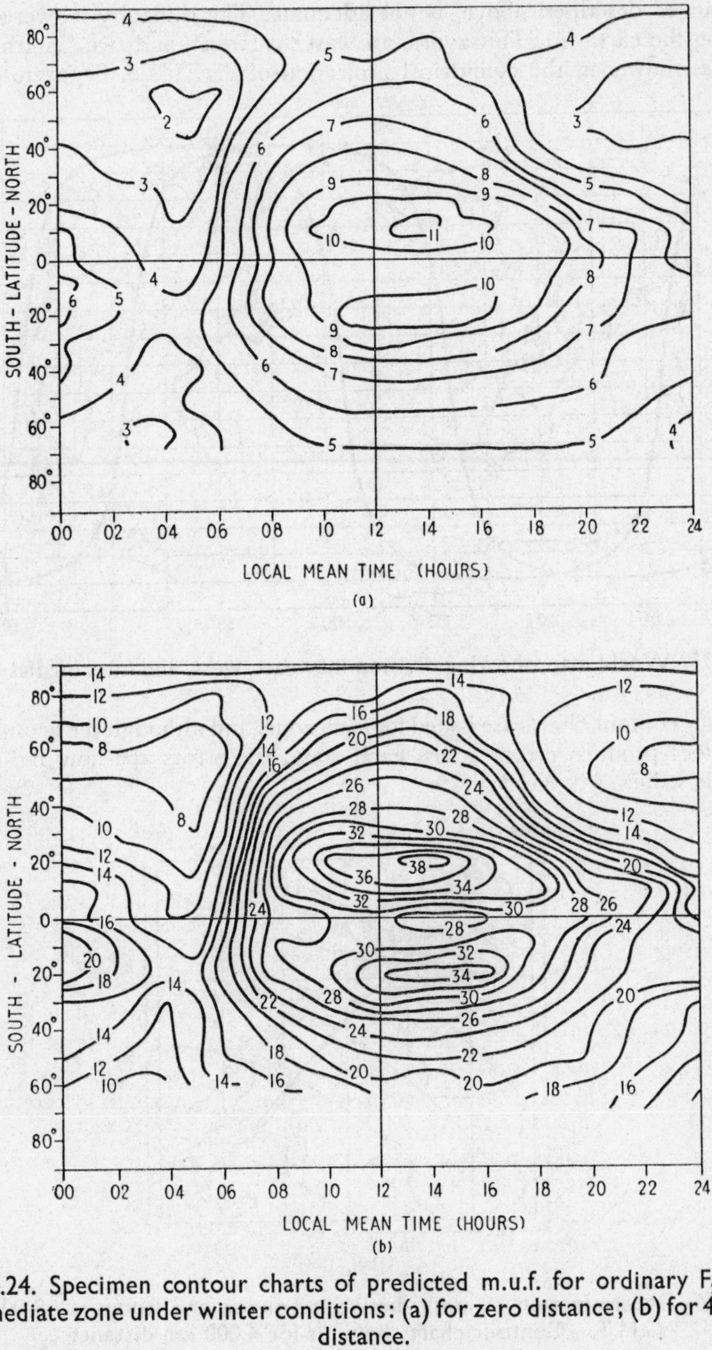

Fig. 14.24. Specimen contour charts of predicted m.u.f. for ordinary F_2 ray in intermediate zone under winter conditions: (a) for zero distance; (b) for 4,000 km distance.

F and F_2 layers, however, is dependent not only on geographical latitude and longitude but also on the magnetic effects of the earth's field, and thus on magnetic latitude and longitude. This means that the transposition of longitude for time, as described above, is not adequate. The difficulty is overcome by dividing the earth into four zones, an 'east', a 'west', and two 'intermediate' zones as shown on the cylindrical projection of Fig. 14.25. Separate critical-

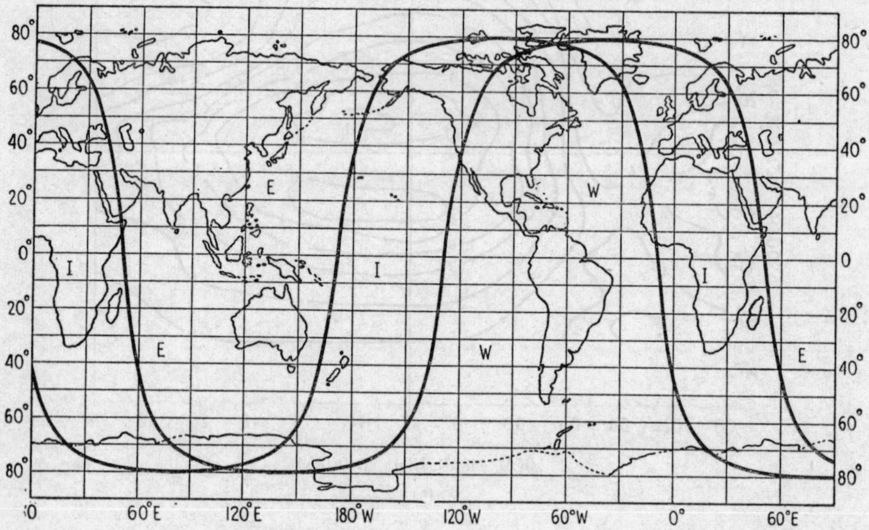

Fig. **14.25. World map, showing division into east, west, and intermediate zones.**

frequency contour charts are issued for each zone, and although the geomagnetic effect does produce errors across each zone, the errors are now reduced to tolerable values.

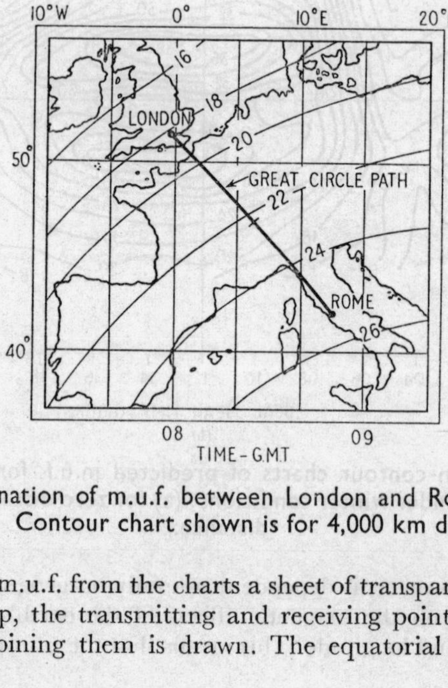

Fig. **14.26. Determination of m.u.f. between London and Rome at 08·00 hours G.M.T. Contour chart shown is for 4,000 km distance.**

To calculate the m.u.f. from the charts a sheet of transparent paper is placed over the world map, the transmitting and receiving points marked, and the great circle path joining them is drawn. The equatorial line and the time reference meridian are also marked in. Usually the Greenwich meridian is used. For paths shorter than 4,000 km (i.e., single-hop paths) the control point is chosen at the centre of the path, and it is ascertained in which zone this lies. The transparency is then laid on the appropriate contour chart, with the time reference meridian coinciding with the ordinate corresponding to the required time. The m.u.f. at the control point is then read off. Contour charts are normally produced for the F_2 layer at zero distance and 4,000 km. Readings are taken for each of these distances and an interpolation made for the required distance. An example is shown in Fig. 14.26.

For distances greater than 4,000 km the procedure is more complicated, two control points being necessary.

Irregular Ionospheric Disturbances

In addition to the regular ionospheric variations previously discussed there are also irregular variations which have an important effect on sky-wave reception. One of these phenomena is the *Dellinger fade-out* (after J. H. Dellinger, of U.S.A.) which causes a complete disappearance of the sky wave, lasting for anything up to two hours. It is caused by sudden eruptions on the sun known as *solar flares*, observable from the earth as flares of bright light. These emit large amounts of radiation, which produce a big increase in ionization extending down to the D layer. This results in a complete absorption of all sky-wave signals of frequencies greater than about 1 Mc/s. The effect is confined to the sunlit hemisphere of the earth, and is more intense in low than in high latitudes. The solar flares appear to be quite random, so that a fade-out is not predictable.

The second major disturbance is the *ionospheric storm*. This is a turbulence produced in the ionosphere by streams of particles emitted from the sun, as a result of which sky-wave reception becomes very erratic. The stream of particles may come from a sunspot, or may arise in a solar flare which causes a Dellinger fade-out—in which case the ionospheric storm will occur something like 30 hours after the Dellinger fade-out, the time taken by the stream of particles to reach the earth. The ionospheric storm usually lasts for several days, during which period signal strength is abnormally low, and subject to a form of rapid fading known as 'flutter' fading. As the higher frequencies are most affected it may be possible to maintain communication by reducing the frequency. The effect is felt equally in the dark and sunlit hemispheres, and is most severe for paths passing near the geomagnetic poles. The phenomenon may be repeated at intervals of 27 days, the period of rotation of the sun, so that its recurrence may sometimes be predicted.

An abnormality of a different type is the occasional appearance in the E layer of drifting electron clouds in which the ionization is much higher than is normal for the layer. These may be of quite small size or extend up to hundreds of kilometres. The layer is therefore given the name *sporadic E*, and is usually represented by E_s. Sporadic E-layer reflections occur most frequently during summer nights, but their occurrence is intermittent and unpredictable, so that they are practically useless for regular short-wave services. The virtual-height curve of Fig. 14.27 is a typical one, showing the E_s critical frequency extending up to 8 Mc/s, although values up to 20 Mc/s are sometimes found. Single-hop propagation up to distances of 2,000 km at frequencies up to 50 Mc/s can be obtained under good sporadic E conditions. The m.u.f. factors for this layer have been included in Fig. 14.19.

Fading

As the ionosphere is subject to continual small fluctuations the returned ionospheric wave is also subject to small fluctuations. The signal reaching the receiver is made up of a large number of 'rays' each of which has travelled by a different path through the ionosphere. As the path length of each ray is subject to continual small variations the relative phases of the waves arriving at the receiver vary in a random manner, and thus the amplitude of their resultant varies continually. This is the effect known as *interference fading*.

In addition the state of polarization of a downcoming sky wave is constantly changing. This is caused by a superposition, with random amplitude and phase, of the ordinary and extraordinary rays, which are oppositely polarized. The polarization relative to the receiving aerial is thus constantly changing, giving rise to changes of amplitude in the receiver and producing *polarization fading*. Fading is always present, to a greater or lesser extent, in sky-wave reception; according to the state of the ionosphere it may be *rapid* or *slow*, *deep* or *shallow*.

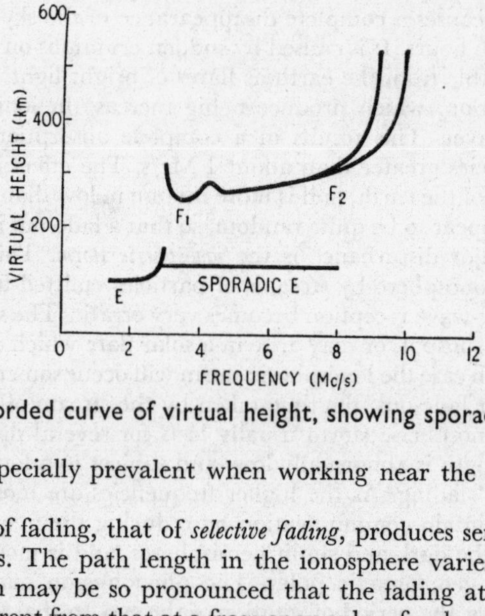

Fig. 14.27. Recorded curve of virtual height, showing sporadic E reflection.

Deep fading is especially prevalent when working near the maximum usable frequency.

Another form of fading, that of *selective fading*, produces serious distortion of modulated signals. The path length in the ionosphere varies with frequency, and this variation may be so pronounced that the fading at one frequency is considerably different from that at a frequency only a few hundred cycles away. Thus the various frequencies in the sidebands are differently affected, giving rise to distortion of the information carried.

Tropospheric Propagation

It has been seen that about 30 Mc/s is the highest frequency at which regular sky-wave signals can be expected. Except under special conditions a wave of higher frequency than this passes through the ionosphere without reflection. Thus the reception of signals at v.h.f. and beyond is almost entirely dependent on the space wave. The space wave, which has already been dealt with briefly, consists of a direct ray and a ray reflected from the earth, as shown in Fig. 14.2 (a). At these frequencies the aerial is normally elevated to heights of at least a wavelength, at which height the surface wave can be neglected in comparison with the space wave.

For propagation in this frequency range, then, we are concerned only with waves travelling through the lower regions of the earth's atmosphere, that is, in the troposphere. We shall show that a major influence on propagation in the troposphere is the variation with height of the refractive index of the air. At frequencies below 30 Mc/s we are not often concerned solely with the space wave propagated in the troposphere, so that the term tropospheric propagation in the following sections will be taken to refer to frequencies above this limit.

From the geometry of Fig. 14.2 (a) it is clear that there will be a slight difference in path length between the direct and reflected rays, the difference decreasing as the distance increases. Thus the two waves arriving at the receiver will be out of phase, and according to circumstances their sum may be greater

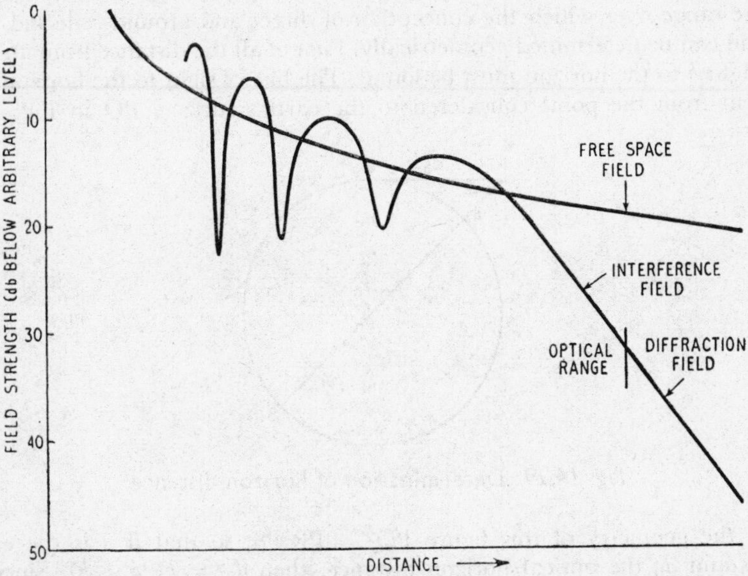

Fig. 14.28. Interference field produced by direct and reflected components of a space wave.

or less than the amplitude of the direct wave alone. It is shown in Appendix 14.5 (see Figs. 14.46–14.49) that for small elevations the reflected wave suffers a phase change of very nearly 180° at the point of reflection, and so when the path difference between the rays is an exact number of wavelengths the two rays will be 180° out of phase and will therefore subtract. They will not cancel completely, since imperfect reflection at the ground makes the reflected ray of smaller amplitude than the direct ray. When the path difference is exactly one half-wavelength, or an odd number of half-wavelengths, the rays are in phase and will add, giving a signal strength greater than that of the direct ray alone.

Thus, as the distance between transmitter and receiver is increased within the optical range, the signal strength will go through successive maxima and minima, giving an interference field of the form shown in Fig. 14.28. The figure shows for comparison the level of the free-space field, decreasing with distance as $1/d$. In the interference field the most distant maximum will occur at the distance where the path difference is one half-wavelength. Beyond that the path difference steadily approaches zero, and the waves interfere destructively, giving a resultant which falls rapidly below the free-space field. The interference pattern is of course dependent upon frequency, the minima crowding together as the frequency is increased, and upon the aerial heights, the pattern moving outwards as the aerial height is increased.

Since the refractive index of the atmosphere decreases slightly with height a ray travelling through the troposphere is slightly refracted as in Fig. 14.30 (a). It is shown in Appendix 14.6 that this is equivalent to straight line propagation over an earth having a fictitious radius which is, on the average, equal to 4/3 of the actual radius, as in Fig. 14.30 (b).

▶ The Space Wave

The range over which the conception of direct and ground-reflected waves is valid can be determined geometrically. First of all the distance from an aerial of height h to the horizon must be found. The line of sight to the horizon is the tangent from the point considered to the earth's surface, PQ in Fig. 14.29.

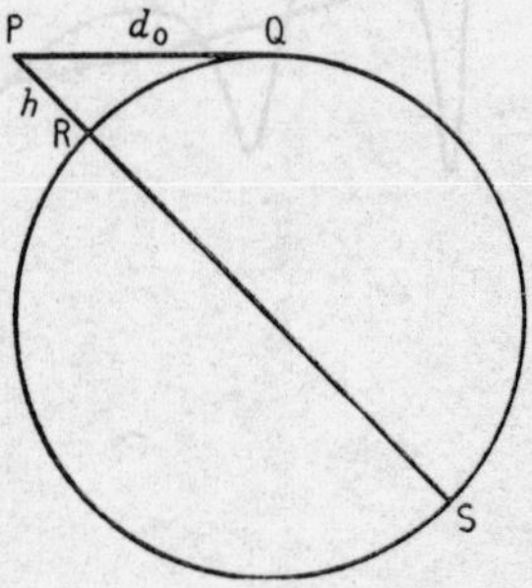

Fig. 14.29. Determination of horizon distance.

From the geometry of this figure $PQ^2 = PR.PS$, so that if a is the earth's radius and d_0 the optical horizon distance, then $d_0{}^2 = h(2a + h)$. Since h is always very small compared with a, this reduces to:

$$d_0 = \sqrt{2ah} \quad . \quad . \quad . \quad . \quad . \quad . \quad . \quad (14.14)$$

From Fig. 14.30 (a) it is clear that the height of the geometric path of a ray above the earth's surface varies continuously over the path. Close to the earth's surface the refractive index of the atmosphere is slightly greater than unity, and this decreases to unity at heights where the air density approaches zero. This gradient of refractive index in the troposphere causes a slight bending of the ray in the direction indicated in Fig. 14.30 (a). This has the effect of increasing the horizon distance, and allows the direct ray to reach points beyond the horizon as determined by a straight-line path.

It is shown in Appendix 14.6 that the effect of refraction can be allowed for by using for the earth's radius an effective value larger than the actual value. The ray paths can then be taken as straight lines, as in Fig. 14.30 (b). When the refractive index n of the atmosphere varies with height at a rate dn/dh the analysis of Appendix 14.6 gives for the effective radius a' the expression:

$$\frac{1}{a'} = \frac{1}{a} + \frac{dn}{dh} \quad . \quad . \quad . \quad . \quad . \quad . \quad (14.15)$$

The value of a' varies with atmospheric conditions, but its average value, for what is known as the *standard atmosphere*, is usually taken as $\frac{4}{3}a$. The value of a is 6,370 km, and thus the standard value of a' is about 8,500 km.

The corrected expression for the horizon distance for radio waves is now given by:

$$d_0 = \sqrt{2a'h} \quad . \quad . \quad . \quad . \quad . \quad . \quad (14.16)$$

If h is expressed in feet and d_0 in miles equation (14.16) takes the very convenient form:

$$d_0 \approx \sqrt{2h} \quad . \quad . \quad . \quad . \quad . \quad . \quad (14.16a)$$

The effect of the standard amount of atmospheric refraction is thus to increase the optical range in the ratio $(a'/a)^{1/2}$, that is, by 15% over its geometric value. If a wave is to propagate between transmitting and receiving aerials of heights h_1 and h_2 without interception by the curvature of the earth then the maximum

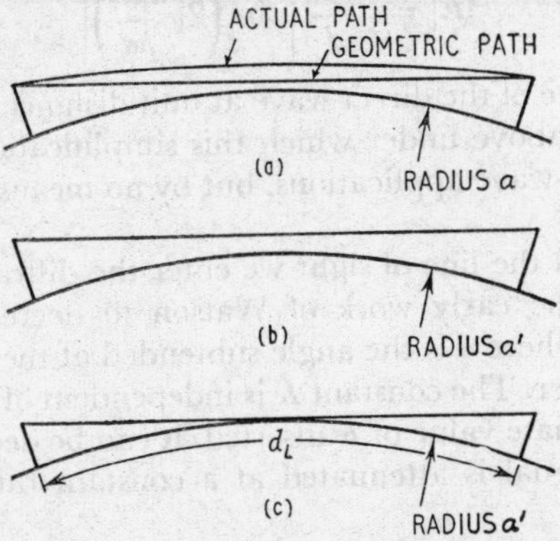

Fig. 14.30. Illustration of (a) curved ray path due to tropospheric refraction; (b) equivalent straight-line path over earth of modified radius; (c) maximum transmission distance for given aerial heights.

separation d_L between them occurs when the direct ray is just tangential to the surface as in Fig. 14.30 (c), that is:

$$d_L = \sqrt{2a'h_1} + \sqrt{2a'h_2} \quad . \quad . \quad . \quad . \quad . \quad (14.17)$$

With h_1 and h_2 in feet and d_L in miles equation (14.17) becomes:

$$d_L \approx \sqrt{2h_1} + \sqrt{2h_2} \quad . \quad . \quad . \quad . \quad . \quad . \quad (14.17a)$$

This is known as the corrected line-of-sight distance. Thus, for example, with $h_1 = h_2 = 100$ m the corrected line-of-sight distance is 82·5 km.

The space wave is dealt with in detail in Appendix 14.7, where it is shown that within the line-of-sight distance the field strength E of the space wave—the sum of the direct and reflected waves—is controlled by an expression which goes through maxima and minima given by:

$$|E| = |E_d|(1 \pm D|\rho|) \quad . \quad . \quad . \quad . \quad . \quad (14.18)$$

where E_d is the field due to the direct ray, $|\rho|$ the amplitude of the reflection factor at the earth's surface, and D a divergence factor to allow for the earth's curvature. It is this expression which determines the form of the curve of Fig. 14.28. The phase difference between the two rays for aerial heights h_1 and h_2 and wavelength λ is given by equation (14.46) as:

$$\phi = \frac{4\pi h_1 h_2}{\lambda d}$$

The distances of successive maxima and minima in (14.18) are given by those values of d which make the phase difference equal to successive multiples of π. The optical region in which this treatment is valid is called the region of interference field.

Where the heights are so low or the wavelength so long that the outermost maximum occurs at a distance small compared with the optical range it is permissible to assume the earth flat and perfectly reflecting, when the expression (14.18) for E becomes (as derived in Appendix 14.7):

$$|E| = \frac{2E_0}{d}\left|\sin\left(2\pi\frac{h_1 h_2}{\lambda d}\right)\right| \quad . \quad . \quad . \quad . \quad . \quad . \quad (14.19)$$

E_0 being the amplitude of the direct wave at unit distance from the transmitter. The condition noted above under which this simplification can be used is met in most normal metre-wave applications, but by no means always at centimetre wavelengths.

At distances beyond the line of sight we enter the diffraction field where the field was shown in the early work of Watson to decrease with distance as $\exp\{-K(a'/\lambda)^{1/3}\theta\}$, where θ is the angle subtended at the earth's centre by the transmitter and receiver. The constant K is independent of the ground constants and, with the appropriate value of K inserted, it can be deduced that in the diffraction region the signal is attenuated at a constant rate by an attenuation factor α, where:

$$\alpha = \frac{26}{\lambda^{1/3}a'^{2/3}} \text{ decibels per metre} \quad . \quad . \quad . \quad . \quad (14.20)$$

Super-Refraction

The atmosphere has not always a uniform gradient of refractive index, as assumed in the previous section. Considerable divergence from the mean often

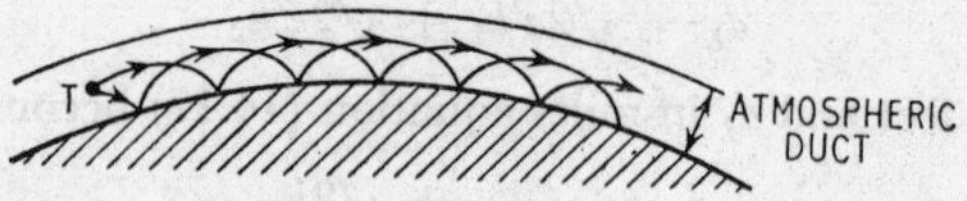

Fig. 14.31. Typical ray paths for a wave trapped in an atmospheric duct.

occurs, particularly in the lower 50 metres of the troposphere. This is important since, at wavelengths small compared with the heights involved, the ray paths are very dependent on variations of index with height. The most important case is that where, over a limited range of height, the refractive index decreases with height much more rapidly than is normal. This gives rise to what is called an *atmospheric duct*, in which the wave is trapped, resulting in a region of abnormally high field strength extending along the surface of the earth without limitation by the horizon. This is the phenomenon of *super-refraction* or *trapping*, illustrated in Fig. 14.31.

Table 14.3 gives some figures of the duct height needed to give complete trapping for different wavelengths.

TABLE 14.3

Maximum trapping wavelength in duct of height b

λ_{max} (cm)	b (m)
1	5
10	23
100	107
1,000	500

Normal duct heights are such that complete trapping occurs only at centimetre wavelengths. Partial trapping may also be found for the shorter metric wavelengths. Only in extreme cases is complete trapping found at metric wavelengths.

In a subsequent section the meteorological conditions giving rise to super-refraction are discussed.

▶ Where the refracting conditions are sufficiently different from standard to cause trapping the concept of an effective earth radius breaks down. The

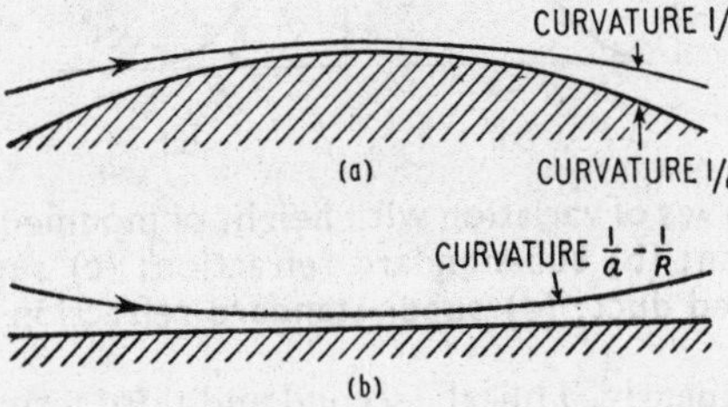

Fig. 14.32. (a) Actual ray path over a curved earth; (b) path of ray of same relative curvature over a flat earth.

alternative then used is to regard the earth as flat and the rays as having sufficient curvature to give the same path relative to the earth's surface as the actual rays. This is illustrated in Fig. 14.32. Appendix 14.8 shows that, for this concept, in order to provide the necessary curvature the actual refractive index n at a height h must be replaced by a *modified index* N defined by:

$$N = n + \frac{h}{a} \quad . \quad . \quad . \quad . \quad . \quad (14.21)$$

Although N is always very close to unity its actual value is important and so it is convenient when dealing with numerical values to introduce the *excess modified index* or *refractive modulus* M, related to N by:

$$M = (N - 1) \times 10^6 \quad . \quad . \quad . \quad . \quad . \quad (14.22)$$

Refractive Index of the Troposphere

The tropospheric refractive index depends on the air temperature and pressure, and on the amount of water vapour present. It is known that the expression for n is:

$$n - 1 = \frac{80}{T} \times 10^{-6}\left(P + \frac{4{,}800w}{T}\right) \quad . \quad . \quad . \quad . \quad (14.23)$$

where P is the atmospheric pressure in millibars, w the partial pressure of the water vapour in millibars, and T the absolute temperature. It is the variation of n with height which is important, and P, w and T all contribute to this. Combining equations (14.21) and (14.23) and taking the gradient, we get:

$$\frac{dN}{dh} \times 10^6 = \frac{80}{T}\frac{dP}{dh} - \frac{80}{T^2}\left(P + \frac{9{,}600w}{T}\right)\frac{dT}{dh} + \frac{80 \times 4{,}800}{T^2}\frac{dw}{dh} + \frac{10^6}{a} \quad (14.24)$$

The first term on the right is always negative, since pressure always decreases with height, and the last term is always positive. The signs of the other two terms depend on atmospheric conditions. In what is defined as the standard atmosphere the temperature decreases with height by 6·5 degrees per kilometre,

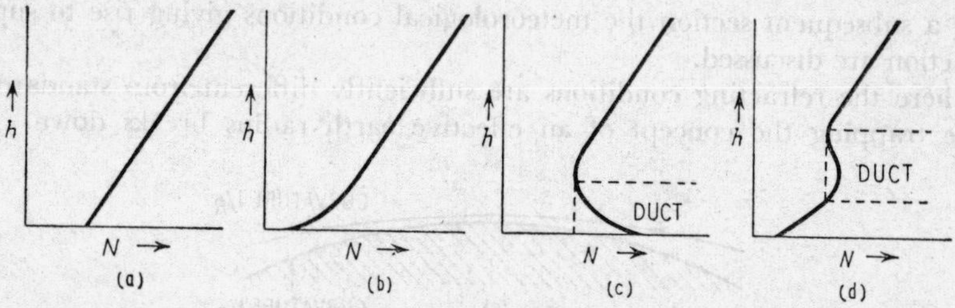

Fig. 14.33. Typical curves of variation with height of modified refractive index for (a) standard refraction; (b) sub-standard refraction; (c) super-standard refraction with ground-based duct; (d) super-standard refraction with elevated duct.

and w also decreases linearly. Thus the second and third terms are both negative, and values in the standard atmosphere are such that dN/dh is positive with a value usually taken as $0{\cdot}118 \times 10^{-6}$ per metre. It is more conveniently expressed in terms of dM/dh as 0·118 *M-units* per metre. This corresponds to the value $dn/dh = -0{\cdot}039 \times 10^{-6}$ quoted in Appendix 14.6.

Under certain atmospheric conditions, however, dT/dh and dw/dh may differ greatly from the standard values. In particular, when warm dry air passes over a cool sea surface the air close to the water will be cooled and thus an increase of temperature with height will occur—the opposite of the normal case. In addition the water-vapour content will decrease with height much more rapidly than usual. It is clear that both factors reduce the value of dN/dh, and under these conditions, dN/dh may become negative over a region close to the sea surface, resulting in what is called a *surface duct*. Under other conditions negative values of dN/dh may appear higher up in the atmosphere, making an *elevated duct*. All conditions giving rise to values of dN/dh less than the standard value are called *super-standard*, since in general they give rise to improved radio propagation. When dN/dh exceeds the standard value conditions are said to be *sub-standard*, giving rise to signals below normal. The various cases are illustrated in Fig. 14.33.

ith height. Ray 1, which leaves the transmitter at an angle α_1 negative) reaches a turning point at the height where $N = N_0 -$ licated on the left of the diagram. Ray 2, which leaves the trans- critical angle α_p (*the angle of penetration*), reaches its turning point op of the duct. A ray such as 3, leaving at an angle greater than α_p, hed the horizontal before it passes above the duct and into a region creasing N bends it upwards. Thus rays having an initial angle less trapped within the duct, and a region of abnormally high field produced, extending without limit along the surface of the earth. shadow region. This is the phenomenon of *super-refraction* or *trapping*, arly most important for long-range reception of signals.

ucting his own diagrams the reader can readily show that rays are d within an elevated duct. He can also show that, under sub- nditions, the upward bending is greater than in the standard case, adow region moves in towards the transmitter, thus reducing the ange.

ation of single rays as in the preceding discussion gives no indication ncy is involved. When, however, all the rays composing a wave are is found that a further condition must be satisfied if the rays are not destructively. This condition gives an upper limit to the wavelength rapping occurs. For a surface duct of height b this maximum wave- be shown to be given by:

$$\lambda_{max} = \frac{8\sqrt{2}}{3} \int_0^b \{N(h) - N(b)\}^{1/2}\, dh$$

e this limitation we can assume that in the duct N decreases linearly t. This makes λ_{max} proportional to $b^{3/2}$, and if we take $-\ 1{\cdot}3 \times 10^{-7}$ ($-\ 0{\cdot}13$ M-units per metre) as an average value for the rate of f N in a duct the values in Table 14.3 are found. As the height of a nmonly a few tens of metres and seldom more than 200 m it is clear ing is most effective for centimetre wavelengths. In super-refraction phere is acting as a kind of waveguide in which the above value of sponds to the critical wavelength.

has, nevertheless, a considerable effect at wavelengths up to several maximum, producing partial trapping. Thus metre wavelengths are not greatly affected by trapping, but as the wavelength is reduced metre the trapping effect increases progressively.

logical Conditions Producing Super-Refraction

vo requirements for super-refracting conditions are an increase in ire with height (temperature inversion) and a rapid decrease of with height, both of which give the necessary decrease of refractive h height. Either of these by itself is effective, if of sufficient magnitude. peaking, super-refracting conditions are associated with fine, calm, nic weather. In cold, rough weather the lower atmosphere is usually d, and the refractive index is more or less standard. We consider now ticular examples of conditions where super-refraction can occur.

nd districts when the day is warm the land and the air both become fter sunset, if the sky remains clear, the land radiates its heat and its ure falls rapidly. The earth cools the lower layers of the atmosphere,

Tropospheric Wave Propagation

It has been pointed out that when a duc technique of the modified refractive index. discussed.

We show in Appendix 14.9 that, for a ra where the modified index is N_0 and at an a at a height where the modified index is N is

$$\alpha = \pm \{\alpha_0^2 + 2(N$$

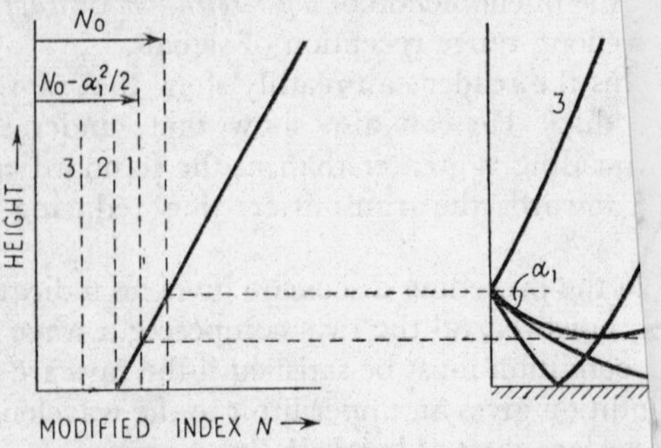

Fig. 14.34. Ray paths associated with lin

The path of the ray can thus be traced by means of N against h. At a height where $N = N_0 - \alpha$

Fig. 14.34 illustrates a family of ray paths fo by means of the modified index curve on the left with height all rays are bent upwards. Ray 1, lea

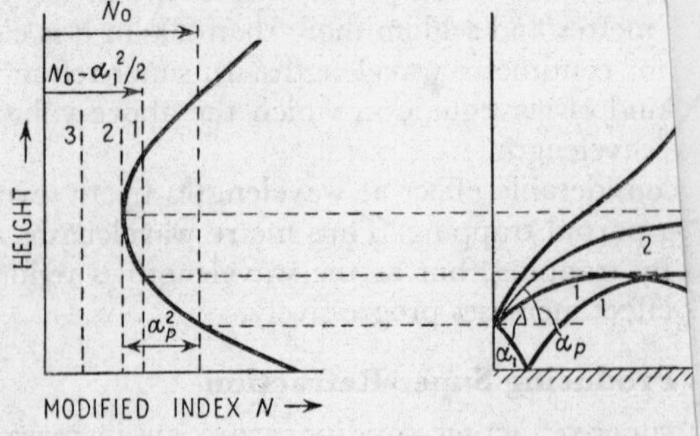

Fig. 14.35. Ray paths associated with gr

wards angle α_1, reaches the horizontal (that is, its where the value of N equals $N_0 - \alpha_1^2/2$ as show Ray 2 just touches the flat earth and thus represents to the right of ray 2 is the shadow region. For ray angle, N does not reach a value sufficiently great to accordingly reflected from the earth's surface.

In Fig. 14.35 is illustrated ray propagation within rays within the duct are bent downwards, since the

decreases w (positive or $\alpha_1^2/2$, as in mitter at a just at the has not rea where an i than α_p ar strength is There is no which is cl

By const also trapp standard c and the sh reception

Conside that frequ summed it to interfer for which length can

To illustr with heig per metre decrease duct is co that trapp the atmos λ_{max} corre

A duct times the normally below on

Meteoro

The t temperat humidity index wi Broadly anti-cycl well mix some pa

In inl warm. A tempera

but the temperature of the upper atmosphere remains almost unchanged. Thus a temperature inversion is set up which, if sufficiently intense, causes super-refraction. This effect is common over deserts, but can occur over any land where the sky is clear and the atmosphere dry. It usually increases to a maximum in the early morning and disappears after sunrise.

The sea, in contrast to the land, shows no marked diurnal variation in temperature. In fine weather the air close to the sea tends to be damp and cool, while the upper air is dry and warm. Thus conditions are appropriate for widespread and continuous super-refraction. It is most marked on the leeward side of land masses, where the warm dry air from the land moves out over the sea, and is widespread off shore in the late afternoon and evening under the effect of the evening land breeze.

In both of the above cases, however, the layer close to the surface may be cooled sufficiently to condense the water vapour into fog. The influence of liquid droplets on the index of refraction is much less than that of the vapour, so that the value of n near to the surface is reduced. This may give rise to sub-standard conditions, with a consequent reduction in signal strength.

A meteorological condition often giving rise to an elevated duct is that of *subsidence*. Subsidence is a sinking of an air mass and its subsequent spreading out over the lower mass of stable air. Across the subsidence there is always a temperature inversion and there may also be a rapid decrease of humidity with height. These effects may be sufficient to produce an elevated duct. Subsidence is usually associated with zones of high pressure.

Equatorial climates, occurring in a small region near the equator, are characterized by heavy rainfall throughout the year, and do not give rise to super-refraction. This includes areas such as the northern half of Brazil and the Belgian Congo. Around and beyond these regions we get the hot tropical and sub-tropical climates, which are dry either throughout the year or during certain seasons. Here strong super-refraction is often experienced throughout a whole season, and on wavelengths up to several metres. Examples are the principal deserts of the world, large parts of India (except during the monsoon), the tropical zone of the Pacific, and to a lesser extent the Mediterranean. In temperate climates usually only centimetric waves are affected, and then only during periods of particularly fine weather. Such areas include the British Isles, the Atlantic coast of Europe, and the coasts of the United States and Canada.

Effects of Super-Refraction

It will be clear that the presence of super-refraction will increase the range of all apparatus using sufficiently short wavelengths, the effects being most marked for the centimetric region. Super-refraction is very obvious on a radar system where the extension of range is shown by the appearance of echoes from distant objects normally beyond the optical horizon. As only rays near to the horizontal are trapped by the duct the phenomenon affects only those radars whose beams are substantially horizontal. Since conditions favourable for super-refraction occur frequently over the surface of the sea, seaborne and low-sited coastal radar are most affected. Determinations of height, for example the altitude of an aircraft beyond the normal horizon, are likely to be seriously in error by reason of the curvature of the rays.

The operational range of reception of a communication system is also increased by super-refraction. The effect here is in general harmful, for it is not sufficiently common or reliable to allow it to be used for regular communication, while on the other hand it may at times permit interception by an enemy of a normally secure communication channel.

Changes in tropospheric refraction have also a considerable effect on the reception of u.h.f. signals at distances within the optical range, the effects being delicately dependent on the continually changing atmospheric structure. The following general observations can be made, however.

For optical or near-optical paths over sea the observed field under standard

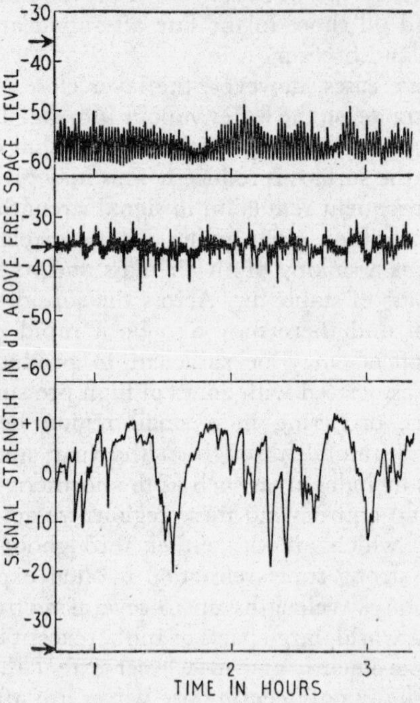

Fig. 14.36. Changes in signal level with atmospheric conditions, showing: (a) rapid fading characteristic of sub-standard conditions; (b) scintillation characteristic of standard conditions; (c) roller fading characteristic of super-standard conditions. Signal level for standard refraction is at − 36 db.

conditions is usually very nearly equal to that calculated for a standard atmosphere. There is a certain amount of rapid fading—*scintillation*—which increases as the range or the frequency is increased. Under sub-standard conditions the signal level falls and rapid fading increases. For super-standard conditions the signal can increase up to about free-space level, but deep long-period *roller fading* can occur. Typical signals are shown in Fig. 14.36, which gives some indication of the wide possible range of level. Generally there is a marked diurnal variation, with the signal fairly steady in the afternoon, changing at night to a form characterized by pronounced fading.

For optical and near-optical paths over land variations are in general less than those over sea. The signal strength is normally steady during the day, while levels on clear, calm nights are high with pronounced fading.

Effect of Surface Irregularities

Thus far the surface of the earth has been assumed to be smooth, which is often far from true. At long wavelengths the surface wave is the important one, and this by its nature follows surface irregularities without appreciable reduction. In the frequency range where transmission depends mainly on the ionospheric wave, this, being well removed from surface irregularities, is also little affected. It is at very high frequencies and beyond, where the propagation is by space wave, that serious disturbances are caused, for example, by buildings, trees, and mountainous or hilly country. Buildings and other obstacles cause reflection, diffraction and absorption. In a built-up area this results in an incalculable field with wide local variations. The losses caused by this absorption and scattering increase with frequency, until, at frequencies of the order of 3,000 Mc/s and beyond, the following can be considered opaque: walls of masonry more than about 20-cm thick, any buildings except those of very light construction, and woods which are visually opaque.

At the higher frequencies the received signal strength is considerably reduced at positions on the shadow side of any hill.

If the hill contour is reasonably smooth, so that it can be considered as part of a sphere, the field reduction on the shadow side can be found approximately

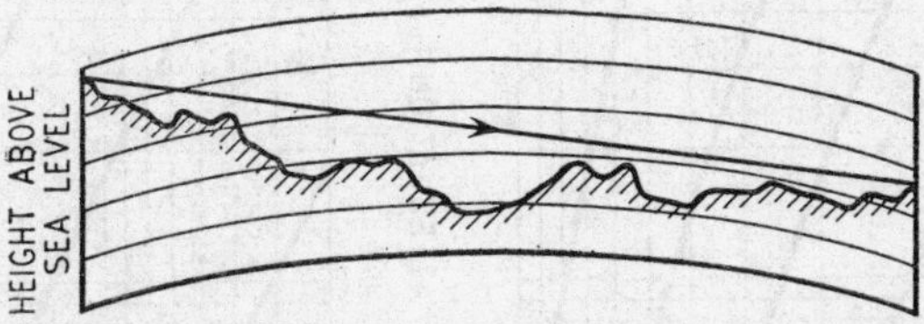

Fig. 14.37. Profile of path between transmitter and receiver.

by the use of equation (14.20) with the earth's radius replaced by a suitable radius to represent the hill.

At v.h.f. and higher frequencies equation (14.17) will not give a useful measure of the line-of-sight distance where the ground is irregular. In the planning of a communication link it is usually necessary to construct a profile of the path, as illustrated in Fig. 14.37, using an effective earth radius of $4a/3$. This enables sites to be chosen so that there is a line-of-sight path. Any reflected ray paths are also evident. Where there are intervening obstacles it is desirable that the direct ray should clear them by a sufficient margin, of the order of $\frac{1}{2}(d\lambda)^{1/2}$. This point is dealt with in Appendix 14.10.

Absorption by Atmospheric Phenomena

We must now consider the effect of rain, snow, clouds, etc., on the propagation of radio waves. For a wave passing over a single spherical droplet part of the energy is absorbed in the droplet and part scattered in all directions. Thus the wave suffers attenuation, which is a function of the wavelength, the drop diameter, and its dielectric constant and losses. For a concentration of drops the attenuation is proportional to the number per unit volume.

Rain. Since the drop size distribution varies in a known manner with the intensity of precipitation it is possible to calculate attenuation conveniently in terms of the precipitation rate. It is found that only in the centimetric waveband is the attenuation appreciable, and its value there is roughly proportional to the precipitation rate. Curves are given in Fig. 14.38 (a) of attenuation as a function of wavelength for different precipitation rates. While rainfall greater than about 20 mm/hour seldom occurs in this country, values up to several hundred mm/hour can occur in the tropics. Thus for wavelengths down to about 3 cm only the heaviest tropical downpours are serious, but for wavelengths of 1 cm and less even moderate rain results in serious attenuation.

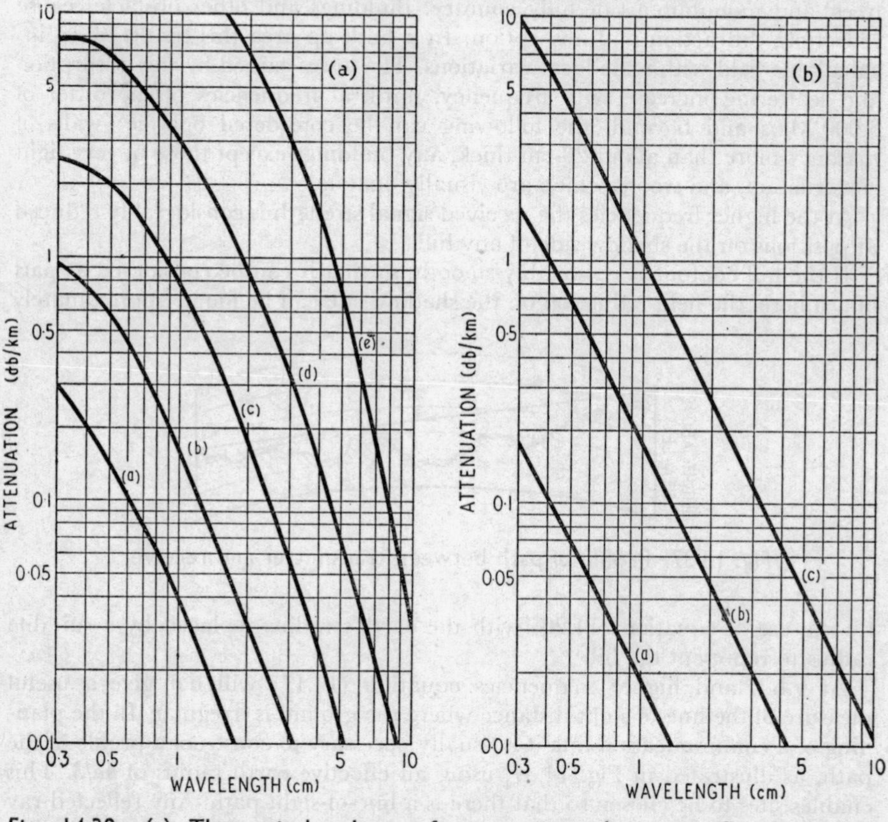

Fig. 14.38. (a) Theoretical values of attenuation by rain, for rates of (a) 0·25 mm/hr (drizzle); (b) 1 mm/hr (light rain); (c) 4 mm/hr (moderate rain); (d) 16 mm/hr (heavy rain); (e) 100 mm/hr (tropical downpour). Temperature 18° C. (b) Theoretical values of attenuation by fog or cloud with water content of (a) 0·043 g/m³ (visibility 500 m); (b) 0·42 g/m³ (visibility 100 m); (c) 2·35 g/m³ (visibility 30 m). Temperature 18° C.

Cloud and Fog. In this case the drop sizes are smaller than for rain, and calculations show that the attenuation is proportional to the mass of water per unit volume. Curves are shown in Fig. 14.38 (b). Again the conclusion holds that it is only below 1 cm wavelength that serious attenuation takes place.

Hail and Snow. The losses in ice are considerably less than in liquid water, and so the attenuation caused by dry hailstones is small compared with that caused by rain of equivalent water content, except in the millimetre wave region, where they are comparable. As the water content in even a heavy snowstorm is quite small, the attenuation caused by snow is always small.

The figures given above are all taken from theoretical work by Ryde in Great Britain. They agree well with measured values.

As was mentioned earlier in this section some energy is scattered by the particles through which the wave passes. If the wave is that of a radar transmitter the energy scattered in the backward direction may be sufficient to be recorded as an echo by the receiver. Such *precipitation echoes* are produced by thunderstorms and by the intense localized precipitation accompanying cyclonic storms.

▶ Atmospheric Attenuation

A further phenomenon affecting wave propagation is absorption by the atmosphere itself. From theoretical considerations it was predicted by Van

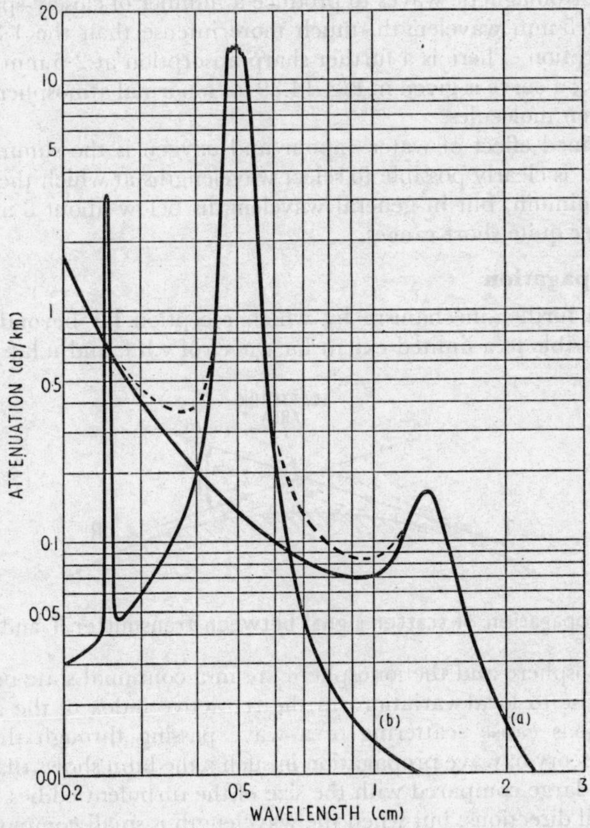

Fig. 14.39. Values of attenuation for (a) water vapour in an atmosphere containing 1% water molecules (7·5 g H_2O per m³); (b) oxygen in an atmosphere containing 20% oxygen molecules. The dashed curve is the sum of the two. Temperature 20° C.

Vleck in the United States that both oxygen and uncondensed water vapour would have absorptions in the centimetre-wave region. This is a molecular phenomenon and its theoretical treatment would lead us deep into atomic physics. It is sufficient for our purpose to state that the water molecule has a permanent electric moment through which interaction occurs between the molecule and an electromagnetic wave. Absorption of energy from the wave takes place at certain wavelengths characteristic of the molecular structure. For water vapour an absorption band occurs with its peak at a wavelength of 1·35 cm, and covers a range of wavelengths on either side. A much more intense absorption takes place around 1·7 mm wavelength and successively higher peaks follow as one proceeds below 1 mm wavelength. Fig. 14.39 shows the attenuation curve for an atmosphere containing 1% of water molecules (7·5 g/m³), the value corresponding to average humidity in a temperate climate. For a saturated atmosphere the attenuation may be two or three times as great.

The oxygen molecule has a small permanent magnetic moment which interacts with electromagnetic waves to produce a number of closely-spaced absorptions around 5 mm wavelength, much more intense than the 1·35-cm water vapour absorption. There is a further sharp absorption at 2·5 mm wavelength. The attenuation curve is given in Fig. 14.39 for a normal atmosphere containing 20% of oxygen molecules.

The combined effect of water vapour and oxygen is the summation of the two curves. It is clearly possible to select wavelengths at which the attenuation is a local minimum, but in general wavelengths below about 8 mm will only be usable over quite short ranges.

Scatter Propagation

There is a further mechanism by which reception far beyond the optical horizon is possible to a limited extent for waves of v.h.f. and u.h.f. frequencies.

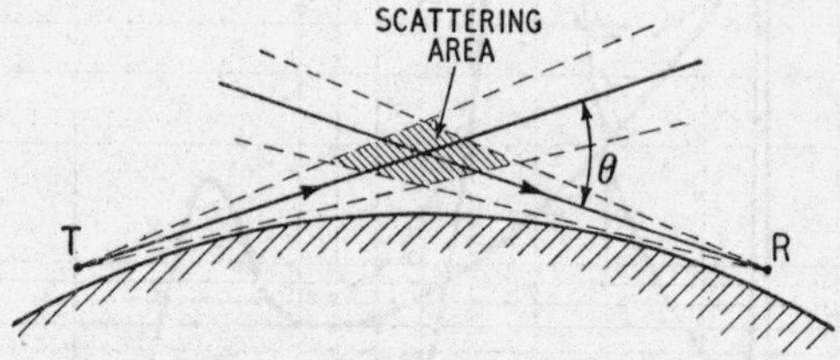

Fig. 14.40. Propagation of scatter signal between transmitter T and receiver R.

Both the troposphere and the ionosphere are in a continual state of turbulence which gives rise to local variations in the refractive index of the atmosphere. These variations cause scattering of a wave passing through the turbulent region. The theory of wave propagation in such a medium shows that, when the wavelength is large compared with the size of the turbulent eddies, the wave is scattered in all directions, but when the wavelength is small compared with the irregularities then most of the scattering takes place within a narrow cone surrounding the forward direction of propagation of the incident radiation.

In order to receive a scattered signal at a point well beyond the horizon the transmitting and receiving aerials must be of high gain and must be orientated so that their beams overlap in a region where forward scattering is taking place, as illustrated in Fig. 14.40. The scattering angle θ should be as small as possible. Because of the random nature of the scattering process the scattered signal is subject to continual random fluctuations in amplitude and phase over a wide range.

Scattering takes place at all frequencies, but there are two distinct frequency regions in which the process is sufficiently marked for practical use to be made of it. One frequency region is in the u.h.f. band, from 500 Mc/s upwards, in which the scattering medium is the troposphere. This is *tropospheric scattering*, and the maximum range attained is of the order of 300–600 km depending on the bandwidth of the transmission. The fact that a received signal consists of components arriving with different amplitudes and phases gives rise to distortion of modulated signals. However, restriction of the scattering area involved, by means of high gain aerials, allows bandwidths up to several Mc/s to be used.

The other frequency region useful for scatter transmissions is the v.h.f. band between about 30 and 50 Mc/s. In this region the scattering takes place in the ionosphere, and is known as *ionospheric scattering*. The part of the ionosphere concerned is the E region—a structure of ionic clouds which undergoes continued turbulent fluctuations in ionization density and hence in refractive index. Fig. 14.40 is applicable here also, but in this case, because the scattering centres are at a much greater height, the maximum attainable range is greater, being of the order of 2,000 km. The level of the scattered signal is usually very low, some 100 db below the free-space signal for the same distance.

In the ionosphere the refractive index, as has been shown earlier, is a function of frequency. This makes ionospheric-scatter signals more dependent on frequency than tropospheric-scatter signals. Because of the much greater height of the ionosphere, the scattering area involved in ionospheric scatter is also much greater than that in tropospheric scatter and the fluctuations are correspondingly greater. A further very variable contribution to the scattered signal is provided by reflections from the ionized trails of meteors, which are constantly being formed in the E region. As a result of all these factors this type of propagation is most suited to the transmission of signals of restricted bandwidth; e.g., telegraphy and commercial telephony with bandwidths not greater than 3 kc/s.

Since the received signal in scatter propagation is composed of numerous components the phase front of the wave reaching the receiving aerial is not uniform over the aperture of the aerial. Under these conditions the full theoretical aerial gain is not attained and the effective gain is variable. This is discussed more fully in Chapter 12.

Summary of Propagation Effects

Having dealt in detail with the various phenomena of propagation, we can now conclude with a summary of how these properties affect the various frequencies. This is best considered under the frequency bands shown in Table 14.4, which is a slight extension of Table 14.1.

TABLE 14.4

Band	Frequency	Wavelength
A	10 kc/s–500 kc/s	30,000 m–600 m
B	500 kc/s–1·5 Mc/s	600 m–200 m
C	1·5 Mc/s–30 Mc/s	200 m–10 m
D	30 Mc/s–300 Mc/s	10 m–1 m
E	> 300 Mc/s	< 1 m

16*

In band A, the long-wave band, transmission by ground wave is stable and reliable for distances up to about 1,500 km, as shown in Figs. 14.5 and 14.6. For very long distances the wave propagates between the two concentric spheres formed by the earth and the lower surface of the ionosphere as described on p.449 and in this case the field strength varies with the distance d as $(1/d)\varepsilon^{-kd\lambda^{-1/2}}$—the Austin-Cohen formula—in which the constant k has the value over water of $4{\cdot}7 \times 10^{-5}$. This property is used in the provision of a limited number of high-grade transoceanic telegraph channels, which are free from service interruptions except during severe magnetic storms.

Band B covers the range of broadcast frequencies, used mainly to provide a high-quality service within a limited area. A station of moderate power has a service radius of the order of 100 km, the field being provided by the ground wave in accordance with Figs. 14.5 and 14.6. Beyond this comes a zone in which fading occurs, and these stations are not normally receivable in daylight beyond a distance of perhaps 250 km over land or 1,000 km over water. In this frequency range the ionospheric wave is strongly absorbed in the ionosphere during the daytime, as discussed in Appendix 14.4. During darkness, however, when ionization is low, the ionospheric wave is only slightly attenuated, and reception by this means is possible up to thousands of kilometres. Such reception is generally unreliable and is particularly subject to selective fading.

The short-wave region covered by band C is that used for the great majority of long-distance communications. The ionospheric wave is used, and frequencies are selected for each particular requirement by means of the m.u.f. predictions and charts discussed earlier in the chapter. The region of the band between 1·5 and 3 Mc/s is erratic and unsatisfactory for distant communication because of absorption effects in the neighbourhood of the gyro-frequency, as discussed in Appendix 14.4. The region between 3 and 6 Mc/s is in use mainly for communications within the limits of a continent, while the remaining part between 6 and 30 Mc/s is used, by reason of the longer skip-distances involved, for long-distance intercontinental services.

Within band C short distances inside the skip distance are covered by the ground wave, with field strengths given by Figs. 14.5 and 14.6. The use is mainly for mobile land communications and ship-to-shore services.

For frequencies above 30 Mc/s it has been shown that the ionospheric wave is not regularly returned, and the surface wave is rapidly attenuated. Thus in range D communication is by the space wave within or somewhat beyond the optical horizon, the variation of field with distance being of the form shown in Fig. 14.28. There is sufficient diffraction round obstacles at these frequencies to allow short-range reception within built-up areas. For frequencies up to about 60 Mc/s reception of signals of limited bandwidth by ionospheric scatter propagation is possible up to distances of the order of 2,000 km.

Range E is useful mainly for line-of-sight distances, usually between fixed stations. Here also the field strength is calculated from the space wave, but wide variations may occur under sub-refracting and super-refracting conditions. From about 500 Mc/s upwards tropospheric scatter provides a limited degree of reception at ranges up to about 300–600 km.

APPENDIX 14.1

Surface-Wave Propagation

The mathematical analysis of wave propagation over an imperfectly-conducting earth gives results in a form where long calculations are needed. These have been reduced to a standard procedure, which the following outline illustrates in the simple case where the distance between transmitter and receiver is so small that the earth's curvature can be neglected.

For a transmitter and receiver placed at ground level the constant A in equation (14.5) is found through two auxiliary parameters, p (the *numerical distance*) and b, defined by the relations:

$$\left.\begin{aligned} b &= \tan^{-1}\left(\frac{\kappa_r + 1}{x}\right) \\ p &= \frac{\pi}{x}\frac{d}{\lambda}\cos b \end{aligned}\right\} \quad . \quad . \quad . \quad . \quad . \quad (14.26)$$

where $x = \sigma/(\omega\kappa_0) = 18 \times 10^9\sigma/f$, λ is the wavelength, κ_r and σ are the relative permittivity and conductivity of the earth and κ_0 is the permittivity of free space. The value of A is then determined from the curves of Fig. 14.41.

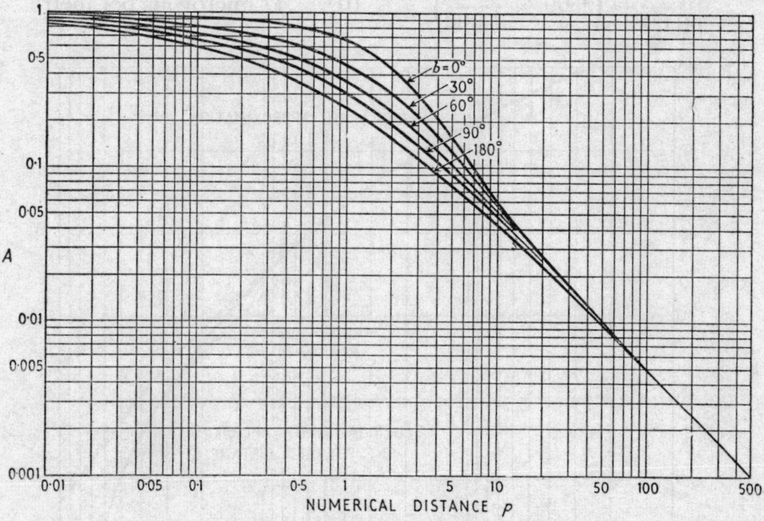

Fig. **14.41. Curves determining the factor A in equation (14.5).**

The above expressions are for vertically-polarized radiation. The same curves can be used for horizontal polarization if b and p are defined by :

$$\left.\begin{aligned} b' &= \tan^{-1}\left(\frac{\kappa_r - 1}{x}\right) \\ b &= 180^\circ - b' \\ p &= \frac{\pi d}{\lambda}\frac{x}{\cos b'} \end{aligned}\right\} \quad . \quad . \quad . \quad . \quad . \quad (14.27)$$

The distance up to which the assumption of a plane earth holds good is about $d = 10^4/f^{1/3}$ km.

Example: Let us find the field at a distance of 60 km from a transmitter of frequency 2 Mc/s radiating 200 W from a vertical half-wave aerial over earth with $\kappa_r = 12$ and $\sigma = 5 \times 10^{-3}$ mho/m.

From equations (14.26):

$$b = \tan^{-1}(13/45) = 16° \, 7'$$

$$p = \frac{\pi}{45} \frac{60{,}000}{150} \cos 16° \, 7' = 26{\cdot}8$$

Hence, from Fig. 14.41,

$$A = 0{\cdot}02$$

Substitution in equation (14.5) gives for the standard field of a 1-kW transmitter:

$$E = \frac{300 \times 0{\cdot}02}{60{,}000} \text{ volts per metre}$$

As the power gain of a half-wave aerial over a short dipole is 1·09, and the radiated power is 200 W, the required value of the field is:

$$\frac{300 \times 0{\cdot}02}{60{,}000}\left(1{\cdot}09 \times \frac{200}{1{,}000}\right)^{1/2} \times 10^6 = 47 \text{ microvolts per metre}$$

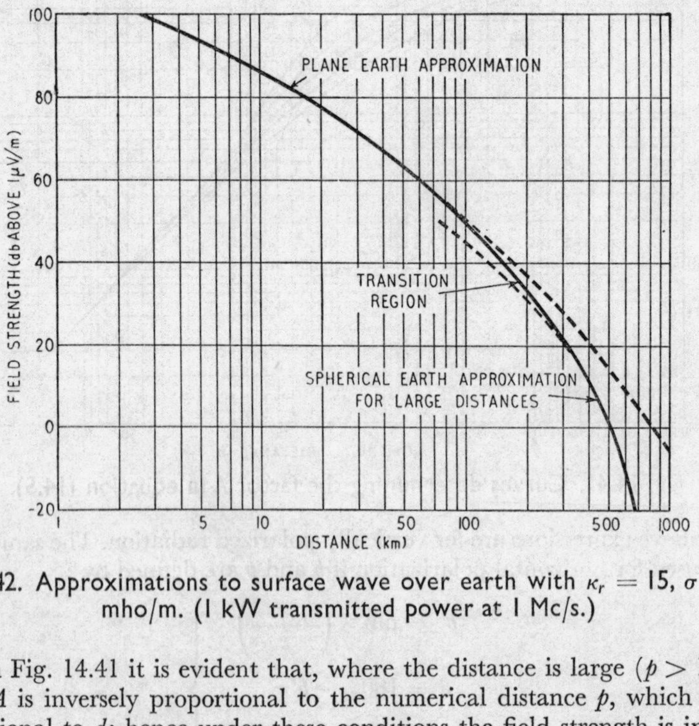

Fig. 14.42. Approximations to surface wave over earth with $\kappa_r = 15$, $\sigma = 10^{-2}$ mho/m. (1 kW transmitted power at 1 Mc/s.)

From Fig. 14.41 it is evident that, where the distance is large ($p > 10$), the factor A is inversely proportional to the numerical distance p, which itself is proportional to d; hence under these conditions the field strength is inversely proportional to the square of the distance.

When the distance exceeds that for which the assumption of a plane earth suffices the procedure becomes much more complex, and several other auxiliary curves and parameters are necessary. These will not be dealt with here, but Fig. 14.42 will illustrate the nature of the difference. It can be seen that the approximations for plane earth and spherical earth do not overlap, and an interpolated curve has to be drawn to join them in the transition region.

APPENDIX 14.2

Height–Gain Factors

When the transmitting and receiving dipoles are elevated at heights h_1 and h_2 above the earth's surface the received field is given by equation (14.5) multiplied by the height–gain factors $f(h_1)$ and $f(h_2)$, so that the field in this case becomes:

$$E = \frac{300}{d} A f(h_1) f(h_2) \qquad (14.28)$$

It is convenient to express aerial heights in terms of a *numerical height*, q, defined by the relations:

$$q = \frac{2\pi h}{\lambda}\left(\frac{\cos b}{x}\right)^{1/2}, \text{ for vertical polarization} \qquad (14.29)$$

$$q = \frac{2\pi h}{\lambda}\left(\frac{x}{\cos b'}\right)^{1/2}, \text{ for horizontal polarization} \qquad (14.30)$$

where x, b and b' have the meanings used in Appendix 14.1. The height–gain factor $f(h)$ is now found in terms of the calculated value of q by means of the curves of Fig. 14.43. These curves are not of universal application, and indeed

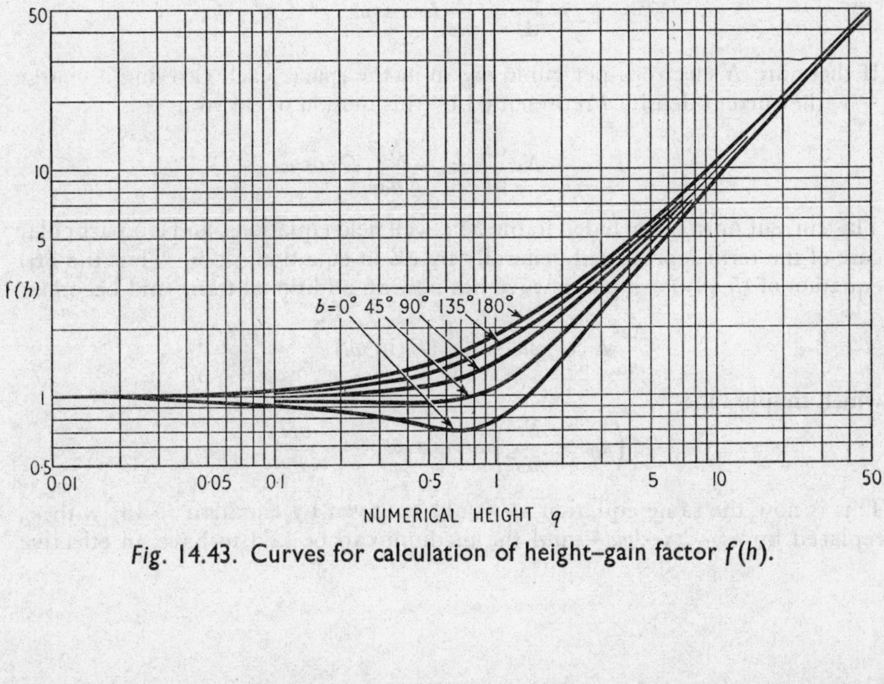

Fig. 14.43. Curves for calculation of height–gain factor $f(h)$.

the limitations imposed on their use are so complicated that it is only possible to deal with a limited range of conditions at one time. If we confine ourselves to the distance limitation $d < 10^4/f^{1/3}$ km used in Appendix 14.1 then equations (14.29) and (14.30) can be applied when the aerial heights are low enough and the numerical distance p is large enough to satisfy simultaneously the relations:

$$\left.\begin{array}{ll} h < 6 \times 10^6/f^{2/3} \text{ metres}, & p > 20 \\ p > 10q_1q_2, & p > 100(q_1 + q_2) \end{array}\right\} \quad . \quad . \quad (14.31)$$

Further extensions of the validity are beyond our scope.
Figs. 14.8 and 14.9 are calculated by this method.

APPENDIX 14.3

Propagation of a Plane Wave in an Ionized Medium

If a plane wave, travelling in the z-direction, and having its electric field along the x-axis and given by $E_x = E \sin \omega t$, moves in a region containing free electrons the electric field will act on each electron with a force F_x given by:

$$F_x = -eE_x$$

The consequent acceleration is in the x-direction, and, from Newton's Law, is given by:

$$m\frac{\mathrm{d}^2x}{\mathrm{d}t^2} = -eE_x = -eE \sin \omega t$$

Integration gives the velocity of the electron as:

$$\frac{\mathrm{d}x}{\mathrm{d}t} = \frac{e}{m\omega}E \cos \omega t$$

If there are N electrons per cubic metre in the space, each carrying a charge $-e$, the current density I represented by this motion of electrons is:

$$I = -Ne\frac{\mathrm{d}x}{\mathrm{d}t} = -\frac{Ne^2}{m\omega}E \cos \omega t$$

This current must be included in the Maxwell field equations, and is a particular case of the term represented generally by $\sigma\mathbf{E}$ in equation (5.29). Thus the first equation of (5.48) for a plane wave has now an additional term, and becomes:

$$-\frac{Ne^2}{m\omega}E \cos \omega t + \kappa_0\frac{\partial}{\partial t}(E \sin \omega t) = -\frac{\partial H_y}{\partial z}$$

which simplies to:

$$\left(\kappa_0 - \frac{Ne^2}{m\omega^2}\right)\omega E \cos \omega t = -\frac{\partial H_y}{\partial z}$$

This is now the same equation as would be given by equation (5.48) with κ_0 replaced by $\kappa_0 - Ne^2/m\omega^2$, and the medium can be said to have an effective permittivity which is less than that of free space. The ionized region thus has a relative permittivity of $1 - Ne^2/\kappa_0 m\omega^2$.

What is known in optics as the refractive index is the square root of the relative permittivity and so we can obtain the refractive index n of an ionized medium as:

$$n = \left(1 - \frac{Ne^2}{\kappa_0 m\omega^2}\right)^{1/2} \quad . \quad . \quad . \quad . \quad . \quad . \quad . \quad (14.32)$$

For an electron $e = 1{\cdot}59 \times 10^{-19}$ coulombs, $m = 9 \times 10^{-31}$ kg, and with f in c/s equation(10.32) becomes:

$$n = \left(1 - \frac{81N}{f^2}\right)^{1/2} \quad . \quad . \quad . \quad . \quad . \quad . \quad (14.33)$$

Equation (14.32) holds equally well for ions or electrons, but from its form it is clear that, for equal numbers and charges, electrons, being very much lighter than ions, will be much more effective in determining the refractive index.

In equation (14.32) n is a function of frequency, and so the velocity of the wave in the medium is also frequency dependent. This is the same phenomenon as occurs in a waveguide, giving rise to two velocities, a phase velocity v_p and a group velocity v_g. The phase velocity is defined by equation (1.36) as $v_p = c/(\kappa_r \mu_r)^{1/2}$, so that, μ_r being unity:

$$v_p = \frac{c}{\kappa_r^{1/2}} = \frac{c}{\left(1 - \dfrac{81N}{f^2}\right)^{1/2}}$$

The discussion in Chapter 6 is of general application, and thus, by equation (6.9) $v_p v_g = c^2$, we can write down the expression for the group velocity as:

$$v_g = c\left(1 - \frac{81N}{f^2}\right)^{1/2} \quad . \quad . \quad . \quad . \quad . \quad . \quad (14.34)$$

In the collisions which take place between the electrons and the gas molecules, however, energy is dissipated in the form of heat, and this energy must be supplied by the wave. The effect may be considered as a 'frictional' force on the electron proportional to its velocity, and proportional to the collision frequency ν.

It can be shown that in this case the refractive index of the medium becomes:

$$n = \left\{1 - \frac{Ne^2}{\kappa_0 m(\nu^2 + \omega^2)}\right\}^{1/2} \quad . \quad . \quad . \quad (14.35)$$

and the medium has in addition an effective conductivity σ given by:

$$\sigma = \frac{Ne^2 \nu}{m(\nu^2 + \omega^2)} \quad . \quad . \quad . \quad . \quad . \quad . \quad (14.36)$$

The collision frequency is dependent on the gas pressure, and is therefore a function of height. Values of ν are estimated to vary from about 6×10^8 per second at a height of 50 km to about 100 per second at a height of 400 km, these heights being the limits of the ionosphere. Below the lower edge of the ionosphere the electron density drops off rapidly; it is therefore around this lower edge that the conductivity is greatest.

In the higher regions of the ionosphere ω is normally much greater than ν, so that the expression (14.35) approximates to equation (14.32), and the value of σ becomes negligible.

APPENDIX 14.4

Effect of Earth's Magnetic Field

If the analysis of Appendix 14.3 is modified to include the effect of the earth's magnetic field the solution becomes very complicated, but it can be shown that there are then two possible values for the refractive index, given in terms of B_L and B_T, the components of the earth's field respectively along the direction of propagation and transverse to it, by:

$$n = \left[1 - \frac{2}{2\alpha - \dfrac{\gamma_T^2}{\alpha - 1} \pm \left\{\dfrac{\gamma_T^4}{(\alpha - 1)^2} + 4\gamma_L^2\right\}^{1/2}}\right]^{1/2} \quad . \quad . \quad (14.37)$$

where $$\alpha = \frac{\kappa_0 m\omega^2}{Ne^2}, \quad \gamma_T = \frac{\alpha}{\omega}\frac{B_T e}{m}, \quad \gamma_L = \frac{\alpha}{\omega}\frac{B_L e}{m}$$

The index corresponding to the upper sign is close to the value given for zero magnetic field by equation (14.32), and governs what is called the *ordinary ray*. The other sign gives the refractive index of the *extraordinary ray*.

In the consideration of the effect of the earth's field, of total value represented by B, an important frequency is that given by the relation:

$$2\pi f = B\frac{e}{m} \quad . \quad . \quad . \quad . \quad . \quad . \quad . \quad (14.38)$$

This is known as the *gyro frequency*. It is the frequency whose period is equal to the period of revolution of an electron in its circular orbit under the influence of the steady magnetic field of flux B. Taking $0{\cdot}5 \times 10^{-4}$ weber/m² as an average value for the earth's field we get the gyro-frequency as approximately 1·4 Mc/s. Near the gyro frequency the wave attenuation in an ionized region is greatly increased over the value existing in the absence of the earth's field. Thus over most of the broadcast band and up to frequencies of about 2 Mc/s the attenuation is too great for reception of a sky wave during daytime. At frequencies beyond about 2 Mc/s the effect of the earth's field on attenuation is small.

As the refractive index for the ordinary ray is very close to that given by equation (14.32), the ordinary ray has therefore the critical frequency f_o of equation (14.8). In the F or F_2 region the critical frequency f_x of the extraordinary ray is always higher than f_o by an amount approximately equal to half the gyro frequency.

APPENDIX 14.5

Reflection Coefficient of Ground

Consider a plane wave in space meeting at a flat surface a medium having a permittivity κ, as indicated in Fig. 14.44. AC is a wave front for the incident rays, BD for the refracted rays, and BE for the reflected rays. In the time in

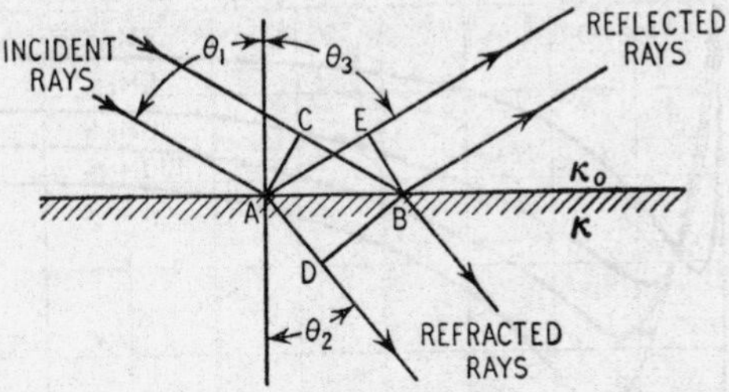

Fig. 14.44. Reflection of plane wave.

which the upper incident ray travels from C to B, the reflected ray originating at A travels from A to E, and the refracted ray originating at A travels from A to D. If v_1 is the wave velocity in space and v_2 the velocity in the medium, these being respectively equal to $(\kappa_0\mu_0)^{-1/2}$ and $(\kappa\mu_0)^{-1/2}$, then CB/AD $= v_1/v_2 = (\kappa/\kappa_0)^{1/2}$. Now CB $=$ AB sin θ_1 and AD $=$ AB sin θ_2, and therefore:

$$\frac{\sin\theta_1}{\sin\theta_2} = \left(\frac{\kappa}{\kappa_0}\right)^{1/2} \quad . \quad . \quad . \quad . \quad . \quad . \quad (14.39)$$

In addition, CB $=$ AE, and therefore:

$$\theta_1 = \theta_3 \quad . \quad . \quad . \quad . \quad . \quad . \quad . \quad (14.40)$$

This demonstrates *Snell's Law* governing the relation of the angles of incidence and refraction, and also the equality of the angles of incidence and reflection.

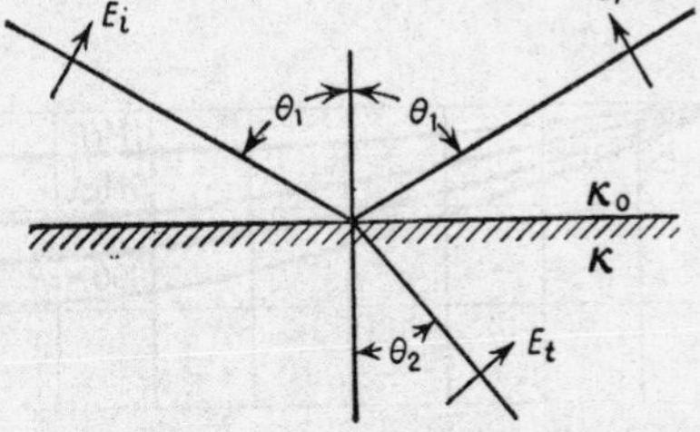

Fig. 14.45. Reflection of vertically-polarized wave.

We further consider the wave to come from a vertically-polarized transmitter, so that the electric vectors of the incident, reflected, and transmitted waves are directed as in Fig. 14.45. Applying the boundary conditions of equations (5.1) to the tangential and normal components of electric field on either side of the boundary we find:

$$E_i \cos\theta_1 - E_r \cos\theta_1 = E_t \cos\theta_2$$
$$\kappa_0(E_i \sin\theta_1 + E_r \sin\theta_1) = \kappa E_t \sin\theta_2$$

By eliminating E_t we deduce that the reflection coefficient ρ_V is given by:

$$\rho_V = \frac{E_r}{E_i} = \frac{\kappa^{1/2} \cos \theta_1 - \kappa_0^{1/2} \cos \theta_2}{\kappa^{1/2} \cos \theta_1 + \kappa_0^{1/2} \cos \theta_2}$$

$$= \frac{(\kappa/\kappa_0) \cos \theta_1 - (\kappa/\kappa_0 - \sin^2 \theta_1)^{1/2}}{(\kappa/\kappa_0) \cos \theta_1 + (\kappa/\kappa_0 - \sin^2 \theta_1)^{1/2}} \quad . \quad . \quad (14.41)$$

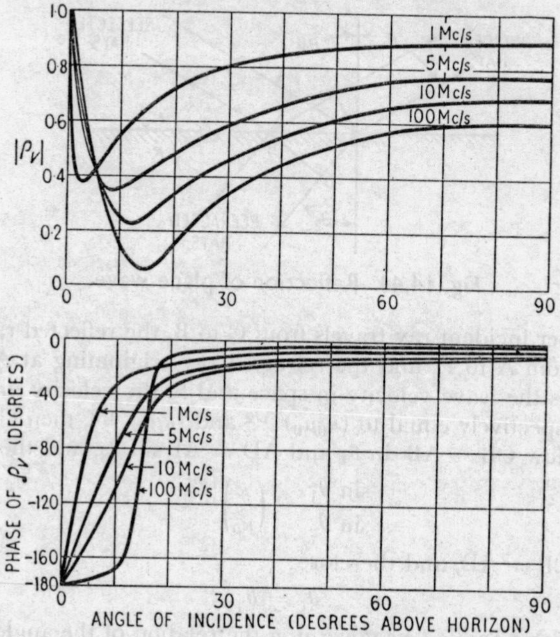

Fig. 14.46. Reflection coefficient for vertically-polarized wave over 'good' ground with $\kappa_r = 15$, $\sigma = 10^{-2}$ mho/m.

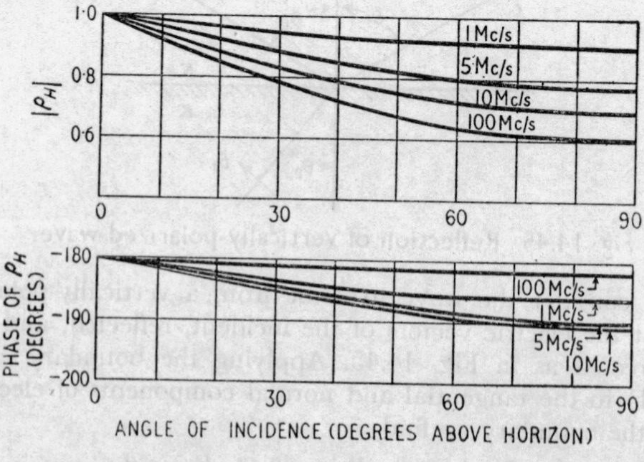

Fig. 14.47. Reflection coefficient for horizontally-polarized wave over 'good' ground with $\kappa_r = 15$, $\sigma = 10^{-2}$ mho/m.

It can similarly be shown that the reflection coefficient ρ_H for a horizontally-polarized wave is:

$$\rho_H = \frac{\cos\theta_1 - (\kappa/\kappa_0 - \sin^2\theta_1)^{1/2}}{\cos\theta_1 + (\kappa/\kappa_0 - \sin^2\theta_1)^{1/2}} \quad . \quad . \quad . \quad (14.42)$$

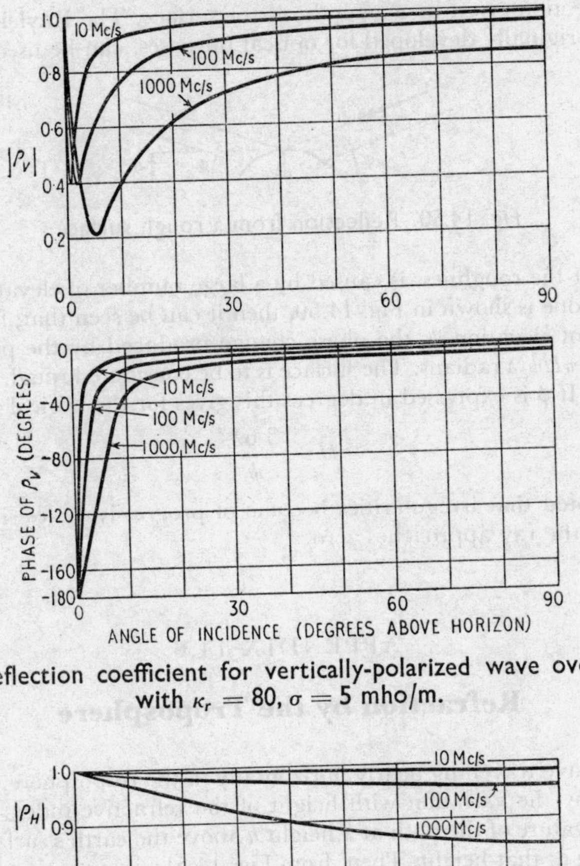

Fig. 14.48. Reflection coefficient for vertically-polarized wave over sea water with $\kappa_r = 80$, $\sigma = 5$ mho/m.

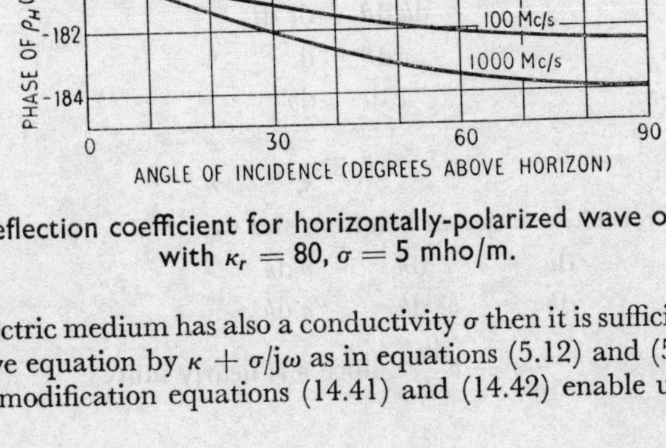

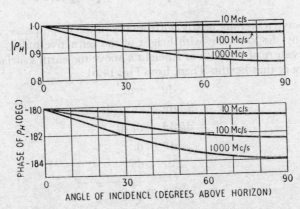

Fig. 14.49. Reflection coefficient for horizontally-polarized wave over sea water with $\kappa_r = 80$, $\sigma = 5$ mho/m.

If the dielectric medium has also a conductivity σ then it is sufficient to replace κ in the above equation by $\kappa + \sigma/j\omega$ as in equations (5.12) and (5.13).

With this modification equations (14.41) and (14.42) enable us to calculate the amplitude and phase of the reflection coefficient for any type of ground at any frequency. Curves of these are given in Figs. 14.46–14.49.

The above results are true only if the reflecting surface is smooth. Roughness of the surface produces a diffuse scattering of the rays. This is of the type which in optics is produced by a dull white surface, in contrast to the normal, or *specular*, reflection given by a smooth mirror surface. The Rayleigh criterion of roughness, originally developed for optical purposes, can be used here. If it be

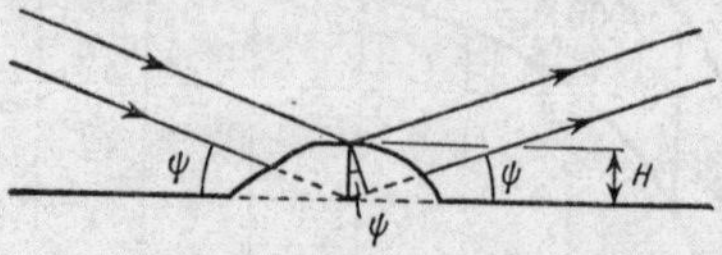

Fig. 14.50. Reflection from a rough surface.

assumed that the roughness is caused by a large number of elevations of height H, of which one is shown in Fig. 14.50, then it can be seen that, for rays with a small angle of elevation ψ, the phase change produced by the presence of the elevation is $4\pi H\psi/\lambda$ radians. The surface is to be considered rough if this exceeds $\pi/4$ radians. If ψ is expressed in degrees this gives for the critical value of H:

$$H = \frac{3 \cdot 6\lambda}{\psi}$$

It will be noted that irregularities become of progressively less importance as the angle of the ray approaches zero.

APPENDIX 14.6

Refraction by the Troposphere

Consider a wave travelling nearly horizontally in the troposphere, its path bent into an arc by the variation with height of the refractive index. Let r be the radius of curvature of the path at a height h above the earth's surface, and v the wave velocity at that height. Then, from Fig. 14.51:

$$r\,\mathrm{d}\theta = v\,\mathrm{d}t$$

and

$$(r + \mathrm{d}h)\,\mathrm{d}\theta = (v + \mathrm{d}v)\,\mathrm{d}t$$

Hence

$$\mathrm{d}h\,\mathrm{d}\theta = \mathrm{d}v\,\mathrm{d}t$$

or

$$\frac{\mathrm{d}\theta}{\mathrm{d}t} = \frac{\mathrm{d}v}{\mathrm{d}h}$$

But

$$v = \frac{c}{\kappa_r^{1/2}} = \frac{c}{n}$$

where n is the refractive index at height h, and so:

$$\frac{\mathrm{d}v}{\mathrm{d}h} = -\frac{c}{n^2}\frac{\mathrm{d}n}{\mathrm{d}h} = -\frac{v}{n}\frac{\mathrm{d}n}{\mathrm{d}h}$$

$$\approx -v\frac{\mathrm{d}n}{\mathrm{d}h}, \quad \text{since } n \text{ is nearly unity.}$$

Therefore, from the above expressions:

$$r = \frac{v}{d\theta/dt} = \frac{v}{dv/dh}$$
$$= -\frac{1}{dn/dh} \quad . \quad . \quad . \quad . \quad . \quad . \quad . \quad . \qquad (14.43)$$

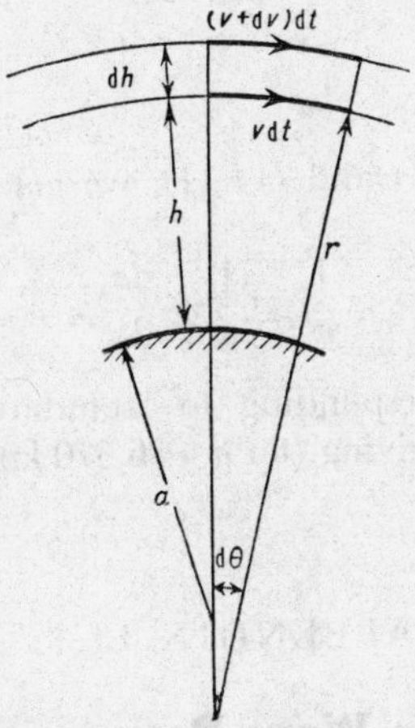

Fig. **14.51. Refraction of wave by the troposphere.**

If we assume that the actual path of Fig. 14.52 (a) can be replaced by an equivalent arrangement in which ray paths are straight lines over an earth of

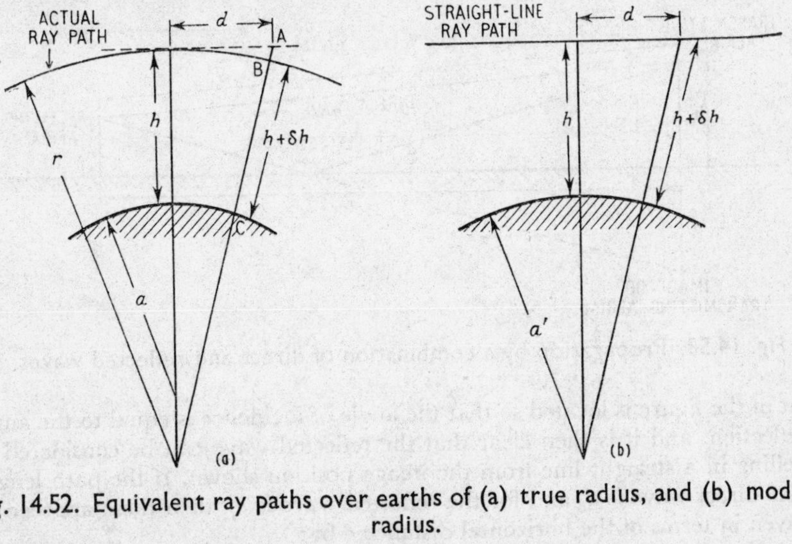

Fig. **14.52. Equivalent ray paths over earths of (a) true radius, and (b) modified radius.**

fictitious radius a', as in Fig. 14.52 (b), then the distance δh must be the same in both cases. From the figure we see that:

$$(a' + h)^2 + d^2 = (a' + h + \delta h)^2$$

whence
$$\delta h = \frac{d^2}{2(a' + h)} \approx \frac{d^2}{2a'}$$

Similarly, from Fig. 14.52 (a):
$$\delta h = \mathrm{AC} - \mathrm{AB}$$
$$= \frac{d^2}{2a} - \frac{d^2}{2r}$$

Therefore:
$$\frac{1}{a'} = \frac{1}{a} - \frac{1}{r} \qquad (14.44)$$

Combining equations (14.43) and (14.44), we get the value for the effective radius as:
$$\frac{1}{a'} = \frac{1}{a} + \frac{\mathrm{d}n}{\mathrm{d}h} \qquad (14.45)$$

The value of $\mathrm{d}n/\mathrm{d}h$ corresponding to 'standard conditions' is taken as $-0{\cdot}039 \times 10^{-6}$ per metre, giving (for $a = 6{,}370$ km) a value of a' equal to $\frac{4}{3}a$.

APPENDIX 14.7

Space-Wave Propagation

Consider two aerials of height h_1 and h_2 separated by a distance d sufficiently small for the earth to be considered as plane. The received signal derived from the space wave is to be calculated for the geometry of Fig. 14.53. The reflection

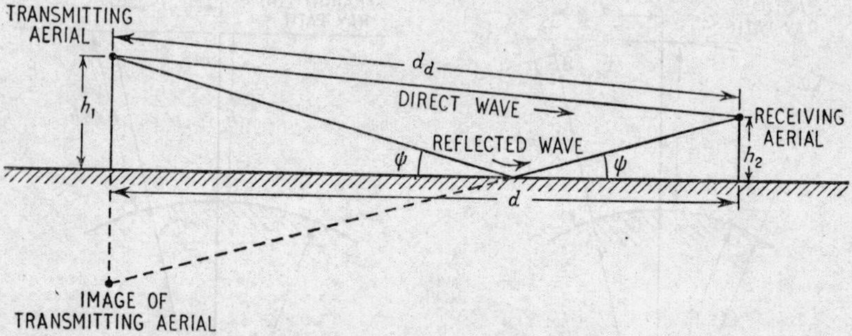

Fig. **14.53.** Propagation by a combination of direct and reflected waves.

point in the figure is located so that the angle of incidence is equal to the angle of reflection, and it is then clear that the reflected wave can be considered as travelling in a straight line from the image position shown. If the path length for the direct wave is d_d and for the reflected wave is d_r, then these are seen to be given in terms of the horizontal distance d by:

$$d_d = \{d^2 + (h_1 - h_2)^2\}^{1/2}$$
$$\approx d\left\{1 + \tfrac{1}{2}\left(\frac{h_1 - h_2}{d}\right)^2\right\}, \text{ by binomial expansion}$$

and

$$d_r \approx d\left\{1 + \tfrac{1}{2}\left(\frac{h_1 + h_2}{d}\right)^2\right\}$$

Hence the path difference, Δd, is:

$$\Delta d = \frac{2h_1h_2}{d}$$

and the corresponding phase difference ϕ is:

$$\phi = \frac{4\pi h_1h_2}{\lambda d} \quad . \quad . \quad . \quad . \quad . \quad . \quad (14.46)$$

We have now to sum the instantaneous values of the two fields at the transmitter.

The direct field at the receiving aerial has an amplitude E_0/d_d, where E_0 is the field amplitude at unit distance, and so will be of the form:

$$E_d = \frac{E_0}{d_d}\sin \omega t \approx \frac{E_0}{d}\sin \omega t$$

For the reflected wave there is the phase difference discussed above and in addition the change of amplitude and phase which occurs on reflection, represented by a reflection coefficient ρ. The reflected field is then given by:

$$E_r = \rho\frac{E_0}{d}\sin(\omega t - \phi)$$

In most practical cases where the angle of elevation is small Appendix 14.5 shows that ρ can be taken as a negative fraction, almost equal to -1. The sum of the direct and reflected waves is then given by:

$$E = \frac{E_0}{d}\{\sin \omega t - |\rho| \sin(\omega t - \phi)\}$$

$$= \frac{E_0}{d}\{(1 - |\rho| \cos \phi)\sin \omega t - |\rho| \sin \phi \cos \omega t\}$$

Hence the magnitude of the field is:

$$|E| = \frac{E_0}{d}(1 - 2|\rho| \cos \phi + |\rho|^2)^{1/2}$$

$$= |E_d|(1 - 2|\rho| \cos \phi + |\rho|^2)^{1/2}. \quad . \quad . \quad . \quad (14.47)$$

The resultant thus passes through maxima and minima given by:

$$|E| = |E_d|(1 \pm |\rho|) \quad . \quad . \quad . \quad . \quad . \quad . \quad (14.48)$$

Because in practice we have to deal with a curved earth it is necessary to multiply ρ by a further factor D, the *divergence factor*. This expresses the reduction in field strength caused by the increased divergence of the beam after reflection from a convex surface, as is evident from Fig. 14.54. Equation (14.48) then becomes:

$$|E| = |E_d|(1 \pm D|\rho|) \quad . \quad . \quad . \quad . \quad . \quad . \quad (14.49)$$

The divergence factor is given by the expression:

$$D = \left(1 + \frac{2h_1'h_2'}{a'd \tan \psi'}\right)^{-1/2}$$

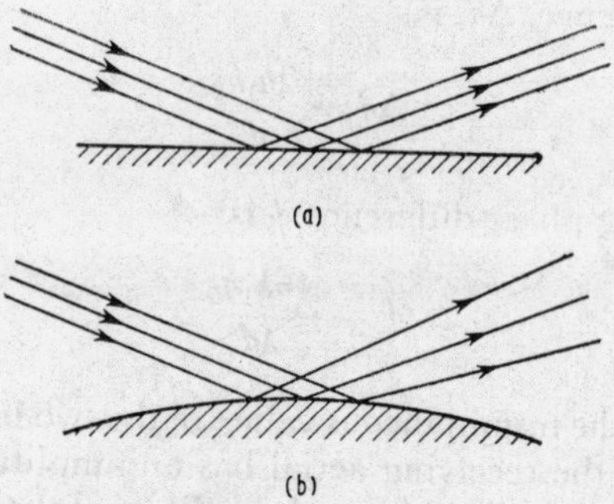

Fig. 14.54. Reflection of parallel rays from (a) plane surface; (b) convex surface, showing divergence.

where h_1', h_2' and ψ' have the meanings shown in Fig. 14.55. For a curved earth the expression for the phase difference ϕ should also be modified by using $h_1'h_2'$ in place of h_1h_2.

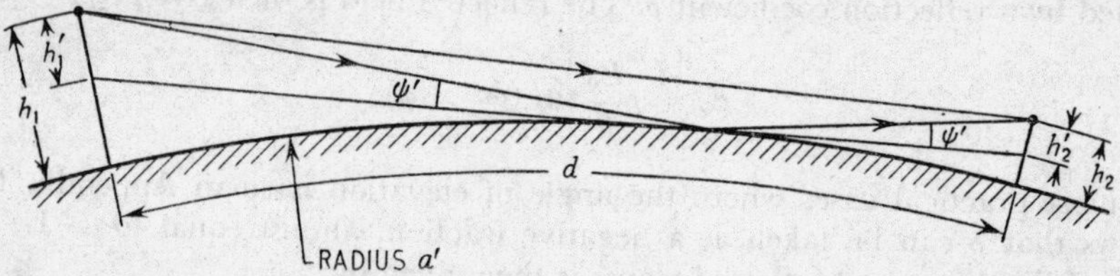

Fig. 14.55. Direct and reflected waves above a curved earth, h_1', h_2', ψ' measured relative to the tangent at the point of reflection.

For many purposes it is sufficient to put $D = |\rho| = 1$, when the expression for the space field reduces to:

$$|E| = \frac{2E_0}{d}\left|\sin\left(\frac{2\pi h_1 h_2}{\lambda d}\right)\right| \quad . \quad . \quad . \quad . \quad . \qquad (14.50)$$

APPENDIX 14.8

Modified Refractive Index

To derive the expression for the modified refractive index consider a spherical earth surrounded by concentric refracting layers of indices n_0, n_1, . . . at the heights shown in Fig. 14.56. A ray with angle of incidence i at the ground is refracted through the layers at the angles shown.

From triangle AOB:

$$\frac{\sin i_1}{a} = \frac{\sin i}{R_1}$$

and by Snell's Law (equation 14.39):

$$\frac{\sin i_1}{\sin r_1} = \frac{n_1}{n_0}$$

Hence
$$a \sin i = R_1 \sin i_1$$
$$= \frac{n_1}{n_0} R_1 \sin r_1$$

and thus:

$$an_0 \sin i = R_1 n_1 \sin r_1 = R_2 n_2 \sin r_2 = \ldots$$

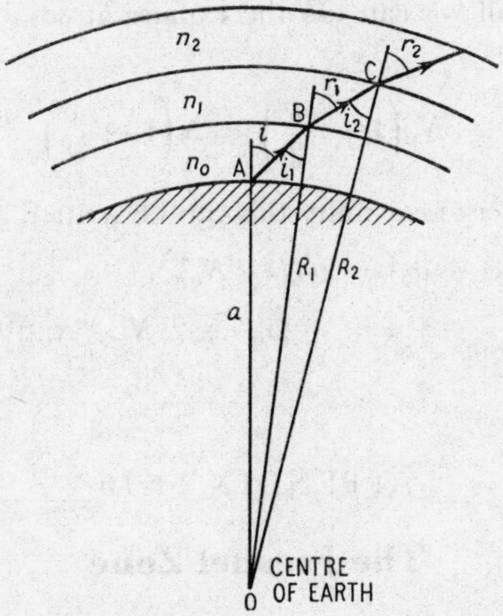

Fig. 14.56. Refraction of ray by concentric refracting layers of successively decreasing refractive indices.

Passing to a continuous variation of n we deduce:

$$an_0 \sin i = Rn \sin r$$

where r is the angle of the ray at the height where the index is n. With $R = a + h$ this equation becomes, in terms of the height h above the earth's surface:

$$n_0 \sin i = \left(1 + \frac{h}{a}\right) n \sin r$$
$$= \left(n + \frac{h}{a}\right) \sin r, \quad \text{approximately, since } n \approx 1 \quad . \quad . \quad . \quad (14.51)$$

Over a flat earth the corresponding expression would be [see Fig. 14.14 and the derivation of equation (14.7)]:

$$n_0 \sin i = n \sin r \quad . \quad . \quad . \quad . \quad . \quad . \quad (14.52)$$

Thus we can treat the earth as flat by replacing the refractive index n by $n + h/a$, which is called the *modified refractive index* and represented by N.

APPENDIX 14.9

Refraction in Variable Medium

For the flat earth and modified index concept consider a ray starting at an angle α_0 to the horizontal at a height where the modified index is N_0. If the angle has changed to α when the modified index has changed to N, then, by comparison with equation (14.52):

$$N_0 \cos \alpha_0 = N \cos \alpha$$

If the angles are small we can use the expansion $\cos \alpha = 1 - \alpha^2/2$, and the above relation becomes:

$$N_0\left(1 - \frac{\alpha_0^2}{2}\right) = N\left(1 - \frac{\alpha^2}{2}\right)$$

Since N and N_0 are very near unity this can be written as:

$$\alpha^2 - \alpha_0^2 = 2(N - N_0)$$

whence

$$\alpha = \pm \{\alpha_0^2 + 2(N - N_0)\}^{1/2} \quad . \quad . \quad . \quad (14.53)$$

APPENDIX 14.10

The Fresnel Zone

Reflection at a surface is not in fact confined to the point where the geometrical rays meet the surface, but is shown by diffraction theory to spread over a limited region surrounding the point. The important region for unobstructed trans-

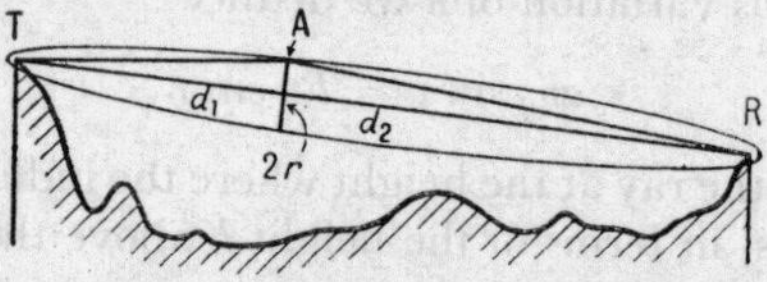

Fig. 14.57. Section of ellipsoid for first Fresnel zone.

mission is that known as the first *Fresnel zone*, whose boundary is defined (Fig. 14.57) as the locus of points A such that TA + AR differs by a half-wavelength from TR. This locus is an ellipsoid of revolution with foci at T and R.

If TA + AR = TR + $\lambda/2$ it follows that:

$$(d_1^2 + r^2)^{1/2} + (d_2^2 + r^2)^{1/2} = d_1 + d_2 + \lambda/2$$

whence approximately

$$r = \left(\frac{d_1 d_2 \lambda}{d_1 + d_2}\right)^{1/2}$$

It is only if this entire zone is clear of obstacles that the direct ray can be assumed to be in free space. If the nearest approach of the ray to the ground is approximately mid-way between transmitter and receiver the minimum clearance required by the above expression is approximately $\frac{1}{2}(d\lambda)^{1/2}$.

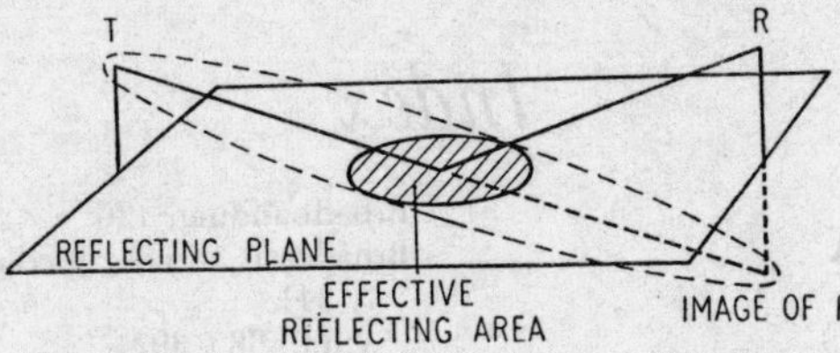

Fig. **14.58. Intersection of Fresnel ellipsoid with reflecting plane.**

When reflection is involved the effective reflecting area is that area in which the Fresnel ellipsoid of the incident ray cuts the reflecting plane, as shown in Fig. 14.58.

Index

E

F

G

H

I

J

K

L

M

N

O

P

Q

R

Printed in Great Britain under the authority of HER MAJESTY'S STATIONERY OFFICE by
WILLIAM CLOWES AND SONS, LTD., LONDON AND BECCLES. Wt. 2253. K. 160.

S.O. Code No. 57-635-5*